GENERAL GENETICS

A SERIES OF BIOLOGY TEXTS

EDITORS   George W. Beadle

Ralph Emerson

Douglas M. Whitaker

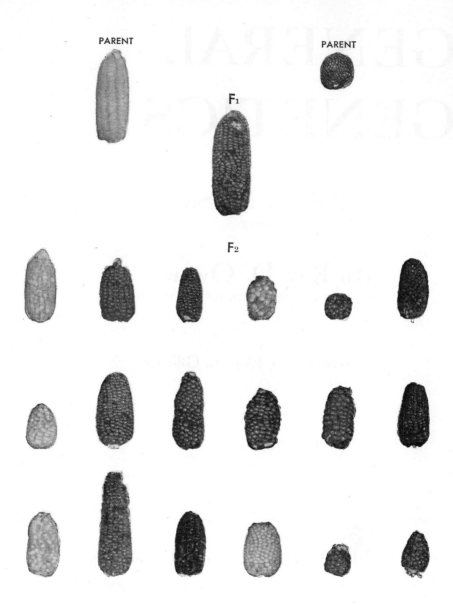

Frontispiece. Plate I. *An inbred sweet corn and "strawberry" popcorn produce very different ears. If such corns are used as the parents in a cross, the F₁ hybrids are uniform. In the next generation (F₂) many different types appear. (Courtesy of E. G. Anderson.)*

GENERAL
GENETICS

BY **Adrian M. Srb**
CORNELL UNIVERSITY

AND **Ray D. Owen**
CALIFORNIA INSTITUTE OF TECHNOLOGY

ILLUSTRATED BY **Evan L. Gillespie**

 W. H. Freeman and Company
SAN FRANCISCO, CALIFORNIA

1958

THE SCIENCE OF GENETICS is relatively young and in a state of exceptionally vigorous growth. It has branched into many fields, deriving sustenance and stimulus from its close interrelationships with cytology, evolution, biochemistry, physiology, morphogenesis, and practical agriculture; its development has depended in significant ways on the application of appropriate mathematical techniques; and, at many levels, genetics has important implications for the welfare of the human individual. These interrelationships are not sidelights but are part of genetics itself. For this reason, genetics offers great opportunities for integration of the student's knowledge of various fundamental aspects of biology. At the same time it offers great challenges to teachers of general genetics and to the writers of textbooks.

We have felt the urge to meet this challenge in our own way. In presenting the subject, we believe it most important that the general biological implications of genetics should never be lost from view. To accomplish this end, we have attempted from the outset to present genetics in terms of the effects of hereditary units, in dynamic interplay with environment, on the development and function of organisms. We have also thought it important to draw examples from a wide variety of living forms, ranging from microorganisms through diverse plants and animals to man. This has meant the abandonment of anything like a systematic historical approach to the subject. On the other hand, we have the strong conviction that genetics, as one of the great experimental sciences of our era, should be viewed as a series of problems and challenges, some of which have been successfully met and been supplanted by others. This means that genetic ideas may be developed along a logical sequence, from the simple to the complex. In following such a sequence, the book should be compatible with the over-all organization of most introductory courses in genetics as they are presently being taught.

Different courses in introductory genetics provide more or less time for presentation of the subject; and instructors may wish to emphasize or neglect certain areas of the field as appropriate to the needs of their students. We have attempted to plan a certain amount of flexibility for this text in anticipation of varying situations. The first sixteen chapters provide elementary coverage of the so-called "classical" areas of genetics. These areas are included in almost every general course in the subject. Chapters 17, 18, and 19 are concerned with some of the details of genic effects that have emerged from recent investigations. Where there is a limitation on time, instructors in certain introductory courses, for example those serving as a prerequisite to work in applied genetics in agricultural schools, may choose to omit portions of these three chapters from formal assignment. On the other hand, students majoring in a basic biological science will find these chapters fundamental. Chapters 20 and 21 present population genetics in fair detail. Here again there is opportunity for selection of material in the light of particular course needs. The final group of three chapters emphasizes application of genetic principles. Chapters 22 and 23 should be of special interest and use to students in colleges of agriculture. But this material may be conveniently omitted, without loss in continuity, if it is inappropriate to a particular course. Chapter 24 summarizes aspects of genetics that relate to the welfare of the human individual. Examples of inheritance in man are found throughout the book.

The illustrations are meant to be an integral part of our presentation of genetics. They should be considered in context. The references at the end of each chapter are no doubt too extensive to be read in entirety by the ordinary undergraduate student. Admittedly, some of this reference material may be overly difficult for a beginner in the field. But the references are meant to serve a variety of needs, including those of students with special interests and capabilities and those of relatively advanced students who are reviewing general genetics. The annotations of references should help the individual student and teacher to select reading suitable to his purposes and interest.

Since genetics is essentially a "problem-solving" kind of science, questions and problems are a major accessory to a genetics text. We have been particularly concerned to confront the student with actual experimental situations for his interpretation. The problems following the different chapters are to some degree graded in difficulty; those toward the end of each sequence are designed to challenge the serious student of genetics.

The order of author names on this book in no way signifies a major and a minor effort or responsibility. We have undertaken the work on as equivalent a basis as possible and must share equally the responsibility for its merits and deficiencies. But for whatever merits there are, we wish to acknowledge gratefully the contributions of many other persons. First of all, our wives, Jo and June, have contributed substantial aid, as well as an uncommon measure of patience and understanding. G. W. Beadle, Ralph Emerson, and D. M. Whitaker, Editors of the W. H. Freeman and Company Biology Series, have provided critical comment on the manuscript. Additional critical reading furnished by the publishers was done by G. H. Mickey. Among our professional associates, many have read various portions of the text and passed on to us their helpful comments. These include D. W. Bishop, I. Blumen, R. W. Bratton, R. L. Cushing, Zlata Dayton, W. T. Federer, E. Hadorn, C. R. Henderson, N. H. Horowitz, E. B. Lewis,

H. M. Munger, Margerie Shaw, H. H. Smith, Curt Stern, A. H. Sturtevant, A. Tyler, C. H. Uhl, and R. P. Wagner. Claude Hinton, Dan Lindsley, Earl Patterson, Carlos Schlottfeldt, and Val Woodward have helped in reading proof and in other ways. Mrs. Alfred B. Clark kindly typed portions of the manuscript.

We also owe numerous debts of gratitude for special materials that have gone into making up the book. The W. B. Saunders Company and A. H. Sturtevant and G. W. Beadle generously loaned us use of the Drosophila eye color plate. Materials for the corn color plate were made available to us and grown especially for our purposes by E. G. Anderson. Color transparencies for the fox color plate were prepared for our use by R. M. Shackelford, of the University of Wisconsin. We are also indebted to A. B. Chapman for the materials illustrating the Wisconsin Swine Selection Cooperative Program, of which we made extensive use in Chapter 23. R. A. Brink provided the photograph of semisterile corn. And H. M. Munger has permitted us to utilize illustrations from an unpublished outline to his course in plant breeding at Cornell. A condensation of an extensive review of the action of colchicine on dividing cells was made available to us by O. J. Eigsti. We are particularly indebted to Dr. Marta S. Walters and Dr. Spencer W. Brown for the photomicrographs reproduced in Figure 7-6. These are selected from a series of twenty large prints that may be obtained from Dr. Walters, 3844 Lincoln Road, Santa Barbara, California. The series shows a mitotic sequence in great clarity and detail. We are indebted to Professor R. A. Fisher, Cambridge, and to Messrs. Oliver and Boyd Ltd., Edinburgh, for permission to reprint Table 3-5 from their book, *Statistical Methods for Research Workers.*

The illustrations of Evan Gillespie speak eloquently for themselves, but we wish to pay personal tribute to our illustrator's insight and imaginative collaboration.

ADRIAN M. SRB
RAY D. OWEN

CONTENTS

CONTENTS

ix

CHAPTER 1

Inherent Patterns
in Living Things

WHENEVER we look at all closely at a plant or animal, it acquires individuality in our eyes. Consciously or unconsciously we begin to describe it in terms of certain of its qualities, such as color, shape, size, or activities. These attributes are peculiarly important to the individual in defining his place in the scheme of things. Clearly, it is of significance to us that we are human beings, and not sweet peas or crayfish. It is also a matter of moment to us whether we are tall or short, bright or dull, whether we have the usual number of fingers and toes, or are uncommonly predisposed to certain kinds of cancers. These things are important because they have a great deal to do with our status among our fellows, with the kinds of jobs at which we are most capable, and with many other aspects of our happiness and well-being. In somewhat the same way, the particular qualities of chipmunks or even of milkweeds must profoundly affect their orientation in their own provinces.

For us as thinking beings, an understanding of the basis of the attributes of living things is fundamental in our attempts to orient and adjust ourselves in a universe in which the importance of living things seems to us to be great. Moreover, we can scarcely afford to be indifferent to what it is that accounts for egg-laying in chickens, or vitamin A in corn, or for the production of rubber by particular kinds of plants. If we are to succeed in altering plants and animals in ways that seem to us desirable, we must learn about the bases of their characteristics.

Genetics is one of the sciences concerned with increasing our knowledge of *why* organisms are the way they are. Genetics, you will find, is characterized by distinctive aims and methods as well as by its accomplishments. All these are limited, and in a sense directed, by the nature of the life attributes with which it deals. As a field, genetics has many facets; and like other experimental sciences, it has not advanced uniformly on all fronts, but has progressed amoebalike, as fingers of successful investigation have pushed out here and there. Because its boundaries are not clearly limited, it is difficult to define in a sentence or two. We shall have to gain our preliminary in-

1

sight into genetics by considering in a general way how its problems and lines of approach have evolved from the basic characteristics of living things —their essential functional similarity, their conformity to regular pattern, and their almost infinite variety.

The Functional Similarity of Living Things. If *genetics* is difficult to define, *life* is even more so. In fact, a brilliant and interesting essay has been written on the "meaninglessness of the terms *life* and *living*." Yet, for the most part, we can readily recognize living things by certain attributes they have in common. These include such properties as reproduction, growth, spontaneous movement, metabolism, and responsiveness.

Accumulating evidence also suggests a striking similarity in much of the fundamental biochemistry of all kinds of living systems. For instance, certain steps in the biological synthesis of the amino acid arginine take place according to the same general reaction scheme in bacteria, in the molds Penicillium and Neurospora, and in guinea pigs, mice, and, probably, in man. Rats and Neurospora convert tryptophane into the vitamin nicotinic acid through similar biochemical mechanisms, and at least some of the functions of thiamine are alike for bacteria and for mammals. A British biochemist, Ernest Baldwin, points to a "common chemical ground plan to which the bloods and tissue fluids of all animals must conform."

The fact that the same chemical reactions are characteristic of cells of such diverse origin as a dog's liver and the mycelium of bread mold does not mean that all organisms are entirely alike; it does serve to emphasize that the many different characteristics of living things have been woven into backgrounds of essentially the same material.

The Conformity to Pattern in Living Things. The processes by which higher plants and animals arrive at their adulthood give striking testimony that living things conform to regular patterns. Consider that, for a given individual, life begins as a single fertilized egg cell. This cell multiplies, and its derivative cells redivide, aggregate, differentiate—all in a most remarkable and well-integrated manner—until the ultimate form characteristic of the adult organism is reached. Usually, the adult produces reproductive cells, either eggs or sperm. These unite with corresponding cells from a member of the opposite sex. Repeating the developmental stages of the generation before, such cells give rise eventually to new adults. Since life as we know it comes only from pre-existing life, each individual is a member of a series which, generation after generation, parades through indefinite time.

It is apparent that there must be governing principles that regulate the continuity of the life forms that you see illustrated in Figure 1-1. The complex embryonic foldings, the growth, and the differentiation of development can in no sense be events occurring at random. They require unusually precise coordination in time and space if the normal life cycle is to be completed.

One way of demonstrating the precision of this coordination is to disrupt

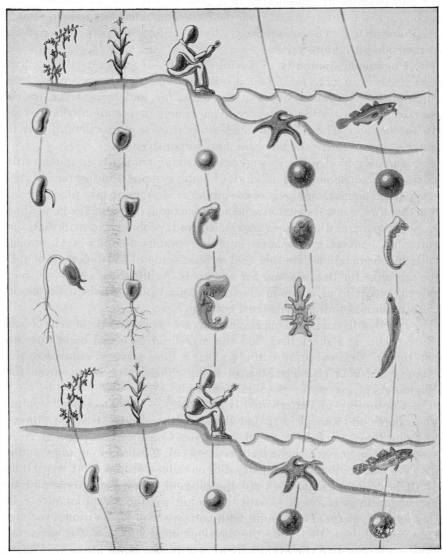

Figure 1-1. *The development of a mature individual from a fertilized egg cell involves a complex series of precisely coordinated events. This developmental sequence is characteristic of the species and displays an uninterrupted continuity from one generation to the next.*

it and observe the consequences. In laboratory experiments the regular sequence in the development of an individual can sometimes be arrested, for example, by so simple an agent as low temperature, or by changing the chemical environment of the embryo. Figure 1-2 illustrates the cyclopean (one-eyed) forms of the Atlantic Coast minnow that may be produced when eggs of this fish are permitted to develop in sea water to which an excess of

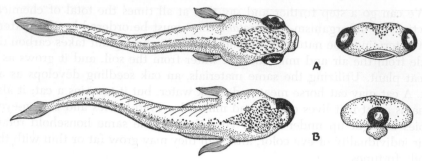

Figure 1-2. *The results of normal and abnormal differentiation in Fundulus, the Atlantic Coast minnow. A, representation of a normal individual with the usual two eyes. B, a cyclopean (one-eyed) individual that developed in sea water to which magnesium chloride had been added. (Redrawn from Figs. 23, 25, and 58 of C. R. Stockard, J. Exp. Zool., 6:303, 325, 1909.)*

magnesium chloride has been added. This profound deviation from normal development, evoked by so slight a change in the environment, emphasizes the delicate precision of the processes through which normal minnows develop in their normal oceanic environment.

Transmission of Pattern Through a Line of Descent. On the basis of the origin of a particular fertilized egg cell, we can make some definite predictions about its potentialities for development. We can take it to be invariable that a radish seed will give rise to a radish and not to some other kind of plant, and that cats can hope for nothing other than kittens in their litters. Of course, tailless cats may sometimes turn up, or, even more rarely, two-headed monsters. Among the progeny of cats, however, not even the grossest exceptions to the normal will be dogs or field mice.

These facts, which seem so very obvious to us because of our undeviating experience with them, are profound in their implications. They imply that organisms have particular characteristics because they have developed according to particular patterns. And since at least the general pattern of an individual always agrees so closely with the parents of the individual, we may suppose it to be *inherited* from parents by progeny. Presumably, this inherited pattern must be transmitted through sperm and egg cells, since these often provide the only genuine physical continuity from one generation to the next.

What is the basis of the pattern of an individual, and how does it impose its design? If it is inherited, in what manner does this inheritance take place? Questions of this kind are amplified when we take into consideration that the morphological events involved in the development of an individual are only an expression of a myriad of complex physicochemical reactions that form the basis for the grosser transformations seen at the anatomical level. Therefore, the chemical processes that give rise to an exact and orderly embryogeny must themselves be under precise control.

We can go a step further and say that at all times the total of chemical reactions of an organism—its *metabolism*—must be ordered by the pattern that determines the nature of the individual. A wheat plant takes carbon dioxide from the air and minerals and water from the soil, and it grows as a wheat plant. Utilizing the same materials, an oak seedling develops as an oak. A cat may eat horse meat and drink water, but it remains a cat; it also remains a cat if it lives on fish and milk. Blue-eyed babies and brown-eyed babies brought up under similar conditions in the same household retain their individuality of eye color, although they may grow fat or thin with the family fortunes.

It is a basic attribute of organisms that, within limits, they can develop their characteristic life form and maintain it against various environmental forces impinging on them. At the same time they utilize selected portions of the environment for their growth and maintenance as individuals. This means that the pattern of an individual is essentially a set of potentialities— primarily potentialities for carrying out certain chemical reactions. The realization of the pattern depends on environment, for it is from environment that the material for carrying out reactions must come. Genetics is not the study of heredity alone but must inevitably deal with environment as well.

The Fundamental Dynamism of Living Systems. From a chemical standpoint the living system is never at rest and never escapes the need for regulation of its physiological processes. With any energy-requiring activity, even the movement of an eyelid, there is set in train a particular series of chemical events, often complex, which faithfully follows a course that is characteristic of the organism and of the activity. Even for an apparently inactive plant or animal, such reactions are so numerous and complex that we can scarcely comprehend their scope, let alone describe them in their entirety.

In efforts to translate life functions into comprehensible terms, biologists have often drawn analogies between organisms and complex machines, such as combustion engines. Foods are likened to fuels that must be fed into an engine to be burned before certain activities can be carried out. Actually, such comparisons give a very imperfect indication of the real dynamism of living systems. This is because we know that the structural units of the organism are themselves undergoing constant chemical transformation and regeneration. You cannot distinguish "fuel" and "machine" in a living organism; the fuel is constantly being incorporated into the machine parts, and the machine parts are constantly being transformed into fuel, in a system that is the essence of dynamic flux.

The fact of these transformations can be demonstrated by introducing "labelled" metabolites, such as fats or amino acids, into the diets of organisms. Labelling molecules involves replacing some normal constituent atom of a molecule with an atom of a radioactive tracer or other isotope of the element involved. (*Isotopes* of an element are different forms of the element that behave alike in chemical and physiological reactivity but may be distinguished on the basis of different physical properties.) Compounds that arise through metabolism of a labelled dietary compound can be detected by the presence of the isotope and then identified. From the results of studies of this kind has emerged the concept that the large molecules of an organism are continually being fragmented into a pool of smaller components of the metabolic system, and that these small components become available for all kinds of biochemical reactions—syntheses, degradations, and regenerations.

The "life machine" itself, then, is a most dynamic sort of entity. To maintain the individuality of the "life machine" and to carry out its different activities demand that the reactions of the body constituents be scrupulously controlled, as, indeed, we know they are. Typically, these reactions are under the immediate control of *enzymes*, which are substances with the catalytic property of greatly accelerating particular biochemical transformations. Usually, at least, a given enzyme is highly specific as to the chemical reaction it promotes. Since an organism's structure and activities depend on its ability to perform particular chemical reactions, it is fair from one point of view to say that the nature of an organism depends on the kinds of enzymes it possesses. This means that part of our thinking about the hereditary pattern of organisms should ultimately refer to enzyme systems.

The Scope of Genetics. Geneticists have been and are concerned with many things in addition to the inherent patterns of metabolism that characterize different organisms. Generally speaking, the characteristics of plants and animals that arrest our interest are not observed in the form of chemical reactions as such, but, rather, as the effects of chemical reactions. And, as a matter of fact, many of the attributes we observe in an organism cannot, in our present state of knowledge, be described in chemical terms. What we know about the physiological bases of morphology permits not so much as a guess as to the particular biochemistry accounting for the absence of sweat glands in some few people or, for that matter, their presence in the large majority of persons. Yet, in the last analysis, this difference among people must be grounded in the biochemistry of development. On the other hand, it is fairly easy to see, and actually to analyze, how the blue color of a delphinium flower is a matter of particular biochemistry. We may hope that ultimately all the characteristics of organisms will be subject to description and understanding in terms of physics and chemistry. Meantime, you will find that geneticists have worked at many levels and from many directions in analyzing the factors underlying the various characteristics of organisms.

The scope of genetics may best be appreciated by summarizing the broad problems with which it deals. From the standpoint of the individual, the development and maintenance of his own unique, inherent pattern in dynamic interplay with the environment are the central problems of life. To the species, the ability to transfer these systems to other generations is the primary requirement for continued existence. For living forms as a whole, the orderly variety of patterns and their changes with time on a geological scale

PLATE II

WILD TYPE (RED)

BLENDED CROSS

SILVER BLACK

WHITE MARKED

PLATINUM

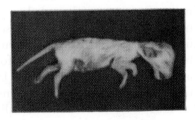

HOMOZYGOUS PLATINUM

Plate II. *A wild-type fox, and foxes showing coat colors that differ from the standard type. (Courtesy of R. M. Shackelford.)*

PLATE III

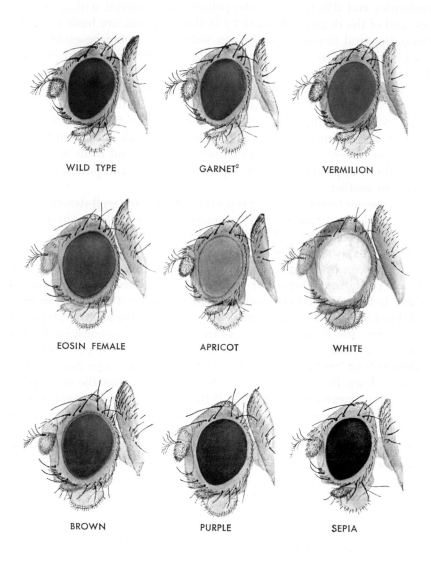

WILD TYPE GARNET[2] VERMILION

EOSIN FEMALE APRICOT WHITE

BROWN PURPLE SEPIA

Plate III. *The wild-type eye-color of* Drosophila melanogaster, *and some of the deviant types that have been found.* (*E. M. Wallace,* pinx. *From Sturtevant and Beadle,* An Introduction to Genetics. *Philadelphia: W. B. Saunders and Co., 1939.*)

constitute the accomplishment of organic evolution. The controlled evolution of plant and animal systems, on a time-scale of human lifetimes, is the challenge of plant and animal improvement through breeding. The definitions of similarities and differences in the patterns encountered within our own species, and of the degrees of plasticity of these systems, are basic to human understanding and important to human welfare. It should be clear that in studying genetics we are dealing with fundamental properties and problems of life and of living.

The Genetic Approach Through Differences Among Living Things. We have emphasized the threads of essential functional identity that run through the varied array of living forms. Superimposed on this basic identity are a vast variety of differences that make the pattern of each individual to some degree unique. These *individual differences* can be useful to us in learning how the individual patterns are developed, maintained, and passed from one generation to another.

For each species being studied it is useful to have some well-described and agreed-upon *standard type* with which individuals can be compared in this analysis of differences. In many plants and animals the selection of the stand-. ard type is relatively easy. The breeder of foxes, for example, knows that the wild, red type constitutes a fairly homogeneous population with regard to the characteristics most important in foxes bred in captivity. It is therefore reasonable to take the wild type as a standard and to treat the different kinds of ranch-bred foxes as deviations from this type. (For the standard type and certain deviants see Plate II.) This is often done quite unconsciously. The breeder who discusses his "cross foxes" does not say in so many words that he is talking about "foxes that differ from wild type in having a darker, cross-shaped area down the back and across the shoulders." But the comparison with wild type is nevertheless implied. If there were no such standard reference, it would be impossible to describe a whole fox with so short a term as "cross." Similarly, in many other animals and plants the existence of a familiar wild type provides a convenient basis for comparisons. In *Drosophila melanogaster,* an insect whose genetics has been extensively studied, a carefully defined wild type has been extremely useful to investigators. Many inherited variations from the wild type have been analyzed, for example the various eye colors illustrated in Plate III.

The selection of a standard type may be more difficult in other species. The real wild ancestor of corn, for example, is unknown, and the corn with which we are familiar could never have survived in nature without help from men in the dissemination of its seed. We know only cultivated corn, and this exists in so many varieties that the choice of a standard type becomes an arbitrary matter. The variety that is most common in our everyday experience is a convenient standard in such a case. When we single out a peculiarity of corn for consideration, we usually mean a peculiarity compared with the yellow dent corn that is the predominant type in our corn belt. For instance, char-

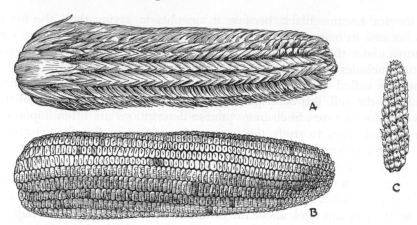

Figure 1-3. *Modern pod corn* (A) *differs from the familiar yellow dent* (B) *in a way reminiscent of a variety cultivated in prehistoric America. C is an artist's reconstruction of primitive pod corn from Bat Cave, New Mexico—a corn in use at approximately 2500* B.C. (*After Mangelsdorf and Smith,* J. Heredity, **40:**39, 1949.)

acteristics like "pod" and "Corn grass," shown in Figures 1-3 and 1-4, may well seem peculiar to us. At least they are clearly different from almost everyone's idea of a standard type of corn. But, actually, either pod corn or Corn grass, or both, may be somewhat more like the wild ancestors of corn than is the standard. On the other hand, yellow dent corn is doubtless about as specialized a product of human selection as is any plant in existence. This serves to illustrate that the definition of a standard type is largely a matter of convenience in the description of individual differences, and that it need not have any profound functional or evolutionary significance in itself.

With a standard type for any species in mind, a virtually endless variety of individual differences within the species becomes apparent. These range from very obvious characteristics to subtle ones detectable only by close observation, measurement, and testing. How do these differences come about? To what extent are they inherited as such, and to what extent may they be the result of differences in the environments in which the individuals develop and live? Most important, what can a consideration of these differences teach us about the transmission of functional potentialities from generation to generation?

The differences themselves are not so important from our present point of view as are the developmental processes that produce them. To observe that a fox is black in contrast to the red of the wild type is essentially a static observation. This fox is black—so what? We are really asking: "Why did this fox become black?" Now, there are at least three kinds of answers to such a question. One is to note that the fox is black instead of red because it has a different kind, or amount, or distribution of pigment in its hair. This is a descriptive answer; in a way it does not make sense as an explanation of why the fox became black, because it amounts to saying that "the fox is black because its hair (which is the part of the fox we are talking about) can be shown under the microscope to be so colored as to look black." If the description includes the observation that the pigment belongs to the class of compounds called melanins, and is often present in the form of discrete granules in the cell, this description certainly adds to our knowledge of the bases of color in foxes. Such more precise descriptions are often important in suggesting ways to study the processes resulting in the characteristics under consideration, but they do not usually explain those processes.

A second kind of answer is to note that the fox is black because the fertilized egg which gave rise to this particular fox contained "genes for blackness" from the father and mother. (We shall have a good deal to say in the early sections of this book about the existence, nature, and physical relationships of such genes, which for the present you may think of simply as units of inheritance.) But this is also a descriptive answer. It is descriptive of the fertilized egg in terms of its potentialities for development. It does not ex-

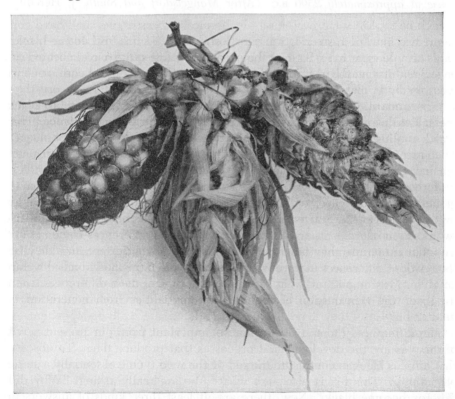

Figure 1-4. *"Corn grass" is a simply inherited, variant characteristic of corn with attributes that might have occurred in the wild ancestors of corn. (Courtesy of W. R. Singleton, Brookhaven National Laboratory, Am. Naturalist, 85:84, 1951.)*

plain why the fox is black; it simply describes the beginning of a potentially black fox.

The third kind of answer would be to note that black foxes may differ from red foxes in an enzyme involved in pigment synthesis. If this were known, it might seem to be the most hopeful kind of answer in explaining why a black fox is black. It would define an essential difference in the system of color development; it would offer a chance of contrasting the developmental proc- esses of which black and red are the different end results; it would even suggest the possibility of test-tube studies of relevant parts of these proc- esses. Here again, however, the answer is only another level of description. We may say that black foxes are black because of an enzyme difference from a wild type. But where does the enzyme difference come from?

It appears that we need all three kinds of answers to get a good idea of why black foxes are black. If we can trace the end product that we call a black fox through the material basis of its blackness, the pigment of its hair, and through the long chain of biochemical processes that are involved in the elaboration of this material, back to the genes with which it started life and which control in some way these biochemical processes, we shall have gone some way toward answering the question: "Why did *this* fox become black?" This simple question must now be seen to involve quite a complicated an- swer; and in fact the answer to this question, or to any similar one, is not yet completely available.

There are other complications. There is more to a black fox than just black- ness. Besides the pigment in his hair, which is probably a relatively super- ficial quality, the fox is made up of innumerable kinds of other molecules that are involved in and produced by thousands of biochemical reaction chains, the results of the specific catalytic activity of tens of thousands of different enzymes, perhaps controlled by about an equal number of separate genes. In dealing with the difference between black and red we have singled out only one of these. If we examined any particular black fox in detail we would certainly find many other differences from wild type—in form and function, in temperament and behavior, in qualities, and in measurable char- acteristics. Insofar as these are independent of the primary difference we are studying, we are justified in ignoring them in this connection. But we cannot be sure, without careful investigation, that any two such characteristics, no matter how little they may appear to be related, are really independent. An example may help to put this and other pertinent points in more concrete form.

Complex Effects of a Single Primary Difference.   One of the most-studied variations from the normal type of chicken is the characteristic called *frizzle*. There are at least two major distinguishable kinds of frizzles. We shall dis- cuss only the more extreme form here, and return to the other in the next chapter.

Frizzle fowls look more or less as one might imagine the proverbial hen

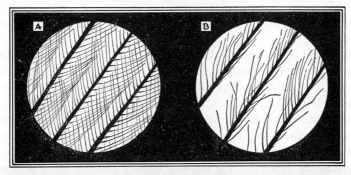

Figure 1-5. *Extreme frizzle fowls have very abnormal feathers. A, feathers from normal birds under low magnification show a closely interwebbed structure. B, frizzle feathers are weak and stringy. C, frizzles at the end of the breeding season are almost naked. D, even when fully feathered, an extreme frizzle has little insulation against heat loss. (A and B after Landauer, p. 131, "Temperature and Evolution," volume VI of* Biological Symposia, The Ronald Press Company, *1942. C and D courtesy of F. B. Hutt,* J. Genetics, **22:**126, 1930.)

to have looked when she got off the hot griddle. Their feathers are brittle, and curly or even corkscrew in shape; they wear off so easily that the birds may be nearly naked for intervals in their lives. Potentially frizzle chicks can be distinguished from normal ones at hatching by their rough down. As shown in Figure 1-5, frizzle feathers show extreme abnormalities of structure under even low magnification.

The striking difference between frizzle and normal seems, therefore, to have quite a simple basis. Frizzle appears to result from an abnormality in the process of feather development. But Landauer and others who have studied these birds have found a galaxy of other abnormalities associated with this primary variation. Frizzle hens do not lay many eggs, and in those fertile eggs that they do lay the embryos frequently die before hatching. The ovaries of frizzle hens remain immature and do not develop normally. Frizzle cocks, too, are of low fecundity. Growing frizzle chicks show a marked inability to adjust to a variable environment; their mortality curve rises sharply when they leave the relatively uniform conditions of the brooder for the fluctuations of the free range. Their metabolic rate is abnormally high, and it shows an interesting relation to environmental temperature. Measured as calories of heat produced per square meter of body surface in 24 hours, their metabolic rate increases by about 4 per cent for every fall of a degree in outside temperature, whereas the metabolic rate of normal birds under the same conditions does not vary. Frizzles, in spite of being much less active, eat more food than do normal birds of the same size and sex. Their hearts are larger, differently shaped, and beat faster. They sometimes die of sudden heart failure. Their blood shows many deviations, both chemical and cellular, from normal composition. The spleen is enlarged, as are the crop, gizzard, small intestine, cecae, pancreas, adrenals, and kidney. The thyroid may show abnormalities of size and microscopic structure. In fact, it appears that almost anywhere you look in the frizzle fowl, you find something wrong.

All these abnormalities, as graphically summarized in Figure 1-6, seem to be related more or less directly to the fact that chickens depend on normal down and feathers for insulation in maintaining a constant body temperature higher than the temperature of their usual environment. The curling, stringy feathers of frizzles, so easily worn away, are of little use as insulation. The result is a constant strain on the metabolic system of the bird in its physiologically dictated effort to compensate for abnormal heat loss. Even under the most favorable conditions, this constant strain is evident in the many, widespread abnormalities displayed by these birds. In the unfavorable environment offered by a changing outside temperature, however, the frizzle fowl is at its most severe disadvantage. Interestingly enough, the disadvantage does not hold for all environments; at high temperature, and under experimental conditions in which rapid heat loss is necessary, frizzles actually get along better than do normal birds. They may even survive conditions that kill ordinary chickens.

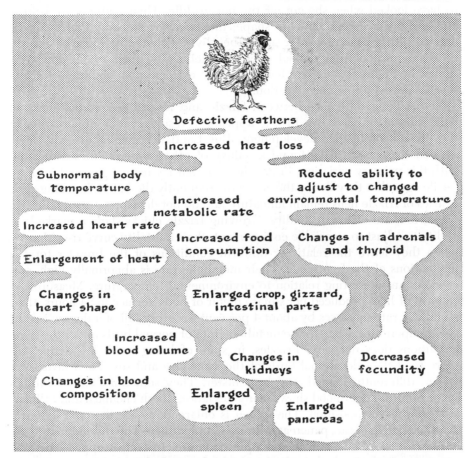

Figure 1-6. *Various abnormalities result from the primary aberration, defective feathers, in the frizzle fowl.* (*Based on Landauer, pp. 127–166, "Temperature and Evolution," volume VI of* Biological Symposia, *The Ronald Press Company, 1942.*)

We have considered the frizzle fowl in some detail to illustrate the multiplicity of secondary effects that may result from a single, simple primary deviation from the normal type. The biochemical basis of this particular unit difference is still obscure, hidden in the complex chemistry of feather development. The genetic basis of the difference, however, is clear-cut and it will be discussed in the next chapter.

Keys to the Significance of This Chapter

It will be understood, of course, that this chapter has been an introduction to a point of view, rather than an establishment of conclusions. A brief restatement of certain principles may help to clear the ground for the more detailed considerations to come:

An endless variety of individual differences are superimposed on the essential functional identity of all living forms. These differences are most easily described as contrasts with a selected standard type for each species. The standard type is often, but not always, a wild type.

Although most of the individual differences noted are morphological ones, they can all be regarded as the results of differences in processes occurring in the development or day-to-day functions of the individual. Emphasis on these processes, rather than simple descriptions of the more static end products of development, will help in understanding heredity as the transfer from generation to generation of *functional potentialities*.

The individual can be considered at all times during development to be an integrated collection of many unit processes in dynamic equilibrium with his environment. A deviation from standard type in any one of these unit processes may result in observable individual differences from type.

A complex of end-product effects may sometimes be traced back to a single primary developmental deviation. The frizzle fowl is a clear example; here a primary variation in feather development affects the regulation of body heat and thus indirectly modifies many parts of the body.

Genetics is concerned with the manner and extent of hereditary control of these primary differences in function.

References

Darlington, C. D., and Mather, K., *The Elements of Genetics*. New York: Macmillan Co., 1949. (Read the introduction, "The Aim and Scope of Genetics.")

Grüneberg, Hans, *Animal Genetics and Medicine*. New York: Paul B. Hoeber, 1947. (Chaps. 1, 2, and 3 introduce the concept of heritable disease as an aspect of developmental genetics. Chap. 3 includes description of a heritable anomaly in the rat where a single primary defect leads to multiple consequences. You may profitably consider this instance in relation to the case of the frizzle fowl.)

Haldane, J. B. S., *New Paths in Genetics*. New York: Harper & Bros., 1942. (Chaps. 1, 2, and 3 form an admirable exposition of modern genetic point of view. Although some of the terminology may be unfamiliar to the beginning student, these chapters should prove to be readable and even fascinating.)

Landauer, W., "Form and Function in the Frizzle Fowl: The Interaction of Hereditary Potentialities and Environmental Temperature." *Biol. Symposia*, 6:127–166, 1942. (Broad treatment of experimental studies with the frizzle fowl.)

Pirie, A. W., "The Meaninglessness of the Terms Life and Living," in *Perspectives in Biochemistry*. Cambridge: The University Press, 1937. (Deals in a fundamental way with the concept of "life.")

Questions and Problems

1-1. J. B. S. Haldane has said that "the aim of physiology is to consider how the internal environment of the body is kept constant in spite of continual alterations in the external environment." Discuss the frizzle fowl as a tool in approaching this aim of physiology.

1-2. Set up a series of criteria for distinguishing things that are alive from those that are not alive. Apply these criteria to yourself, a rock, a virus, and a "dead" cat.

1-3. Why should geneticists be interested in enzyme systems in relation to the hereditary patterns of individuals?

1-4. In view of the variety of individual differences found within the same species, even among wild plants and animals, how can one justify the adoption of "the wild type" as a standard for comparison?

1-5. We have described heredity as "the transmission from generation to generation of an integrated pattern of functional potentialities." Discuss the significance, in this connection, of the terms: (a) transmission, (b) generation, (c) integrated pattern, (d) functional potentialities.

1-6. Define, in appropriate detail, a "standard type" for an analysis of human differences. Cite a few apparently simple deviations from this type. To what extent do you regard each of these deviations as hereditary?

1-7. List a few of the individual differences that are of economic importance in (a) a cultivated plant, (b) a domestic animal. To what extent can you discern "single, primary differences" here?

CHAPTER 2

Units of Inheritance

W ITH THE principles developed in the first chapter in mind, we can now proceed to a more careful investigation of the bases of inherited differences among individuals. A brief general statement will help to put the problem in relatively specific form.

Sexual Reproduction. Throughout our introductory discussion we shall be primarily concerned with the type of reproduction in which the individual begins life as a fertilized egg, or *zygote*. There are, of course, other ways in which new individuals may originate. Strawberries, for example, like many other higher plants, may multiply by sending out "runners," which can take root and function as independent plants. Among other plants, new individuals are frequently developed by means of cuttings, or by grafting or budding. Many unicellular plants and animals may reproduce simply by dividing into "daughter cells." Molds and other organisms may produce asexual spores—specialized pieces of the parent organism capable of germinating to form new individuals. In honey bees the males usually develop from unfertilized eggs, and similar *parthenogenetic* development of the egg is not infrequent in other animals and plants. These and many other examples that might be cited illustrate *asexual* or *vegetative reproduction*. In none of them does the individual originate as a zygote, formed by the fusion of egg and sperm. Parthenogenesis is not strictly asexual, since one of the elements of sexual reproduction, the egg, is involved. Neither is it sexual reproduction in a complete sense, since the egg is not fertilized.

There are several good reasons for our emphasis on sexual reproduction. One is the fact that our own species, and the higher animals in which we are generally most interested, almost invariably reproduce by means of fertilized eggs. Sexual processes are also most important in the propagation of the higher plants. At the other end of the scale of plant and animal life, some of the most exciting and clever of recent researches have suggested that reproduction of a sexual type must sometimes occur among bacteria, and even among the ultramicroscopic parasites of bacteria called *bacteriophages*. Indeed, among most of the varied forms of life from bacteriophage to human, sexual reproduction plays a prominent role.

Another reason for emphasizing sexual reproduction is that it provides better opportunities for the analysis of inheritance than does vegetative propagation. When individuals multiply asexually, their offspring are almost literally "chips off the old block." The investigator cannot combine or extract inherited differences in asexually reproduced generations, and the lack of inherent variation in such a line of descent leaves few "handles" for the experimenter to grasp. In sexually reproducing material, on the other hand, differing individuals can be *crossed*, and the consequences of such combinations can be observed through successive generations. Thus sexual reproduction offers techniques useful for the investigation of the processes of inheritance, and the knowledge accumulated through such studies in turn helps in understanding the sexual reproduction that made the investigations possible. We shall be able to get some idea, as we progress, of why sexual reproduction is so important and so widespread in plants and animals; and through familiarity with the transmission of inherited potentialities in sexual reproduction we will find it easy to understand also the bases of asexual multiplication.

Sexual reproduction is so familiar a method of organic multiplication that few of us have had occasion to consider how remarkable it is. The sperm, the egg, and their fusion product, the zygote, are notable for their small size and for the precision of their organization and activity. It has been estimated that the sperm involved in the fertilization of all the eggs from which the present human population of the world developed could be packed into a volume about twice the size of a pinhead. The eggs, since they carry some stored materials for early development, are somewhat larger; nevertheless they are also small by our everyday standards. A half-gallon jug would hold almost all the eggs from which humans living in the world today originated. All of the biologically inherited qualities of human beings—the similarities as well as the differences that distinguish one human from another and from all other living things—have their basis in two pinheadsful of sperm and little more than half a gallon of eggs!

The minute and delicately organized material that forms the physical basis for the transmission of inherited qualities has been called *germ plasm*. We will be concerned with the analysis of the architecture and the activity of this germinal material.

Inheritance of Frizzle Characteristic in Chickens. As a first approach to a study of the nature of germ plasm, we can turn again to the frizzle fowl. It will be recalled that there are at least two major distinguishable kinds of frizzles; in Chapter 1 we spent some time describing the more extreme of these. What can we find out about the inheritance of this characteristic, apparently so simple in its primary effect on feather development but so profound in its consequent effects on the individual?

We first observe that frizzle is, in fact, a biologically inherited characteristic. When both of the parents of a family of chicks are extreme frizzles, all the chicks develop into extreme frizzles. When both of the parents are normal, all the chicks are normal. It is clear that the potentiality for frizzle is inherent in the germ plasm of frizzle fowls, and that the difference between frizzle and normal is transmitted as a controlling difference in their germinal materials.

To study the nature of this difference, we can begin by combining the two kinds of germ plasm in the same individual. This is done simply by crossing frizzle and normal birds. Thus, when we mate a frizzle rooster with a normal hen, we get fertilized eggs in which the male's contribution to the germ plasm, brought in by the sperm, includes the potentiality for frizzle, while the female's contribution, through her eggs, includes the potentiality for normal feathers. Alternatively, the *reciprocal* cross might be made—a normal cock mated with a frizzle hen. It turns out that the progeny of the reciprocal crosses are identical in this and a great variety of other similar instances with which we shall be concerned in the early part of this book.

We refer to the progeny of crosses between inherently unlike strains of individuals as *hybrids,* and to the process of producing them as *hybridization.*

Now, when the fertilized eggs containing a combination of the two kinds of germ plasm develop, we find that the hybrids are a new, milder kind of frizzle, almost intermediate between the two parental types (Fig. 2-1). Their feathers curl to some degree, but are less brittle and less modified

Figure 2-1. A *"mild"* frizzle fowl results from mating an extreme frizzle with a normal bird (cf. the extreme frizzles of Fig. 1-5). (Courtesy of F. B. Hutt, J. Genetics, **22:**126, 1930.)

Blood of great-grandparents

-Paternal :   -Maternal :

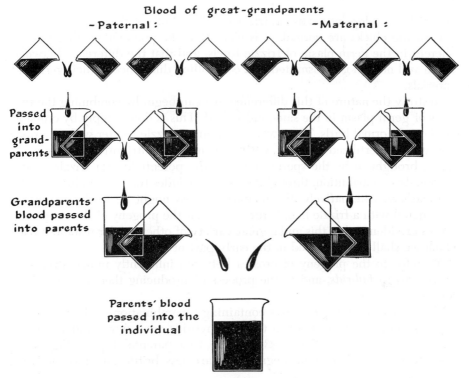

Passed into grand-parents

Grandparents' blood passed into parents

Parents' blood passed into the individual

Figure 2-2. *According to an outmoded idea of inheritance, the heredity of an individual was believed to depend on intermixture of the parents' blood. (After Scheinfeld,* The New You and Heredity, *Lippincott, 1950, p. 521.)*

than the feathers of extreme frizzles. The other abnormalities characteristic of frizzles are correspondingly less extreme, presumably because the more nearly normal feathers of these mild frizzles are better able to perform their function as insulators. These "mild" frizzles represent the second, major distinguishable type of frizzle to which previous reference has been made.

The first working hypothesis that one could suggest to explain this result of crossing extreme frizzle and normal chickens might be to assume that the two different "germinal fluids" had combined to form a homogeneous mixture. The developmental result of this blending could be the intermediate observed as the mild frizzle hybrid. This *blending* concept of the basis of inheritance is more or less like that involved when we talk about the inherent relationship of animals and of men in terms of "percentages of blood" (Fig. 2-2). The use of the term *blood* in a literal sense in this connection is, of course, archaic; we know that blood as such is not a vehicle of inheritance and that it is not passed as a germinal fluid from parent to offspring. Instead, the germ plasm within the sperm and egg is the essential physical bridge between sexually produced generations. But if (as no doubt is commonly the

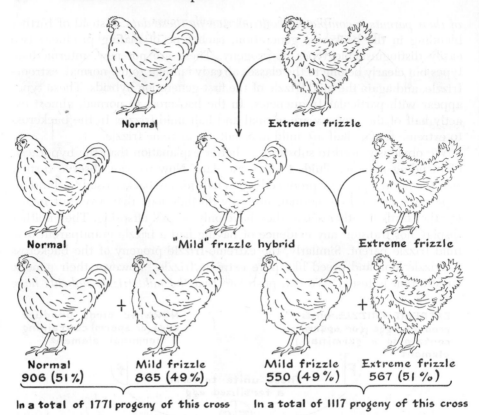

Normal   Extreme frizzle

Normal   "Mild" frizzle hybrid   Extreme frizzle

Normal   Mild frizzle   Mild frizzle   Extreme frizzle
906 (51%)   865 (49%)   550 (49%)   567 (51%)

In a total of 1771 progeny of this cross   In a total of 1117 progeny of this cross

Figure 2-3. *When "mild" frizzle hybrids are backcrossed to the parental types, the progeny do not display blending inheritance, but segregate into sharply distinct classes. (Data from Landauer, p. 134, "Temperature and Evolution," volume VI of* Biological Symposia, The Ronald Press Company, 1942.)

case nowadays) in speaking of "blood relationship" we mean "percentage of blending germinal fluids," then the intermediate frizzle hybrid could be understood as the result of such a blending process. We will need to check this working hypothesis further.

One good check is to breed the hybrids with the parental types. Such crosses, involving the mating of hybrids back to individuals like their parents, are called *backcrosses*. We can predict that, if the blending hypothesis holds, the result of mating mild frizzles to normals should be milder frizzles —again intermediates between the parental types in the cross. The result of mating mild frizzles to extreme frizzles should also be intermediate—birds more extreme than the mild hybrids but less so than the extreme frizzle. The actual results of these breeding experiments are given in Figure 2-3.

If you have accepted the blending hypothesis up to this point, you should be startled by this result. *The prediction based on the assumption that the mild frizzle hybrids represented a homogeneous blend of the germinal fluids of their parents is completely controverted by these data.* Instead of further blending in the backcross generation, each type of mating produces two easily distinguishable types of progeny. These are not new, intermediate types but clearly belong to the classes already familiar to us: normal, extreme frizzle, and again the mild frizzle of the first-generation hybrids. These types appear with particular frequencies. In the backcross to normal, almost exactly half of the progeny are normal and half mild frizzle. In the backcross to extreme frizzle, half are mild and half are extreme frizzle.

We obviously need to substitute a better explanation than the hypothesis of blending germinal fluids to fit these data. Now we can observe further that the normal progeny produced when hybrids are backcrossed to standard type birds are entirely normal; not only do they look that way, but mated to other birds like themselves they have only normal offspring. They neither display nor transmit any evidence of having had a frizzle grandparent or a mild frizzle parent. Similarly, the extreme frizzle progeny of the backcross to frizzle look and breed like pure extreme frizzles, however their genetic constitution is tested. We can postulate that *the mild frizzle hybrids have*

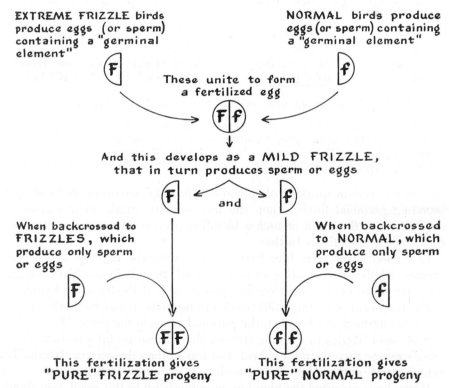

Figure 2-4. *The appearance of pure frizzles and pure normals in the backcrosses illustrated in Figure 2-3 can be understood in terms of germinal elements that do not blend or change.*

received a germinal element of some kind from each parent, and that these elements can be transmitted unchanged to their backcross progeny. The element controlling the potentiality for normal feathers, inherited from the normal parent, and the element for frizzle, from the frizzle parent, coexist in the hybrids without contaminating each other or blending with each other in any way, and are transmitted unchanged to their progeny. Figure 2-4 will help in understanding this new hypothesis.

This postulate accounts for the formation of pure normal and pure frizzle progeny in the respective backcrosses. But it is only part of the story. Half of the progeny of each backcross are mild frizzles like the first-generation hybrids. How would our new hypothesis explain them? (Try answering this from a consideration of Figure 2-4 before you read the next paragraph.)

You probably have the answer. We have postulated that the hybrids produce two kinds of germ cells, *f* and *F;* the normal progeny of the backcross to normal result from the combination of the *f* hybrid germ cell with a normal egg or sperm, while the extreme frizzle progeny of the backcross to frizzle come from a combination of the *F* hybrid germ cell with frizzle egg or sperm. But another combination is possible in each backcross, as shown in Figure 2-5.

The backcross results diagrammed in Figures 2-4 and 2-5 can now be considered together. When mild frizzle, first-generation hybrids are backcrossed to normal birds, they produce two, and only two, kinds of progeny: true normals and mild frizzles that look and breed like hybrids. The fact that these two types are produced *in approximately equal numbers* suggests that *two distinct kinds of germ cells, f and F, are produced by the hybrid in*

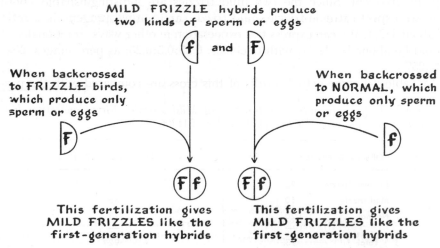

MILD FRIZZLE hybrids produce
two kinds of sperm or eggs

f and F

When backcrossed
to FRIZZLE birds,
which produce only
sperm or eggs

When backcrossed
to NORMAL, which
produce only sperm
or eggs

F

f

Ff   Ff

This fertilization gives
MILD FRIZZLES like the
first-generation hybrids

This fertilization gives
MILD FRIZZLES like the
first-generation hybrids

Figure 2-5. *The other possible combinations of germinal elements from the "mild" frizzle hybrids complete the explanation begun in Figure 2-4.*

Sperm from → Eggs from → Fertilized →   Type of
male hybrid   female hybrid   eggs   individuals produced

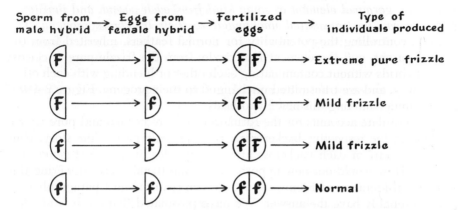

Figure 2-6. *The particulate concept of heredity makes a clear-cut prediction of the results of crossing "mild" frizzles together.*

equal proportions. The results of the backcross to frizzle are consistent with this observation.

We can test our hypothesis again by using it to predict the results of another type of mating. What kinds and proportions of progeny will be expected when the mild frizzle, first-generation hybrids are mated with each other? (Try reasoning out this prediction before reading the next paragraph.)

We have postulated that the hybrids produce two kinds of germ cells in equal numbers. The germ cells of two hybrids can then combine in four ways, as shown in Figure 2-6. These four combinations should be about equally frequent. Since the two mild frizzles are indistinguishable (both *Ff*), we expect extreme frizzle, mild frizzle, and normal progeny in a ratio of about 1:2:1. We can express this expectation in other ways: fractionally, it would be about ¼: ½:¼; with decimals, 0.25:0.5:0.25; as percentages, 25%: 50%:25%.

In Table 2-1 some actual results of this cross are compared with the pre-

TABLE 2-1. *Results of Intercrossing Mild Frizzle, First-Generation Hybrids. (Landauer and Dunn, J. Heredity,* **21**:*300, 1930.)*

OBSERVED NUMBERS		PREDICTED (1:2:1)
Extreme frizzle	23	23
Mild frizzle	50	46
Normal	20	23
	—	—
Total	93	92†

† Avoiding the absurdity of predicting fractions of chickens.

dictions. The agreement between experimental observation and prediction is obviously good enough to lend strong support to the hypothesis.

The Particulate Basis of Heredity. The points arising from this consideration of the inheritance of frizzle are of sufficient importance to justify their precise restatement:

1. The differences between normal and frizzle fowls depend on particulate elements in the germ plasm.

2. These particles are *paired* in an individual. One member of the pair is introduced by the sperm and comes from the father; the other, in the egg, comes from the mother.

3. When an individual forms germ cells, the paired particles, of paternal and maternal origin, respectively, separate cleanly without having influenced each other and go into different germ cells.

4. The determination of hereditary similarities and differences is therefore not a matter of blending germinal fluids but of separations and combinations of units in the germ plasm—units that maintain their separate identity from generation to generation.

5. We have already suggested (Chap. 1) that the differences between normal and frizzle fowls can all be explained as consequences of a single (unit) deviation from the normal processes of feather development. It now appears that the basis of this developmental deviation is a unit difference in the germ plasm. The relationships between germinal unit and primary developmental effect, and between primary effect and extensive secondary consequences, appear in this case to be direct and straightforward. On the foundation of this and similar considerations we can hope to build a better understanding of how living organisms originate, develop, and function.

Terminology. Situations and concepts that are encountered frequently are commonly designated in a shorthand way by giving them special names. Genetics is a problem-solving kind of science, and we hope to minimize the memorizing aspects of it. But it would be inefficient to go on using sentences or long phrases to represent ideas for which single-word symbols are available. Accordingly, we will pause at this point to equip ourselves with the rudiments of a genetic vocabulary. The following are not intended as formal definitions to be memorized, but as descriptions of useful terms. Two, *hybrid* and *backcross*, have already demonstrated their utility.

A unit of heredity, exemplified by the element or particle controlling the potentiality for frizzle, is called a *gene*.

The members of a pair of such units, like F and f controlling the frizzle-normal alternative, are called *alleles*.

An individual's genetic constitution is called its *genotype*. Thus the genotype of a mild frizzle, first-generation hybrid is, with regard to this pair of alleles, Ff; a normal bird's genotype is ff. When the members of a given pair of alleles are alike in an individual (e.g., FF or ff), he is described as being *homozygous*. When they are unlike (e.g., Ff) the individual is *heterozygous*.

Thus a mild frizzle is heterozygous for the frizzle alleles, while an extreme frizzle is homozygous for frizzle, and normal birds are homozygous for the normal allele of frizzle. The corresponding nouns are sometimes used. For example, one may refer to the mild frizzle as a *heterozygote,* and to extreme frizzles or normals as *homozygotes.*

In typical laboratory investigations, true-breeding parent forms are crossed to produce a hybrid generation. The parents are frequently referred to as the P generation, and the hybrid generation as the F_1. The term F_1 is an abbreviation for "first filial generation." When F_1's are crossed with each other they produce an F_2 generation; these may produce an F_3, and so on.

Dominance. Studies of inheritance in a great variety of plants and animals have revealed a number of examples similar to that of the frizzle fowl. Blue Andalusian chickens, for example, are heterozygous for a pair of alleles that in homozygous condition produce white-splashed and black Andalusians, respectively. Roan shorthorn cattle are heterozygous for an allelic pair in which the corresponding homozygotes are, respectively, red or white. Crossing snapdragons having red flowers with those having white flowers yields plants bearing pink flowers; the latter are heterozygous. A rare allele in man, producing a very severe anemia (*thalassemia major*) in the homozygous condition, causes only a mild anemia (*thalassemia minor*) when heterozygous. A little practice with this kind of inheritance is offered by Problems 2-3 to 2-6.

Very frequently a minor complication is encountered in studying the inheritance of unit differences. This may be illustrated by fat color in rabbits. The fat beneath the skin is white in wild rabbits, yellow in certain domestic breeds. When rabbits from true-breeding strains of the two types are crossed, and the hybrids used in subsequent backcrosses and intercrosses in a classical genetic analysis, the results (in terms of ratios) are as shown in Figure 2-7. You will note in this figure three differences from the kind of results obtained with the frizzle fowl:

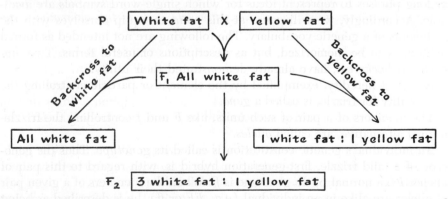

Figure 2-7. *Fat color in rabbits shows a pattern of inheritance in F_1, F_2, and backcrosses differing somewhat from the example of the frizzle fowl.*

1. The F_1's are not intermediate between the parental types, but are like one of the parents. Their fat is white, not light yellow.

2. The F_2 ratio is not 1:2:1, but 3:1. As in the F_1, no intermediate type appears.

3. The backcross to a particular one of the parental types (white fat) does not give progeny segregating into two classes; instead, all the progeny of this backcross are like this parent type.

There is a simple explanation of all this. First, we can observe in the backcross to the yellow-fat parental type that the hybrids do in fact possess and transmit a genetic unit for yellow fat. This allele, inherited by the hybrids from their yellow-fat parent, is passed on unchanged to their yellow-fat progeny in this backcross. Figure 2-8 shows that the situation here is comparable to that in the frizzle fowl.

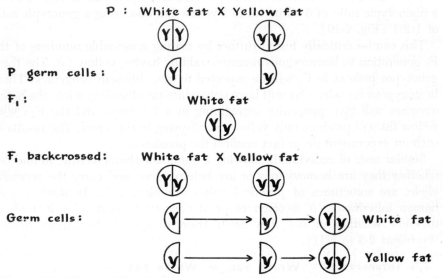

Figure 2-8. *When rabbits heterozygous for the fat color alternative are backcrossed to the recessive parent, the particulate basis of this alternative is revealed.*

The key consideration is the observation that, while the F_1 heterozygotes carry and transmit the factor for yellow fat, they do not show it. In some way, the Y gene (for white fat) appears to cover up or obscure the expression of its allele, y (for yellow fat). A shorthand description of this situation is to say that the Y allele is *dominant* to its alternative for yellow fat. The y allele is *recessive*.

You can see how this works in the other crosses. When the F_1 is backcrossed to the white-fat parental type, two genotypes are present in equal proportions in the progeny, but they all look alike (Fig. 2-9).

A more elegant way of saying that the progeny all look alike is to say that they have the same *phenotype*. Thus the term *phenotype* refers to the way

F₁ backcrossed: **White fat X White fat**

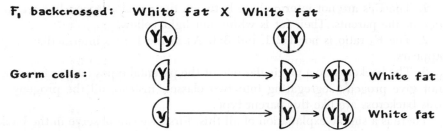

Figure 2-9. *Progeny of the backcross to the dominant parent do not segregate phenotypically.*

an individual looks, while his *genotype* describes his genic formula and the way he breeds.

When the F_1's are intercrossed to produce an F_2 generation, one observes a phenotypic ratio of 3 white fat to 1 yellow fat, obscuring a genotypic ratio of 1:2:1 (Fig. 2-10).

This can be critically tested further by mating reasonable numbers of the F_2 generation to homozygous recessive rabbits having yellow fat. The three genotypes present in F_2 will be expected to give different progenies: Those homozygous for white fat will have only white-fat offspring, while the heterozygotes will give progenies segregating in a 1:1 ratio, and the F_2's with yellow fat will produce only yellow-fat offspring in this cross. The results of such an experiment do in fact confirm the prediction.

Similar tests of individuals showing a dominant characteristic, to find out whether they are homozygous or are heterozygous and carry the recessive allele, are sometimes of practical value (Problem 2-7). In dealing with human inheritance, it is often of great concern to particular individuals to know whether or not they are carriers of specific hereditary defects (Problems 2-8 to 2-11).

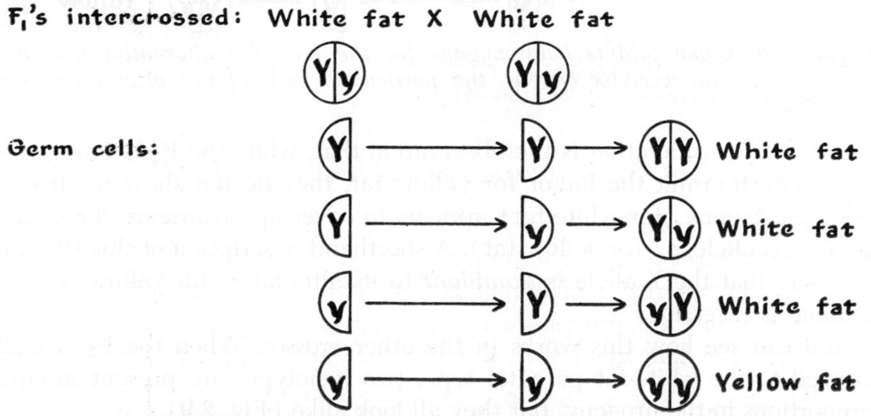

Figure 2-10. *Intercrossing individuals heterozygous for a dominant characteristic gives a 3:1 phenotypic ratio among the progeny. Dominance obscures the underlying 1:2:1 genotypic ratio.*

Physiological Aspects of Dominance. It would be a mistake to believe that by describing and naming the phenomenon of dominance, we have in any sense explained it. Instances of incomplete dominance, like the frizzle fowl, the Blue Andalusian, the roan shorthorn, thalassemia minor, and the pink snapdragon, are really rather exceptional. They are numerous enough, but they are far outnumbered by unit differences in which dominance of one allele over its alternative appears, at least on casual consideration, to be complete. What explanations, in terms of gene action in development, can we offer for this general tendency of one allele to obscure the expression of its alternative when both are present in an individual?

The example chosen to introduce dominance is one of a relatively few for which a material explanation is now at hand. When a wild rabbit eats green plants, one of the digestive processes that goes on in the rabbit's body is the breakdown of certain yellow-colored components (xanthophylls) of this kind of food. A specific enzyme in the liver controls this process. When a rabbit does not have the enzyme, the breakdown of xanthophylls to color-less derivatives does not occur, and they are instead stored intact in the animal's fat, giving it a yellow color. It is this difference, between the presence and the apparent absence of the enzyme, that is the immediate, physiological cause of the difference between white fat and yellow fat in rabbits. And the presence or absence of the enzymatic function is determined by the allelic alternatives Y and y.

This aspect of the way the Y and y alleles operate suggests a reasonable interpretation of their dominance relationship. An enzyme is an organic catalyst; probably only a relatively small amount of the appropriate enzyme is required to break down the xanthophyll in a rabbit's normal diet. When we observe that the two genotypes YY and Yy are phenotypically indistinguishable, we are observing that a single "dose" of the Y allele is sufficient to produce all the enzyme needed by a rabbit to break down all the xanthophyll he is likely to eat. It seems reasonable that this should be so. Perhaps the very frequency of dominance suggests that most genes produce their effects in essentially similar ways.

Keys to the Significance of This Chapter

In sexual reproduction, the fertilized egg constitutes a minute but precisely organized physical continuity between generations. The biologically inherited characteristics of plants and animals must be represented in an orderly way in the germ plasm contributed to the zygote by the egg and sperm. We are concerned with the structure and the activity of this germ plasm.

With regard to its structure, the germ plasm appears to include paired particles (*genes*) which maintain their separate identity from generation to generation.

With regard to its activity, the particles of germ plasm appear to produce their effects on the development and functions of the individual at least in part through the control of specific enzymes. A general relationship, *Unit Difference in Germ Plasm → Unit Difference in Development or Function*, seems to be emerging from our preliminary consideration of the nature of biological inheritance.

References

Mendel, G., "Versuche über Pflanzen Hybriden," 1866. (This classic of genetics is available in the original German as Vol. 42, No. 1 of the *Journal of Heredity*, 1951, and in English translation from the Harvard University Press, Cambridge, 1948.)

Neel, J. V., "The Detection of Genetic Carriers of Hereditary Disease." *Am. J. Human Genetics*, 1:19–36, 1949. (Somewhat technical in spots, but a very interesting and competent review of an important aspect of this subject.)

Scheinfeld, A., *The New You and Heredity*. Philadelphia: Lippincott Co., 1950. (This popular but accurate book provides an interesting survey of human heredity. Not a textbook, but a fine example of science writing for laymen.)

Stern, C., *Principles of Human Genetics*. San Francisco: W. H. Freeman and Co., 1949. (Especially, at this point, Chap. 3, "Genic Action," for an extension of our introduction to unit differences in heredity and development.)

Questions and Problems

2- 1. What do the following terms signify?

alleles	gene	parthenogenesis
backcross	genotype	phenotype
bacteriophage	heterozygote	recessive
dominance	homozygous	reciprocal crosses
F_2	hybridization	xanthophyll

2- 2. How does the particulate basis of inheritance we now recognize differ from the outmoded concept of "blending inheritance" with respect to the kind and amount of variation to be expected among the children in a family?

Thalassemia is a type of human anemia rather common in Mediterranean populations, relatively rare in other peoples. The disease occurs in two forms, minor and major; the latter is much more severe. Severely affected individuals are homozygous for an aberrant gene; mildly affected persons are heterozygous. Persons normal in this regard are homozygous for the normal allele. The following four questions relate to this situation.

2- 3. A man with thalassemia minor marries a normal woman. With respect to thalassemia, what types of children, and in what proportions, may they expect? Diagram the germ-cell unions producing children in this marriage, letting T = the allele for thalassemia, t = its normal alternative.

2- 4. Both father and mother in a particular family have thalassemia minor. What is the chance that their baby will be severely affected? Mildly affected? Normal? Diagram the possible germ-cell unions in this family.

2- 5. An infant has thalassemia major. According to the information so far given you, what possibilities might you expect to find if you checked the infant's parents for anemia?

2- 6. Thalassemia major is almost always fatal in childhood. How does this fact modify your answer to Question 2-5?

2- 7. Purebred Holstein-Friesian cattle are black and white. A recessive allele that, when homozygous, results in red and white is present but rare in this breed. Red-and-white calves are barred from registration, and therefore it is economically important to avoid using for breeding purposes black-and-white individuals that carry the undesirable recessive allele hidden in the heterozygous condition. How might you detect such heterozygosity in a bull to be used extensively in artificial insemination?

Huntington's chorea is a human nervous disorder characterized by purposeless, uncontrolled movements and progressive mental deterioration. The disorder does not occur in young people; affected individuals experience its gradual onset during the third or fourth decade of life.

2- 8. Persons with Huntington's chorea regularly have a parent who was similarly afflicted, and they regularly transmit the disorder to about half their children. What does this suggest as to the genetic basis of the disorder?

2- 9. If your answer to Question 2-8 is right, what chance has a young man whose father has Huntington's chorea to develop the disorder himself? What might you say to such an individual if he asked your advice about marrying and having children?

2-10. Recent studies suggest that young people who will later develop Huntington's chorea show abnormal electroencephalographic patterns ("brain waves"). If this is true, how might you modify your answer to Question 2-9?

2-11. Dr. James Neel (see "References" at the end of this chapter) lists thirty-four human disorders in which a genetic "carrier state" may be recognized. Of these, twelve are clear examples, and the remaining twenty-two are considered more dubious. Discuss the potential value to human welfare of clearing up the dubious instances, and of obtaining similar information about the many other hereditary disorders in which the carrier state cannot at present be recognized.

At the February and March, 1865, meetings of the Brünn (Austria) Natural History Society, a monk named Gregor Mendel read a paper destined to become the foundation of modern genetics. He reported a series of careful experiments with garden peas.

2-12. When Mendel used pollen from a dwarf strain of peas to fertilize the flowers of a true-breeding tall line, and planted the resulting seeds, only tall plants grew from them. But when he crossed these hybrids to dwarf plants, he observed among the progeny 87 tall and 79 dwarf plants. Diagram the basis of this early example of "Mendelian inheritance."

2-13. When Mendel allowed the F_1 hybrids of Problem 2-12 to self-fertilize, the resulting seeds produced an F_2 generation of 787 tall : 277 dwarf plants. How close are these to the expected numbers for an F_2 of 1064 plants?

2-14. Mendel took a sample of 100 of the tall plants of the F_2 generation in Problem 2-13 and allowed them to self-fertilize. Twenty-eight of them produced all tall progeny, and 72 produced some tall and some dwarf. How close is this to the expected distribution among the F_2 talls?

Hans Nachtsheim, of the Free University, Berlin-Dahlem, over a period of several years investigated an inherited anomaly of the white blood cells of rabbits. This *Pelger anomaly*, in its usual condition, involves an arrest of the typical segmentation of the nuclei of certain of the white cells. The rabbits do not appear to be seriously inconvenienced by this anomaly.

2-15. When rabbits showing the typical Pelger anomaly were mated with rabbits from a true-breeding normal stock, Nachtsheim counted 217 offspring showing the Pelger anomaly to 237 normal progeny. What appears to be the genetic basis of the Pelger anomaly?

2-16. When rabbits with the Pelger anomaly were mated to each other, Nachtsheim found 223 normal progeny, 439 showing the Pelger anomaly, and 39 *extremely abnormal progeny*. Besides having defective white blood cells, these very abnormal progeny showed severe deformities of the skeletal system, and almost all of them died soon after birth. What do you suppose these extremely defective rabbits represented in genetic terms? Why do you suppose that there were only 39 of them?

2-17. What additional experimental evidence might you collect to support or disprove your answers to Question 2-16?

2-18. About one human being in a thousand (in Berlin) shows a Pelger anomaly of white blood cells very similar to that described in rabbits. It is also inherited, in man, as a simple dominant, but in man the homozygous type has not been observed. Can you suggest why, if you are permitted an analogy with the condition in rabbits?

2-19. Again by analogy with rabbits, what might be expected among the children of a man and wife each showing the Pelger anomaly?

2-20. In Plate I (Frontispiece), two lines of corn, one with light colored ears and one with dark red, were crossed and produced a red F_1. Count the red and light colored (yellow or white) ears among the 18 successive F_2 ears illustrated. How does this color difference in corn appear to be inherited?

2-21. In the color plate illustrating Drosophila eye colors (Plate III) note the contrast between sepia eyes and the red eyes of the wild type. The difference depends on a single pair of alleles, in which the allele for sepia is recessive to its wild-type alternative. What eye colors would you observe, and in what proportions, in F_1, F_2, and both possible backcrosses, if sepia flies were crossed with a true-breeding wild-type strain?

2-22. Wild red foxes occasionally have a silver-black pup appearing as a "sport" in their litters (see Plate II). These "sports" had long been prized by trappers, when it was found that two such black foxes, reared and mated in captivity, at once established a true-breeding silver-black strain of foxes.

What is the most likely explanation of the rather frequent appearance of these "sports" in nature, and why was it so easy to establish true-breeding blacks that did not throw red progeny?

2-23. Suppose that in the future it should be found that individuals with thalassemia could be "cured" by giving them frequent massive injections of a particular vitamin. Would this modify our present opinion that thalassemia is a genetic condition? If so, how?

2-24. Under the assumptions of Question 2-23, would you expect that vitamin treatment of an affected individual would modify the expectation of thalassemia in his descendants?

CHAPTER 3

Two or More Pairs of Alleles:

Independence of Genetic Transmission

W E HAVE considered the transmission of one pair of alleles at a time. But we have also noted that many different units of heredity must be concerned in the many different unit processes occurring in the development and function of an organism. Do the members of different allelic pairs separate in the formation of germ cells and recombine at fertilization independently of each other, or does the behavior of one pair of alleles affect the pattern of transmission of another? Does the fact that many different genes are simultaneously affecting the development and functions of an individual result in the modification of the action or expression of one gene by another? The problem has two separate facets: The first comprises the extent to which the *patterns of transmission* of different pairs of particles in the germ plasm may be interdependent or independent. The second is the extent to which the *dynamic effects of different genes* may interact in controlling the processes that go on in the individual. We will be concerned with the first of these facets in this chapter and the second in Chapter 4.

A Dihybrid Cross in Tomatoes. First, we shall consider two pairs of unit differences in tomatoes (Fig. 3-1).

Tall Stature Versus Dwarf. Dwarf tomatoes differ from the familiar tall type in having short, thick stems and deeper green, puckered, and somewhat curved leaves.

Cut Versus Potato Leaves. The leaves of most tomatoes typically have cut margins, but some varieties are called potato-leaf types because their leaves are broad and entire, like the leaves of potato plants.

MacArthur, a Canadian geneticist, published extensive studies of these and many other characteristics of tomatoes. We will utilize his data and conclusions.

Considered separately, these pairs of differences behave in inheritance in a fashion now familiar:

Figure 3-1. A, *standard (tall) tomato plant.* B, *dwarf plant, the same age as A and grown under similar circumstances, but differing from it in a unit of inheritance.* C, *cut leaf.* D, *potato leaf in the tomato, differing from C in a unit of inheritance.* (*Photographs by R. H. Burnett.*)

P	tall × dwarf	cut × potato
F_1	tall	cut
F_2	3 tall : 1 dwarf	3 cut : 1 potato

When the tall F_1 is backcrossed to dwarf, one observes a ratio of 1 tall : 1 dwarf in the progeny. Similarly, F_1 cut backcrossed to potato gives 1 cut : 1 potato. It is evident that the difference between tall and dwarf behaves as a unit difference in inheritance, with tall being dominant; and similarly, the difference between cut and potato leaves is a unit difference, with cut dominant. (You can fill in genotypes, germ cells, and genotypic ratios for review. In doing so, let D = tall, d = dwarf; and C = cut, c = potato.)

Our problem is to consider how these two different pairs of alleles behave with respect to each other in inheritance. A way of studying this is to cross individuals that differ in both characteristics:

$$\text{tall, cut} \times \text{dwarf, potato}$$

When this cross is made, the F_1 shows both dominant characteristics, tall and cut. It is heterozygous for two pairs of alleles. Such an individual is called a *dihybrid*.

Now, a good method of testing the behavior of these two pairs of alleles with respect to each other is to backcross the F_1 to the dwarf, potato-leaf parent plant type.

Actual data obtained from this backcross are as follows:

> 77 tall, cut
> 62 tall, potato
> 72 dwarf, cut
> 73 dwarf, potato

There are four types among the backcross progeny—the original parental types and two new combinations, tall, potato and dwarf, cut. These four types appear in very nearly equal numbers.

It would appear that when the F_1 forms germ cells, the two different line-ups shown in Figure 3-2 occur with equal frequency. Subsequent fertilizations give the observed ratio in the backcross (Fig. 3-3).

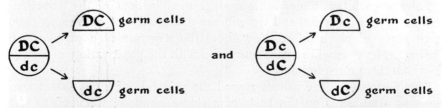

Figure 3-2. *When a dihybrid forms germ cells, there are two equally likely ways in which the germinal elements may line up. This results in the formation of four kinds of germ cells, in equal numbers.*

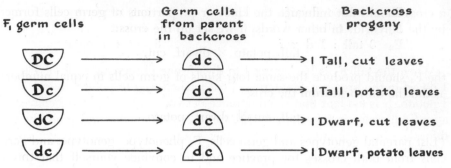

Figure 3-3. *The four kinds of germ cells produced by the dihybrid result in four distinct and equally frequent phenotypes among the progeny of a backcross to the double-recessive parent type.*

Segregation and Independent Assortment. There are two important implications in the dihybrid example just discussed.

First, the members of a given pair of alleles always separate from each other when an individual forms germ cells. We observed this in connection with single allelic pairs in the preceding chapter, and our present consideration of the dihybrid offers no occasion for modifying this rule. The backcross in the example above shows that about half of the progeny received the *D* allele from the dihybrid parent, and the other half the *d* allele. (The actual figures are $77 + 62 = 139D$, $72 + 73 = 145d$.) Similarly, about half received the *C* allele and half the *c*. (The figures are $77 + 72 = 149C$, and $62 + 73 = 135c$.) In working with and understanding genetics, it is important to observe this *principle of segregation* first of all: *The members of a pair of alleles separate cleanly from each other when an individual forms germ cells.*

The second rule is that *the members of different pairs of alleles assort independently of each other when germ cells are formed.*

In the dihybrid $\dfrac{D}{d}\dfrac{C}{c}$, *D* is just as likely to be included in a germ cell with *c* as it is to be with *C*, and *c* is equally likely to be with *D* or *d*. Another way of looking at the behavior of the *D-d* and the *C-c* allelic pairs as independent phenomena is suggested in Figure 3-4.

Later we will encounter some regular modifications of the principle of independent assortment, and we will see that studies of such modifications have provided much information about the structure of germ plasm. But for the present we will remain concerned with the great variety of instances in which this principle holds.

The Testcross. We cannot regard the principle of independent assortment as established on the basis of a single example; we need to test it further. Of the several possible tests, the first might involve this reasonable extension: The combinations in which two pairs of alleles are introduced in a cross should not influence the kinds or proportions of germ cells formed by the dihybrid. In other words, if we set up the cross:

tall, potato × dwarf, cut,

the F_1 should produce the same four kinds of germ cells in equal numbers, as did the dihybrid from the cross:

tall, cut × dwarf, potato.

(List parental genotypes and germ cells; F_1 phenotype, genotype, and germ cells from both crosses for practice and to convince yourself that this is indeed expected on the basis of independent assortment.)

Many tests of this sort have given results consistent with the predictions.

It will be obvious that in all such tests the F_1 should be crossed with individuals homozygous for both recessive characteristics. If, in the cross:

tall, potato × dwarf, cut

the F_1 is simply *backcrossed* to the tall parent, all the offspring will be phenotypically tall, since the tall parent contributes the dominant D allele to each backcross offspring. The segregation and assortment of the tall-dwarf alternative is therefore obscure. Similarly, a simple backcross to the cut parent will give only the cut phenotype in the progeny. Crossing to the double-recessive type (dwarf, potato) has the great virtue of *making the*

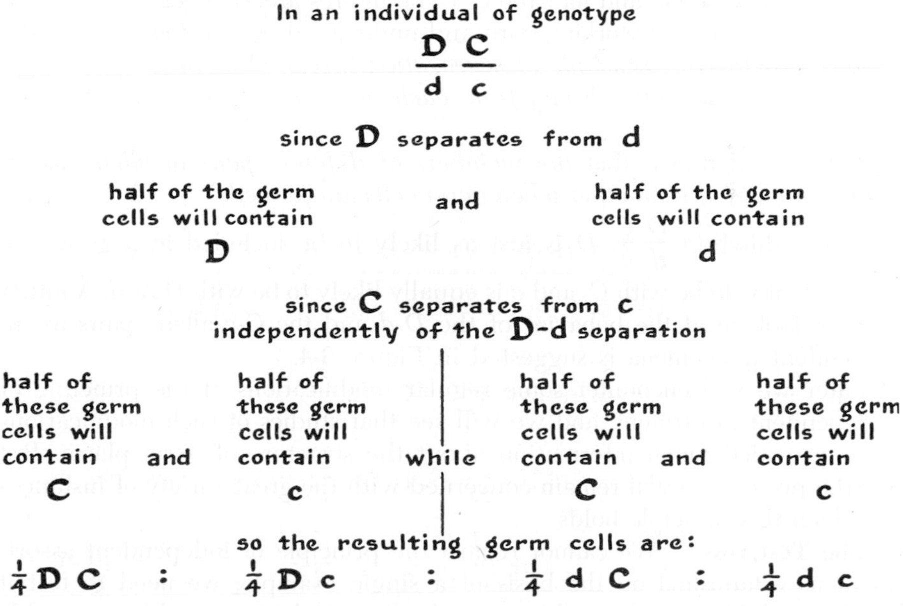

In an individual of genotype

$$\frac{D\ C}{d\ \ c}$$

since **D** separates from **d**

half of the germ cells will contain	and	half of the germ cells will contain
D		**d**

since **C** separates from **c**
independently of the **D-d** separation

half of these germ cells will contain	and	half of these germ cells will contain	while	half of these germ cells will contain	and	half of these germ cells will contain
C		c		**C**		c

so the resulting germ cells are:

$\frac{1}{4}$ **D C** : $\frac{1}{4}$ **D** c : $\frac{1}{4}$ d **C** : $\frac{1}{4}$ d c

Figure 3-4. *The separation of the C-c allelic pair, and of the D-d allelic pair, respectively, can be treated as independent events.*

segregation and assortment of both allelic pairs immediately apparent in the phenotypes of the progeny of the cross.

The cross with the double-recessive type is called a *testcross* to characterize it as distinct from a *backcross,* which is a cross of the F_1 with either of the parent types. Some backcrosses are testcrosses, and some testcrosses are backcrosses, but the two terms are not equivalent.

Dihybrid Ratios in the F_2 Generation. Another test of the principle of independent assortment involves carrying a dihybrid cross to the F_2 generation. The F_1 individuals are assumed to produce four kinds of germ cells in equal numbers. Under this assumption, what ratios do we predict among the progeny when two such individuals are crossed?

An easy way to illustrate the possible fertilizations is through the use of a "checkerboard," in which the four kinds of germ cells from one parent are listed in a row along the top, and the four kinds from the other parent are put in a column down the left margin. The 16 combinations are then obtained by "filling in" the checkerboard:

Sperm from Dihybrid Male

	$D\ C$	$D\ c$	$d\ C$	$d\ c$
$D\ C$	$\dfrac{D\ C}{D\ C}$	$\dfrac{D\ C}{D\ c}$	$\dfrac{D\ C}{d\ C}$	$\dfrac{D\ C}{d\ c}$
$D\ c$	$\dfrac{D\ c}{D\ C}$	$\dfrac{D\ c}{D\ c}$	$\dfrac{D\ c}{d\ C}$	$\dfrac{D\ c}{d\ c}$
$d\ C$	$\dfrac{d\ C}{D\ C}$	$\dfrac{d\ C}{D\ c}$	$\dfrac{d\ C}{d\ C}$	$\dfrac{d\ C}{d\ c}$
$d\ c$	$\dfrac{d\ c}{D\ C}$	$\dfrac{d\ c}{D\ c}$	$\dfrac{d\ c}{d\ C}$	$\dfrac{d\ c}{d\ c}$

Eggs from Dihybrid Female

Collecting like genotypes, we predict the following genotypes and phenotypes:

$$\tfrac{1}{16}\ \frac{D\ C}{D\ C} + \tfrac{2}{16}\ \frac{D\ C}{d\ C} + \tfrac{2}{16}\ \frac{D\ C}{D\ c} + \tfrac{4}{16}\ \frac{D\ C}{d\ c} = \tfrac{9}{16}\ \text{tall, cut}$$

$$\tfrac{1}{16}\ \frac{D\ c}{D\ c} + \tfrac{2}{16}\ \frac{D\ c}{d\ c} = \tfrac{3}{16}\ \text{tall, potato}$$

$$\tfrac{1}{16}\ \frac{d\ C}{d\ C} + \tfrac{2}{16}\ \frac{d\ C}{d\ c} = \tfrac{3}{16}\ \text{dwarf, cut}$$

$$\tfrac{1}{16}\ \frac{d\ c}{d\ c} = \tfrac{1}{16}\ \text{dwarf, potato.}$$

Table 3-1 shows an actual result of this cross as compared with the prediction. The observation is close to the prediction and confirms our hypothesis that these two pairs of alleles are independently transmitted. If one wanted to check the matter even further, the *genotypic* ratio of the F_2 could be tested by further matings. This has been done in many cases, and the results again confirm the hypothesis. (What further matings can you suggest that would be efficient in checking the F_2 genotypic ratio?)

TABLE 3-1. Results in F_2 of a Cross Between Tall, Potato and Dwarf, Cut Tomatoes. (MacArthur, Trans. Royal Can. Inst., 18:8, 1931.)

	TALL, CUT	TALL, POTATO	DWARF, CUT	DWARF, POTATO
Observed	926	288	293	104
Expected	906	302	302	101
(9:3:3:1)				

Probability

A shortcut to avoid the rather tedious completion of the checkerboard can be suggested for computing the F_2 ratios. The shortcut is based on one of the laws of chance that may be phrased as follows:

If two events are independent, the chance that they will occur together is the product of their separate probabilities.

It will be simpler to illustrate an application of this law than to engage in further definition. With regard to the tall-dwarf alternative in the F_2 generation, the expected 3:1 phenotypic ratio tells us that:

The chance (probability) that an individual plant will be tall = ¾; the chance that an individual plant will be dwarf = ¼.

Similarly, with regard to the cut-potato alternative:

The chance that an individual plant will be cut = ¾; the chance that an individual plant will be potato = ¼.

Assuming independence between these two pairs of alternatives, we can compute:
The chance that an individual plant will be:

$$
\begin{aligned}
\text{tall, cut} &= ¾ \times ¾ = 9/16 \\
\text{tall, potato} &= ¾ \times ¼ = 3/16 \\
\text{dwarf, cut} &= ¼ \times ¾ = 3/16 \\
\text{dwarf, potato} &= ¼ \times ¼ = 1/16
\end{aligned}
$$

This is the same result the checkerboard gave us.

TABLE 3-2. Distribution of Genotypes in F₂.

TALL-DWARF ALTERNATIVE		CUT-POTATO ALTERNATIVE	
GENOTYPE	PROBABILITY	GENOTYPE	PROBABILITY
DD	¼	CC	¼
Dd	½	Cc	½
dd	¼	cc	¼

Table 3-2 shows that essentially the same method can be used to compute genotypic ratios. You can pick out any genotype and compute its expected frequency separately, without filling in and collecting genotypes for the whole checkerboard. For example, the genotype $\dfrac{D\,c}{D\,c}$ occurs with the frequency ¼ × ¼ = ¹⁄₁₆, the genotype $\dfrac{D}{d}\dfrac{C}{c}$ with the frequency ½ × ½ = ¼ (= ⁴⁄₁₆), and so on. These computations check with the more laborious collections of the same genotypes from the checkerboard.

Chance Deviations from Expected Ratios. Another aspect of the operation of chance in genetic systems must be considered. We have had repeated occasion to compare expected ratios with those observed experimentally. Those chosen for illustrative purposes have seemed close enough to expectation, when the expectation was properly computed. But two questions have perhaps bothered you: Why does the observed not turn out to be *identical* with the expected if the hypothesis on which the expected distribution is based is correct? Just how large a difference can we permit between the observed and the expected before we suspect that the hypothesis being tested is false or inadequate?

An answer to the first question will have occurred to you if you have flipped pennies. The working hypothesis in this game is that a penny is equally likely to fall heads or tails. Or, to put the matter more formally, the probability that a penny will fall heads is equal to ½, and the chance that it will fall tails is also ½. Then, if you toss a penny 100 times, you expect that it will fall heads about 50 times (½ × 100) and tails about 50 times. But if you undertake this experiment in probability and toss a penny 100 times, you will find that only very seldom is the ideal expectation of 50 heads : 50 tails exactly realized. It is much more likely that you will observe a distribution somewhere between 45 heads : 55 tails on the one hand, and 55 heads : 45 tails on the other. The ideal expectation, based on probability considerations, is a sort of average expectation in an infinite number of trials, but in any finite number of trials it is unlikely to be realized exactly.

Now, we observe that these same laws of probability operate when a mixture of pollen types fertilizes the female parts of flowers, or when sperm fertilize eggs. For example, when pollen from a plant of genotype *Dd* is placed on flowers of a homozygous recessive plant *dd,* two types of pollen grains, each present in large numbers, are available for the fertilization of a finite number of female germ cells. We can predict, if no consistent bias of any kind favors one type of pollen over the other, that about half the embryos will come from eggs fertilized by *D* pollen, and half from eggs fertilized by *d* pollen. But we cannot expect that this prediction will be exactly realized in this case any more than in the strictly similar case of the tossed penny. Nor will any repetition of the experiment involving the same number of trials be likely to give numbers in each class identical with those observed in the first experiment. Each "sample" of the ideal, infinite population will give somewhat different values. Each is subject to *sampling errors*—to chance deviations from the ideal expected values.

This brings us to our second question regarding chance deviations from expected ratios: How large a difference can we permit between the observed and the expected before we suspect that something other than chance alone is involved in the deviations observed? This is a more difficult question, because any answer must be arbitrary. If, in a game of penny tossing, your friend tossed a penny 100 times and threw a head every time, you would probably ask to see the penny, suspecting that it must be so abnormal as to have heads on both sides. If he threw 90 heads and 10 tails you would probably consider this ratio so far off as to suggest that the penny might not be properly balanced, or you would watch the tosses carefully to be sure that the penny turned over in the air. Would you accept the ratio of 80:20 as a chance deviation? 70:30? 60:40? Just where would your skepticism stop?

The question can be rephrased in more concrete fashion. Take the ratio between tall and dwarf observed in the backcross discussed earlier in this chapter:

	Tall	Dwarf	Total
Observed	139	145	284
Expected (1:1)	142	142	284
Deviation	3	3	

We are really wondering *how often*, in backcrosses involving 284 progeny, we would expect chance alone to produce as large a deviation as three plants in each class. Would it happen in nine such trials out of ten? Then certainly we could accept this particular trial as only a chance deviation. Would it happen only once in ten repetitions? Then we might be rather doubtful, but, being conservative, we would probably accept this as a chance deviation. If it would happen only once in twenty trials, we might well be skeptical, and suspect that something other than chance alone might be involved in the deviation observed in this particular trial. In other words, few of us would risk a positive conclusion on a "twenty-to-one shot." And if the odds were a hundred or more to one against it we would regard it as a poor gamble indeed.

Statisticians, in general, accept these reasonable standards of evaluation of chances. If a deviation can be shown to occur more often than once in twenty trials, on the basis of chance alone, the observations are conventionally accepted as a satisfactory fit to the expected. If the chance is less than twenty to one ($\frac{1}{20} = 0.05$), the deviation is regarded as "significant"; that is, something other than chance is suspected to be operating. If the probability is less than a hundred to one (0.01), the deviation is "highly significant," and it is considered very unlikely that the difference between observed and expected is due to chance alone.

The Chi-Square Test. The only problem remaining is to get a measure of the odds for or against a given deviation. Now, it should be clear that the significance of a given deviation is related to the size of the sample. If we expect a 1:1 ratio in a test involving six individuals, an observed ratio of 4:2 is not at all bad. But if the test involves six hundred individuals, an observed ratio of 400:200 seems rather far off. Similarly, if we test 40 individuals and find a deviation of 10 in each class, this deviation seems serious:

Observed	30	10
Expected	20	20
Deviation	10	10

But if we test 200 individuals, the same numerical deviation seems reasonably enough explained as a purely chance effect:

Observed	90	110
Expected	100	100
Deviation	10	10

The statistical test that is most commonly used on such problems is about as simple in design and application as any that might be conceived. Each deviation is *squared,* and each squared deviation is then divided by the expected number in its class. The resulting quotients are then all added together to give a single value, called the *chi-square* (χ^2), for the distribution. To substitute symbols for words, let d represent the respective deviations, e the corresponding expected values, and the Greek letter Σ "the sum of." Then

$$\chi^2 = \Sigma\left(\frac{d^2}{e}\right).$$

We can calculate χ^2 for the two arbitrary examples above to show how this value relates the magnitude of the deviation to the size of the sample (see Table 3-3).

TABLE 3-3. Calculation of Chi-Square Values.

	SAMPLE OF 40 INDIVIDUALS		SAMPLE OF 200 INDIVIDUALS	
Observed	30	10	90	110
Expected (e)	20	20	100	100
Deviation (d)	10	10	10	10
d^2	100	100	100	100
$\dfrac{d^2}{e}$	5	5	1	1
$\chi^2 = \Sigma\left(\dfrac{d^2}{e}\right)$	$\chi^2 = 10$		$\chi^2 = 2$	

You will note that the value of χ^2 is much larger for the smaller population, even though the absolute deviations in the two populations are the same. In view of our earlier common-sense comparison of the two, this is a practical demonstration that the calculated value of χ^2 is related to the significance of a deviation. It has the virtue of reducing many different samples, of different sizes and with different numerical deviations, to a common scale for comparison.

The chi-square test can also be applied to samples including more than two classes. For example, Table 3-4 shows the value of chi-square for the testcross ratio introduced early in this chapter.

TABLE 3-4. Calculation of Chi-Square for a Dihybrid Testcross Ratio.†

	TALL, CUT	TALL, POTATO	DWARF, CUT	DWARF, POTATO
Observed	77	62	72	73
Expected (e)	71	71	71	71
Deviation (d)	6	9	1	2
d^2	36	81	1	4
$\dfrac{d^2}{e}$	0.51	1.14	0.01	0.06
$\chi^2 = \Sigma\left(\dfrac{d^2}{e}\right)$	$\chi^2 = 1.72$			

† Cases in which the expected numbers are all the same are more quickly calculated by adding the squared deviations and making a single division by the expected number. We have retained the longer method of computation in order to avoid confusion in extending the calculation to other ratios, like the 9:3:3:1, in which the expected numbers differ in respective classes.

The number of classes upon which the χ^2 value is based must somehow be considered in any conclusion about its significance. A value for a two-class distribution includes only two squared deviations. But a value for a four-class distribution is based on four squared deviations, and it seems reasonable that here a larger value of χ^2 should be permitted before we question the hypothesis that chance alone explains the deviation. Conventionally, the effect of number of independent classes is recognized in the phrase *degrees of freedom*.

The number of degrees of freedom in tests of genetic ratios is almost always *one less than the number of classes*. Thus in tests of 1:1 or 3:1 ratios there is one degree of freedom. A test of 1:2:1 ratio would have two degrees of freedom. A test of a 1:2:2:4:1:2:1:2:1 would have eight degrees of freedom. The general idea of degrees of freedom is very much like the situation encountered by a small boy when he puts on his shoes. He has two shoes, but only one degree of freedom. Once one shoe is filled by a foot, right or wrong, the other shoe is automatically committed to being right or wrong too. Similarly, in a two-place table, one value can be filled arbitrarily, but the other is then fixed by the fact that the total must add up to the precise number of observations involved in the experiment, and the deviations in the two classes must compensate for each other. When there are four classes, any three are usually free, but whatever they are the fourth is fixed. Thus, when there are four classes, there are usually three degrees of freedom.

Application of the Chi-Square Test. We are now in a position to take the single additional step necessary to the application of the χ^2 test. This is a very simple step in practice, although the mathematical processes and assumptions upon which it is based are rather complex. We must ignore the complexities here and proceed in arbitrary fashion.

Once the value of χ^2 is computed, and the number of degrees of freedom noted, the odds for a strictly chance deviation *as large as or larger than* that observed can be read directly from a table of χ^2 (Table 3-5). This table is entered at the left according to the number of degrees of freedom; the value of χ^2 is bracketed as your eye follows across the proper row, and the probability of the observed deviation is read as the appropriate probability across the top of the table. After you have examined the table briefly, we will illustrate its use.

In Table 3-3, on page 43, we calculated $\chi^2 = 10$ for one degree of freedom for the sample of 40 individuals. The largest value of χ^2 given in the table, for one degree of freedom, is 6.635; and this applies to a probability of 0.01 (1 in 100). You will note that the probability decreases as the value of χ^2 increases. In this case, therefore, chance alone would be expected in considerably less than one in a hundred independent trials to produce as large a deviation as that observed. We cannot reasonably accept chance alone as responsible for this particular deviation; it represents an event that

TABLE 3-5. Table of Chi-Square. (Abridged from Table III of Statistical Methods for Research Workers by R. A. Fisher, published by Oliver and Boyd Ltd., Edinburgh, by permission of the author and publisher.)

DEGREES OF FREEDOM	P = 0.99	0.95	0.80	0.50	0.20	0.05	0.01
1	0.000157	0.00393	0.0642	0.455	1.642	3.841	6.635
2	0.0201	0.103	0.446	1.386	3.219	5.991	9.210
3	0.115	0.352	1.005	2.366	4.642	7.815	11.341
4	0.297	0.711	1.649	3.357	5.989	9.488	13.277
5	0.554	1.145	2.343	4.351	7.289	11.070	15.086
6	0.872	1.635	3.070	5.348	8.558	12.592	16.812
7	1.239	2.167	3.822	6.346	9.803	14.067	18.475
8	1.646	2.733	4.594	7.344	11.030	15.507	20.090
9	2.088	3.325	5.380	8.343	12.242	16.919	21.666
10	2.558	3.940	6.179	9.342	13.442	18.307	23.209
15	5.229	7.261	10.307	14.339	19.311	24.996	30.578
20	8.260	10.851	14.578	19.337	25.038	31.410	37.566
25	11.524	14.611	18.940	24.337	30.675	37.652	44.314
30	14.953	18.493	23.364	29.336	36.250	43.773	50.892

would occur, on a chance basis, much less often than the one-time-in-twenty that we have agreed on for our standard, and even less often than the one-time-in-a-hundred that we decided to regard as highly significant.

On the other hand, we calculated $\chi^2 = 2$ for the sample of 200 individuals in the same table. Here the probability, according to the χ^2 table, falls between 0.05 and 0.20. In other words, independent repetitions of this experiment would produce chance deviations as large as those observed a little less often than one time in five, but more often than one time in twenty. We can reasonably regard this observed deviation as simply a sampling, or chance, error.

In Table 3-4, on page 43, we calculated $\chi^2 = 1.72$ for a dihybrid testcross. With four classes, the table is entered at three degrees of freedom; the probability is between 0.8 and 0.5. Clearly, the deviations can be accepted as chance ones. The dihybrid F_2 ratio of Table 3-1, page 39, can be used to illustrate the entire chi-square test (Table 3-6).

Somewhere between five and eight times in ten, chance alone would produce a deviation as great as or greater than that observed by MacArthur in this F_2. The data represent a good fit to the expected.

Improper Use of Chi-Square. The two most important reservations regarding ordinary use of the χ^2 method in genetics are:

1. Chi-square can be applied only to numerical frequencies themselves, never directly to percentages or ratios derived from the frequencies. For

TABLE 3-6. Chi-Square Test of Dihybrid F_2 Data.

	TALL, CUT	TALL, POTATO	DWARF, CUT	DWARF, POTATO
Observed	926	288	293	104
Expected 9:3:3:1 (e)	906.3	302.1	302.1	100.7
Deviation (d)	19.7	14.1	9.1	3.3
d^2	388.09	198.81	82.81	10.89
$\dfrac{d^2}{e}$	0.43	0.66	0.27	0.11
$\chi^2 = \Sigma \left(\dfrac{d^2}{e} \right)$	$\chi^2 = 1.47$; p is between 0.8 and 0.5			

example, if in an experiment one expects equal numbers in each of two classes, but observes 8 in one class and 12 in the other, he might recalculate these numbers as 40 per cent and 60 per cent observed, with 50 per cent expected in each class. A χ^2 value computed from these percentages could not be used directly for the determination of p. When the classes are large and correction for continuity is not necessary, a χ^2 value computed from percentages can be used, if it is first multiplied by $n/100$, where n is the total number of individuals observed.

2. Chi-square cannot properly be applied to distributions in which the frequency of any class is less than 5. In fact, most statisticians suggest that a particular correction be applied if the frequency of any class is less than 50. However, the approximations involved in χ^2 are close enough for most practical purposes when there are more than 5 expectations in each class.

Trihybrid and Higher Multiple-Gene Ratios

The preceding sections on probability and the chi-square method are to a certain degree parenthetical in this chapter. We can now return to a brief extension of our consideration of the independent transmission of different pairs of alleles.

Individuals heterozygous for three independently assorting pairs of alleles produce eight types of germ cells in equal numbers. The types and a method of listing them are illustrated in Figure 3-5.

When such a trihybrid is testcrossed to the triple recessive, eight phenotypes are present in equal proportions among the progeny. The F_2 calculations are also straightforward, though tedious. If you use a checkerboard for them, it has to have 64 (8 × 8) squares. With complete dominance in all

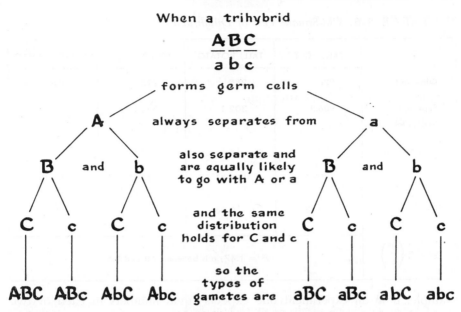

When a trihybrid

ABC
abc

forms germ cells

A always separates from a

B and b

also separate and are equally likely to go with A or a

B and b

C c C c

and the same distribution holds for C and c

C c C c

ABC ABc AbC Abc

so the types of gametes are

aBC aBc abC abc

Figure 3-5. *A trihybrid forms eight equally frequent kinds of germ cells when the members of the three allelic pairs assort independently.*

three pairs of alleles, this gives a phenotypic ratio of 27:9:9:9:3:3:3:1. Eager readers of this book will want to verify this for themselves.

Probability calculations are particularly timesaving in these more complicated combinations. For example, what proportion of the F_2 individuals in a trihybrid cross will be expected to be heterozygous for all three genes? You could answer this from a checkerboard by counting 8 out of 64 F_2 progeny that are $\dfrac{A\ B\ C}{a\ b\ c}$. But it is much quicker to compute:

The probability of heterozygosity for A = ½
The probability of heterozygosity for B = ½
The probability of heterozygosity for C = ½
The probability of heterozygosity for
all three = ½ × ½ × ½ = ⅛.

There are, of course, other similar applications of probability calculations in this kind of situation.

Crosses involving individuals heterozygous for more than three pairs of alleles are subject to the same kinds of regular analysis. The size of experimental populations necessary to display these multiple-gene ratios is so great, however, that it is only rarely that the analysis has been complete or critical.

In later chapters we shall consider an important class of inherited characteristics in which many genes are involved. Additional statistical techniques will be introduced at that time for the more convenient handling of these complicated examples.

Certain regularities appear as we progress from monohybrids to dihybrids to trihybrids and on to heterozygosity for n pairs of alleles when n may be any whole number. These regularities, which are summarized in Table 3-7, are worthy of careful attention.

TABLE 3-7. Characteristics of Crosses Involving n *Pairs of Alleles.*

NUMBER OF HETEROZYGOUS ALLELIC PAIRS	NUMBER OF TYPES OF GERM CELLS	NUMBER OF PHENOTYPES IN TESTCROSS	NUMBER OF GENOTYPES IN F_2	NUMBER OF PHENOTYPES IN F_2†
1	2	2	3	2
2	4	4	9	4
3	8	8	27	8
4	16	16	81	16
n	2^n	2^n	3^n	2^n

† Assuming complete dominance in each allelic pair.

Mendel and Mendelism

In Chapters 2 and 3 we have come to recognize that hereditary differences are based on particulate differences in the germ plasm, that these particles are present in pairs, and that they obey the laws of segregation and independent assortment. All of these facts were established by a monk named Gregor Johann Mendel in a paper published in 1866. Mendel's paper is conveniently available both in the original German and in English translation (see "References," Chap. 2), and it is well worth reading. Appreciation of its brilliance grows as one becomes familiar with the deficiencies of other studies of heredity up to, during, and even long after, Mendel's time. To many of us, the innovations of thought and experiment included in Mendel's concise paper rank among the most admirable accomplishments of the rational human mind.

Mendel's work was ignored and virtually forgotten for thirty-four years after its publication. It was not until 1900 that its rediscovery, by three different biologists independently, burst upon a biological world that had, in the interval since the publication of the paper, progressed sufficiently to appreciate it. Today, we remember Mendel in terms like *Mendelian inheritance, Mendelian laws, Mendelian factors,* and others. It is pathetic that such recognition should have had to wait until long after Mendel's death. His sound and painstaking work with common peas, in a monastery kitchen garden, forms the foundation of our present knowledge of heredity.

Keys to the Significance of This Chapter

The subject matter of this chapter falls into two related parts, each of which can be summarized briefly.

Consideration of the transmission of two or more pairs of alleles at a time leads to the conclusion that the members of a particular pair always separate from each other when an individual forms germ cells. The members of different pairs can assort into the germ cells independently of each other, and they then recombine at random at fertilization.

Probability computations can serve as significant timesavers in calculating the frequencies of various phenotypes and genotypes in crosses involving two or more pairs of alleles. It is important to have at hand arbitrary techniques for evaluating the statistical significance of deviations observed in any experiment testing a Mendelian hypothesis. The chi-square test has been discussed and applied in this connection.

References

Babcock, E. B., *The Development of Fundamental Concepts in the Science of Genetics*. Washington: American Genetic Assoc., 1951. (An evaluation of highlights in the history of genetics. 60¢ per copy; 40¢ in groups of 12 or more.)

Fisher, R. A., *Statistical Methods for Research Workers*, 10th ed. London: Oliver and Boyd, 1946. (Clear, authoritative, and concise; the standard reference in the field.)

Iltis, H., *Life of Mendel*, trans. by E. and C. Paul. New York: W. W. Norton & Co., 1932. (Interestingly written, thorough biography.)

MacArthur, J. W., "Linkage Studies with the Tomato." *Trans. Roy. Can. Inst.*, 18 (Part 1):1–19, 1931. (Source of data on inheritance in tomatoes included in text and problems of this chapter.)

Roberts, H. F., *Plant Hybridization Before Mendel*. Princeton: Princeton University Press, 1929. (This historical account will fortify your appreciation of Mendel.)

Snedecor, G. W., *Statistical Methods Applied to Experiments in Agriculture and Biology*, 4th ed. Ames: Iowa State College Press, 1946. (An eminently readable textbook.)

Stern, C., *Principles of Human Genetics*. San Francisco: W. H. Freeman and Co., 1949. (Especially, at this point, Chap. 8, "Problems of Genetic Advisers," and Chap. 9, "Genetic Ratios," for extensions of probability considerations to problems of human heredity.)

The Birth of Genetics, C. Stern, ed. Supplement to *Genetics*, 35:No. 5, Part 2, 1950. (Includes Mendel's letters to Carl Nageli, 1866–1873, and the papers by DeVries, Correns, and von Tschermak reporting the rediscovery of Mendelism in 1900.)

Tschermak-Seysenegg, E. von, "The Rediscovery of Gregor Mendel's Work." *J. Heredity,* 42:163–171, 1951. (A fascinating firsthand report by one of the rediscoverers of Mendel's work.)

Questions and Problems

3- 1. What do the following terms signify?

backcross	multiple-gene ratios
chi-square	probability
degrees of freedom	sampling errors
dihybrid	segregation
independent assortment	significant deviation
Mendelism	testcross

Besides the cut-leaf/potato-leaf and the tall/dwarf alternatives introduced in this chapter, MacArthur studied a number of additional inherited characteristics of tomatoes. Among these, his data on two will be useful in several problems:

1. Usually, tomato plants have purplish stems, but in some varieties the purple pigment (an anthocyanin) is lacking, and the stem is green. The difference is evident from the time the seedling first emerges. Let A = purple stem (having the anthocyanin), and a = green stem.

2. Red fruit flesh color (R) *vs.* yellow (r) refers to the color of the "meat" of the ripe fruit.

3- 2. True-breeding, purple-stemmed tomatoes crossed with green-stemmed plants gave all purple-stemmed F_1's. When these F_1's were backcrossed to green-stemmed plants, the progeny were: 482 purple-stemmed, 526 green-stemmed. Diagram the crosses, showing all pertinent genotypes, phenotypes, and germ cells.

3- 3. Verify that, in the backcross ratio of Problem 3-2, $\chi^2 = 1.92$, and p is greater than 0.05. Can this deviation be accepted as a sampling error?

3- 4. The F_2 of the cross in Question 3-2 consisted of 3084 purple-stemmed and 1093 green-stemmed plants. Does this fit the expected ratio satisfactorily? (Verify that p is greater than 0.05.)

3- 5. Purple-stemmed, cut-leafed plants $(AACC)$ crossed with green-stemmed, potato-leafed plants would give what genotype and phenotype in F_1? What would be the backcross ratio when these F_1's are crossed with the green-stemmed, potato-leafed parent strain if the A-a and C-c allelic pairs assort independently?

3- 6. In an F_2 grown from the F_1's in Question 3-5, MacArthur counted:

purple, cut	purple, potato	green, cut	green, potato
1790	620	623	222

Is this consistent with our postulate of independent assortment of these two allelic pairs? (Verify that p here is a little less than 0.5.)

3- 7. When a purple-stemmed, potato-leafed true-breeding strain was crossed with a true-breeding green-stemmed, cut-leafed strain, MacArthur observed in F_2:

purple, cut	purple, potato	green, cut	green, potato
247	90	83	34

Calculate the expected number of purple, cut F_2's in this cross (454 total F_2 progeny), using (a) the checkerboard method and (b) the probability, or fraction, method described on page 39.

3- 8.   Diagram a backcross of the F_1's of Question 3-7 to the purple, potato parent. To the green, cut parent. Diagram a testcross of these same F_1's. What will be the phenotypic ratio in each cross?

3- 9.   In the table below, results are given for six separate matings of tomato plant phenotypes. What are the most probable genotypes for the parents in each instance? (These are not experimental data, but are postulated for illustrative purposes.)

Phenotypes of Parents	*Number of Progeny*			
	Purple, Cut	Purple, Potato	Green, Cut	Green, Potato
(a) purple, cut × green, cut	321	101	310	107
(b) purple, cut × purple, potato	219	207	64	71
(c) purple, cut × green, cut	722	231	0	0
(d) purple, cut × green, potato	404	0	387	0
(e) purple, potato × green, cut	70	91	86	77

Example: In cross (a) we know that the purple, cut parent had the dominant allele of each pair, but we do not know from its phenotype whether it was homozygous or heterozygous. It may therefore be written: $A?C?$. Similarly, the other parent is $aaC?$, and our problem is to remove the question marks.

The simplest way to do this is to note that the green, potato progeny ($aacc$) must have received the recessive allele of *each* pair from *each* parent. The parental genotypes therefore must be: $AaCc \times aaCc$. You could reach the same conclusion in other ways. As a check, note that the expected ratio, 3:1:3:1, in this cross agrees well with the observed result.

3-10.   How would you test to see whether the D-d (tall-dwarf) allelic pair in tomatoes assorted independently of the A-a pair?

3-11.   A true-breeding tall, purple-stemmed, cut-leafed strain is crossed with a dwarf, green-stemmed, potato-leafed strain. What types of germ cells, and in what proportions, will be produced by the F_1 plants, assuming independent assortment of all three allelic pairs?

3-12.   What porportion of the F_2 progeny will be genotypically like the dwarf, green, potato parent strain? Phenotypically? Genotypically like the tall, purple, cut strain? Phenotypically?

3-13.   Suppose that the F_1's in Question 3-11 were also heterozygous for the R-r allelic pair affecting fruit-flesh color. (See introduction to this series of questions.) How many types of germ cells would these *tetrahybrid* F_1's produce? How many phenotypes in F_2? Genotypes? What proportion of the F_2's would be expected to be tall, purple, potato-leafed, with red fruit flesh? What proportion of the F_2's would have the genotype Dd Aa cc Rr?

In man, the most frequent type of albinism (itself quite rare) is inherited as a simple recessive characteristic. Albinos lack the normal pigment of skin, hair, and eyes, so that their hair and skin are white and their eyes pink. Standard symbols are C = normal color; c = albino. Recall also thalassemia (Problems 2-3 to 2-6), where TT = thalassemia major (severe anemia, usually fatal in childhood); Tt = thalassemia minor (mild anemia, often unnoticed); tt = normal blood character. Assume that the genes for thalassemia and albinism assort independently.

3-14. A husband and wife, both normally pigmented and neither with severe anemia, have an albino child who dies in infancy of thalassemia major. What are the probable genotypes of the parents?

3-15. If these people have another child, what are its chances of being phenotypically normal with respect to pigmentation? Of having entirely normal (i.e., non-thalassemic) blood? Of being phenotypically normal in both regards? Of being homozygous for the normal alleles of both genes?

3-16. What would you expect to be the genotypic and phenotypic ratios among the children of numerous marriages like that in Question 3-14?

A rather frequent inherited difference among people is in the ability to taste a compound called *phenylthiourea*. To about 70 per cent of North American Whites this compound tastes very bitter; the remaining 30 per cent find it virtually tasteless. The ability to taste phenylthiourea is dominant, so that we can let TT and Tt = "tasters"; tt = "nontasters." Assume that this allelic pair is independent of albinism in genetic transmission.

3-17. Two tasters, normally pigmented, have an albino son and a nontaster daughter, not albino. What is the chance that the albino son is a taster? That the nontaster daughter is a "carrier" of albinism?

3-18. The nontaster, nonalbino daughter in Question 3-17 marries a taster man, normally pigmented, whose mother was a nontaster albino. What chance has their child of being a taster? Albino? Taster albino?

Mendel studied, besides the tall-dwarf alternative (see Problems 2-12 to 2-14), six other pairs of characteristics in garden peas. These were:

Characteristic	Dominant	Recessive
Seed coat	Round (W)	Wrinkled (w)
Seed color (endosperm)	Yellow (G)	Green (g)
Seed coat color (and flower color)	Colored (C)	White (c)
Pod form	Smooth, inflated (I)	Constricted between seeds and wrinkled (i)
Pod color (unripe)	Green (Y)	Yellow (y)
Flower position	Distributed along stem (T)	Bunched at top of stem (t)

(The symbols assigned are arbitrary.)

3-19. With regard to all seven characteristics, whenever true-breeding strains differing in any two pairs of characteristics were crossed, Mendel observed a 9:3:3:1 phenotypic ratio in F_2. Trace the logical steps that would suggest, from these observations:
a. The particulate basis of inheritance
b. The fact that the critical particles are present *in pairs* in an individual
c. Dominance
d. Segregation
e. Independent assortment

3-20. From the F_2 results indicated in Question 3-19, what would you predict if any of the dihybrid F_1's in Mendel's experiments were crossed with the corresponding double-recessive strain? Indicate how Mendel's confirmation of this prediction strengthened the principles listed in 3-19, perceived originally from his experience with the F_2's.

3-21. Suppose that Mendel had produced an F_1 heterozygous for all seven allelic pairs. What would be the minimum number of F_2's he would need to display the expected F_2 phenotypic ratio?

3-22. What advantages do the opportunities for segregation, assortment, and recombination give a sexually reproducing species over an asexually reproducing form?

3-23. Why is a marriage like that in Question 3-14 a very rare event? Why would its occurrence appear more plausible if it had been stated that the husband and wife were cousins, and of Mediterranean origin?

3-24. It is a matter of common observation that, except for identical twins, the children of the same family differ in many respects. This variation is even greater among the members of less closely related groups. What does this suggest as to the amount of heterozygosity in man? How does it reflect on the concept of "pure races," and the assignment of groups of men to racial stereotypes conceived in genetic terms?

CHAPTER 4

Two or More Pairs of Alleles:

Interactions in Phenotypic Expression

THE FIRST of the two aspects of the behavior of different pairs of alleles with respect to each other has now been discussed in detail sufficient for our present purposes. We have answered the first question raised in the introduction to the preceding chapter: Different pairs of alleles may be independent of each other in their segregation and recombination patterns—in their patterns of genetic transmission from one sexual generation to the next.

Another aspect remains to be discussed. It might be well to repeat the question at issue: Does the fact that many genes are simultaneously affecting the development and functions of an individual result in modification of the action or expression of one gene by another? In turning to this question, we leave for a while the field of the *transmission of hereditary particles* and again take up the problems of *gene action in development and function.*

Independence of Gene Action. So little is certainly known about the real nature of the *primary action* of any gene that it is impossible at present to make any positive statement about the independence or interdependence of the first, immediate effects of different genes on the biochemically active materials in cells. Concerning the interaction of the *products* of genes in the cell and in the organism, however, there is no doubt. In terms of its final expression in the phenotype of the individual, *no gene acts by itself.* A difference between two individuals may be traced to a particulate difference in their germ plasm. But the individuals themselves, complex as they are in their development and functions, are the results of innumerable integrated reactions. Without the active collaboration of the totality of genes that together make the individual a functioning whole, no single gene could express itself.

When we specify two particular pairs of alleles and consider their interactions in terms of the final phenotype, we may encounter either independence of expression or almost any degree of interdependence between the two pairs, depending on what genes we are considering. Usually, the degree of interdependence can be predicted to some extent from a knowledge of the effects of the different genes separately. In the example of tall *versus* dwarf and cut leaves *versus* potato leaves in tomatoes we need not expect that the stature of the plant and the shape of its leaves should be related. In fact, the 9:3:3:1 phenotypic ratio in the F_2, in which the alternatives tall-dwarf and cut-potato both occur in their characteristic 3:1 ratios, demonstrates the independent expression of these two allelic pairs just as it is an evidence of their independent transmission. One can find variations from the 9:3:3:1 phenotypic ratio based on independently expressed allelic pairs showing lack of dominance within one or both of the pairs. For instance, the poultry cross:

$$\text{Extreme Frizzle,} \quad \text{Black} \quad \times \quad \text{Normal,} \quad \text{White-Splashed}$$

$$\frac{F}{F} \qquad \frac{bl}{bl} \qquad \frac{f}{f} \qquad \frac{Bl}{Bl}$$

gives an intermediate F_1:

$$\text{Mild Frizzle,} \quad \text{Blue}$$

$$\frac{F}{f} \qquad \frac{bl}{Bl}$$

and an F_2 in which each of the nine genotypes is separately recognizable as a distinct phenotype. In this case, although both pairs of alleles affect feathers, they do so independently, one affecting color and the other structure. And here, because dominance is lacking in both pairs, the F_2 phenotypic ratio is not 9:3:3:1, but 1:2:2:4:1:2:1:2:1—the same as the genotypic ratio. (For practice, identify the phenotypes in this ratio.)

There are many instances in which a true interaction might be expected from a knowledge of the separate allelic pairs. We can list a few examples, briefly:

Comb Shape in Chickens. When fowls of a *rose*-combed breed (like the Wyandotte, Fig. 4-1A) are crossed with a *pea*-combed breed (like the Brahma, Fig. 4-1B), the F_1 birds have a new and different comb type, called *walnut,* because it looks like half a walnut meat (Fig. 4-1C). Walnut combs are characteristic of the Malay breed.

The F_2 shows a ratio of:
9 walnut
3 rose
3 pea
1 single

A result like this must seem inexplicable to a breeder unfamiliar with genetics. A new type, unlike either parent and characteristic of an unrelated breed, occurs in the progeny of the first cross; and still a fourth type (*single,*

Figure 4-1. *Two different allelic pairs interact in affecting comb shape in the fowl. A, rose* (R–pp). *B, pea* (rrP–). *C, walnut* (R–P–). *D, single* (rrpp).

characteristic of the Leghorn, Fig. 4-1D) appears in the next generation. But it will be easy for you to recognize this as a dihybrid ratio, in which single is the double-recessive class, and in which one dominant was contributed by each parent in the original cross. Let:

$$R\text{–}P\text{–} = \text{walnut} \quad (9)$$
$$R\text{–}pp = \text{rose} \quad (3)$$
$$rrP\text{–} = \text{pea} \quad (3)$$
$$rrpp = \text{single} \quad (1)$$

(The dashes are meant to signify that the indicated phenotype may be either homozygous or heterozygous for the dominant allele.) You can work backwards from the appearance of single-combed birds in F_2, and of walnut combs exclusively in F_1, to confirm that the genotypes of the parents were

RRpp × *rrPP*. (What types will appear, and in what proportions, in F$_1$ and F$_2$, if single-combed birds are crossed with birds of a true-breeding walnut-combed strain?)

This is a good example of *independently transmitted* pairs of alleles that are *not independent in their expression*. The final phenotypic effect of alleles of the *R-r* pair in an individual depends on which alleles of the *P-p* allelic pair are present, and vice versa. Some interaction in expression is not unexpected, since both pairs of alleles affect the same characteristic—comb shape. It would, however, be difficult to predict on any *a priori* ground that this interaction would take the form it does.

Color in Mammals. In a variety of mammals, several different genes affect the coat color. These are of particular interest to breeders of fur animals, since new and different furs command premium prices on the market, at least until they become common through breeding programs designed to increase their frequency. In mink, for example, the wild type, long a standard for breeders, ranges from dark brown to nearly black. At least twelve different allelic pairs are known to be concerned with this color. Considered as separate deviations from the wild type, they can be described as follows:

Wild Type: *PP IpIp AlAl BB BgBg BiBi CC OO ss ff ebeb cmcm*
Unit Deviations: (wild-type genotype except for the substitution of indicated genes for their wild-type alleles)

p p	= platinum	⎫ phenotypically indistinguishable,
ip ip	= imperial platinum	⎬ blue-grey color
al al	= aleutian	blue-grey color
b b	= brown-eyed pastel	⎫
bg bg	= green-eyed pastel	⎬ chocolate brown color
bi bi	= imperial pastel	⎭
c^H c^H	= albino	very light color
o o	= "goofus"	pattern like a Siamese cat

(The above eight, as indicated by small letters in duplicate, are all recessive to their wild-type alleles.)

S– = black cross; *F–* = blufrost; *Eb–* = ebony; *Cm–* = colmira.

(The above four are each at least partially dominant to their wild-type alleles. They are called "pattern" color phases because they affect some areas of the pelt more than others. One other allele, that for royal silver, will be mentioned in Problem 19-5.)

You can imagine the variety of color types that can be obtained by using different combinations of these twelve allelic pairs. Even the commercial names of some of the better-known combinations are remarkable; for example:

$$Ff\ pp\ \ \ \ = \text{breath-of-spring platinum}$$
$$Ff\ bb\ \ \ \ = \text{breath-of-spring pastel}$$
$$alal\ ipip = \text{sapphire}$$
$$bb\ pp\ \ \ \ = \text{platinum blond}$$

and so on.

The list of genes for the wild type will emphasize that no gene affecting color ever acts alone on this characteristic. The allele for platinum (p), for example, produces an obvious effect when substituted, in the homozygous condition, in an otherwise wild-type genotype. But all of the other wild-type genes are there and acting too, and the final effect of the platinum substitution will be different if there are other changes as well in this "residual" genotype. Substituting platinum in a genotype that is wild type except for its being bb, for instance, will give a platinum blond. The F_2 dihybrid ratio for these two allelic pairs is:

9 wild type	(P– B–)
3 platinum	(pp B–)
3 brown-eyed pastel	(P– bb)
1 platinum blond	(pp bb)

Color in Onions. Often one allelic pair can suppress the expression of another. As one of many examples we can consider color in onion bulbs. Here, a gene c (for "colorless"), recessive to its standard-type allele, produces clear, white bulbs; plants having the dominant C allele produce colored bulbs. Another allelic pair governs the difference between red (R) and yellow (r) bulb color. We can list the F_2 ratio in a cross involving both pairs of alleles:

$$C\text{--}R\text{--} = \text{red} \quad (9)$$
$$C\text{--}rr = \text{yellow} \ (3)$$
$$\left.\begin{array}{l} ccR\text{--} = \text{white} \ (3) \\ ccrr = \text{white} \ (1) \end{array}\right\} = 4$$

It is obvious that a difference in the R-r allelic pair can express itself only when there is some color in the bulb to display the difference between red and yellow. This means that the R-r allelic pair can be expressed only in the presence of C; in colorless bulbs, when c is homozygous, diversity for other genes affecting color is obscured.

Another gene produces white in onions, this one *dominant* to its allele for color. In a dihybrid F_2 segregating with the R-r allelic pair, the dominant white (I—the symbol stands for an "inhibitor" of color) gives this ratio:

$$\left.\begin{array}{l} I\text{--}R\text{--} = \text{white} \ (9) \\ I\text{--}rr = \text{white} \ (3) \end{array}\right\} = 12$$
$$iiR\text{--} = \text{red} \quad (3)$$
$$iirr = \text{yellow} \ (1)$$

Here, the ratio is 12 white : 3 red : 1 yellow, while with the recessive white the ratio was 9 red : 3 yellow : 4 white. An interesting dihybrid ratio combines the dominant and the recessive whites:

$$\left.\begin{array}{rll} I\text{–}C\text{–} = & \text{white} & (9) \\ I\text{–}cc = & \text{white} & (3) \\ iiC\text{–} = & \text{colored} & (3) \\ iicc = & \text{white} & (1) \end{array}\right\} = 13 \text{ white} : 3 \text{ colored}$$

Actually, the dominant white is only incompletely dominant to its allele for color. Heterozygotes (Ii) often have a little color around the neck of the bulb, while II bulbs, like cc ones, are all white. These genes are of more interest than simply as color genes and as academic examples. Colored bulbs are resistant to smudge, an important disease of onions. This resistance results from the presence in colored bulbs of certain compounds that inhibit the growth of the smudge-producing pathogens. These compounds are related to the production of pigment, and recessive whites, lacking both the pigment and the "resistance compounds," are very susceptible to the disease. Dominant whites are rather resistant to smudge; apparently the block in pigment development in dominant whites does not block completely the synthesis of the "resistance compounds." There is also some indication that the allele I may be associated with smaller bulb size.

Cyanide in White Clover. The modifications of the dihybrid ratio illustrated above are reasonable on the grounds of what we know of the particular gene effects, but the real, material bases of these interactions still escape us. Another dihybrid ratio, for cyanide content of white clover, is a more revealing choice in this regard.

Some strains of white clover are high in cyanide content, while others are low. Rather surprisingly, in spite of the usual toxicity of cyanide, its presence in clover eaten by cattle does not seem to hurt the animals. On the contrary, high cyanide lines of white clover, because of their generally richer vegetative growth, are agriculturally desirable.

Usually, when a high and a low cyanide strain are crossed, the F_1 is high, and the F_2 gives a ratio of 3 high : 1 low, indicating that a single pair of alleles controls this difference. This suggests that low cyanide strains, being homozygous recessives, should always give low cyanide progeny when intercrossed. However, in rather rare instances the following result has been noted:

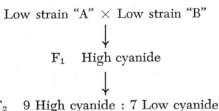

Low strain "A" × Low strain "B"

↓

F_1 High cyanide

↓

F_2 9 High cyanide : 7 Low cyanide

This result is at first unexpected, but with a little thought you will be able to explain it.

The F_2 ratio in this instance is a dihybrid ratio, modified so that the phenotype having both dominants, with a frequency of $\frac{9}{16}$, is high; the remaining $\frac{7}{16}$, having either or both recessives homozygous, are low in cyanide content. To explain this, assume two different allelic pairs each affecting cyanide in such a way that:

$$L- = \text{high} \qquad\qquad H- = \text{high}$$
$$ll = \text{low} \qquad\qquad hh = \text{low}$$

P $\qquad\qquad LLhh \times llHH$
$\qquad\qquad\qquad$ low $\qquad$ low

F_1 $\qquad\qquad\qquad LlHh$
$\qquad\qquad\qquad\qquad$ high

F_2 $\qquad\qquad\quad L-H- = \text{high} \ (9)$
$\qquad\qquad\qquad llH- \ = \text{low} \ (3)$
$\qquad\qquad\qquad L-hh \ = \text{low} \ (3) \bigg\} = 7 \text{ low}$
$\qquad\qquad\qquad llhh \ = \text{low} \ (1)$

The observed 9:7 ratio in the F_2 and all other aspects of this cross are consistent with this explanation.

Now, something is known about the chemistry of cyanide production in white clover. Cyanide (or, more properly, hydrocyanic acid, HCN) is liberated under the action of a specific enzyme from a specific source or substrate known as a *cyanogenic glucoside*. The reaction can be represented as follows:

$$\text{Substrate} \xrightarrow{\text{enzyme}} \text{Cyanide}$$

One of the low-cyanide lines ($LLhh$) in the cross can easily be shown to have very little, if any, of the enzyme. We can diagram:

$$\text{gene } H$$
$$\downarrow$$
$$\text{Substrate} \xrightarrow{\text{enzyme}} \text{Cyanide}$$

But, in the absence of H (i.e., when its allele, h, is homozygous), there is little or no enzyme, and little or no cyanide is formed.

It can be shown that the other low parental line ($llHH$) has plenty of the enzyme, but lacks the substrate. We can diagram:

$$\text{gene } H$$
$$\downarrow$$
$$\xrightarrow{\text{gene } L} \text{Substrate} \xrightarrow{\text{enzyme}} \text{Cyanide}$$

But in the absence of L (i.e., when its allele, l, is homozygous), there is little or no substrate, and little or no cyanide is formed.

It is likely, though not yet demonstrated, that gene L also governs the specificity of an enzyme that is concerned with the conversion of some precursor to the substrate upon which the H enzyme works. For the sake of unity, we will diagram this partly speculative relationship:

gene L gene H

enzyme   enzyme

$\longrightarrow$ Precursor $\longrightarrow$ Substrate $\longrightarrow$ Cyanide

Plant leaf extracts can be tested for cyanide, and by adding substrate and enzyme separately the four types of F_2 can be demonstrated (Table 4-1).

TABLE 4-1. Tests of Leaf Extracts for Cyanide Content.

	PHENOTYPE	LEAF EXTRACT ALONE	LEAF EXTRACT AND SUBSTRATE	LEAF EXTRACT AND ENZYME H
(9)	L–H–	+	+	+
(3)	L–hh	0	0	+
(3)	llH–	0	+	0
(1)	llhh	0	0	0

"+" indicates a positive test for cyanide.
"0" indicates little or no cyanide.

One can therefore observe phenotypic ratios of 9:7, or 12:4 (two different ways), or 9:3:3:1 (taking all tests into account) in this dihybrid F_2, depending on how the plants are tested and classified.

This consideration of cyanide in white clover suggests a basis that is doubtless quite common for gene interaction. One gene may depend for its expression on the product of the action of another gene. There are, of course, other bases for other types of interaction. You may enjoy speculating about the possible material bases, in terms of gene action and interaction, of some of the other modified dihybrid ratios that have been discussed.

General Aspects of Independence and Interaction. In some ways the interaction between two different genes, in which one gene may suppress the expression of another, will remind you of the phenomenon of dominance. The two phenomena are essentially different, however, and *dominance* always refers to the modification of the expression of one member of a pair of alleles by the other, never to an interaction between different genes. *Epistasis* is the term generally used to describe effects of nonallelic genes on each other's expression; thus the recessive allele of the gene for white (c) in the onion is epistatic to the *R-r* allelic pair. Sometimes it is convenient to use the term *hypostatic* to indicate the opposite direction of dependency; thus the *R-r* allelic pair is hypostatic to the recessive allele of the gene for white.

There is very little point in trying to memorize the bases for all the modified dihybrid ratios that we have discussed, or for the several others that are sometimes encountered. But it is important to be able to recognize a dihybrid ratio and to work out its basis. Several of the problems at the end of this chapter will help you to practice.

Aside from their academic interest, the subjects of the *transmission* and the *action* of two or more gene pairs considered together, as discussed in Chapters 3 and 4, are of profound practical significance. Here, one of the main advantages of sexual reproduction first becomes evident. The formation of germ cells, each containing a random sample of one allele from each of the many allelic pairs in an individual, and the recombinations of these diverse samples at fertilization, gives a degree of plasticity to sexually reproducing populations impossible without sex. New combinations are always turning up, and these may involve more than simply new ways of adding the old characteristics together. Through the interactions of the genes in these new combinations, very different new types may emerge, and some of these new types may have real advantages over their parents. In natural evolution, and in the controlled evolution that we characterize as plant and animal improvement, the segregation, assortment, recombination, and interaction of genes provide a most powerful means of progress towards better adapted or more useful plants and animals.

Certain aspects of human inheritance involving these same phenomena might well be introduced at this time. But aside from examples in several of the problems, where important illustrations can be utilized, we shall postpone this particular discussion until the last chapter in our book. There the applications of genetics to human welfare will be drawn together as a unit.

Keys to the Significance of This Chapter

While the *primary* action of any gene may usually be independent of other genes, the *products of the primary actions of different genes* certainly interact in the development and function of the individual. No gene produces its effect on the phenotype by itself. Considering two pairs of alleles at a time, either independence of effect on phenotype or almost any degree of interdependence in interaction can be observed, depending on the genes involved.

References

Atwood, S. S., and Sullivan, J. T., "Inheritance of a Cyanogenetic Glucoside and Its Hydrolyzing Enzyme in *Trifolium repens*." *J. Heredity,* **34:**311–320, 1943. (A report of studies on cyanide in white clover, discussed in this chapter.)

Castle, W. E., *Mammalian Genetics.* Cambridge: Harvard University Press, 1940. (Lists and discusses many simply inherited mammalian characteristics.)

Falls, H. F., "Congenital and Hereditary Eye Disorders." National Society for the Prevention of Blindness, Inc., 1790 Broadway, New York 19, N.Y. Publication 496. Price 10¢. (A brief consideration of an important aspect of medical genetics.)

Hutt, F. B., *Genetics of the Fowl.* New York: McGraw-Hill Book Co., 1949. (Note the progress in poultry genetics between 1923 [see Punnett, below] and 1949, as exemplified in this book.)

Punnett, R. C., *Heredity in Poultry.* London: Macmillan Co., Ltd., 1923. (A classic summary of poultry genetics as known in 1923.)

Rieman, G. H., "Genetic Factors for Pigmentation in the Onion and Their Relation to Disease Resistance." *J. Agr. Research,* **42:**251–278, 1931.

Shackelford, R. M., *Genetics of the Ranch Mink.* New York: Pilsbury Publishers, 1950. (A book for breeders, with much interesting information.)

Questions and Problems

4- 1.   What does gene interaction mean? Epistasis? How does epistasis differ from dominance?

Many kinds of wild mammals have a peculiar distribution of pigment in their hair. The hair is mostly black or dark brown, but each hair has, just below the tip, a yellow band. This color pattern, called the *agouti* pattern after a wild animal displaying it, gives wild mice, rats, and rabbits, for example, their peculiar "mousy" color, almost indescribable in ordinary color terms.

4- 2.   In black mice and other black animals the subapical yellow band is not present; the hair is all black. This absence of the wild agouti pattern is called *non-agouti.* When mice of a true-breeding agouti strain are crossed with non-agoutis, the F_1's are all agouti, and in F_2 three agoutis appear to one non-agouti. Diagram this cross, letting A = agouti and a = non-agouti, and giving: parental phenotypes, genotypes, and germ cells; F_1 phenotype, genotype, and germ cells; and F_2 genotypes and phenotypes.

4- 3.   Another inherited color deviation in mice substitutes brown for the black color in the wild-type hair. Brown agouti mice are called "cinnamons," a good descriptive term for their color. When wild-type mice are crossed with cinnamons, the F_1's are all wild type, and the F_2 consists of three wild type to one cinnamon. Diagram this cross as in Question 4-2, letting B = the black of the wild type, b = the brown of the cinnamon.

4- 4. When mice of a true-breeding cinnamon strain are crossed with mice of a true-breeding non-agouti strain (black), the F_1 are all wild type. Explain this "reversion" to wild type by means of a genetic diagram.

4- 5. In the F_2 of the cross in Question 4-4, besides the parental types (cinnamon and non-agouti blacks), and the wild type of the F_1, a fourth color, called chocolate, shows up. Chocolates are a solid, rich-brown color. What do the chocolates represent genetically?

4- 6. Assuming that the A-a and the B-b allelic pairs assort independently of each other, what would you expect to be the relative frequencies of the four color types in the F_2 above? Diagram the crosses of Questions 4-4 and 4-5, showing phenotypes, genotypes, and germ cells.

4- 7. What phenotypes, and in what proportions, would be observed in the progeny of a backcross of the F_1's in Question 4-4 to the cinnamon parent stock? To the non-agouti (black) parent stock? Diagram these backcrosses.

4- 8. Diagram a testcross for the F_1's of Question 4-4. What colors would result and in what proportions?

4- 9. Albino (pink-eyed white) mice are homozygous for the recessive member of an allelic pair (C-c), independent of the A-a and B-b pairs in its genetic transmission. Suppose that you had four different highly inbred (and therefore presumably homozygous) albino lines, and you crossed each of them with a true-breeding wild-type strain and raised a large F_2 progeny in each case. What genotypes for the albino lines would you deduce from the following F_2 ratios:

	Numbers of F_2 Progeny				
F_2 of Line	Wild Type	Non-agouti (Black)	Cinnamon	Chocolate	Albino
1	87	0	32	0	39
2	62	0	0	0	18
3	96	30	0	0	41
4	287	86	92	29	164

Example: F_1 mice in all crosses are known to have received ABC from their wild-type parent and c from their albino parent. Crosses to produce the F_2 can therefore be written $A?B?Cc \times A?B?Cc$, in which the males and females in any given F_1 have the same genotype.

In the F_2 of line 1, the cinnamon mice must have received the b allele from each parent. All of the colored mice, however, have the agouti color pattern. The F_1's of line 1 must therefore have been $AABbCc$. Since these received ABC from their wild-type parent, they must have received Abc from their albino parent, and since the albino line 1 is presumed to be homozygous, its genotype must be $AAbbcc$.

As a check, note that the particular 9:3:4 ratio expected in such an F_2 agrees well with the observed result. You could get the answer more quickly by noting that this is a modified dihybrid ratio (9:3:4) involving heterozygosity for albinism and for the B-b pair of alleles.

The following three questions refer to general genetic situations, in which the particular phenotypes are not specified.

4-10. A particular cross gives in F_2 a modified dihybrid ratio of 9:7. What phenotypic ratio would you expect in a testcross of the F_1's in this cross?

4-11. What phenotypic ratio would you expect from the testcross of an F_1 giving a 13:3 ratio in F_2? A 9:3:4 ratio? A 12:3:1 ratio? A 15:1 ratio? A 9:6:1 ratio? A 1:2:2:4:1:2:1:2:1 ratio? A 3:6:3:1:2:1 ratio? A 9:3:3:1 ratio?

4-12. Indicate how each of the nine dihybrid ratios listed in Questions 4-10 and 4-11 may come about.

Example: The 13:3 ratio results when a dominant allele of one gene produces a phenotypic effect indistinguishable from that produced by the homozygous recessive allele of an independent gene. Thus, the dihybrid phenotypic ratio of 9A–B–:3A–bb: 3aaB–:1aabb becomes 13:3, since only the third phenotype is different; the first, second, and fourth are alike.

When silver (black) foxes were first successfully bred in captivity, it was found easy to maintain true-breeding black lines. Black was *recessive* to red; the wild red color was therefore not carried hidden in the heterozygous condition, to appear unexpectedly in later generations (see Problem 2-22).

4-13. Some time after the establishment of the ranch-bred silver fox industry, it was found that black foxes of Canadian origin (called Standard Silvers), when crossed with blacks of Alaskan origin (Alaskan Silvers), instead of breeding true for black, gave reddish hybrids with a dusky cross over their shoulders (see Plate II). How would you explain this apparent contradiction to the observation that black is recessive to red? How would you test your explanation?

4-14. The F_1's, when Standard and Alaskan Silver foxes are crossed (Problem 4-13), are called "blended-cross" foxes. When two blended-cross foxes are mated, the progeny range in color from wild red to intense black. Numerous such crosses suggest the following ratio: 1 Red : 2 Smoky Red : 2 Cross-Red : 4 Blended Cross : 1 Standard Silver : 2 Substandard Silver : 1 Alaskan Silver : 2 Sub-Alaskan Silver : 1 Double-Black. On this basis, what advice could you give a breeder who wished to establish a true-breeding blended-cross strain of foxes?

4-15. What breeding system could you recommend to assure the rancher in Question 4-14 of a high frequency of blended-cross foxes without having to dispose of numerous mongrel types of little market value?

4-16. In the discussion of color in mammals on page 57, several color variants in mink were listed as examples. Note that platinum (pp) and imperial platinum ($ip\ ip$) depend on the recessive alleles of different genes, but that the two are phenotypically indistinguishable, each having a blue-grey color. What could you advise a breeder who reported to you that he was having trouble with his "platinum" mink because many of his matings between "platinums" were producing wild-type progeny?

Many apparently similar, inherited human disorders show different patterns of inheritance in different family histories. *Retinitis pigmentosa*, for example, is an eye defect associated with the deposition of pigment on the retina, resulting in more or less severe impairment of vision. In some human pedigrees, this disorder behaves as a simple dominant, transmitted directly by affected individuals to about half their children. In other families, the disorder is evidently recessive. Still other bases for similar disorders are known; we will confine our attention to the two specified, for the present.

The dominant form of retinitis pigmentosa is usually rather mild and typically occurs relatively late in life. The recessive form is usually severe, often leading to blindness at an early age, and frequently accompanied by deafness.

Exceptions to these generalizations occur.

In the questions that follow, assume that the dominant and the recessive forms of retinitis pigmentosa depend on independent genes having similar phenotypic effects, such that

$R-$ = dominant form $P-$ = normal vision
rr = normal vision pp = recessive form

Further assume that both the R allele and the p allele are rare, so that unless direct evidence to the contrary is cited in the question, any individual may be considered homozygous for the normal alleles of these genes.

(Answer the questions on the basis of the information and assumptions given, but if you should have occasion to consider problems of real persons in this connection, be cautious; all the facts are not yet available.)

4-17. A young man whose father and paternal grandfather developed retinitis pigmentosa late in life wants to know the chances that he, in turn, will in time develop the disorder. What might you tell him?

4-18. Suppose you found that the mother of the young man in Question 4-17 had been blind since childhood, and that there was evidence for the recessive type of retinitis pigmentosa in her and her family. One of her parents had normal vision; the other had the disorder in its recessive form. Would this modify your answer to Question 4-17?

4-19. The young man in Questions 4-17 and 4-18 is contemplating matrimony, and wonders what chance his children will have of developing retinitis pigmentosa. What could you tell him:
a. If his fiancée has normal vision, and there is no record of retinitis pigmentosa in her family history?
b. If he hopes to marry a first cousin, the daughter of his mother's sister? Neither the cousin nor her mother has shown any indication of the disorder.

4-20. Dr. Harold Falls (see "References") has cautioned medical advisors that "genetic advice should not be given without sufficient, careful, and meticulous study of the specific family concerned." What aspects of this chapter and its problems relate to Dr. Falls' admonition?

4-21. In Problem 2-20, referring to the corn color plate, Plate I, you were asked a question leading to the answer that the two strains of corn crossed in that figure probably differed in a particular allelic pair affecting kernel color. You probably concluded that the light parent was homozygous for a recessive light kernel coat color, while the dark-red parent was homozygous for the corresponding dominant allele. This was consistent with the ratio of 13 red to 5 light (yellow or white) illustrated in 18 successive F_2 ears.
Now, suppose that there are two different recessives in corn, either of which when homozygous gives a light kernel color. What ratio would you observe in F_2, if the light parent strain were homozygous for both of these, assuming that the two allelic pairs assort independently? Is the ratio illustrated in the figure inconsistent with this hypothesis?

4-22. What data would you collect to distinguish between the hypothesis that the parent strains differ in a single allelic pair, and the hypothesis that they differ in two allelic pairs, interacting as postulated in Question 4-21?

4-23. In a large F_2 of the type illustrated, suppose that you observed 876 red : 324 light ears. Test both hypotheses of Question 4-22 against these observed data using the χ^2 test. Which of the hypotheses now seems more likely?

4-24. A mouse fancier crossed an albino mouse with a solid black in his colony and found that about half the progeny were black-and-white spotted, the remainder solid black. The breeder was not surprised at the black-and-white offspring, since it seemed reasonable to him that mice with one white and one black parent would be black-and-white. But he wondered how the black progeny came about. Could you diagram the cross for him, using the information you gained in Problem 4-9, plus the knowledge that a recessive white spotting is common in mice?

CHAPTER 5

The Impact of
Environment

THERE IS a saying that one may miss seeing a forest because of the trees. For students of genetics a parallel proverb might be devised to say that one may fail to understand genetics because of the genes. Let us see what is meant by this paradoxical statement.

Most of us would concede that a forest is made up, at least in large part, of trees, and that trees largely determine the character of a forest. To understand a forest, then, we must examine the trees. But as we stand close to a tree to scrutinize it carefully, it bulks large, and may cut off our view of other trees and other objects in the forest. Especially, it may obscure various cross relationships among the components of the forest. For comprehension of a complex whole made up of many parts, it is necessary to look near, far, and all about.

Similarly, all present evidence leads us to conclude that genes have great importance in determining the character of an organism. If we are to get at an understanding of heredity and life, we must analyze the nature and behavior of genes. But if genes are to be studied effectively, they must be dealt with only a few at a time. Otherwise the problems of the geneticist become too complex to analyze. This difficulty begins to become apparent even in the relatively simple analyses dealing with segregations of Mendelian trihybrids. And remember that to deal with the segregation of genes is to consider only a single aspect of their behavior.

Actually, in calling an organism a Mendelian trihybrid, and in using similar terms and concepts, we create an artificial kind of situation. Real genes are never found in the situation we give them when one or two genes are set apart, designated by letters or other arbitrary symbols and shown in splendid isolation on a printed page. Geneticists estimate that the different kinds of genes in most organisms number in the hundreds or even the thousands. As a given gene functions in an organism, it has a chemical environment determined not only by itself but also by many other genes and by agents of the external environment of the organism. More or less specifically, and to a greater or lesser degree, the functioning of a gene always depends on this environment.

Relationships Between Genes and Characters

Genes are generally recognized by the characters primarily determined by them. They are also named after the characters they determine. These are expedient procedures and well justified. But you must remain aware that genes and characters are not identical. The expression of a given character, even though it is primarily associated with a single gene, is the product of many interactions between genotype and environment. If you fail to understand this, one of the major concepts of genetics will have escaped you. We will try to reinforce this concept by means of the illustrations that follow.

A Pedigree for Severe Blistering of the Feet in Man. Figure 5-1 is a pedigree showing the distribution of severe blistering of the feet in four

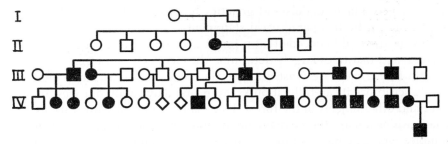

Figure 5-1. *Shaded symbols in this pedigree indicate individuals affected with severe foot blistering. The circles designate females; the squares, males.* (*From Haldane and Poole,* J. Heredity, **33**:17, 1942.)

generations of persons in families related by descent. According to the conventions for such representations, a circle represents a female and a square a male individual. Unshaded circles or squares designate people normal for the characteristic being studied. Shaded circles or squares represent "affected" individuals, in this case persons showing severe foot blistering. Each horizontal row, or tier, of circles and squares designates a generation, with the most recent generation shown lowest on the page. The generations are identified in sequence by Roman numerals.

In generation I of this pedigree, the horizontal line connecting the circle (woman) and square (man) is the typical indication of a mating between the two. Counting off from the left, individuals 1, 2, 3, 4, 5, and 7 in generation II are children of the man and wife above. Individual 6, not directly connected by lines with 1 and 2 above, is the husband of 5 in generation II. Individuals 9 and 11 in generation III are two different wives of 10. Which wife was second is not necessarily indicated by their sequence in the diagram. The diamonds in generation IV are used to indicate a number of individuals of unknown sex. Not all pedigrees in the literature of genetics conform entirely to fixed usage, but if you learn to read this one with facility, variant forms will give you no real trouble.

Now, what genetic meaning may we derive from the pedigree? In the first place, it can be seen that once the character for blistering appears in the ancestral line, no individual shows the character unless one of his parents also is affected. (How the gene for this character may have arisen in the first instance is something we will consider later on.) Also, in families with an affected parent, both normal and affected progeny may occur, and usually do. Applying what we have already learned about inheritance, we see that these things would be true if foot blistering were conditioned by a single dominant gene. Just *how dominant* the gene may be is unknown, since these families offer no opportunity to observe the effects of homozygosity for the gene. See whether you can answer why, under the explanation just presented, all affected individuals in the pedigree must be heterozygotes.

If the individuals in this study were experimental animals or plants, the question of relative dominance might be readily resolved. From brother-sister or cousin matings between affected individuals we could expect about one-fourth of the progenies to be homozygous for the gene for foot blistering. Marriages among near relatives are rare in our society, however. And as this gene for foot blistering is apparently a fairly scarce one in the population at large, the question about relative dominance of the gene may remain unanswered for some time.

There is one other piece of simple genetic reasoning that can be applied to the pedigree under examination. If all the affected individuals are heterozygous for a gene for blistering, and the normals are homozygous for its normal allele, matings between normals and affecteds should give rise to affecteds and normals in a ratio of 1:1. In other words, $Aa \times aa \rightarrow \frac{1}{2} Aa + \frac{1}{2} aa$. Referring to the pedigree itself you will find that out of such matings 11 normal and 17 affected offspring have been identified. You should ask yourselves whether this deviation from the theoretically expected 14:14 is a significant one. In the opinion of Haldane and Poole it is not. (What tool do you have at hand to help in formulating and justifying *your* answer?)

Let us accept the genetic interpretation that has been applied to the preceding pedigree as being correct. A common way of summarizing the situation would be to say that a certain severe blistering of the feet is a dominant heritable character. Of course, it is obvious to all of us that we are speaking figuratively when we imply that the *characteristic* is inherited, for the notion of a sperm or an egg cell with blistered feet is clearly ridiculous. What we really mean is that people may inherit a dominant gene for blistered feet. But, although this statement may cover the situation from one limited point of view, it is quite inadequate—except as shorthand—if we are to pursue our major purpose of inquiring *why* organisms are the way they are.

In this particular instance we are confronted with the question of why certain people show severe blistering of the feet. Examination of the pedigree shows, over several generations, a distribution of the characteristic which fits in with the inheritance pattern of a single dominant gene. Blistered feet and the gene, however, are not identical. Neither does the gene alone give rise to blistered feet. For example, we learn from the original paper by Haldane and Poole that the blisters always appear in hot weather but seldom in cold. As one might expect, occupation also has something to do with the blistering, for Mr. III-13 found that while in military service his feet blistered even during the winter. In a study of a different pedigree of what appears to be the same condition, one of the affected persons was found to show the additional symptom of hand blistering, but only after a hard day at golf. We cannot doubt that these persons to whom we have been referring each had his own same genes, winter or summer, walking or being hauled around in a motor truck. It is therefore not inappropriate to speculate what the pedigree would look like if these people had lived in Eskimo land and had been afflicted with a severe aversion to pedestrian activity. Naturally we have no real way of knowing what would have happened. The point is that under certain circumstances severe foot blistering might never occur even in persons carrying the appropriate dominant gene.

External Environment and the Development of Yellow Fat in Rabbits. To reinforce the point that has just been made, let us think back to a genetic situation already examined in some detail. In rabbits, yellow fat occurs in individuals homozygous for a recessive gene y (p. 25). The dominant allele of y conditions colorless fat because this gene determines the presence of an enzyme that breaks down the yellow-colored xanthophylls that frequently occur in the food of rabbits. But suppose there were no xanthophylls in the diet of a rabbit of the genotype yy? The answer, of course, is that on a xanthophyll-free diet even animals lacking the enzyme for xanthophyll destruction will have white fat. This should re-emphasize an idea that was suggested earlier: Genes determine *potentialities;* the realization of these potentialities depends on the environment in which the genes perform their functions.

Internal Environment and Cyanogenesis in Clover. In rabbits of genotype yy, typical phenotypic expression depends ultimately on an *external* environmental circumstance—the presence of green food in the diet. In other words, to distinguish readily between genotypes yy and $Y-$, it is necessary that an external source of substrate be at hand for an enzyme system whose presence or absence is genetically determined. *Internal* environment as conditioned by genotype can bear the same kind of relationship to the realization of the genetic potentialities of an organism. This can be illustrated with the already familiar example of cyanide production in clover (p. 59).

Even if the gene determining an enzyme for cyanogenesis (gene H) is present in a plant, no cyanide will be formed unless appropriate substrate is at hand to permit the reaction to proceed. In the clover plant the presence of substrate is itself dependent on at least one gene we know about specifically, and doubtless on many others as well. If all other conditions are favorable to the event, cyanide production may be used as a basis for identifying the presence of gene *H;* lack of cyanogenesis may then be taken as evidence for the absence of this gene. The gene is only a unit of inheritance, however, and does not by itself produce cyanide.

Cooperation Among Genic and Nongenic Factors in Chlorophyll Production. Green plants are widespread on our planet, and because of their capacity to synthesize carbohydrates from water and carbon dioxide, they are highly important in the economy of living things. Both the faculty of photosynthesis and the characteristic color of green plants depend on the presence of the pigment substance chlorophyll. Occasionally, among members of a group normally composed of green plants, one finds a white individual. Since without chlorophyll such a plant cannot make its food, it literally starves to death, perishing in the seedling stage as soon as the reserve food of the seed is exhausted.

The fact that there are occasionally white seedlings as well as normal greens provides an opportunity for investigation of the genetic basis of the formation of the key compound chlorophyll. Particularly in corn, chlorophyll inheritance has been closely studied by several geneticists. In experiments conducted in the years just prior to 1920, E. W. Lindstrom self-pollinated green corn plants heterozygous for white. (*Self-pollination* means fertilizing the female gametes of a plant with male cells from the same individual.) Progeny arising out of the controlled mating were 1513 green seedlings and 555 albinos. The result is in close agreement with a 3:1 ratio, and implies that white seedling is inherited as a simple Mendelian recessive. We might represent the mating as having been $Ww \times Ww$, or as Ww selfed.

Not all instances of white seedling are due to the effects of the same gene, however. This fact emerged after self-pollination of certain plants gave phenotypic results falling into a 9:7 ratio of green seedlings to white. Such a mating and its results may be summarized as follows:

$$W_1w_1W_2w_2 \; Self\text{-}pollinated$$

$$
\begin{array}{ll}
W_1\text{--}W_2\text{--} & = \text{green } (9) \\
W_1\text{--}w_2w_2 & = \text{white } (3) \\
w_1w_1W_2\text{--} & = \text{white } (3) \quad \Big\} = 7 \\
w_1w_1w_2w_2 & = \text{white } (1)
\end{array}
$$

In other words, here is an instance where dominant alleles of two independent genes, W_1 and W_2, are each shown to be essential for the production of chlorophyll.

From still other heterozygous stocks of corn, Lindstrom was able to obtain ratios of 27 green to 37 white after self-pollination of the parent plants. Here the situation is analogous to that presented just above, but a segregation of three instead of two independently inherited allelic pairs is involved. At the present time, we know that more than twenty different dominant genes in corn must be present if chlorophyll is to be formed. The effect of the absence of any one of these genes is chlorophyll deficiency.

Besides white seedlings in corn, other kinds of genetic variants from the normal green are known. One of these is the *virescent* type. Virescents usually begin as albinos but gradually become yellow-green, and eventually may be indistinguishable in color from the normal. Several different virescents are known to act as simple recessives to normal green. The speed with which chlorophyll develops among virescents not only varies from one genetic type to another but also depends very strongly on light and on temperature. Under conditions of weak light and low temperature, color development tends to be suppressed. In the full sun and with temperatures from 90° to 110°F, chlorophyll may develop so rapidly that virescent seedlings are difficult to tell from normal green seedlings after the plants are more than a few days old.

Self-pollination of heterozygous normal green plants that carry recessive genes for both white seedling and virescent gives rise to a 9:3:4 ratio.

$WwVv$ *Self-pollinated*
$$W\text{--}V\text{--} \ = \ \text{green} \qquad (9)$$
$$W\text{--}vv \ = \ \text{virescent} \ (3)$$
$$wwV\text{--} \ = \ \text{white} \qquad (3) \left.\begin{array}{c} \\ \end{array}\right\} = 4$$
$$wwvv \ = \ \text{white} \qquad (1)$$

The result implies that the normal allele of the white seedling gene must carry out its function if virescent color development is to occur.

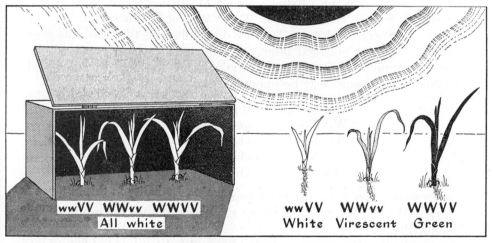

Figure 5-2. *Corn plants grown in the absence of light will not develop chlorophyll. Grown in sunlight, corn plants may develop chlorophyll rapidly, slowly, or not at all, as determined by their genotype.*

The relation of sunlight to virescent seedlings is one limited aspect of a general association between light and the development of chlorophyll. No matter what their genotype, seedlings will not develop chlorophyll in the absence of light. For different genotypes, however, light may elicit various responses depending on the genetic constitution of the individual. This relationship is shown in Figure 5-2. One might say that light here acts like a finger on a trigger, in each different case releasing particular inherent potentialities of the organism.

Heredity, Environment, and Lethality. Suppose that as a little summer experiment in genetics you were to plant some corn seed from self-pollinated plants of the genotype Ww. On the basis of what you have learned about chlorophyll inheritance, you would expect a progeny population having about three normal greens to one white. If just after the planting you were to leave on a vacation trip, you might well return to find only green plants in your experimental plot. Suitable genetic tests would show these green plants to be in the genotypic proportions of ⅓ WW to ⅔ Ww. On the other hand, if you were to stay around and observe the seedlings emerge, you would probably find both green and white seedlings in about their expected ratio. The reason for the different observations you might make is that plants of genotype ww always die after a short time in the field. Appropriately, then, white seedling is called a *lethal* character. You can appreciate that genes for lethal characters not only affect individuals in a drastic way but also have important implications for populations in which they segregate. Recessive lethal characters tend to disappear from our view, since individuals homozygous for the allele die out. But recessive lethal alleles may be carried along in individuals that are heterozygous, and thus be preserved in a population, possibly to appear again when heterozygotes mate.

Lethal characters occur among people, as well as among other organisms, so that our study of them has a certain direct and practical application in our own species. This is a good place for us to consider briefly some attitudes toward heredity and environment that are important for us both as people and as students of genetics. To many of you, the term *lethal character* doubtless has a terribly final sound. The impression it conveys fits the fairly common notion that heredity fixes on us an unalterable destiny. Heredity indeed has very much to do with what we are, but it generally fixes limits of potentiality rather than imposes specific characters. Within these limits, there may be the possibility of realizing any one of a number of different potentialities.

Consider the lethal character albino in maize. Lethality in this instance is not due to lack of chlorophyll as such but to nutritional deficiencies resulting from the lack of chlorophyll. H. A. Spoehr, of the Carnegie Institution's Division of Plant Biology, was able to show this when he kept albino corn plants alive and growing by introducing sugar solutions into them through their leaves (Fig. 5-3). Curiously enough, attempts to culture albino corn by

Figure 5-3. *Albino corn plants usually die in a very short time, because they cannot manufacture carbohydrate. But if such plants are artificially nourished by means of sugar solution introduced through their leaves, they may survive for several months, gain in weight, produce as many leaves as normal plants, and develop inflorescences.* (Courtesy of H. A. Spoehr, Plant Physiol., **17**:400, 1942.)

placing its roots into similar solutions of sugar are not nearly so effective. One lesson that we may draw from Spoehr's experiments is that genetic lethality is a conditional rather than an absolute matter. If certain conditions maintain, lethality expresses itself; under other circumstances it may not.

The preservation of albinos in maize by feeding them sucrose has obvious analogies to the preservation of diabetic people by giving them injections of insulin. In both instances, an inborn deficiency in metabolism is remedied by applying from the outside a chemical substance which in normal individuals is synthesized by the organism itself. These remedies, however, are not "cures for the genes"; they do not alter the genes or restore their activity for synthesis.

There are other means by which certain genetic defects may be remedied. *Retinal glioma* is a rare heritable condition in man manifested as a malignant tumor of the retina. Unless the affected eye is removed before the cancer spreads into the tissue beyond, the condition is lethal. Prompt surgery may save the lives of affected individuals, but not even the most dextrous surgeon can selectively remove the genes for retinal glioma. An affected individual whose life is saved by a timely operation will still retain defective genes in the germ line, and may pass them on to progeny.

Having in mind a number of examples of relationships between heredity and environment, we can generalize on a concept that was suggested earlier: The genetic characters we observe are not inevitable merely by reason of the presence of a particular gene. On the other hand, the fact that appropriate environment is required for development of genetic traits does not mean that genes fail to exert a decisive influence on characteristics of the organism. Neither can one assume that genetic characters may be altered at will, for either circumstances or our own ignorance may prevent this. If in retinal glioma the heart instead of the eye were cancerous, removal of the affected organ would scarcely evade the incipient lethality. Conceivably, though, if enough were known, application of just the right chemicals at just the right time might arrest the cancer or prevent it entirely. We may justifiably hope that increased understanding of the bases of our heritable characteristics will lead to increased possibilities for altering these characteristics when we find it desirable to do so.

The Variety of Environmental Agents That Act on Genetic Characters

There is no escaping the conclusion that genes work in terms of the chemistry of the organism. A considerable amount of direct evidence supports this view, and in any event no other possibility is conceivable. You should not be surprised, therefore, that characteristics controlled by genes are affected by agents known to influence the rates, the initiation, and the cessation of chemical reactions in general. In the first place, you know from experience that almost any extreme of environment can produce disruption and disintegration of all the life qualities of an organism. Very high or low temperature, extreme desiccation, or any one of a variety of drastic conditions may lead to death. But variations within the range of everyday environments compatible with life are also important to an organism, and may markedly affect the expression of certain of its genetic characters.

pH and the Colors of Flowers. Many of the flower colors we see are determined by pigments called *anthocyanins*. These pigments can act as pH indicators. In other words, they give color changes as the relative acidity of their medium is altered. For the anthocyanin produced under a particular genotype, different color possibilities exist, and pH may determine the possibility that ultimately is realized. The relative acidity of the cellular environment in which a genotypically determined anthocyanin exists may be affected by external conditions, such as the pH of the soil; or it may vary with the genotype of the organism itself. In the sweet pea, a gene d has been found to give rise to a cell sap that averages 0.6 of a pH unit higher than that found in plants of comparable genotype where allele D is present instead. Comparing sweet peas having the same anthocyanin, d types are appreciably bluer than D types. This example illustrates the important principle that gene products or by-products may be essentially the same as environmental agents arising outside the organism, and that these may act in similar fashion to give similar effects in the organism.

Effect of Temperature on the Bar-Eye Character in Drosophila. The compound eyes of the fruit fly Drosophila are made up of many subunits, or facets. In the wild type these facets number 800 or more. A striking difference from the wild-type eye is found in the so-called bar-eyed individuals, where the facet number is considerably reduced. The bar character is determined by a single gene. As shown in Table 5-1, however, the number of facets found in bar flies is markedly affected by the temperature at which the flies are grown. The mechanism accounting for the effect of temperature

	15°C	20°C	25°C	30°C
Bar-eyed ♂♂	270	161	121	74
Bar-eyed ♀♀	214	122	81	40

TABLE 5-1. Average Facet Number in the Eyes of Bar-Eyed Drosophila Grown at Different Temperatures. (Data from Krafka, J. Gen. Physiol., 2:413, 1920.)

on reduction of facet number in bar-eyed flies is not yet understood. Obviously, however, the explanation of this phenomenon must be sought among the physical conditions for particular biochemical reactions in the organism.

The Relation of Light to Sun-Red Corn. For corn plants to develop the color called "sun red," the cooperation of at least three genes, as designated by the genotype A–B–$plpl$, is required. Moreover, pigmentation occurs only on those parts of the plant exposed to sunlight, so that the outer husks, for example, are usually red colored, but the inner husks are not. Anthers and glumes in these plants are normally pigmented red, but if a tassel is covered with a black paper sack, red fails to develop.

A colorful demonstration of precision and localization of the effects of sunlight on pigmentation may sometimes be found on husks of a type of corn designated as "weak sun red." It is characteristic of young, rapidly growing ears of corn that portions of certain husks are continually emerging from beneath previously overlapping husks. In weak sun-red plants, portions of husks that emerge during bright daylight hours develop red color. Portions that emerge at night stay green. Thus, as illustrated in Figure 5-4, weak sun-red husks often exhibit a banding pattern of alternate red and green stripes which lie parallel to the upper edge of an overlapping husk.

Effects of Cultural Conditions on Certain Drosophila with Abnormal Abdomens. In certain strains of Drosophila the regular banding pattern

Figure 5-4. *The barred pattern seen on the husks of weak sun-red corn is a response of pigment development to light. Portions of growing husks that emerge during bright daylight turn red; portions emerging at night remain green. The dark shading represents red color, the light shading green.* (*After Emerson,* Cornell Univ. Agr. Exp. Sta. Mem. No. 39, *1921.*)

typical of the abdomens of wild-type adults may be drastically altered (Fig. 5-5). The deviant characteristic has been given the name *abnormal abdomen,* and the results of appropriate crosses indicate that it has a simple genetic basis. Deviation from the normal, however, is not always in the same degree, even in stocks homozygous for abnormal abdomen. Flies that emerge from fresh, moist culture medium usually show abnormal abdomen in its most extreme form. With increasing age and dryness of "fly food," individuals come out looking more nearly normal. Ultimately, flies emerge that are indistinguishable from wild type. If special precautions are taken to keep larvae from abnormal abdomen stocks on properly fresh, moist medium, normal appearing individuals may fail to turn up at all. On the other hand, regular and familiar phenotypic ratios which should occur after matings of heterozygous individuals may be entirely concealed by raising the flies on dry medium from the outset. It will be important for you to keep in mind that genotypic segregation is not always accompanied by the appearance of individuals that are phenotypically different. Again, this is because genes

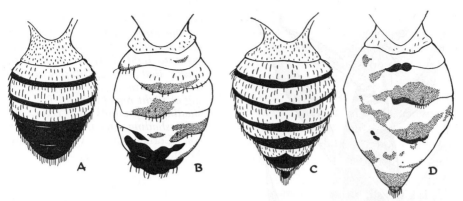

Figure 5-5. *Drosophila with the abnormal abdomen characteristic may be strikingly different from wild type. A, abdomen of wild-type male; B, of "abnormal" male; C, of wild-type female; D, of "abnormal" female. (After Morgan,* The Physical Basis of Heredity. *Lippincott, 1919, p. 29.)*

by themselves do not produce characteristics, but do so only through interactions with environment.

Other Instances of Interactions Between Genotype and Environment. Our list of examples showing the effects of different environmental factors on the expression of particular genetic characteristics could be greatly expanded. For instance, the availability of riboflavin (vitamin B_2) in the culture medium affects the expression of a gene which determines absence of antennae in Drosophila. Wild type of the mold Neurospora synthesizes pyridoxin at pH levels both above and below 5.8. But a strain differing from wild by only a single gene is unable to make this vitamin at pH levels below 5.8; it can manufacture pyridoxin where pH values are somewhat higher. Also in Neurospora, presence of a gene r leads to an inability to synthesize riboflavin at temperatures above 28°C. Wild-type Neurospora makes this substance at temperatures anywhere from 15° to 40°C, or perhaps even over a slightly wider range.

These instances, and others that might be mentioned, strongly indicate that environmental factors affect genetic characteristics by influencing the inherent biochemistry of the organism. But although this general situation is clear, the details of relationships between environmental factors and gene-controlled biochemical reactions remain to be worked out. When such relationships are subjected to more refined investigations than have so far been possible, unexpectedly subtle associations between hereditary and nonhereditary factors probably will be revealed.

The Idea of a Threshold

Apparently inconsequential differences in environment may assume special importance at critical times in the development of an organism. This principle can be seen in characteristics of a *giant* race of Drosophila, where a single genotype may produce adult individuals falling into two distinct categories, normal-sized flies and giants that average 70 per cent greater in weight than do wild-type adults. In a culture of Drosophila of this genotype, frequency of giants depends rather directly on the cultural conditions as expressed in food available for each larva. When conditions are crowded, and when there is rigorous larval competition for food, few giants emerge. With plentiful food available for each individual, potential giants actually become giants in high percentage. Wild-type Drosophila do not become giants even under the most favorable nutritional circumstances that have been devised.

It is interesting that in homozygous giant cultures grown under conditions where nutrition may be a limiting factor, it is not so much the *size* of the giants but their *number* that is affected. The few giants that do appear are about as large as those emerging in culture bottles where nutritional conditions are uniformly excellent. This suggests that there is some kind of genetically controlled *threshold* for the reaction that produces the giant characteristic. The reaction itself seems to be set in train by factors of the environment, in this instance probably nutritional factors. Under the somewhat variable conditions of a crowded Drosophila culture, these factors may reach threshold intensity for some individuals but not for others. The threshold concept is a useful way of looking at a number of the relationships between heredity and environment that will come to your attention. You should realize, however, that it provides only a point of view and is not in itself an explanation of particular cases where a genotype shows irregular expression.

Stability of Expression of Many Genotypes. By now you may be wondering how geneticists have ever made any progress in their studies, since relatively trivial alterations in the environment can produce large differences in phenotypic expression. If it were true that genetic characters in general were highly sensitive to environment, there would be great difficulty in following patterns of gene segregation by observing the distributions of characteristics among particular progenies. Geneticists try to meet this difficulty by conducting their experiments under carefully controlled conditions, insofar as is feasible. Moreover, organisms are fairly well insulated against quite a few of the possible variations in their external environment. But at least equally important to the success of genetic studies is the fact that many genes express themselves quite uniformly and predictably over a wide range of intensities of the agents of environment ordinarily met.

The genotype that produces blue eyes in man, for example, seems to be expressed very much the same irrespective of diet or of climate. Even the gene for foot blistering, which we described earlier as requiring a particular type of environment for its expression, produces an effect which enables it to be identified under a variety of circumstances. After all, the pedigree for foot blistering (Fig. 5-1) includes four generations of persons who not only lived at different times but must have been distributed among various households and been active in various occupations. Whatever the dissimilarities in environment of the persons involved, however, the threshold for foot blistering was reached often enough for a pattern of single-gene transmission to be shown with reasonable exactness. This fact does not preclude the possibility that more drastic variations in environment might have obscured the pattern of inheritance.

Alterations of Genes by Environment

Up to this point we have been considering various aspects of interactions of genes and environment with reference to the realization of genetic characters. These interactions are supposed, although they cannot always be specifically proved, to operate through chemical reactions originated by the genes. In the ordinary interplay of genotype and environment, the genes themselves are not altered, at least not permanently. Sometimes, however, a gene does undergo sudden, permanent, apparently spontaneous alteration into a different allelic form. Such permanent heritable alterations of genes are called *mutations*. The conditions responsible for the processes by which spontaneous mutation occurs have not been identified. But it is known that treatment with certain drastic environmental agents, like X-rays, ultraviolet light, or mustard gas, greatly accelerates the mutation frequencies of genes. These agents do not appear to act selectively in the sense of reacting only with particular genes, but rather they seem to increase mutation rates in general. In addition, there is evidence that a few particular genes may be able to induce, or at least facilitate, the mutation of other genes. This is not unexpected, since genes play a large role in determining the internal chemical environment of the organism. Problems of mutation are exceedingly important in genetics, and will be dealt with in detail in Chapter 12.

Keys to the Significance of This Chapter

The characteristics of organisms are not inherited as such. Heredity is transmitted in the form of genes, and it is these entities that determine potentialities that may be fulfilled by the developing organism.

Genes do not exist within an environmental vacuum; neither do they function entirely without reference to their fellow genes. The activities of genes may be influenced by the internal environment of the organism or by factors of the external environment.

The same genotype may give rise to different phenotypes under varying circumstances of environment. In turn, one environmental factor may act to elicit various responses, depending on the genotype of the organism. In some instances, it is helpful to think of genotypes as determining thresholds for response.

Occasionally, environment influences processes by which genes undergo permanent heritable alterations called *mutations.*

References

Allee, W. C., *Animal Aggregations.* Chicago: University of Chicago Press, 1931. (Thoughtful and original treatment of a subject with which too few students in biology are familiar. Chap. 18, "The Morphological Effects of Crowding," has particular interest for geneticists.)

Goldschmidt, R., *Physiological Genetics.* New York: McGraw-Hill Book Co., 1938. (First 45 pages contain discussion of *phenocopies,* environmentally induced, nonheritable variants from wild-type forms, which simulate the phenotypic effects of particular gene mutations.)

Haldane, J. B. S., *Heredity and Politics.* New York: W. W. Norton & Co., 1938. (A stimulating and well-written book. Chap. I discusses heredity and environment as the basis for biological differences.)

Hogben, L., *Nature and Nurture.* London: G. Allen & Unwin, Ltd., 1939. (Chap. I, pp. 9–33, discusses relationships between heredity and environment as background for the medical application of genetic principles.)

Landauer, W., "Rumplessness of Chicken Embryos Produced by the Injection of Insulin and Other Chemicals." *J. Exp. Zool.*, 98:65–77, Feb. 1945. (Use of insulin to induce a character in the fowl similar to that produced by a mutant gene.)

Lindstrom, E. W., "Chlorophyll Inheritance in Maize." *Cornell Univ. Agr. Exp. Sta. Mem. No. 13,* 1918. (Summarizes early studies on this subject and is the source for some of the examples discussed in this chapter.)

Osborn, D., "Inheritance of Baldness." *J. Heredity,* 7:347–355, 1916. (Gives pedigrees for baldness, and the interpretation which is the basis for Questions 5-8 to 5-12.)

Stern, C., "Gene and Character," in *Genetics, Paleontology, and Evolution.* Princeton: Princeton University Press, 1949. (Brief essay on fundamental aspects of the relationships between genes and characteristics.)

Stokes, J. L., Foster, J. W., and Woodward, C. R., "Synthesis of Pyridoxin by a 'Pyridoxinless' X-ray Mutant of *Neurospora sitophila.*" *Arch. Biochem.*, 2:235–245, 1943. (Describes the effect of pH on the synthesis of pyridoxin by a Neurospora mutant.)

Questions and Problems

5- 1.   What do the following terms signify?

anthocyanin   pH
genetic potentiality   riboflavin
mutation   threshold
pedigree

5- 2. Using Figure 5-1 as a type example, begin to construct pedigrees showing the distributions of different alternative characteristics within your own family. Differences for which you might establish pedigrees include: (a) presence or absence of hair on the middle segments of the fingers (excluding the thumb); (b) ability or inability to turn up the lateral edges of the tongue; (c) adherent or free ear lobes; (d) curly, wavy, or straight hair. Or, if you are able to obtain some phenylthiocarbamide test paper, perhaps from your instructor, you might classify yourself and other members of your family for ability or inability to taste this compound. There are, of course, many other characteristics you might wish to work with.

As soon as you establish reasonably complete pedigrees, attempt to interpret them in terms of the genetic knowledge you have at the time. Retain these pedigrees, and re-examine them as you near the end of your course in genetics. See then whether your increased knowledge of genetic principles throws additional light on these pedigrees. (Naturally, the larger the numbers of individuals, the more likely your pedigrees are to be meaningful.)

5- 3. Distinguish carefully between a lethal gene and a lethal character.

5- 4. Why do you suppose no testcross data are available from investigations of the inheritance of albino corn?

5- 5. Which would you expect that the early workers who elaborated the principles of Mendelian inheritance found most useful for their studies: (a) genes having constant expression over a wide range of environments, or (b) genes sensitive to environmental influence in their expression? Why?

5- 6. List some factors of both the internal and external environment of organisms that are known to influence the expression of particular genes.

5- 7. Are *internal* and *external* environment mutually exclusive categories? Discuss.

5- 8. According to one theory, pattern baldness depends on an allele recessive to its normal alternative in women but dominant in men, thus:

Genotype	Phenotype	
	Women	Men
B^1B^1	nonbald	nonbald
B^1B^2	nonbald	bald
B^2B^2	bald	bald

In terms of internal environmental influence on gene action, suggest a possible explanation for the difference in dominance relations of this allelic pair in the two sexes.

5- 9. (Assume that the scheme presented in Question 5-8 is a valid one.) A bald woman marries a nonbald man. What is the probability that a son of theirs will be bald? A daughter?

5-10. A nonbald woman whose mother was bald marries a bald man whose father was nonbald. What is the probability that a son of theirs will be bald? A daughter?

5-11. A nonbald woman whose mother was bald marries a nonbald man. What is the probability that a son of theirs will be bald? A daughter?

5-12. The parents designated in Question 5-10 have a son and a daughter. What is the probability that both will be bald? Both nonbald?

5-13. In some breeds of sheep, both the males and females have horns. In other breeds, both sexes are hornless. When certain of these breeds are crossed, the F_1 males are all horned; the F_1 females are all hornless. Develop a simple hypothesis which would explain this situation. (Keep in mind the relations between genotype and phenotype in the case of baldness in men and women.)

5-14. On the basis of your hypothesis developed in answer to Question 5-13, draw diagrams to show what would happen if the F_1 individuals were crossed to produce an F_2.

5-15. What genotypes and phenotypes would be expected if you crossed an F_1 ram back to ewes of the hornless parent breed? If you crossed this ram back to ewes of the horned parent breed?

5-16. What genotypes and phenotypes would be expected if you crossed F_1 ewes with a ram of the horned parent breed? If you crossed F_1 ewes with rams of the hornless parent breed?

5-17. In certain breeds of sheep, yellow-fatted individuals occasionally appear. The yellow-fat character, which is accounted for by failure to oxidize the fat-soluble plant pigment xanthophyll, is undesirable from the standpoint of the meat purchaser. Assume that its genetic basis is the same as for the analogous character in rabbits. If you were a sheep breeder and found sheep in your flock with yellow fat, what kind of breeding program would you institute in order to eliminate the appearance of yellow-fatted individuals in the future? (Note: Sheep breeders usually use a single ram per flock.) Would you need to take environment into account in planning your breeding program?

5-18. Discuss in what respects genes appear to you to behave independently and in what respects they do not.

5-19. Not too long ago it was popular to debate whether heredity or environment is more important in determining the characteristics of organisms. Is this a proper question for debate? Why? How might the question be rephrased to make it more meaningful?

5-20. Because of advances in medical science, the effects of an increasing number of man's "lethal" genes can be circumvented by proper manipulation of environment. Is this all to the good, or do you see any possible dangers in the situation? Discuss.

CHAPTER 6

Sex Chromosomes and Sex Linkage

A LITTLE CONSIDERATION of the individual difference called *sex*, most familiar to us in animals and in our own species, suggests that this characteristic may depend on a unit difference in inheritance. Normally, the sex difference is a clear-cut one, and it generally appears in a fairly regular ratio, generation after generation. Using the symbol ♂ ("Mars' shield and spear") to represent a male, and ♀ ("Venus' looking glass") for a female, we can diagram this progression of generations:

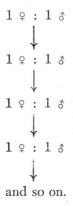

and so on.

There are, of course, frequent deviations from this 1:1 ratio—in some species rather extreme and regular ones. And occasional individuals are more or less intermediate between the two sex classes. The Greeks, in fact, had words for six sexes. We shall consider these complications and others in Chapter 14. For our present introductory discussion we will assume the normal, general situation to be based on the occurrence of two clearly distinct sex classes in a ratio approximating 1:1.

The 1:1 ratio is already familiar to us as the expression of a unit difference in germ plasm, segregating in crosses in which one parent is heterozygous and the other homozygous. If we let X represent one of the elements of a

85

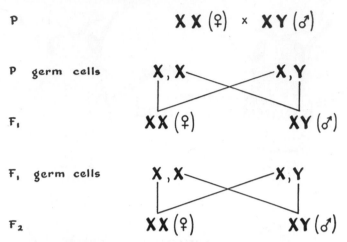

Figure 6-1. *The 1:1 sex ratio may depend on a pair of germinal elements, homozygotes for which are female and heterozygotes male.*

pair of units, and Y its alternative, we can suggest the diagram for the inheritance of sex shown in Figure 6-1. Simply by assuming that homozygosity for a pair of germinal elements controlling sex produces a female, while heterozygosity produces a male, we can explain the regular appearance, generation after generation, of males and females in approximately equal proportions.

Of course the fact that this simple explanation, as far as we have tested it, fits the situation so neatly does not prove that the explanation is correct. It happens that, among a number of lines of confirmatory evidence, one can be singled out as most convincing. Under proper conditions, the germinal elements involved in the sex difference can be seen, identified, and described. They are called *sex chromosomes.*

Sex Chromosomes. When plant or animal tissue is placed on a microscope slide, in slices or smears so thin that light can pass through, and the tissue is examined under magnification sufficient to make out its cellular structure, small, discrete bodies can often be seen within the nuclei of the cells. The examination is facilitated by staining the tissue with certain dyes, like *hematoxylin* or *acetocarmine.* The regular bodies within the nuclei take up these dyes more intensely than do other parts of the nucleus or of the cell. For this reason they have been known for many years as *chromosomes* (colored bodies). It is worth noting that their *color* is strictly an artificial quality—something new that is added by cytological staining technique to make them more easily visible under ordinary light microscopes. Other types of microscopes, like the phase microscope, that depend on principles different from those operating in the light microscope, can be used more effectively on unstained, living material than can the ordinary light microscope. It is comforting to find that observations on the chromosomes of dead,

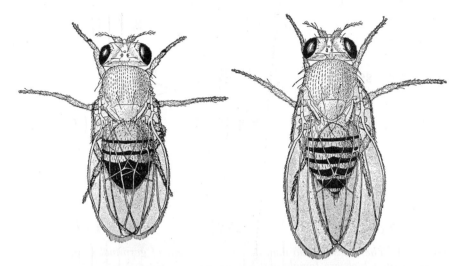

Figure 6-2. Drosophila melanogaster *has contributed greatly to our knowledge of heredity.* Left, *male.* Right, *female.* (*After Sturtevant and Beadle,* An Introduction to Genetics, *W. B. Saunders Co., 1940, frontispiece.*)

stained cells are adequately confirmed by the studies of living tissues made possible by newer tools like the phase microscope.

As an illustration of the visible basis of the inheritance of sex, we can consider this phenomenon in *Drosophila melanogaster* (Fig. 6-2). You have doubtless noticed this small fly around fruit in stores or kitchens and around garbage cans in the summer. Since its first extensive utilization early in the present century by T. H. Morgan and his co-workers, Drosophila has contributed more than any other organism to our knowledge of the physical basis of heredity. The fly has many advantages for such studies; its life cycle is short, and large populations can be maintained in small space, at little expense. The geneticist studying Drosophila can keep under his experimental control, on a shelf in his laboratory, the equivalent for the student of cattle genetics of many large barns full of cows. And in a year of intensive fly breeding, the equivalent of a long lifetime of large-scale cattle breeding

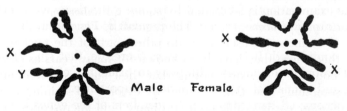

Figure 6-3. A *female* D. melanogaster *has four pairs of chromosomes in her body cells, including a pair of X-chromosomes. A male has an X-Y pair instead of X-X, but is otherwise like the female in his chromosomal makeup.* (*After Dobzhansky, in Morgan,* The Scientific Basis of Evolution, *W. W. Norton, 1932, p. 80.*)

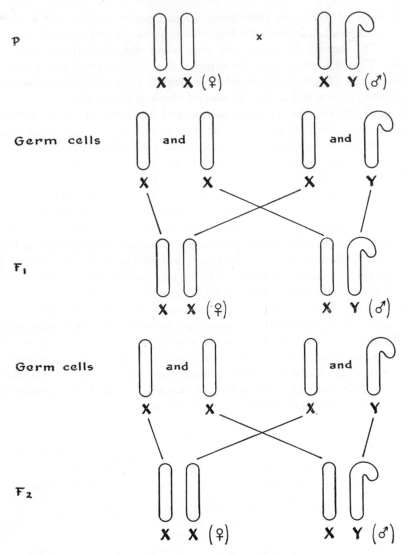

Figure 6-4. *The X- and Y-chromosomes follow the inheritance patterns postulated for the sex-determining germinal elements of Figure 6-1.*

can be accomplished. It is small wonder, therefore, that studies of inheritance in Drosophila have shown the way to principles of broad application to plants and animals of greater economic importance.

It has become customary to refer to members of the genus Drosophila as "fruit flies." It should be emphasized, however, that Drosophila are not part of another group of flies, including the Mediterranean fruit fly and other harmful insects, of concern to economic entomologists. In fact, Drosophila generally have little direct economic significance at all.

The cells of a female *Drosophila melanogaster* contain eight chromosomes, recognizable as four distinguishable pairs—a pair of small dots, two pairs of "V"-shaped elements (one pair larger than the other), and a pair of rods. The cells of a male Drosophila also contain the pair of dots and the two pairs of V's. But instead of a pair of rods, males have an unlike membered pair—a rod and a "J"-shaped element (Fig. 6-3).

We will discuss the general nature and behavior of chromosomes in some detail in the next chapter. For the present we can note that the differences between male and female Drosophila are associated with a regular difference in one particular pair of chromosomes, and we can focus our attention on this one pair. They are the sex chromosomes.

When a Drosophila of either sex forms germ cells, the members of the pairs of chromosomes separate, one member of each pair going into each germ cell. The effect of this process, and of the restoration to the paired condition at fertilization, is diagrammed for the sex chromosome in Figure 6-4. You will observe that, by labelling the rod-shaped member of the pair as X and the "J"-shaped element as Y, we can provide the presumptive diagram of Figure 6-1 with a clear and visible material basis.

Sex Linkage. One of the many interesting inherited characteristics of Drosophila, mentioned earlier in this book, involves a marked reduction in the number of facets in the fly's normally large, round, compound eyes. This difference from wild type is called "bar eye," because when it is obtained in true-breeding stocks, the eyes of both sexes are reduced to narrow red bars (Fig. 6-5C and D). When flies of the bar-eye stock are crossed with wild type, the following results are obtained in F_1:

Round eye ♀ × Bar eye ♂   Bar eye ♀ × Round eye ♂
(wild type)   (wild type)
F_1: ♂♂—Round eye F_1: ♂♂—Bar eye
       ♀♀—Wide Bar eye   ♀♀—Wide Bar eye

("♂♂" and "♀♀" are conventional plural symbols, like "pp." for pages.)

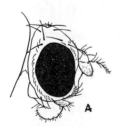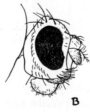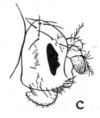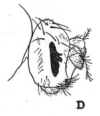

Figure 6-5. *Wild-type Drosophila* (A) *have round eyes, but the eyes of bar-eye females* (C) *and males* (D) *are small and narrow because of a greatly reduced number of facets. Only females may show the intermediate "wide-bar" phenotype* (B). (*After Morgan,* The Theory of the Gene, *Yale University Press, 1926, p. 87.*)

In two respects, these observations are unexpected in terms of our previous experience in this text. First, the phenotypes of F_1 males and females differ; and second, the reciprocal crosses give different results.

Now, in both crosses the females seem to fit what we have learned about heredity so far. They occur in three classes, *round, wide bar,* and *bar* (Fig. 6-5A–C), and the intermediate, wide-bar type occurs when we would expect an ordinary heterozygote. Furthermore, the reciprocal crosses do give identical results, as far as their female progeny are concerned. We could assign genotypes to the females as follows, letting B represent the allele for bar eye, and B^+ its normal alternative:

$$BB = \text{bar}$$
$$BB^+ = \text{wide bar}$$
$$B^+B^+ = \text{round}$$

It is the males that are out of line. They occur in only two types, *bar* and *round,* and we do not observe the wide-bar type even when a heterozygote would normally be expected. Each male seems to possess only one member of this pair of alleles, B or B^+. *He seems to inherit this allele from his mother, and to receive nothing, with regard to this pair of alleles, from his father. Each male transmits his single allele, for bar or for round eyes, to his daughters, but not to his sons.*

We can list the males as:

$$B(-) = \text{bar}$$
$$B^+(-) = \text{round}$$

in which $(-)$ stands for the missing member of the pair, and can diagram the crosses as in Figure 6-6.

The diagram is entirely consistent with the observations, which is perhaps not too surprising, since it was tailored to fit. But a comparative glance at Figures 6-1, 6-4, and 6-6 may surprise you. The pattern of inheritance of the

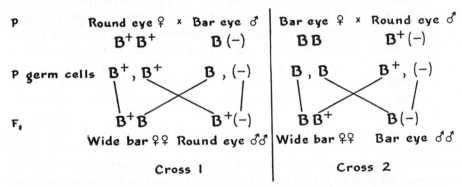

Figure 6-6. *Reciprocal crosses between bar-eye and wild-type Drosophila show a pattern of inheritance like that of the sex chromosomes.*

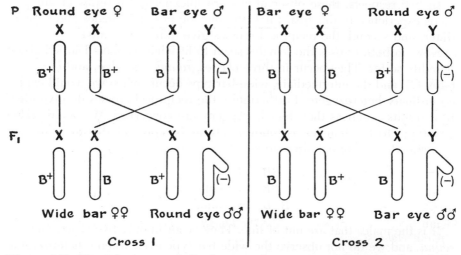

Figure 6-7. *The inheritance of the bar-eye characteristic behaves as though the responsible gene were in the X-chromosome. The Y-chromosome appears to be empty in this regard.*

bar-eye allele and its normal alternative is the same as that of the X-chromosome. The bar-eye gene has nothing apparent to do with the sex difference between individuals; either it or its normal alternative may appear in flies of either sex. But it goes with the X-chromosome in inheritance.

We can set up the following working hypothesis: Besides its role in the determination of sex, the X-chromosome also carries a gene that affects the number of facets in the eyes of a fly. A given X-chromosome may carry either the allele for bar or its normal alternative. The Y-chromosome is empty with regard to this pair of alleles. A diagram of the crosses, on this hypothesis, would look like Figure 6-7.

Now how can this be checked? One way is to predict on this basis what kind of an F_2 would be produced in each cross, and then compare what is actually obtained with this prediction. A checkerboard for cross 1 of Figure 6-7 is shown in Figure 6-8. We would predict a ratio of approximately 1 round ♀ : 1 wide bar ♀ : 1 round ♂ : 1 bar ♂ in the F_2 of this cross. This is the result actually observed. (Show that the observed ratio of 1 bar ♀ : 1 wide bar ♀ : 1 round ♂ : 1 bar ♂ in the F_2 of cross 2 is also in agreement with expectation.)

Other predictions based on the same hypothesis—expected backcross results, for example—have also been tested repeatedly. The uniform agreement between observed and expected provides convincing evidence that the bar-round alternative is controlled by a pair of alleles on the X-chromosome. This pattern of inheritance is called *sex linkage.*

Attached-X. One day several decades ago, an unusual fly turned up in

Sperm from F_1 ♂♂

		$X \underline{\text{B}^+}$	$Y \underline{(-)}$
Eggs from F_1 ♀♀	$X \underline{\text{B}^+}$	$X \underline{\text{B}^+}$ $X \underline{\text{B}^+}$ (Round eye ♀)	$X \underline{\text{B}^+}$ $Y \underline{(-)}$ (Round eye ♂)
	$X \underline{\text{B}}$	$X \underline{\text{B}^+}$ $X \underline{\text{B}}$ (Wide bar ♀)	$X \underline{\text{B}}$ $Y \underline{(-)}$ (Bar eye ♂)

Figure 6-8. *The F_2 prediction from the hypothesis in Figure 6-7 is subject to experimental test.*

the Drosophila cultures of L. V. Morgan (Mrs. T. H. Morgan). While it was being examined by some of the Drosophila workers in the laboratory, the ether anesthesia under which the fly was held wore off, and with little warning it left the stage of the microscope and flew away. There were other flies about, and there seemed little chance of recapturing this particular one. But it, a female, had been a queer-looking specimen, and considerable effort was made to find her. She was finally caught on a window pane.

This story may seem trivial. But we have already pointed out that in the development of knowledge of heredity an individual fly has often been more important than a cow. And this particular fly was an unusually important one, because she was the beginning of an exceptional stock. Incidentally, the fact that she looked queer had nothing to do with her eventual utility.

A typical experimental result with females of this stock is this: When bar-eye males are crossed with females of the exceptional stock, the offspring are just the opposite of the normal and usual result of this cross:

Exceptional ♀♀ × Bar eye ♂♂ → Bar eye ♂♂ , Round eye ♀♀
(Round eye)

Here, the *males* seem to get their allele of the bar pair *from their fathers*, while the *females are like their mothers*—the reverse of ordinary sex linkage. How can this remarkable result, uniformly obtained with the exceptional stock, be explained?

After thinking about her experimental observations, Mrs. Morgan arrived at the hypothesis that the X-chromosomes of the exceptional females might be attached to each other, so that they failed to separate when germ cells were produced. The two kinds of eggs formed by such females would then

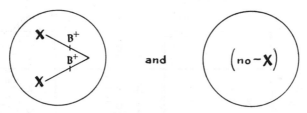

Figure 6-9. *A female Drosophila homozygous for* B+, *whose X-chromosomes were attached to each other, would form two kinds of eggs.*

be as shown in Figure 6-9. Their predicted behavior in a cross with a bar-eye male is shown by the checkerboard in Figure 6-10.

The checkerboard shows some important points in common with the actual breeding results. It provides for XX progeny lacking the bar allele; these might well be the round-eye females in the cross. And it provides for one-X progeny with the bar allele from their fathers; these may be the bar-eye male progeny. It also raises some obvious questions. If the hypothesis is correct, what happens to the expected "three-X" and "no-X" progeny? And how does the Y-chromosome fit into the picture?

At any rate, the hypothesis showed sufficient promise to be worth checking. The confirmation was straightforward: Microscopic observation of sex chromosome behavior in germ-cell formation by the exceptional females showed without question that the two X-chromosomes were attached to each other. Besides the attached-X's, the exceptional females had a Y-chromosome (like those predicted in the upper right block of our checkerboard). We need to revise our checkerboard slightly in line with this observation (Fig. 6-11).

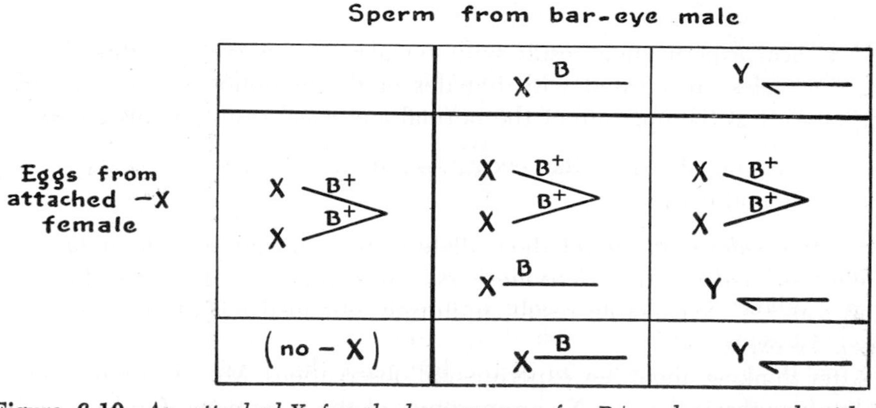

Sperm from bar-eye male

	$X \xrightarrow{B}$	$Y \xleftarrow{}$
Eggs from attached -X female $\quad X \xrightarrow{B+} X \xrightarrow{B+}$	$X \xrightarrow{B+} X \xrightarrow{B+}$ $X \xrightarrow{B}$	$X \xrightarrow{B+} X \xrightarrow{B+}$ $Y \xleftarrow{}$
$(no - X)$	$X \xrightarrow{B}$	$Y \xleftarrow{}$

Figure 6-10. *An attached-X female homozygous for* B+, *when crossed with a bar-eye male, would produce round-eye female and bar-eye male progeny, and two additional exceptional classes as well.*

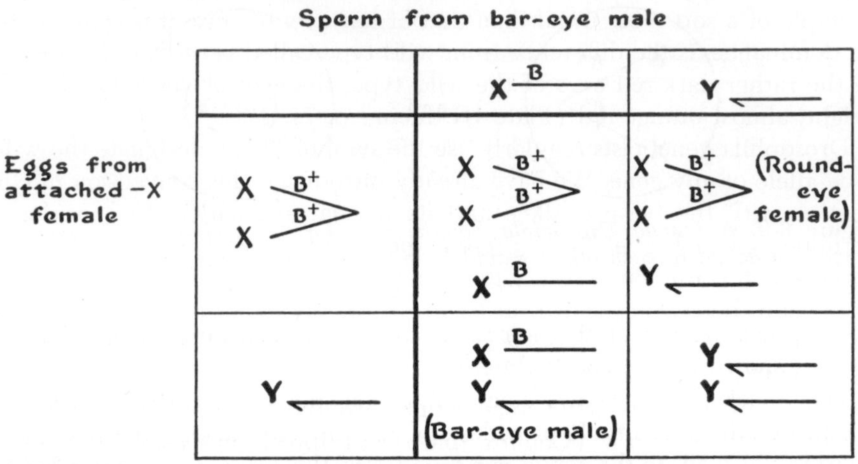

Sperm from bar-eye male

	$X \xrightarrow{\text{B}}$	Y
Eggs from attached−X female $\quad$ $X \diagdown^{\text{B}^+}$ $X \diagup_{\text{B}^+}$	$X \diagdown^{\text{B}^+}$ $X \diagup_{\text{B}^+}$ $\quad X \xrightarrow{\text{B}} \quad Y$	$X \diagdown^{\text{B}^+}$ $X \diagup_{\text{B}^+}$ (Round-eye female)
Y	$X \xrightarrow{\text{B}} \quad Y$ (Bar-eye male)	$Y \quad Y$

Figure 6-11. *The attached-X condition in the exceptional stock, postulated from genetic evidence, is confirmed by cytological observation. Attached-X females also have a Y-chromosome, which modifies the hypothetical diagram in Figure 6-10 slightly.*

Knowing that the checkerboard is based on concrete fact, it is now possible to dispose of the questions it raises.

1. Individuals lacking an X-chromosome (lower right corner of checkerboard) die before hatching from the egg.

2. Individuals with three X's (upper left) usually die. The few that survive are so different from other flies that they are easily identified. Such individuals have contributed to genetic knowledge. We shall refer to them again in Chapter 14.

3. The presence of a Y-chromosome in an attached-X (symbol: $\widehat{XX}$) female does not affect her sexual characteristics at all. It has also been shown, in other cases, that one-X flies lacking a Y are normal males in appearance, although they are sterile. It is evident that it is the "one-X or two-X" alternative that is essential in the normal determination of sex in Drosophila; the presence or absence of the Y is largely irrelevant.

Observations like those on $\widehat{XX}$ provide the most convincing kind of confirmation that the allele for bar eye and its normal alternative are actually located on the X-chromosomes. We have already found that this pair of alleles coincides with the X-chromosomes in its normal pattern of inheritance. When a visible and regular abnormality in the distribution of the X-chromosomes can be shown always to be associated with an identical abnormality in the distribution of the bar gene, the relationship becomes an established fact.

Other Sex-Linked Characteristics in Drosophila. In addition to bar eye, a large number of other genes not concerned with the sexual differences between males and females are known to be located in the X-chromosome. An example of a sort more usual than that of bar eye, because it is complicated by dominance, is the difference from wild type called *vermilion*. In contrast to the rather dark-red eyes of the wild type, the eyes of vermilion flies are bright, almost orange-red (Plate III, facing p. 7).

Drosophila geneticists regularly use the symbol "+" to designate the wild-type allele of any gene. We have already introduced this convention in connection with the bar-eye allele and its normal alternative. In considering vermilion eye color, let "+" represent the wild-type allele of vermilion, and v represent vermilion. Then a cross between vermilion females and wild-type males behaves as shown in Figure 6-12. Vermilion follows the genetic pattern of a sex-linked characteristic, and the normal allele is dominant to its alternative, for vermilion.

The complication of dominance is not a troublesome one, because we are already familiar with it. (Confirm that the reciprocal cross, wild type ♀ × vermilion ♂, would produce *all wild-type flies* in F_1, and a ratio of *2 wild type* ♀♀: *1 wild type* ♂ : *1 vermilion* ♂ in F_2.)

The wild-type allele of vermilion is known to govern the production of a diffusible or circulating substance involved in eye-pigment synthesis. This substance, which is not produced by vermilion flies, is called the v^+ *hormone*. Embryonic eye discs from vermilion larvae transplanted into wild-

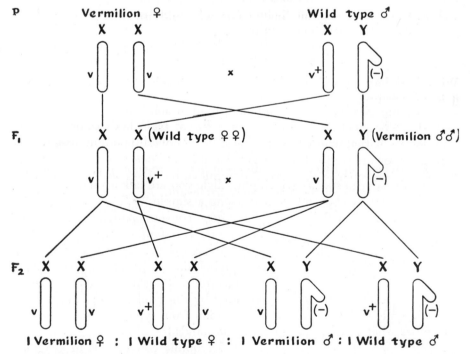

Figure 6-12. *Vermilion eye color in Drosophila is a sex-linked recessive characteristic.*

type hosts develop wild-type eye color, since the host provides the graft with its missing v^+ substance. We mention this here only in connection with the dominance of the wild-type allele; as in the example of yellow fat in rabbits, one "dose" of the dominant allele appears to produce enough of an active substance to do the necessary job, so that the heterozygote is phenotypically indistinguishable from the homozygous wild type.

Genetic Symbols: The use of a "+" to distinguish the wild-type allele of any gene, as in the vermilion and bar examples, automatically identifies a given allele as that found in the standard type. *By using a capital letter to designate a dominant deviation from type, and a small letter to designate a recessive one,* the dominance relationships of allelic forms of a gene are clear from the symbolism. For example, in Drosophila genetics, B^+ is the symbol for the wild-type allele of the *dominant* deviation from type, bar eye (B). On the other hand, b^+ is the symbol for an entirely different gene, the wild-type allele of the *recessive* deviation from type, black body color (b). On occasion, when there can be no doubt of which particular wild-type allele is under consideration, the symbol is shortened to a simple "+." Thus, in crosses involving only the bar-normal alternative, we can conveniently use:

$$B = \text{bar eye}$$
$$+ = \text{wild type,}$$

and in crosses involving only body color, we could use

$$b = \text{black body color}$$
$$+ = \text{wild type,}$$

When both bar eye and black body color are involved in a cross, however, it is safer to use:

B = bar eye	b = black body color
B^+ = wild-type eye shape	b^+ = wild-type body color.

In fact, whenever two or more different *genes* are concerned in a cross, it is generally safer to specify which plus-allele you are talking about by using the appropriate symbol, rather than using a simple "+."

The letter used for the symbol of the gene conventionally comes from the *name of the characteristic, different from the standard, controlled by a deviant form of the gene.* Thus, a gene controlling eye color, giving a white-eye/red-eye alternative, has w as its basic symbol, since *white* is the deviant type; the symbol r would be wrong here, since *red* is the standard characteristic. Consider the information, then, provided by the symbol w^+: It represents the wild-type allele of a recessive deviation from type, and we can easily remember what this deviation is, since w stands for white.

Many geneticists have adopted the Drosophila conventions in assigning symbols to genes in other animals and in plants. However, many other geneticists retain older and less informative conventions. Recall the cut-leaf/

potato-leaf alternative for tomatoes, in Chapter 3, for example. Here, the standard symbolism does not include the "+" convention at all; the symbol C comes from the *standard type* (cut leaf), and c stands for a recessive deviation from type called potato leaf!

You may at first find the convention in which a capital letter represents a dominant, and the corresponding small letter the recessive allele, and in which the particular letter chosen is arbitrary, the least confusing method of assigning symbols to genes. It undertakes to give less information in itself, and it therefore appears less complex. If you go on in genetics, however, you will increasingly appreciate the Drosophila conventions, and in reading outside literature in genetics you will find it important to be able to follow both types of representation with equal ease. For these reasons, we will use both methods in this book.

Sex Linkage in Other Organisms. The determination of sex by sex chromosomes, and the location of genes in these chromosomes, is similar in a variety of species to the situation described for Drosophila. In man, for instance, a rather large proportion of the known, simply inherited characteristics are controlled by sex-linked genes. Examples are the sex-linked recessive gene for ordinary red-green color blindness, and the "bleeder's disease," *hemophilia,* in which the blood fails to clot normally—also a sex-linked recessive.

Knowledge of the genetic pattern for such a defect often helps in making definite predictions relative to the children of concerned individuals. It is clear, for example, that a man whose blood clots normally cannot transmit to his children the allele for hemophilia, no matter how high the incidence of this disease may be in his family. A man has only one X-chromosome; if the allele for hemophilia is present on that chromosome, the man is a "bleeder," and if he is not a "bleeder," then his X-chromosome does not carry the defective allele. A normal woman whose father was hemophilic, on the other hand, can expect that about half of her sons will be hemophilic. (Chance, of course, enters into the experience of any particular family in this respect.)

It is of interest to note that a few dogs show a condition similar to human hemophilia, and that here too the allele responsible is a sex-linked recessive. Sex linkage is remarkably rare in other mammals; in spite of extensive studies of inheritance in rats and mice, for example, until very recently no clear instance of sex-linked inheritance was known to occur in either of these species. There is, however, an interesting probable example in cats. The black and yellow pigments in the coats of cats seem to be controlled by a sex-linked pair of alleles such that the heterozygote is the familiar "tortoise shell," having areas of black and areas of yellow in the coat. We can list:

Females	*Males*
yy = yellow	$y(-)$ = yellow
Yy = tortoiseshell	$Y(-)$ = black
YY = black	

You are therefore justified in giving good odds in a wager that the calico cat in the next block is a female. Winning your bet would not be quite certain, however, since tortoise tomcats do very rarely appear. The fact that they are almost always sterile shows that there is something abnormal about their sexual development.

Some animals do not have a Y-chromosome at all. Their sex determination is described as the "X-O" type. This departure from the Drosophila model is not an extreme one, since we have already suggested that the Y-chromosome may be virtually empty of genes.

Plants like corn and our common garden vegetables have both sexes represented in the same individual. There is therefore no sex difference between individuals; there are no sex chromosomes, and no sex linkage is possible. But some plant species are bisexual (*dioecious*, "two houses"). Hemp, the date palm, and the willows are examples. In some dioecious plants, sex chromosomes have been identified, and sex linkage is known.

Birds differ from the Drosophila type of sex determination in one impor-

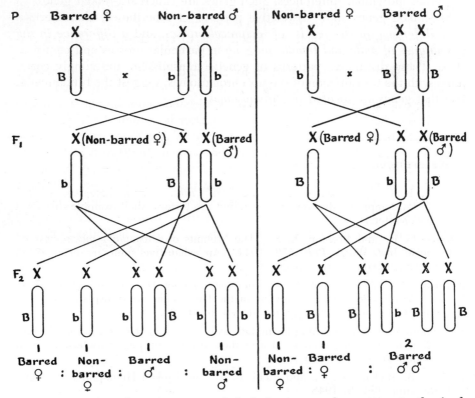

Figure 6-13. *Barred feathers, a sex-linked dominant color pattern in the fowl, shows the pattern of inheritance characteristic of forms in which it is the female that has a single X-chromosome.*

tant respect: The *male* has two sex chromosomes, and it is the female that has an unpaired chromosome or an unlike-membered pair. The effect of this is to reverse the pattern of sex-linked inheritance now familiar to us in Drosophila. To illustrate the difference, observe the inheritance of the sex-linked dominant for barred feathers in poultry—a color pattern characteristic of the Barred Plymouth Rock breed (Fig. 6-13).

Besides the birds, the moths and butterflies, all the reptiles that have been carefully examined, and some kinds of fish and amphibia have the XX = male, XY or XO = female type of sex determination. Other kinds of animals, and many dioecious plants for which a sex-chromosome mechanism of sex determination holds, have the Drosophila type.

Keys to the Significance of This Chapter

Sex is controlled by a pair of *sex chromosomes*. Besides affecting the sexual characteristics of the individual, the sex chromosomes carry genes controlling other individual differences. Such genes are called *sex-linked* genes.

Sex-linked genes show distinctive patterns of inheritance, characterized by *a difference in the results of reciprocal crosses*, and *a difference in the phenotypes of male and female progeny* in particular crosses and combinations. These distinctive patterns of genetic transmission, unfailingly correlated with the transmission of the sex chromosomes, suggest the fundamental fact that *genes are located in chromosomes*.

References

Bamber, R. C., "Genetics of Domestic Cats." *Bibliographia Genetica*, 3:1–86, 1927. (A comprehensive review, including the tortoise shell example discussed in this chapter.)

Bridges, C. B., and Brehme, K. S., "The Mutants of *Drosophila melanogaster*." *Carnegie Inst. Wash. Pub.* 552, 1944. (An exhaustive summary of reported hereditary variants in this species.)

Ephrussi, B., "Chemistry of 'Eye Color Hormones' of *Drosophila*." *Quart. Rev. Biol.*, 17:327–338, 1942. (A review of the Drosophila eye-transplant work, including the vermilion example mentioned in this chapter.)

Hollander, W. F., "Auto-Sexing in the Domestic Pigeon." *J. Heredity*, 33:135–140, 1942. (An interesting account of a method of breeding pigeons whose sex will be evident from their color.)

Hutt, F. B., Rickard, C. G., and Field, R. A., "Sex-Linked Hemophilia in Dogs." *J. Heredity*, 39:2–9, 1948.

Morgan, L. V., "Non-Criss-Cross Inheritance in *Drosophila melanogaster*." *Biol. Bull.*, 42:267–274, 1922. (Reporting the discovery and genetic behavior of attached-X.)

Morgan, T. H., and Bridges, C. B., "Sex-Linked Inheritance in *Drosophila.*" *Carnegie Inst. Wash. Pub.* 237, 1916. (A classic consideration of early work in this field.)

Stern, C., *Principles of Human Genetics.* San Francisco: W. H. Freeman and Co., 1949. (See Chap. 13, "Sex Linkage," for extensions of our consideration of this subject, emphasizing human inheritance.)

Winge, Ø., "X- and Y-Linked Inheritance in *Melandrium.*" *Hereditas,* **15**:127–165, 1931. (Studies of sex linkage in a flowering plant.)

Questions and Problems

6- 1. What are sex chromosomes? What does the symbol $\widehat{XX}$ stand for?

6- 2. In terms of standard Drosophila gene symbolism, what can you deduce from the symbol y^+, if you know that a useful inherited deviation from type in this species is yellow body color?

6- 3. The standard type of tomato plant has cut leaves, is tall (not dwarf), has an anthocyanin pigment that makes the stems purple, and the ripe fruit has red flesh. Unit deviations from type in these characteristics include, respectively, potato leaves, dwarfism, green stems (lacking the anthocyanin), and yellow fruit-flesh color. Standard symbols for the allelic pairs are: C-c for cut *vs.* potato leaves; D-d for tall *vs.* dwarf; A-a for the presence *vs.* the absence of the anthocyanin; and R-r for red *vs.* yellow fruit-flesh color. The deviations from type are recessive to the type allele in each case.

a. How would this symbolism be modified if the Drosophila system for designating alleles prevailed in tomato genetics?
b. What are advantages and disadvantages of each convention of nomenclature?

6- 4. How would your answer to Question 6-3a be changed if the conventional standard type of tomato had green, rather than purple, stems?

In man, *hemophilia,* the "bleeder's disease" in which the time required for the blood to clot is greatly prolonged, depends on the recessive allele of a sex-linked gene. There are at present about 40,000 cases of the disease in the United States. In the following questions, let $h^+ =$ the allele for normal clotting time; $h =$ the allele for hemophilia.

Note: In all problems involving sex linkage, list the phenotypes of sons and daughters separately.

6- 5. A man whose father was hemophilic, but whose own blood clotting time is normal, marries a normal woman with no record of hemophilia in her ancestry. What is the chance of hemophilia in their children?

6- 6. A woman whose father was hemophilic, but who is not herself a "bleeder," marries a normal man. What is the chance of hemophilia in their children?

6- 7. What is the chance of hemophilia among the sons of a daughter of the marriage in Question 6-6 if she marries a normal man?

6- 8. It has been reported that women heterozygous for hemophilia are distinguishable from homozygous normal women; the clotting time of the heterozygotes appears to be longer, but not sufficiently long to constitute a hazard to survival. How might you apply this information to Problem 6-7?

Note: The probable sex linkage of alleles for yellow and black pigments in cats was described on page 97.

6- 9. A calico cat has a litter of eight kittens: one yellow male, two black males, two yellow females, and three calico females. Assuming a single father for the litter, what was his probable color?

6-10. A black cat has a litter of seven kittens: three black males, one black female, and three calico females. Comment on the probable paternity of this litter.

6-11. A yellow cat has a litter of four kittens: one yellow and three calico. Assuming a single father for the litter, what is the probable sex of the yellow kitten?

Vermilion eye color in Drosophila (Plate III) is inherited as a sex-linked recessive.

6-12. What phenotypes would be found in the progeny of a cross between a vermilion female and a wild-type male?

6-13. Suppose that the vermilion female in Question 6-12 were $\widehat{XX}$. What phenotypes would the surviving progeny of this cross show? Diagram the cross, showing parental genotypes, phenotypes, and gametes; F_1 genotypes and phenotypes.

6-14. Like vermilion eye color, white eye color (w) in Drosophila depends on a sex-linked recessive. Suppose that a particular white-eyed female, when crossed with a wild-type (w^+) male, gave white-eyed daughters and red-eyed sons. How might this result be explained? How would you check your explanation?

Recall the discussion of the inheritance of comb shape in poultry in Chapter 4, and of the barred feather pattern in Chapter 6.

6-15. A homozygous barred walnut-comb cock is mated with a nonbarred, single-comb hen, and 320 eggs from this cross hatch. How many chicks would you expect in each phenotypic class?

6-16. Progeny of the cross in Problem 6-15 are mated to produce an F_2 generation. If 320 F_2's are produced, how many would you expect in each phenotypic class?

Rarely, a hen's ovary may lose its function (presumably as a result of a local infection), and a testis develops instead. Such "sex-reversed" hens have even become fathers of chicks. No change in the chromosomal makeup of the hen occurs under these conditions.

6-17. What types of sperm, with regard to X-chromosome constitution, would a sex-reversed hen be expected to produce?

6-18. What sex ratio would you expect among the progeny of a sex-reversed hen and a normal hen?

6-19. Suppose that the barred walnut "cock" in Question 6-15 were really a sex-reversed hen. What answer would you give to Question 6-15?

Recessive lethals (recall Chap. 5) are known in the X-chromosomes of many species. Letting $l =$ such a lethal, the usual results in Drosophila are:

$$\begin{array}{cc}
\text{Males} & \text{Females} \\
l^+(-) = \text{normal} & \left.\begin{array}{l} l^+l^+ \\ ll^+ \end{array}\right\} = \text{normal} \\
l(-) = \text{dies} & ll = \text{dies}
\end{array}$$

6-20. What sex ratio do you expect among the progeny of a female Drosophila heterozygous for a sex-linked lethal?

6-21. Under similar circumstances in poultry, what sex ratio do you expect among the progeny of a male heterozygous for a sex-linked lethal?

6-22. A flowering plant of the pink family, called Melandrium, has a sex-determining mechanism such that XY = "male," XX = "female." Winge has described a recessive on the X-chromosome that is lethal when homozygous in "female" plants, but produces a yellow-green uneven color when present in the single X-chromosome of a "male" plant. Normal "males" and "females" and heterozygous "females" are dark green. What phenotypic ratio would result from crossing heterozygous "females" with yellow-green "males"?

6-23. Edward Lambert, a "porcupine man," was born in England in 1717. His skin was covered with bristly scales and quill-like structures an inch or so long. He had six sons, all "porcupine men" like himself, and the characteristic appeared in all of the sons of affected fathers through four further generations. No daughter ever displayed or transmitted the characteristic. What was the probable chromosomal basis of this abnormality?

6-24. A useful technique in studying the ability of agents like X-rays to induce new mutations with visible effects is to mate X-rayed (or otherwise treated) males with $\widehat{XX}$ females. What advantages can you discern in this technique?

CHAPTER 7

The Vehicles of Inheritance

IN THE preceding chapter the mere establishment, beyond a reasonable doubt, of the facts that sex chromosomes are involved in the determination of sex, and that they also carry genes affecting characteristics other than sex, left little room for a discussion of the broader significance of these facts. It should be pointed out that in Chapter 6 for the first time we encountered a visible, material basis for the behavior of the units of heredity that had, up to that point, a logical but only a rather abstract reality.

We do not need to know about chromosomes to feel sure of the existence of genes. Mendel established the particulate and duplicate basis of inheritance without knowing anything about chromosomes—in fact, several years before chromosomes had been named or described in any detail. Even the fact that a single sperm fertilizes a single egg to give rise typically to a single individual had not been established beyond doubt at the time when Mendel did his work, although the assumption that this was true seems implicit in some of his reasoning. The Mendelian approach was, and to a large extent still is, based on breeding experiments. The particles of concern to the geneticist have enjoyed about the same order of reality as do the molecules of the chemist or the particles of the modern physicist—their nature and properties deduced from their effects in groups, rather than from their direct visual observation singly.

Similarly, it was not necessary to know about Mendelian units to be reasonably sure that chromosomes are intimately concerned with inheritance. During the thirty-four years that Mendel's paper lay unnoticed, chromosomes were described, and their behavior was followed with great care and enthusiasm. It was appreciated that in their regular and precise duplication and distribution at ordinary cell division, their neat parcelling-out to the germ cells, and their behavior during fertilization and development, the chromosomes gave every evidence of unique importance to the cell. And chromosome theories of heredity had been suggested while Mendelism was still virtually unknown.

Shortly after the rediscovery of Mendel's work, during the period when elementary Mendelism was being enthusiastically extended to many plants and animals, it was realized that what was known about chromosomes fitted remarkably well what was being learned about genes. Within a brief period of time, these two previously independent subjects of investigation became fused along their common boundary, and today we recognize as the science of *cytogenetics* a field that is an integral part both of the study of heredity and of the study of cells. This hybrid field has enriched, and has been enriched by, both of its parent disciplines. To us, as students of heredity, it is imperative that we become familiar with the nature and behavior of chromosomes, the vehicles of inheritance.

The Nature of Chromosomes. It is not known, as yet, what physical and chemical properties endow the chromosomes with their most remarkable and essential qualities, the ability of specific self-duplication and the control of specific processes in the cell. We know that a class of compounds called *nucleoproteins* plays a prominent part in their structure, and there is independent evidence, from studies of viruses, for example, that the nucleoproteins are concerned not only with the structure but also with the unique functions of self-duplicating units of life. But how these complex molecules govern the production of more molecules exactly like themselves, and how they control specific reactions in the cell, are riddles for future research to answer.

On the level of visual observation, a good deal is known about the structure of chromosomes. They change in form and character from stage to stage in the continuous processes of cell growth and multiplication. These changes are in general cyclic; as the cell prepares to divide, and proceeds through division, the chromosomes pass through a regular progression of structural alterations until, at the end of the division cycle, the characteristics of the original cell are again restored in two daughter cells. Through all these changes each chromosome maintains its integrity.

The core of this continuity is a fine thread (or bundle of threads) called the *chromonema* (plural: *chromonemata*). This thread is often, though not always, coiled. The chromosomes often change in length through the division cycle, in part by the coiling more tightly or by the uncoiling of the chromonemata. Several different types of coiling have been described, so that cytologists speak of standard, relic, or relational coils; of major and minor coils; of molecular coils, twists, and so on. These terms are necessary to the cytologist, but we need not discuss them here.

Around the chromonema is the *matrix* of the chromosome—an envelope that varies from stage to stage in amount and in staining reaction. Often, special staining techniques are necessary to make the structure of the chromosome's interior visible through this matrix.

Among the diverse characteristics of chromosomes that assist in the visual distinction of one from the other are the following:

The Centromere. Each chromosome has (almost always) a single differentiated region somewhere along its length that seems to act as the point at which force is exerted in the movement apart of dividing chromosomes. The structure has been called by a number of names, among which the terms *centromere* and *kinetochore* probably are used most generally. It has also sometimes been called the *spindle-fiber attachment,* or the *attachment region.* The force that accounts for the movement apart of the dividing chromosomes is associated with a visible cellular structure, which, because of its shape, is called the *spindle.* The spindle, when stained, appears to be made up of fibers; hence the term *spindle-fiber attachment* for the centromere, the point at which the spindle fiber appears to affect the movement of the chromosome.

The position of the centromere along the length of a chromosome contributes in a direct manner to the shape of the chromosome as the nucleus divides. If the centromere is near the middle, the chromosome becomes "V"-shaped as this central spot leads the way to the poles of the cell, the "arms" of the chromosome trailing behind. If the centromere is nearer one end, the chromosome becomes "J"-shaped, since the arms are of unequal length. If the centromere is very near one end, the chromosome moves as a straight rod. There is some doubt that a centromere is ever truly terminal under normal conditions.

The centromere is typically a permanent, well-defined "organelle" of the chromosome, and not a vague, transient, or generalized region. In favorable material it can be demonstrated all through the cell's division cycle; in most cells it is lost to view through changes in the staining qualities and general character of the nucleus during part of the cell's history. But there is every reason to believe that in such instances the "loss" is purely a visual illusion. For example, when it is really lost, through the breaking off of a part of a chromosome, a centromere cannot be regenerated by the fragment lacking it. Like other structures and regions of the chromosome, continuity of pattern from cell generation to cell generation is characteristic of the centromere. The chromosome duplicates all its parts with almost undeviating fidelity and only rarely ventures into novelty.

Chromomeres, Knobs, and Constrictions. In many species, the chromosome is seen to be not a smooth or regularly coiled thread, but to have bumps and constrictions along its length. When this is true, the pattern of such specialized regions is reasonably constant for any given chromosome. The smaller "beads on the string" are called *chromomeres,* while the larger ones are often called *knobs.*

Nucleolus-Forming Regions. Within the nucleus, there are often one or more spheres of darkly staining material called *nucleoli* (singular: *nucleolus*). The organization of the nucleolus seems usually to be the function of a specific point on a particular chromosome, and when the nucleolus is visible it can be seen to be attached to this *nucleolus-forming region* or *nucle-*

olus organizer. Chromosome 6 in corn, for instance, can usually be identified in proper stages of cellular division through its possession of the nucleolus organizer.

Satellites. In the region of the nucleolus organizer, the chromosome is often constricted to so fine a thread that it may be difficult to see. If another section of the chromosome then extends beyond this point, it appears as an "appendage" to the chromosome, and is called a *satellite.* Satellite chromosomes are among the easiest to identify. (See the fox chromosomes in Fig. 7-1.)

Heteropyknosis. Certain chromosomes or parts of chromosomes become darkly staining earlier in the division cycle and retain their dense appearance longer than do others. This dense-staining property is called *heteropyknosis* (literally: "difference in density"). Major parts of the sex chromosomes in many species are heteropyknotic, and this, together with the fact that the sex chromosomes often are the first to move apart on the spindle,

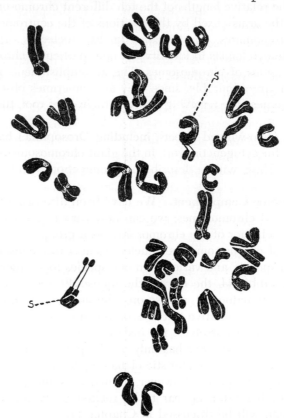

Figure 7-1. *A pair of satellite chromosomes* (s) *is particularly conspicuous in this equatorial plate from the seminiferous tubules of a red fox. Count 34 chromosomes, each longitudinally double, in this mitotic division.* (*From Wipf and Shackelford,* Proc. Nat. Acad. Sci., **28:**266, 1942.)

has been useful in the tentative identification of the sex chromosomes in these species.

Heterochromatin and Euchromatin. Two general kinds of material can be identified in chromosomes on the basis of staining reactions. Differences between chromosomes in the relative amounts of these two materials are responsible for the phenomenon of heteropyknosis, mentioned above. The first, a darkly staining and relatively undifferentiated material, is called *heterochromatin.* It seems to be largely empty of genes; the Y-chromosome of Drosophila, for instance, is mostly heterochromatin. But it does have certain effects on gene expression.

The other kind of chromosomal material is called *euchromatin.* It is the substance with which we shall be most concerned as we proceed to discuss chromosome behavior and its genetic aspects.

These and other characteristics of chromosome structure make it possible to identify particular chromosomes in favorable material. In corn, for example, charts of the relative lengths of the ten different chromosomes, the relative lengths of the arms (fixed by the positions of the centromeres), and the patterns of chromomeres, constrictions, knobs, nucleolus organizers, and satellites, enable cytologists to identify not only particular chromosomes but even specific regions of chromosomes. The accomplishments of cytologists in this direction are admirable, since they are sometimes observing objects so small as to be near the resolving limits of their chief tool, the light microscope.

The Diptera (two-winged insects, including Drosophila) have a remarkable advantage for cytogenetic work in the giant chromosomes of their larval salivary glands. These will be described, in connection with their chief uses, in Chapter 10.

The Chromosome Complement. We have been discussing the characteristics of individual chromosomes; we can now turn to the consideration of the nature and behavior of the chromosomes as a group.

The number of chromosomes per nucleus is as a rule constant for all the individuals of a species, and varies from one species to another. Man has 48, the fox 34, the rabbit 44, the rat 42, the mouse 40, red clover 14, garden peas 14, corn 20, tomatoes 24, and so on. The number of chromosomes has no general significance relative to the evolutionary achievement of any species. We cannot pride ourselves, for instance, on having 48 chromosomes while *Drosophila melanogaster* has only 8. The potato, among other organisms, shares with us the characteristic of having 48 chromosomes. Within a series of related plant species, however, regular multiples of the same basic chromosome number often appear to be related to evolutionary changes. This phenomenon will be discussed in Chapter 11.

The chromosomes are present in pairs, and, with the exception of certain sex chromosomes, the members of a pair of chromosomes cannot normally be distinguished under the microscope. It is often convenient to speak of the

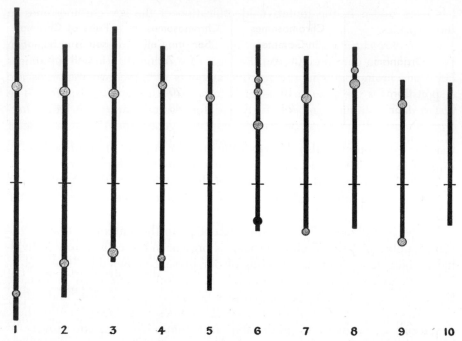

Figure 7-2. *The ten different chromosomes of corn are distinguishable in terms of their length (chromosome 1 is the longest, 10 the shortest); the relative lengths of their arms (the centromere, shown as a dash across the chromosome, divides the chromosome into two arms); the nucleolar-forming region of chromosome 6; and knobs. (After Longley,* Botan. Rev., **7:266, 1941.)**

chromosome number of a species in terms of the number of *pairs* of chromosomes present; thus human beings have 24 pairs, foxes 17, red clover 7, corn 10, and so on. This is what was meant when it was casually stated above that corn has 20 chromosomes; actually a corn plant has ten different *pairs* of chromosomes in each somatic cell; the members of each pair are alike, but the different pairs are distinguishable. The different chromosomes are symbolized by numbers, from chromosome 1 (the longest) to chromosome 10 (the shortest) (Fig. 7-2). A nucleus of a root cell, for example, will generally contain two chromosomes 6, two chromosomes 9, and so on.

There are at least six kinds of exceptions to the statement that a constant number of chromosomes is present in pairs in the cells of any individual of a species. The first of these is very important:

1. The mature germ cells (*gametes*) of a sexually reproducing individual contain only half the usual number of chromosomes—one member of each pair. In this respect, the germ cells are different from the body cells, or *somatic cells,* of the individual. Conventionally, the gametes are described as *haploid* in chromosome number, and the somatic cells as *diploid.* The symbol *n* is used to signify the haploid chromosome number; you will note

Organism	Chromosomes in Gametes (= n)	Chromosomes in Somatic Cells (= 2n)	Pairs of Chromosomes in Somatic Cells (= n)
Corn	10	20	10
Man	24	48	24

that the same number also describes the number of *pairs* of chromosomes in diploid tissues. The table above will make the relationship clear:

We will be concerned, during much of the remainder of this chapter, with the mechanisms and the significance of the maintenance of these regularities.

2. The importance of the second exception to the statement that a constant number of pairs of chromosomes is present in the cells of any individual is difficult to evaluate in terms of our present knowledge. The fact is, however, that occasional deviations from the rule occur even in somatic tissues; some body cells can sometimes be shown to have less and others more than the normal diploid number of chromosomes. Occasionally, these deviations are regular and predictable. In legumes like peas and clover, for example, the root nodules, which are the site of activity of the nitrogen-

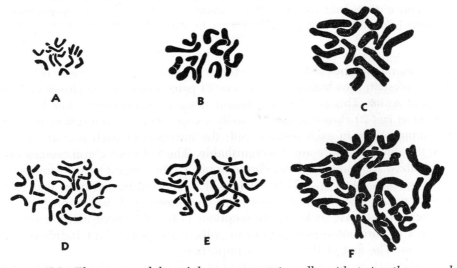

Figure 7-3. *The root nodules of legumes contain cells with twice the normal chromosome number. A, red clover, ordinary root tip cell; count 2n = 14. D, nodule tissue of red clover; count 28 chromosomes. B, common vetch, ordinary root tip cell; count 2n = 12. E, nodule of common vetch; count 24 chromosomes. C, garden pea, ordinary root tip cell; count 2n = 14, two beginning to appear double. F, nodule of garden pea; count 28 chromosomes, many longitudinally double.* (From Wipf and Cooper, Proc. Nat. Acad. Sci., **24**:88, 1938.)

fixing bacteria so important in the maintenance of soil fertility, contain plant cells whose chromosome number is consistently doubled (Fig. 7-3). In other tumorlike growths, in cancers, and even in normal organs like animal liver, an increase of chromosome number in multiples of the basic number (called *polyploidy*) also appears with some degree of regularity. In the other direction, a diminution in chromosome number in somatic tissues may occur. Rarely, this diminution can be shown to be a regular process; in certain forms, for example, particular chromosomes are limited to the "germ line" and are uniformly lost in the formation of somatic tissue.

In man, the chromosome complement of normal somatic cells appears to vary within wide limits, some cells having considerably fewer, and other cells having many more, than the normal diploid number of 48. It is not yet clear, however, whether these differences bear any consistent, cause-and-effect relationship to the other differences among the cells of the individual.

3. The third kind of exception to the statement that a constant number of pairs of chromosomes is present in the cells of any individual of a species is almost certainly of little general significance. For example, some types of corn (particularly Black Mexican Sweet Corn) have extra chromosomes in addition to the normal ten pairs. These extra chromosomes are called "B-type" chromosomes. They seem to have no essential genetic activity; they can be either entirely absent or present in rather large numbers in a plant without appreciably affecting the plant's characteristics. The B-type chromosomes have provided the basis for some very interesting and significant work in experimental cytology, but in terms of normal development they are unimportant.

4. An important part of the seed of higher plants regularly has three, rather than two, sets of chromosomes. This structure, the *endosperm*, plays a dynamic part in seed development, and it later contributes to the nourishment of the young seedling. Its origin will be described in Chapter 8.

5. Variations in number of chromosomes or sets of chromosomes among individuals of the same species are of considerable importance with regard to the mechanisms of evolution, the improvement of plants, and the understanding of gene action in development.

6. Finally, as we have previously noted, the sex difference within a species is often associated with a difference in chromosome number. One sex may be XX and the other XO; or one sex may be diploid and the other haploid, resulting from the development of unfertilized eggs, as in the honey bee and other Hymenoptera.

Mitosis

We turn now to the mechanisms through which the regularities in chromosome complement are maintained. The problem has two facets. First, how is the regular diploid complement of chromosomes kept constant through the successive nuclear divisions involved in the growth and development of a multicellular individual from a single cell, the fertilized egg? And, second, what special phenomena in germ-cell formation result in haploid gametes, each with one member of each pair of chromosomes, so that diploidy is restored at fertilization? The process responsible for the maintenance of the first of these two bases of regularity is ordinary somatic nuclear division, and is called *mitosis*. It will provide a frame of reference for the second process basic to uniformity—germ-cell formation, or *meiosis*.

We can begin with the kind of nuclear division through which the fertilized egg of a human being, for example, gives rise to the 26 billion or so cells of the adult human body. The process of mitosis is uniform in its essentials through all the somatic divisions that occur (with the exceptions noted in the previous section). And the essential characteristics of mitosis are very simple: *Each chromosome duplicates itself*, and the duplicates are separated from each other at cell division, one going into the nucleus of one daughter cell, and its "twin" into the other. The daughter cells are therefore identical with each other and with their parent cell in chromosome constitution. Figure 7-4 diagrams this essential characteristic of mitosis. It is to be hoped that the following more detailed account of the process will not mask or confuse its essential simplicity.

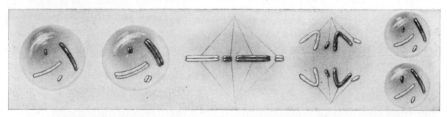

Figure 7-4. *In mitosis, each chromosome duplicates itself. The duplicates separate as the nucleus divides, so that the daughter nuclei are identical in chromosomal constitution. The process is shown in greater detail in Figures 7-5 and 7-6. (By permission after* Fundamentals of Cytology, *by Sharp, Copyright 1943, McGraw-Hill Book Co., p. 64.)*

It has already been emphasized that nuclear division is a continuous and a cyclic process. A cell proceeds smoothly through a series of changes that result in the formation of two daughter cells, and a very precisely synchronized part of this process is the division and distribution of the chromosomes of the nucleus to the daughter cells. The daughter cells may then follow the same cycle, giving rise in turn to two cells each, and so on. Cell multiplication is therefore a geometric progression: $1 \rightarrow 2 \rightarrow 4 \rightarrow 8 \rightarrow 16 \rightarrow 32 \rightarrow 64$, and so on. At this rate, it would take less than 36 consecutive divisions for a single egg to produce 26 billion cells. Since the division rates vary in different tissues during development, this average figure has little actual significance except as an order of magnitude.

Because the process of nuclear division is a continuous series of changes, only by arbitrary distinctions can we break up the process into "stages" or

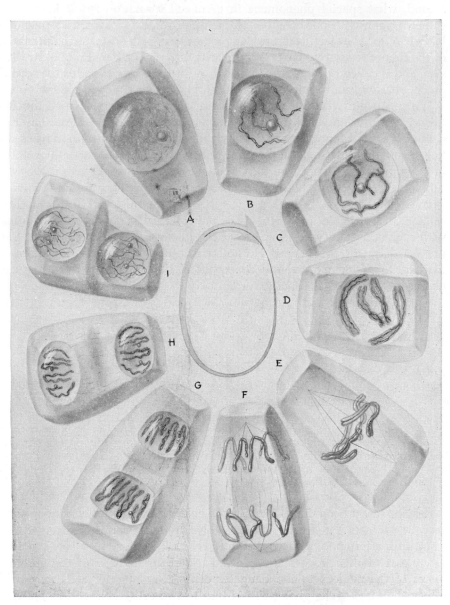

Figure 7-5. *In mitosis, a resting nucleus* (A) *undergoes a continuous sequence of changes called prophase* (B, C, D,), *metaphase* (E), *anaphase* (F), *and telophase* (G, H, I). *Either or both of the two daughter nuclei so formed may then enter the division cycle again.* (*By permission after* Fundamentals of Cytology, *by Sharp, Copyright 1943, McGraw-Hill Book Co., p. 60.*)

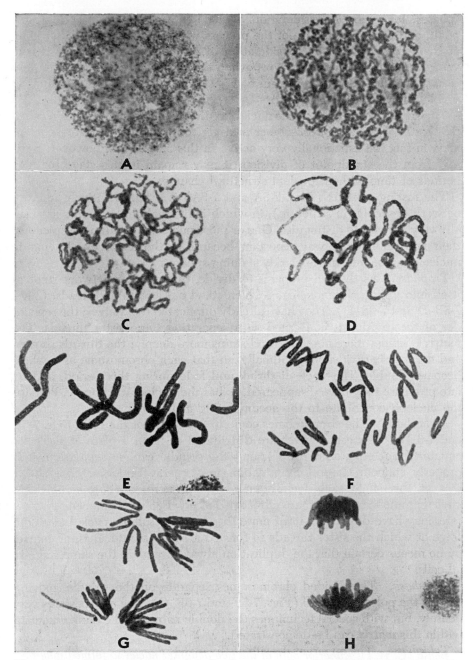

Figure 7-6. *Photomicrographs of dividing tapetal cells of young anthers in the Californian coastal peony show the chromosomes enlarged about 900 diameters. Compare with the diagram of Figure 7-5. A, resting nucleus. B, C, D, early, middle, and late prophase. E, metaphase. F, G, middle and late anaphase. H, telophase. (Courtesy of M. S. Walters and S. W. Brown.)*

"phases" for separate consideration. We can enter the division cycle at any point, and the cyclic nature of the process will bring us back to that point at the completion of our consideration of one nuclear division. It is convenient to enter between divisions, when the active cell is metabolizing but is not dividing. (See the diagram of Fig. 7-5 and the photomicrographs of dividing plant cells in Fig. 7-6.)

The "Resting" Nucleus. The nucleus of the metabolic stage is often called the "resting" nucleus—a misnomer in a general sense, because the nucleus may, in fact, be functionally very active in this stage. It is, however, "resting" from the standpoint of division; it may remain in this stage for long periods of time without evident structural change.

The resting nucleus (Figs. 7-5A and 7-6A) is a fine, relatively uniform network (*reticular* in structure), in which individual chromosomes are usually very difficult to distinguish. One or more nucleoli are often conspicuous; their number is not always constant because of the tendency of separate nucleoli to fuse into single, darkly staining spheres.

Prophase. As the cell prepares to divide, the reticular network resolves itself into visible chromonemata, which stand out as double threads. (Figs. 7-5B–D and 7-6B–D). They have already duplicated themselves; the remainder of the division is concerned with separating these sister threads. The matrix becomes more abundant and stains more deeply; the threads shorten and the matrix divides longitudinally, so that each chromosome as a whole becomes double. The nucleoli shrink and fade during this period, and by late prophase they have disappeared, as has the nuclear membrane. Perhaps the nucleoli contribute to the accumulating matrix material.

Metaphase. The chromosomes come to the center of the cell (Figs. 7-5E and 7-6E). Their centromeres are distributed as if on a plate at the cell's equator (the "equatorial plate"), and the spindle can be seen when it is properly stained. Careful examination in very favorable material shows that at this stage each longitudinal half-chromosome (*chromatid*) contains chromonemata that are already double. Each chromonema, therefore, may have duplicated itself more than a whole mitotic cycle before the stage at which the sister threads so formed are to separate. It is, of course, by no means certain that the duplication always occurs at the same stage in all cells.

Anaphase. The divided chromosomes separate on the spindle, moving toward the poles of the cell (Figs. 7-5F and 7-6F, G). The matrix stains very densely, but with special techniques the double nature of the chromonemata within this matrix can be demonstrated.

Telophase. The apparent density of the matrix decreases, and the netlike character of the metabolic nucleus begins to develop. Nucleoli again grow into prominence (Figs. 7-5G-I and 7-6H). Two cells, with identical metabolic nuclei, are now present where one existed before.

We have considered only the nuclear behavior in division. Late in ana-

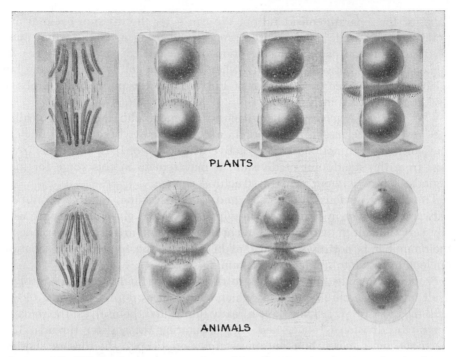

PLANTS

ANIMALS

Figure 7-7. *While the processes of nuclear division in plants and animals are very similar, the cells typically divide somewhat differently. In plants, a plate develops between the daughter cells; in animals, the cells "pinch apart." (By permission after* Introduction to Cytology, *by Sharp, Copyright 1934, McGraw-Hill Book Co., p. 109.)*

phase or early in telophase the cells themselves divide. This process is typically somewhat different in plants and in animals (Fig. 7-7).

General Aspects of Mitosis. The precision of mitosis makes it a remarkable phenomenon. A more direct mechanism than this one, to guarantee the equal distribution of essential materials to the daughter cells, is difficult to conceive. If we can assume that the chromonemata are essentially the visible evidence of linear strings of genes (and we shall be able to marshal convincing evidence for this assumption), then the point-for-point reduplication of these linear strings, and their longitudinal separation into the daughter nuclei, represents a beautiful solution to the problem of providing each daughter cell with an identical set of genes.

But the very precision of this process raises some difficult questions. If, as a result of mitotic division, all or almost all of the cells of the body have the same set of genes, then what makes the cells in different tissues so different both in structure and in function? This is probably the most elusive riddle in biology today, and we cannot solve it in this book. We shall, however, be able to bring some further information to bear upon it, and will return to its systematic consideration in Chapter 18.

Meiosis

The special kind of nuclear division that results in the formation of haploid gametes, each with one member of each pair of chromosomes, now demands our attention. Meiosis is not really a single division, but two successive ones, the first and the second meiotic divisions. The process of meiosis in its essentials is simple and straightforward. The members of each pair of chromosomes come to lie side by side in the nucleus. Each chromosome is double, so that four strands are associated in a *tetrad;* there are therefore n (the haploid number) tetrads. The tetrads are separated into *dyads* at the first meiotic division, and the dyads into single chromosomes by the second meiotic division. The resulting nuclei are the nuclei of the germ cells; each, you will observe, must have one member of each pair of chromosomes.

Figure 7-8 diagrams the essentials of the process of meiosis. If you study the figure at this time, the more detailed consideration of meiosis below should not obscure its true simplicity.

The "Germ Line." As an embryo grows and differentiates, certain cells are sooner or later set aside as potential gamete-forming tissues. The location, nature, and time of formation of these tissues vary greatly from one kind of plant or animal to another. In chickens and other birds, for example, there is good evidence that the "primordial germ cells" originate in an area outside the embryo itself, very early in development, and that they later migrate into the developing sex organs (gonads). In mammals, the bulk of the evidence seems to favor the view that the primordial germ cells differentiate in the testes or ovary, as part of the progeny of cells destined also to contribute to other structures in the gonad. In some of the lower animals, the cells of the "germ line" are clearly set apart from ordinary somatic cells

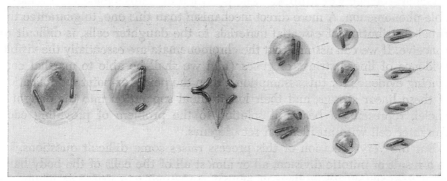

Figure 7-8. *In the formation of sperm, duplicated members of each pair of chromosomes come to lie side by side in "four-strand" configurations. Two successive nuclear divisions then result in the formation of four sperm, each with one member of each pair of chromosomes. (By permission after* Introduction to Cytology, *by Sharp, Copyright 1934, McGraw-Hill Book Co., p. 251.)*

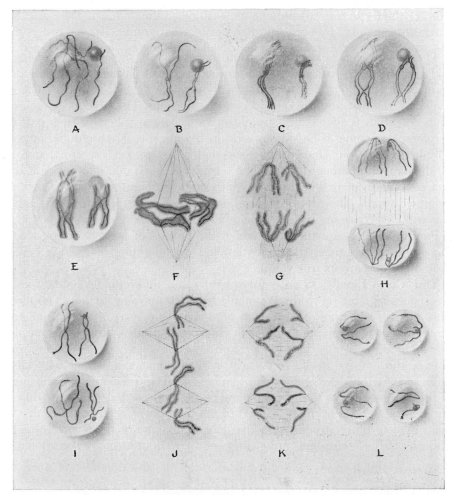

Figure 7-9. *Meiosis involves two successive divisions, which in the male give rise to four sperm nuclei* (L) *from each primary spermatocyte. Each sperm has one member of each pair of chromosomes. The diagram is described in detail in the text.* (*By permission after* Fundamentals of Cytology, *by Sharp, Copyright 1943, McGraw-Hill Book Co., p. 107.*)

at extremely early stages in development. In plants, similar extreme variations occur in the time at which the germ line becomes distinct from somatic tissues.

But whenever, however, and wherever the cells of the germ line originate, their behavior in the process of gamete formation is remarkably similar in all sexually reproducing forms. We can take a male mammal as a standard, and list the major deviations from this model after the model has been described.

Spermatogonia. Arranged around the basement membranes of the tubules of the testes are rather large cells called *spermatogonia*. They are the direct descendants (by mitosis) of the primordial germ cells, and are eventual sources of gametes. The spermatogonia multiply by mitosis, and in this process give rise to somewhat smaller, different cells called *primary spermatocytes*.

Primary Spermatocytes: The First Meiotic Division

Prophase I. The reticulum of the nucleus of the primary spermatocyte resolves itself, in early prophase of the first meiotic division, into the diploid number of long, very slender threads. These threads sometimes appear to be already double or in the process of doubling. This stage is called the *leptotene* (Fig. 7-9A).

The slender threads come to lie side by side, in units corresponding to the number of pairs of chromosomes (Fig. 7-9B). The process of side-by-side conjunction is called *synapsis;* the stage at which it occurs is called *zygotene*.

The paired threads shorten and thicken somewhat, and each thread is now clearly double, except that the centromere does not divide. Four strands are associated in a *tetrad* of four *chromatids* for each original pair of chromosomes. This stage is called *pachytene* (Fig. 7-9C).

In each tetrad, two chromatids fall apart from the other two, so that each chromatid has a single pairing partner in each region. But the chromatids often seem to exchange pairing partners along their length, so that cross-shaped figures are formed (Fig. 7-9D). These cross-shaped figures, or *chiasmata* (singular: *chiasma*), may constitute cytological evidence for genetic phenomena with which we shall be concerned in Chapters 8 and 9. The stage in which the chiasmata are first evident is called *diplotene*.

The chiasmata seem to progress toward the ends of the chromatids (to *terminalize*) at least in many plants and animals, as the chromatids continue to shorten and to stain more heavily through the development of a dense matrix (Fig. 7-9E). This stage, called *diakinesis,* is an important one, because the number of chromosomes is often easier to count at this stage than at any other, and our information about chromosome numbers in many plants and animals is based on diakinesis figures. The distribution of matrix about the tetrads at this stage varies in different species.

Metaphase I. The tetrads take their usual positions at the cell's equatorial plate, with their centromeres at the equator. (Fig. 7-9F).

Anaphase I. The two chromatids of a tetrad that are still connected at their centromere separate from the other two of the tetrad, and these *dyads* go to opposite poles of the cell (Fig. 7-9G). With regard to each original pair of chromosomes, the separation of centromeres has now been accomplished; the centromere of each chromosome has been separated from that of its pairing partner. We shall see later that, because of exchanges between pairing partners at intervals along their length, the separation of other regions of the original pair of chromosomes is not effected until the second meiotic division. The chiasmata often seem to offer some resistance to the separation of the dyads, but eventually they pull free, and the two chromatids of each dyad then spread away from each other. They usually remain connected at their centromeres.

Telophase I. There is considerable variation, from one species to another, in the nature and duration of the subsequent telophase (Fig. 7-9H). This period between the two meiotic divisions is designated by the special term *interkinesis.* It may be rather long, but typically it is very short, and the cells press immediately into the second meiotic division.

Secondary Spermatocytes: The Second Meiotic Division

Prophase II. In the usual prophase of the second meiotic division, the dyads of the preceding telophase are still associated at their centromeres, but they diverge widely elsewhere. The members of the dyads themselves can sometimes be observed to be already double or doubling, in evident preparation for the next cell division, which in animals comes after fertilization. The matrix becomes prominent during this prophase (Fig. 7-9I).

Metaphase II. The dyads line up at the equatorial plate again, with their centromeres at the equator (Fig. 7-9J).

Anaphase II. With the division of the centromeres, and the separation of the chromatids on the spindle, each chromatid now becomes a complete and separate chromosome (Fig. 7-9K).

Telophase II. The nuclei, four from each original primary spermatocyte, now each contain one member of each pair of chromosomes (Fig. 7-9L). These are the nuclei of the spermatids, which, without further division, reorganize to form the major part of the head of the sperm cell. This process of reorganization of spermatids into sperm cells includes not only nuclear changes but cytoplasmic modifications as well, leading to the formation of the sperm with its tip, head, midpiece, and tail. The general process of sperm-cell formation, including especially the meiotic divisions, is called *spermatogenesis.*

Germ-Cell Formation in Female Animals. As indicated earlier, the processes of meiosis are similar in all sexually reproducing plants and animals of either sex. The following tabulation of comparative terms will serve to emphasize the similarities between male and female animals:

Male	*Female*
Spermatogonium	Oögonium
Primary spermatocyte	Primary oöcyte
Secondary spermatocyte	Secondary oöcyte
Spermatid	Oötid (or ovum)
Sperm cell	Egg cell

There is, however, one important difference between male and female gamete formation. In the male, four functional sperm cells are formed from each primary spermatocyte. The egg must often provide stored food mate-

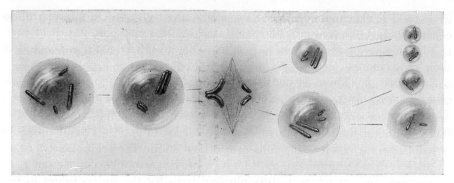

Fig. 7-10. *Meiosis in a female animal gives rise to only one functional egg from each primary oöcyte. (By permission after* Introduction to Cytology, *by Sharp, Copyright 1934, McGraw-Hill Book Co., p. 251.)*

rial for the developing embryo, and the division of this stored material, accumulated by the egg during its development, among four functional female gametes would have real disadvantages. Accordingly, a regular modification of cell division has been fixed by evolution among females. Three of the four products of meiosis in females are small, abortive cells called *polar bodies.* These contain little cytoplasmic material. They simply "bud off" from the egg as meiosis proceeds (Fig. 7-10). Thus, in females one primary oöcyte gives rise to only a single egg cell.

The meiotic divisions in the eggs of some species occur *after* the sperm has entered the egg. In other species, sperm entrance occurs after the first, but before the second, meiotic division. In others, meiosis is completed before fertilization.

In many animal species, in addition to the food material stored as yolk in the egg cell, additional material is added outside the cell as it passes down the oviduct. Birds carry this trend to something of an extreme; albumin is secreted around the egg cell, and the whole is packaged within a membrane and a porous shell—a neat arrangement for an independently developing embryo.

Gamete Formation in Plants. The germ-cell-forming tissues in plants behave in meiosis in much the same way as do those of the corresponding sexes in animals. In plants, however, the situation is somewhat complicated by the occurrence of two or more *mitotic* divisions of the haploid products of meiosis before fertilization occurs. The subject will be discussed in detail in the next chapter.

Genes and Chromosomes

Autosomal Inheritance. The implication has been clear throughout this chapter that all the chromosomes of an individual, not just his sex chromosomes, carry genes. But our demonstration, in the preceding chapter, that genes are in fact located on chromosomes was limited to sex-linked genes on the X-chromosomes.

The chromosomes that are not sex chromosomes are called *autosomes*. It should be obvious that the autosomes provide a reasonable basis for the inheritance of characteristics that are not sex-linked, just as the sex chromosomes can be shown to be involved in sex-linked inheritance. The autosomes are present in pairs, just as are the non-sex-linked Mendelian units. They maintain their individual identity, just as do genes. The members of a pair separate when germ cells are formed, as do the members of a pair of alleles. And the independent behavior of the members of different pairs of chromosomes provides a clear physical basis for the independent assortment of different pairs of alleles. Still more convincing evidence that the autosomes are the vehicles of non-sex-linked inheritance will be forthcoming when we begin to consider correlations between abnormalities of chromosomal number, behavior, and structure, and abnormalities of gene distribution (Chaps. 10 and 11).

Genes, Meiosis, and Mitosis. If we accept the conclusion that the autosomes as well as the sex chromosomes carry genes, we can consider further the genetic significance of the two types of nuclear division we have been discussing. The cytologist is often limited by the fact that the members of a pair of autosomes are not distinguishable; with his methods they appear to be identical. But if one chromosome of a pair carries a given gene, and its homologue an allelic form of this gene, then the members of this pair of chromosomes are distinguishable to the cytogeneticist. Figure 7-11 illustrates mitosis and meiosis, labelling three pairs of chromosomes on this basis.

You will observe that mitosis (Fig. 7-11,I) produces daughter cells that are genetically identical with the parent cell and with each other. Meiosis, on the other hand, results in the formation of different types of haploid gametes; it involves the segregation and assortment of genes. Subsequently, fertilizations result in a variety of new combinations.

In a male, a given meiotic division will produce, under the conditions of Figure 7-11,II, two different kinds of sperm. You can easily see, from the abbreviated diagram in Figure 7-11,III, how different alignments of the paired chromosomes at the first meiotic metaphase would result in all eight kinds of gametes actually produced by the trihybrid illustrated. In the female, since only one functional egg is formed in each meiotic series, it would take at least eight different primary oöcytes to produce the eight possible kinds of eggs, depending on the chance alignment of chromosome pairs when the first polar body is formed. But the qualitative consequences of meiosis are alike in the two sexes—eight kinds of germ cells are produced by the trihybrid, in approximately equal numbers.

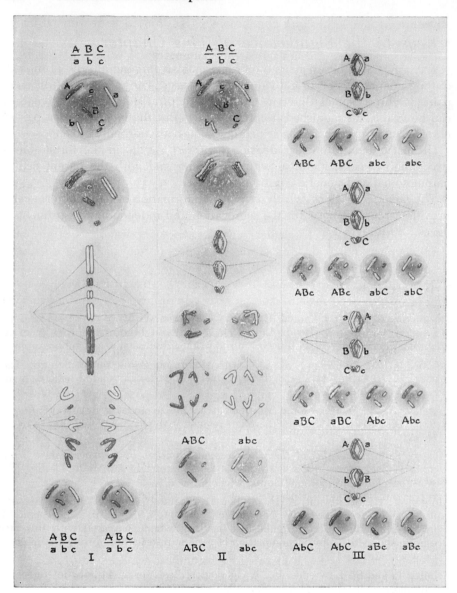

Figure 7-11. *Mitosis* (I) · *in a trihybrid, when the three allelic pairs mark three different pairs of chromosomes, results in daughter cells identical with each other and with the parent cell. Meiosis* (II) *provides the basis for segregation and assortment of alleles. The different possible alignments* (III) *at the first meiotic metaphase result in the production of eight kinds of gametes, in equal proportions.* (*By permission, based in part on* Introduction to Cytology, *by Sharp, Copyright 1934, McGraw-Hill Book Co., p. 253.*)

Keys to the Significance of This Chapter

A constant number of pairs of chromosomes is in general present in each of the somatic cells of all individuals of a species. The members of different pairs of chromosomes differ in constant structural details, and often they can be visibly distinguished from each other. But the members of a pair of chromosomes, except for the sex chromosomes, are normally alike.

Ordinary somatic nuclear division (*mitosis*) results in the formation of two daughter cells, identical with each other and with the parent cell in chromosomal and genetic constitution.

The *meiotic* divisions, which result in the formation of haploid germ cells, provide a physical basis for the segregation and independent assortment of genes.

References

Darlington, C. D., and Ammal, E. K. J., *Chromosome Atlas of Cultivated Plants*. London: G. Allen & Unwin, Ltd., 1945. (A thorough compilation of reported chromosome numbers, with useful introductions, discussions, and bibliography.)

Huskins, C. L., and Cheng, K. C., "Segregation and Reduction in Somatic Tissues." *J. Heredity*, **41**:13–18, 1950. (One of a series of related articles, with references to others.)

Longley, A. E., "Chromosome Morphology in Maize and Its Relatives." *Botan. Rev.*, **18**:399–413, 1952. (A thorough review of this subject, with many references.)

Makino, Sajiro, *An Atlas of the Chromosome Numbers in Animals*. Ames: Iowa State College Press, 1951. (A compilation for animals similar to Darlington's work on plant chromosome numbers, cited above.)

Morgan, T. H., Sturtevant, A. H., Muller, H. J., and Bridges, C. B., *The Mechanism of Mendelian Heredity*. New York: Henry Holt & Co., 1915. (A classic. A later edition of this book, published in 1923, when compared with this first edition shows the rapid accumulation of genetic information during the interval between editions.)

Schultz, J., and St. Lawrence, P., "A Cytological Basis for a Map of the Nucleolar Chromosome in Man." *J. Heredity*, **40**:30–38, 1949.

Sharp, L. W., *Fundamentals of Cytology*. New York: McGraw-Hill Book Co., 1943. (Concise and interestingly presented, the chapters on mitosis [Chap. 5], chromosomes [Chap. 7], and meiosis [Chap. 8] are particularly pertinent here.)

Therman, E., and Timonen, S., "Inconstancy of the Human Somatic Chromosome Complement." *Hereditas*, **37**:266–279, 1951. (Reports wide variations in the chromosome numbers of human somatic cells.)

Wipf, L., and Shackelford, R. M., "Chromosomes of a Fox Hybrid." *Proc. Nat. Acad. Sci.*, **35**:468–472, 1949. (Source of the material in Problems 7-13 and 7-14.)

Questions and Problems

7· 1. What do the following terms signify?

anaphase	heteropyknosis	prophase
autosomal	interkinesis	satellite
centromere	knob	secondary spermatocyte
chiasma	leptotene	somatic
chromatid	matrix	spermatid
chromomere	meiosis	spermatogenesis
chromonemata	metaphase	spermatogonia
cytogenetics	mitosis	spindle
diakinesis	nucleolus	synapsis
diplotene	oötid	telophase
euchromatin	polar body	tetrad
heterochromatin	primary spermatocyte	zygotene

Characterize the four chromosomes carried by an X-bearing Drosophila sperm, in terms of the centromeres of these chromosomes, as X_m, 2_m, 3_m, 4_m (letting m stand for a centromere of *male* origin). Similarly, label the centromeres of a Drosophila egg as X_f, 2_f, 3_f, 4_f; and those of a Y-bearing sperm as Y_m, 2_m, 3_m, and 4_m.

7- 2. In terms of the above symbolism, what will be the "chromosomal centromere formula" of a fertilized egg that will develop into a male? A female? Of male somatic cells generally, assuming no abnormality in somatic mitosis? Female somatic cells?

7- 3. What is the centromere formula of a spermatogonium? A primary spermatocyte? (Remember that the centromeres do not usually divide until the second meiotic division.) Give a formula for any particular secondary spermatocyte. A spermatid. A sperm.

7- 4. What is the centromere formula of an oögonium? A primary oöcyte? Any particular secondary oöcyte? An egg, after meiosis, but unfertilized? A polar body?

7- 5. What is the chance that a particular sperm has all four centromeres from the father of the individual producing the sperm? From the mother?

7- 6. What is the chance that a fertilized egg that will develop into an F_2 has all eight of its centromeres from the male in the original parental cross?

7- 7. Mankind has 23 pairs of autosomes plus an XX pair in women and an XY pair in men. What proportion of a man's sperm will contain all of the centromeres he received from his father?

7- 8. Assume an ancestral, sexually reproducing organism in which there was originally only one pair of chromosomes but that produced gametes without meiosis, so that the germ cells in each generation were diploid. What consequences would this have in terms of the chromosome number of successive generations? In terms of genetic variation?

7- 9. In a normal male, how many functional sperm will be expected from 100 primary spermatocytes? 100 secondary spermatocytes? 100 spermatids?

7-10. How many functional eggs will be expected from 100 primary oöcytes? 100 secondary oöcytes? 100 oötids?

7-11. What advantage for the species has the process of polar body formation in females, compared with the possibility of forming four functional eggs from a primary oöcyte?

7-12. Assume a plant with six chromosomes—a pair of rods, a pair of V's, and a pair of dots. After three successive generations of self-fertilization, what proportion of the population will have all "V"-shaped chromosomes? What proportion will be like the original plant, with a pair of rods, a pair of V's, and a pair of dots?

Fox breeders have sometimes hoped to improve the size, productivity, and color variety of the red fox (*Vulpes vulpes*) by hybridizing it with the Arctic fox (*Alopex lagopus*). Numerous such hybrids have been produced, but they are always completely sterile.

7-13. The red fox has 17 pairs of relatively large, long chromosomes (Fig. 7-1). The arctic fox has 26 pairs of shorter, smaller chromosomes. What do you expect to be the chromosome number in somatic tissues of the hybrid?

7-14. The first meiotic division in the hybrid shows a mixture of paired and single chromosomes. Why do you suppose this occurs? Can you suggest a possible relationship between this fact and the sterility of the hybrid?

7-15. Cattle breeders often speak of "full-sisters" (i.e., heifers with the same sire and dam) as being of "100% the same blood." On this basis, breeders often find it difficult to understand that full sisters may be quite different in their inherent qualities. Contrast the discarded "blending concept" of inheritance with Mendelian genetics in explaining this situation.

7-16. Before the rediscovery of Mendelism, Galton formulated a "Law of Ancestral Inheritance" according to which a person shows about half of the hereditary characteristics of each parent, a quarter of those of each grandparent, and so on. The law was based on studies of such characteristics as height in man. Can you account for the "law," in terms of chromosomes and genes?

Assume a corn plant that is missing the knob at the end of one of its ninth chromosomes, and has a knob at the end of one of its tenth chromosomes (*cf.* Fig. 7-2). Letting K stand for *knob*, the plant's chromosomal formula may be designated $\left(\dfrac{9K}{9}, \dfrac{10K}{10}\right)$. In corn, as in animals, the "male" tissues form four functional meiotic products, while in the "female" tissues three degenerate and only one is functional.

7-17. Suppose that you examined cytologically the meiotic products in the "male" tissues of this exceptional plant. What proportion would you expect to find with both knobs (9K, 10K)? What other types would you expect to find, and in what proportions?

7-18. Answer the questions in 7-17 with regard to the chromosomal constitution of the functional products of meiosis in the "female" tissues.

7-19. If this exceptional plant is self-fertilized, what proportion of the zygotes would you expect to be like the standard type of corn $\left(\dfrac{9K}{9K}, \dfrac{10}{10}\right)$?

7-20. Discuss the value of material like that in the preceding three questions with regard to the visible recognition of the independent assortment of chromosomes.

7-21. In Drosophila, an allelic pair concerned with body color
  y, a sex-linked recessive for yellow body color, and
  y^+, the wild-type allele
is known to be located very near the end of the X-chromosome (the opposite end from the centromere). If we had used this pair of alleles to "mark" the X-chromosomes of a female fly, rather than using the centromere, how would your answers to Question 7-4 have been different?

7-22. Diagram the process of egg formation in a female Drosophila, with X-chromosomes marked as follows:

(X_m and X_f refer to the centromeres.) Show tetrad formation, but do not at this time show chiasmata or exchanges between chromatids. Show how two different kinds of functional eggs may be formed under these circumstances.

7-23. Now, diagram the process as in Problem 7-22, but show an exchange between two of the four strands of the tetrad, between the position of the y gene and the centromere. What new types of eggs may result from this kind of exchange?

7-24. Rabbit eggs have been stimulated to develop without fertilization, and certain of the parthenogenetic rabbits so formed have been reported to be heterozygous for certain allelic pairs. How might this be explained?

CHAPTER 8

Life Cycles

OVER THE COURSE of the preceding chapters, attention has been drawn to certain principles that provide the foundation upon which much of your further understanding of genetics will rest. They may be summarized briefly as follows:

1. Life, as we know it, is derived only from previously existing life.
2. Each of the different kinds of living things characteristically gives rise to other living things of the same general kind.
3. Many of the similarities and differences of organisms have a biologically heritable basis residing in units of heredity called genes.
4. Genes are located in chromosomes in the nuclei of cells.
5. There are two well-defined kinds of nuclear division—*mitosis* and *meiosis* —and they are known to have special and far-reaching implications for the life histories of organisms.

These well-established principles, especially when considered in expanded form, tell a good deal about life as a general phenomenon. But to bring them into sharp focus, and extend and apply them, you need to consider them in relation to particular organisms. In order to do this, you must know about the *reproduction* of particular organisms, since all these principles relate more or less directly to reproduction.

This chapter will give some idea of the diversity of reproductive processes in various forms of life. It should also help you to appreciate that a knowledge of reproduction is essential to successful genetic analysis.

The Summarization of Reproductive Processes in Life Cycles. The significant stages in the processes by which a plant or animal gives rise to others of its kind make up the *life cycle* of that plant or animal. Biologists often represent a particular life cycle by diagramming in a circle the salient events of a completed life history. Thus a simplified life cycle of man might be shown as indicated in Figure 8-1. Schematic representations of this kind provide simple, flexible frameworks for summarizing significant knowledge that may be difficult to apply unless it is remembered in a meaningful, sequential arrangement.

Chromosome Cycles and Life Cycles. Chromosomes play an unseen but

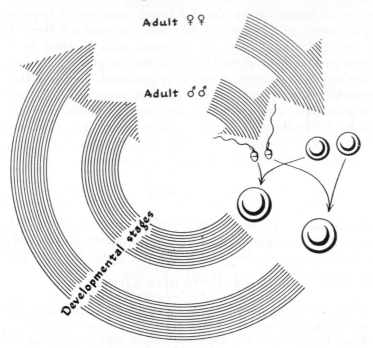

Figure 8-1. *A simplified life cycle of man.*

highly important role in life cycles. In sexually reproducing organisms, life begins as a single cell formed from the union of two parental germ cells, or *gametes.* This fusion cell has the combined chromosome complements of the germ cells and, therefore, normally has twice the chromosome number of either gamete alone. The subsequent growth and development of a mature multicellular organism from a fertilized egg cell, or *zygote,* are based on cellular divisions where the nuclei divide mitotically, so that somatic cells typically have the same chromosome complement as the fertilized egg. Reproduction by the new adult, however, is preceded by a reduction of chromosome number through meiosis of the nuclei in certain cells. This whole series of events repeated through succeeding reproductive cycles insures that, generation after generation, the adults of a species have the same number of chromosomes and give rise to gametes with half that number. With few known exceptions, chromosome cycles in higher animals follow the pattern just outlined. The life cycle of man, already presented briefly, can now be made more complete by adding the information about haploid and diploid stages in the cycle, and showing where reduction in chromosome number and resumption of diploidy occur. For details of spermatogenesis and oögenesis in higher animals, refer to Chapter 7.

In many groups of plants, the life cycle involves a regular alternation of a sexual with an asexual generation. This is true of angiosperms, gymnosperms, ferns, mosses, liverworts, and certain members of lower groups. In the typical situation, a zygote develops into a *sporophytic* plant. The *sporophyte*, through meiosis, gives rise to spores, each of which by itself may produce a *gametophytic* plant. *Gametophytes* are plants that form gametes. With the union of gametes, a zygote is produced, and from the zygote a new sporophyte comes into being. The alternation of a gamete-producing generation with a spore-producing generation in plants coincides with an alternation in chromosome number in these forms. For ease of reference, the relation of chromosome complement to prominent stages in the life cycles of higher animals and plants can be summarized in the following way:

	Haploid Chromosome Complement	Diploid Chromosome Complement
Most animals	Gametes	Zygote, animal body
Many plants	Spores, gametophyte, gametes	Zygote, sporophyte

The Life Cycles of Particular Organisms

In turning to examine the life cycles of particular kinds of organisms, we shall have to limit ourselves to the detailed consideration of a few examples. Our choice of examples is admittedly rather arbitrary but has been governed by these considerations: (1) that the organisms chosen have life histories that, in general aspect at least, are representative of large groups; (2) that the organisms chosen be important objects of genetic investigation, either because they have been widely studied, or because they offer exceptional opportunities for investigation, or both. As you read about reproduction in corn, Sphaerocarpos, Neurospora, and Paramecium, take note that life cycles not only summarize fundamental genetic information but also point to important questions and problems to be solved.

You will see at once that most of our illustrative types have been selected from the plant kingdom. In the different kinds of organisms whose genetics has been studied extensively, greater variation has been found among the life cycles of plants than of animals. Moreover, the general scheme and some of the typical details of life cycles of higher animals should be familiar to you after your reading of Chapter 7 and the first part of this chapter.

The Life Cycle of Corn

Reproduction in corn (*Zea mays*) is typical enough of what happens in most seed plants for us to make broad applications from the outlines of its life history to analogous events in different members of the group. A more particular reason for concentrating attention on corn is that of all plants its genetics has probably been investigated most thoroughly. Why have geneticists spent so much time on corn? Its agronomic importance, the fact that

a single ear of corn represents a large progeny, the early discovery of interesting deviant characters, and the relative ease of controlled matings are all
involved. In addition, corn chromosomes are of a size and morphology that
make them well suited for cytogenetic study. These advantages of corn as
an object of genetic research have far outweighed such disadvantages as its
comparatively long life cycle. Finally, it should be remarked that some exceptionally gifted investigators simply happen to have been fascinated by
the genetics of corn, and have devoted their time and thought to its study.

Sporophytic Generation and Spore Production. At least for preliminary
purposes, we can identify the sporophyte of corn as the large green corn
plant familiar to everyone and conspicuously present as a major crop in the
fields of the middle west of the United States. Corn is *monoecious,* which
means that both *pistillate* ("female") and *staminate* ("male") flowers occur

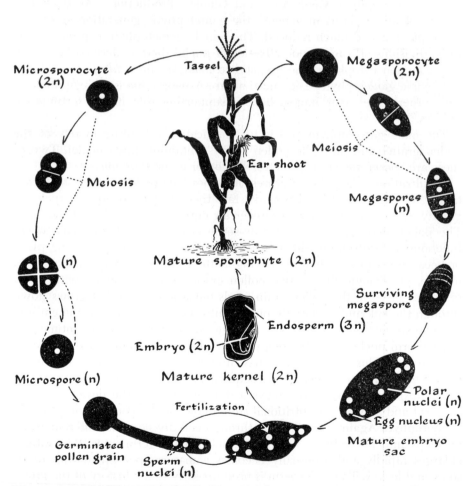

Figure 8-2. *The life cycle of corn* (Zea mays)

on the same plant. The pistillate flowers are borne in the *ears* of corn; the staminate flowers are in the *tassel* at the top of the stalk (see Fig. 8-2). In the flowers are formed spores that give rise to the gametophytic generation.

Megaspores are produced in the ovules of pistillate flowers. The cells that undergo meiosis to produce megaspores are called *megasporocytes*. Each megasporocyte gives rise to four megaspores, of which three degenerate. The remaining megaspore develops into the female gametophyte. Notice how the fate of the four products of meiosis of a megasporocyte nucleus corresponds to what happens to the meiotic products of a primary oöcyte in animals.

Microspores are produced from *microsporocytes* (pollen mother cells) within the anthers of the staminate inflorescence. Each microsporocyte gives rise by meiosis to four functional microspores.

The Gametophytic Generation and Gamete Production. As is characteristic of angiosperms in general, the gametophytic generation of corn is inconspicuous and much reduced. The female gametophyte is produced by three divisions of a megaspore. The eight nuclei thereby derived lie at first in a common cytoplasm, and are said to make up the *embryo sac*. This is the female gametophyte. The nuclei all are haploid. One is the egg nucleus. Two others, the polar nuclei, have a supporting role in the fertilization process.

The male gametophyte also is uncomplicated, consisting merely of the pollen grain (and later the pollen tube) containing three nuclei. Two of these are *sperm nuclei*, or gametes. The other is the *tube nucleus*.

Fertilization. As pollen matures, it comes free of the anthers that contain it. Under natural conditions, its fate thereafter is governed largely by gravity and by the whim of whatever air currents are flowing at the time. The pollen may either travel far or settle near home. Much pollen never functions in fertilization, either because it comes to rest in the wrong place or because it dries out before arriving at the right place. However, when a mature, physiologically reactive pollen grain comes in contact with a silk of an ear of corn, the pollen grain sends out a long tube that grows down through the silk and eventually pushes into the embryo sac. In the embryo sac, one sperm nucleus fuses with the egg, forming a zygote. Meantime, the other sperm nucleus and the two polar nuclei of the embryo sac unite in a triple fusion. This fusion nucleus has three sets of chromosomes, and hence is said to be *triploid*. Through subsequent mitotic divisions, it gives rise to the *endosperm,* a tissue that plays a dynamic role in the development of the seed and serves as a nutritional storehouse for the young sporophyte.

Sporophyte Again. The zygote, through cell division and differentiation, develops into an embryo. When a kernel of corn germinates, the embryo enlarges rapidly and eventually becomes a mature sporophyte with roots, stem, and leaves. The endosperm is used up early in the history of the growing seedling plant.

Controlled Matings in Corn. Genetic analysis in corn or any other organism is facilitated if the investigator is not forced to deal with instances of unknown or uncontrolled parentage. To control matings in most animals is relatively simple, and may be accomplished merely by isolating individuals from members of the opposite sex and then pairing off males and females at an appropriate time. Practical problems of controlling matings in higher plants may be somewhat different, especially in those species where both male and female sex organs occur in single individuals.

In order to control matings in corn, two kinds of precautionary measures must be taken: (1) The pistillate inflorescence must be protected from pollen other than that the investigator wishes to apply. (2) The desired pollen must be collected and applied in such a way that no mixture with other pollen occurs. Separation of the staminate and pistillate inflorescences in different parts of the corn plant makes these objectives readily attainable. A paper bag tied over the ear shoot before the silks appear will prevent chance fertilization, and the pollen to be used in making the cross can be collected by enclosing an appropriate tassel in a different paper bag. Since corn pollen is fairly short-lived, bagging a tassel the day before its pollen is to be used is good insurance against active contamination by foreign pollen which may have settled on the tassel. The pollination process itself can be accomplished by removing the ear-shoot bag and pouring pollen from the tassel bag directly onto the silks. Then the ear-shoot covering must be replaced promptly. Such techniques permit corn, at the will of an investigator, either to be entirely self-pollinated or to be cross-pollinated from a given source. Under uncontrolled conditions (open-pollination), a few of the kernels on an ear of corn usually have resulted from self-pollination and the majority from cross-pollination.

It is worth pointing out at this time that problems of controlling matings in seed plants may differ considerably from group to group, depending in a large part on the kind of inflorescence encountered. When both stamens and pistils are within the same flower (a *perfect flower*), self-fertilization may be the rule under "natural" conditions. Controlled cross-pollination must then be preceded by timely emasculation of the flower to be pollinated, in order to prevent self-pollination. In tomatoes, for example, emasculation can be accomplished simply by removing the male organs of the flower with forceps. In some other plants, this straightforward approach may not be practical. Techniques for genetic investigation must in each instance be adapted to the characteristics of the particular kind of plant to be studied. There are good reasons, then, for geneticists to know a great deal about the actual details of reproductive processes as well as generalized life cycles.

Genetic Applications. You understand, of course, that we cannot attempt to review the entire genetics, or even any considerable portion of it, for the organisms whose life cycles we are examining in detail. But it should be profitable to consider a few of the genetic challenges and opportunities that relate rather directly to the particulars of each life cycle under consideration.

Genetics of the Male Gametophyte. You have learned that a meiotic division in a plant heterozygous for an allelic pair *Aa* gives rise to two nuclei of genotype *A* and two nuclei of genotype *a*. This is seldom observed directly. The rule is usually inferred from microscopic observations of chromosomal distribution at meiosis and from the fact that Mendelian ratios presuppose equal numbers of the different genotypes occurring in gametes produced by a hybrid. There are two chief impediments to obtaining direct evidence for the basic 1:1 segregation at meiosis in organisms heterozygous for a single allelic pair: (1) Meiotic products such as pollen grains seldom have phenotypic characters that permit determination of their genotype. Usually, a meiotic product needs to take part in fertilization before its genetic constitution can be identified. (2) It is difficult in most organisms to obtain for analysis all the products of a single meiosis. This is certainly true of corn, where on the female side three of the four products of each meiosis degenerate, and where on the male side the four pollen grains arising from a single meiosis intermingle with other male gametophytes.

Nevertheless, we can in general be certain that there really is a 1:1 segregation of members of allelic pairs at meiosis. Phenotypic ratios obtained among the progeny of hybrids (*Aa*) prove that in large populations of pollen there must be roughly equal members of *A* and *a* pollen grains. Similarly, Mendelian ratios among segregating characters in sporophytes are consistent with the supposition that there are equal chances of either the *A* or the *a* allele being present in the single nucleus that survives after meiosis of a megasporocyte.

In a few special instances it is possible to detect segregation directly in pollen grains and in female gametophytes. A clear example is found in the segregation of alleles for the characters *waxy* and *nonwaxy* in corn. The two alternative phenotypes depend on a difference in the chemical nature of starch reserves that can be tested for by the simple expedient of treating with an iodine solution. Pollen with the *wx* gene is red in iodine; pollen carrying the normal allele, *Wx*, turns blue. If pollen from a plant of the genetic constitution *Wxwx* is stained with iodine, about half is red and about half turns blue. In an experiment of this kind by Demerec, 3437 pollen grains were found to stain blue and 3482 were red-staining. The results provide direct evidence for the basic 1:1 segregation expected after meiosis in a heterozygote. Since the pollen collected in such an experiment is only a sample of an entire population, chance deviations from a 1:1 ratio are expected to, and do, occur. Such chance deviations in gametic ratios account in part for deviations from the ideal Mendelian ratios expected for the diploid generation following.

Female gametophytes from a *Wxwx* hybrid also may be subjected to the iodine treatment. If this test is applied to a good sample of gametophytes, approximately equal numbers of individuals show the blue as against red color. This result is a straightforward indication that alleles Wx and wx have equal chances of being in the surviving member of the quartet of mega-spores originally formed by a meiosis.

Rice is another organism in which gametophytic segregation has been observed. In this plant, *starchy* endosperm is dominant over *waxy*. F_1 hybrids between parents of the different types give rise to pollen about half of which stains red and half of which develops blue color in weak iodine solution. Counts made from a series of anthers showed that 48.1 per cent of the pollen stained blue, i.e., was starchy. This example from rice genetics seems to parallel exactly the example of waxy endosperm in corn.

A third analogous instance has been described for sorghum. Figure 8-3 is a photographic demonstration that in sorghum heterozygous for the waxy gene, approximately half the pollen stains blue, for *starchy*, and about half stains red, indicating *waxy*.

Endosperm Genetics. All the nuclei in a male gametophyte of corn are genotypically alike, and the same is true for a female gametophyte.

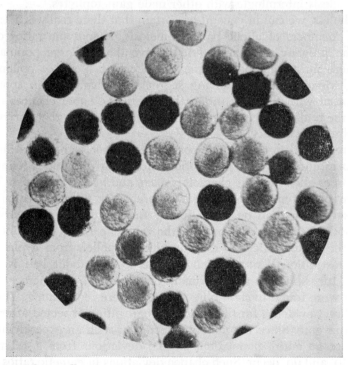

Figure 8-3. *When pollen from sorghum heterozygous for the waxy gene is treated with iodine, about half stains blue (dark in the photo) and half stains red. The pollen grains shown here are magnified 200 times. (Courtesy of R. E. Karper, J. Heredity, 24:259, 1933.)*

Therefore an embryo and its surrounding endosperm have the same alleles represented. But because the endosperm arises from a triple rather than a double fusion of gametic nuclei, the allelic balance in the endosperm differs from that in the embryo. Endosperm that is heterozygous always has two of one allele and one of the other. This permits a view of dominance relations different from that usually observed in the sporophyte. Difference in allelic balance in endosperm as against embryo can be seen in Figure 8-4, which shows reciprocal crosses involving the characters *sugary vs. starchy* endosperm. In both the hybrids indicated in the figure, the endosperm turns out to be starchy, no matter which allele enters through the female line. One *Su* gene, then, is dominant over two *su* alleles.

Sugary ♀ ×	Starchy ♂	
su su	*Su Su*	
(egg) *su* ×	(sperm) *Su* → (embryo) *Su su*	
(polar nuclei) *su + su* ×	(sperm) *Su* → (endosperm) *Su su su*	
Starchy ♀ ×	Sugary ♂	
Su Su	*su su*	
(egg) *Su* ×	(sperm) *su* → (embryo) *Su su*	
(polar nuclei) *Su + Su* ×	(sperm) *su* → (endosperm) *Su Su su*	

Figure 8-4. *Reciprocal crosses in corn involving the alternative characters* starchy *and* sugary *illustrate the fact that the endosperm obtains two identical alleles from the maternal parent and a third allele from the paternal parent.*

Other alleles, however, may not show the same kind of dominance relations in the endosperm. This can be seen in certain genotypes that result from crosses involving *floury* (*f*) as against *flinty* (*F*) endosperm. The genotype *Fff* is found to determine the floury character; *FFf* endosperm is flinty.

An advantage of endosperm genetics is that the investigator can keep one jump ahead of the game of genetic analysis as it is ordinarily played. In the usual investigation of inheritance of a sporophytic character, seed must be planted for the parental generation, and then again for the F_1, and a third time for the F_2. In the study of endosperm characters, however, kernels that form on the parent plants show the F_1 hybrid characteristics for endosperm. One more planting, and the "F_2" endosperm characteristics appear. Two plantings, then, give the same amount of information about endosperm characters that three plantings give about sporophytic characters. Geneticists, of course, have not concentrated entirely on the study of endosperm characters in corn, since the characters of the sporophyte are much more numerous and, on the whole, more important.

The value of knowing life histories becomes quite obvious when you consider the genetic intricacies of the apparently simple kernel of corn. Covering the kernel is a protective layer called the *pericarp*. This consists of maternal tissue, and its characteristics are determined by the genotype of the mother plant. Beneath it is the endosperm, including its outer layer the *aleurone,* whose characteristics appear quickly following pollination. Still deeper inside is the embryo, having a genotype one generation removed from that of the pericarp—a genotype whose phenotypic expression is largely deferred until germination and the emergence of the new sporophyte take place. If the origin of structures in the kernel of corn were not known and properly fitted into the life cycle, genetic interpretation of the inheritance of kernel characteristics might go rather far astray.

The Life Cycle of Sphaerocarpos

Sphaerocarpos, one of the liverworts, is not a conspicuous plant in nature. Neither is it economically important. In the literature of genetics it is far from bulking as large as man, corn, Drosophila, tobacco, the mouse, Oenothera, or any one of quite a variety of other organisms. Nevertheless, there is a good deal to be learned from Sphaerocarpos. Certainly, in the interests of general biological orientation and awareness, we should be acquainted with organisms that stand at different evolutionary levels. Sphaerocarpos is a reasonable sort of representative of groups of plants that have a more conspicuous and longer-enduring gametophytic than sporophytic phase. Beyond this, it can be said that investigations of the life cycle and the genetics

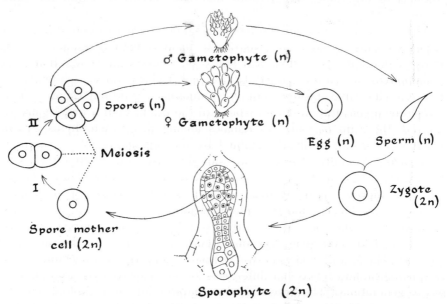

Figure 8-5. *Essential features of the life cycle of Sphaerocarpos.*

of Sphaerocarpos have uncovered information of special interest. Essential features of the life cycle of Sphaerocarpos are found in Figure 8-5.

Gametophytic Generation. In contrast to the gametophytes of corn, those of Sphaerocarpos are independent plants and nutritionally self-sustaining. The gametophytic plants of Sphaerocarpos show sex differences. Male plants produce sperm; female gametophytes give rise to egg cells. The entire gametophytic generation is haploid, and may reproduce itself asexually as well as give rise to sporophytes through unions of gametes.

Sporophytic Generation. A sporophyte develops from a fertilized egg cell and, therefore, is typically a diploid generation. As indicated before, the sporophyte is simple and inconspicuous. It is nutritionally dependent on the gametophyte. Within the maturing sporophyte, spore mother cells (sporocytes) divide meiotically, so that each gives rise to four spores. The germination of such spores leads to the development of haploid gametophytic plants.

Genetic Applications. The four spores resulting from meiosis of a spore mother cell adhere to one another, even after maturity, in many species of Sphaerocarpos. This circumstance is favorable for the analysis of mechanisms of inheritance, since it means that the geneticist may recover and identify all the products of a single meiosis. You should compare the situation here with that in corn, where in megasporogenesis three of the products of each meiosis degenerate, and in microsporogenesis the products of a single meiosis do not adhere but become inextricably mixed with the products of other meiotic divisions that have occurred within the same anther.

When the four spores derived from a single spore mother cell of Sphaerocarpos are germinated, two give rise to male gametophytes and two to female gametophytes. Cytological study of S. *donnellii* shows that male gametophytes are distinguished by a small Y-chromosome, while female gametophytes have a prominent X-chromosome. Sporophytes are XY in chromosome constitution. Here, where all the products of a meiosis are recovered, the ratio of males to females among the gametophytes can be observed as mechanically determined by the segregation of sex chromosomes and is not subject to errors of sampling. Genetic results of this kind are as stylized as those predicted in checkerboard diagrams. They corroborate most impressively the brilliant deductions of Mendel and of the pioneer students of sex linkage and sex determination.

Certain aberrant phenomena in the life cycle of Sphaerocarpos have also been turned to good genetic account. These throw light on the important question: Do the differences between diploidy and haploidy account for the morphological and functional differences between sporophytic and gametophytic generations? The answer is that they do not, since diploid gametophytes sometimes do occur. It is interesting that in Sphaerocarpos, diploid gametophytes with two Y-chromosomes are males; those with two X-chromosomes are females; and those with an X- and a Y- are intersexes. The evidence from Sphaerocarpos is consistent with that from other sources, which also indicates that chromosome cycles in themselves do not explain alternation of generations. For instance, haploid sporophytes are known in corn, Datura, and other plants, and so are diploid gametophytes.

The Life Cycle of Neurospora

Most beginning students in genetics are unlikely to be familiar with the mold Neurospora. Some bakers remember it well, however, as a once aggressive pest in their establishments. Children in Java no doubt think of it in kindlier terms, since it is a necessary participant in the manufacture from peanut meal of a Javanese delicacy called "ontjom." We are interested in Neurospora because in many ways it offers exceptional opportunities for genetic study. If we were to create in our minds an ideal being for genetic investigation, this synthetic creature would need to have many of the qualities found already put together in a simple mold.

What are these qualities? Neurospora has a brief life cycle, and is well adapted for investigation on a mass-production scale. Since it may be readily propagated asexually, unlimited populations of a given genotype may be had for very little trouble. Moreover, it is easily kept in pure culture—a great advantage for physiological research. The physiology of Neurospora has provided an enormously fruitful area of investigation. Finally, the nature of its life cycle permits unusually close genetic analysis.

Reproduction in *Neurospora crassa*. There are several different species of the genus Neurospora. We are to discuss *N. crassa*, the species on which the bulk of genetic investigation has been carried out. When simply the generic name Neurospora is employed in genetic writing, the species *crassa* is usually meant. In the same way, Drosophila, unless further qualified, in practice refers to *D. melanogaster*.

Figure 8-6 summarizes the life cycle of Neurospora. You will note that reproduction of this organism may be sexual or asexual. Asexual reproduction occurs by means of spores called *conidia* or simply by propagation through unspecialized fragments of mycelium. The vegetative hyphae of Neurospora are segmented, with each segment normally containing many haploid nuclei. Asexual reproduction, then, is based on mitotic divisions of haploid nuclei.

Neurospora has two mating types, designated *a* and *A*. Sexual reproduction occurs only when cells of opposite mating type unite. The fusion nucleus which forms is the sole diploid stage in this organism. The zygote quickly undergoes meiosis in a saclike structure called the *ascus*. As is represented in our diagram of the life cycle of Neurospora, the narrow contours of the ascus hold the division figures so that their long axes coincide

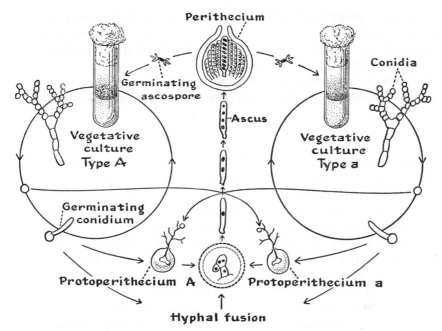

Figure 8-6. *The life cycle of* Neurospora crassa. (*After Beadle, from Hardin,* Biology: Its Human Implications, *W. H. Freeman and Co., 1949, p. 377.*)

with the long axis of the sac. The ascus is narrow enough that divisions following the first division of meiosis occur in tandem, and the resultant nuclei do not slip past each other. The meiotic divisions are typical of their kind, and give rise to the usual four nuclei. Each product of meiosis, still in place, then divides once mitotically, giving rise to eight nuclei in linear order in the ascus. Heavy spore walls form around each of these nuclei, and eventually the eight nuclei are contained in eight *ascospores*. Starting at either end of an ascus one may count off four pairs of spores, each pair representing one of the products of meiosis. Within a pair of ascospores, members are genetically alike.

Eventually, an ascus of Neurospora ruptures. Then the ripe ascospores that were within mingle with other ascospores from different sources. In order to identify individuals arising from crosses between strains of Neurospora, ascospores must be isolated and cultured separately. The germination of an ascospore begins a new generation of haploid mycelium of whatever genetic constitution has been determined by the shuffling of genotypes at meiosis.

Genetic Applications.   Until an ascus breaks up, the eight linearly arranged ascospores provide an accurate diagrammatic record of what has happened at meiosis. This is because: (1) All of the products of a single meiosis are preserved within one structure and cannot be confused with products of other meiotic divisions; and (2) the position of a particular ascospore within its ascus can be referred to the actual position of a nucleus in meiosis, as determined by the orientation of separating chromosomes on a division spindle.

Under appropriate conditions, geneticists can read and interpret the apparently enigmatic diagram represented by eight ascospores within an ascus. Interpretation is possible when ascospores are removed singly from an ascus while retaining their original order. Dissection of ascospores in order is a task that requires some pains and skill, inasmuch as a single spore is only about 0.028 mm long, but with the use of a microscope and a fine glass needle the job can be done successfully. After isolations are made in order, the ascospores may be placed in separate culture tubes and

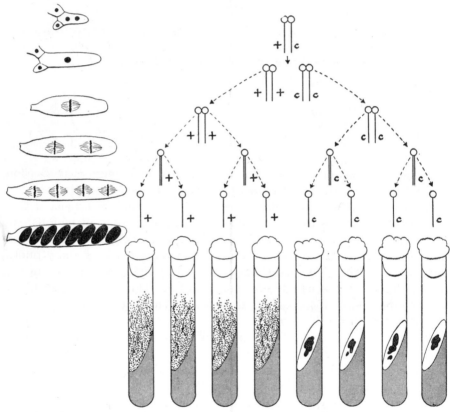

Figure 8-7. *The basis of first-division segregation within an ascus of Neurospora. The sequence at the left shows the general nuclear behavior synchronized with a detailed sequence for a particular chromosome pair at the right. Gene c determines a colonial type growth, while its wild-type allele determines the usual mycelial growth habit. The centromeres of the chromosomes are represented by clear circles. (After Beadle; Baitsell, Science in Progress, Fifth Series. Yale University Press, 1947, p. 180.)*

germinated. Then the genetic attributes of cultures so derived may be referred to segregations of genes at meiosis. In summary, if eight such culture tubes are lined up in the same order as maintained for their corresponding ascospores in the ascus, one can observe directly which alleles went to which nuclei at meiotic segregation. This kind of situation is illustrated pictorially in Figure 8-7, which shows the segregation of a wild-type gene as against an allele which affects the morphology of the mold. The variant-type morphology is characterized by buttonlike, colonial growth on agar medium as contrasted with the weblike, spreading habit typical of the wild type grown under similar cultural conditions.

You will note that after a meiosis such as has been illustrated in Figure 8-7, the first four spores to the left would germinate to give wild-type mycelium and that the next four would produce colonial cultures. The spore order may be represented simply as $+ + + + c c c c$. An order $c c c c + + + +$ would be equally possible. This kind of difference in orientation depends on whether the chromosome carrying gene c lines up to the right or to the left of its homologue at the first division of meiosis.

The recovery of precisely four variant and four wild-type spores from a complete ascus is just what is expected when a single allelic pair is segregating. Remember that when all the products of a meiosis are recovered, genetic ratios are mechanically, not statistically, determined. Naturally, observed ratios in Neurospora vary from the theoretical if certain ascospores fail to germinate. Also, if ascospores were isolated at random, instead of in order out of single asci, following the cross $+ \times c$, deviations from the expected ratio of 1 colonial : 1 wild-type mycelium would be expected to occur. Some of these deviations would certainly be due to the operation of chance during the process of selecting ascospores to isolate and germinate.

Although a single allelic pair characteristically gives rise to a segregation of 4 variant spores to 4 wild-type spores within an ascus, the segregation need not always have a *linear arrangement* of 4:4, but may be some combination of 2:2:2:2 instead. From a cross like that discussed above, the following types of spore arrangements are sometimes found:

$$+ \; + \; c \; c \; + \; + \; c \; c$$
$$c \; c \; + \; + \; c \; c \; + \; +$$
$$+ \; + \; c \; c \; c \; c \; + \; +$$
$$c \; c \; + \; + \; + \; + \; c \; c$$

To understand how arrangements of this kind occur, it is necessary first to have clearly in mind the basis of 4:4 segregations. If you look back to Figure 8-7, you will see that 4:4 segregations occur when a gene and its allele separate from one another at the first division of meiosis. Now look at Figure 8-8 to see what accounts for 2:2:2:2 segregations, called *second-division segregations*. Observe that second-division segregations are accounted for by actual physical exchanges of corresponding segments of chromatid strands

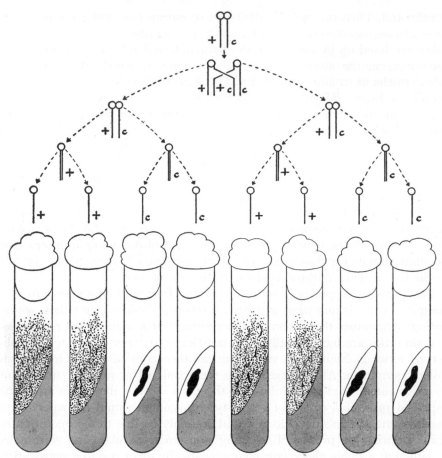

Figure 8-8. *Exchange between chromatids results in second-division segregation within an ascus of Neurospora. (After Beadle; Baitsell,* Science in Progress, Fifth Series, *Yale University Press, 1947, p. 182.)*

of homologous chromosomes. This process of exchange of chromosomal material is called *crossing over*. When crossing over occurs between a gene and the centromere of its chromosome, segregation of the alleles does not occur at the first division of meiosis but is deferred to the second division. The centromeres of homologous chromosomes seem always to segregate from one another at the first division of meiosis. In Neurospora, segregation within an ascus showing a 2:2:2:2 spore arrangement indicates crossing over between the segregating gene and the centromere of its chromosome.

The Life Cycle of Paramecium

Paramecium is a Protozoan (one-celled animal) which, over the past decade or more, has been studied intensively from the genetic point of view.

Among the more important results of these studies has been the emergence of new concepts of the relationships between nucleus and cytoplasm in inheritance. Besides acquainting you with one of the organisms of consequence in genetic research, study of the life cycle of Paramecium will bring to your attention another enlightening example of the great diversity to be found among reproductive systems.

Most college students in biology, at one time or another, look at Paramecium under the microscope. Those who have done this realize that a single-celled animal may have a highly complex structural organization. Also in the functional sense, Paramecium is far from simple. In fact, there are so many complexities in the reproductive processes of Paramecium that for our purposes only a considerably simplified version of the life history can be given.

Again you should be aware that Paramecium is a generic name and that there are numbers of species of this type of organism. Our discussion will be based largely on *P. aurelia*.

Binary Fission. The life cycle of Paramecium is not well defined in the sense that each individual goes through the same rigid sequence of reproductive events. Depending upon circumstances, a variety of nuclear processes of reproductive significance may occur. However, there is only one way by which paramecia give rise to more paramecia. This is through *binary fission,* which is essentially a division of one individual into two individuals that are alike in genetic constitution. A complete description of nuclear behavior at this time of asexual reproduction would be complicated by the fact that paramecia have two kinds of nuclei, *macronuclei* and *micronuclei*. The macronuclei, as their name implies, are much the larger of the two kinds. They appear to be the physiologically active nuclei, in terms of general cellular function, and are essential for survival. However, in our incomplete version of the life history of Paramecium, we can neglect macronuclei in order to concentrate on the micronuclei. For it is the micronuclei that act as germinal nuclei, taking part in conjugation and other processes of importance in the life cycle. Micronuclei are able to give rise to macronuclei.

At fission, micronuclei divide mitotically. Reproduction in Paramecium, then, is fundamentally like the usual manner of proliferation of body cells in multicellular plants and animals. In either instance, single cells through mitosis and cell division give rise to daughter cells that are genetically identical with their progenitors. Paramecium cells, however, separate entirely from one another, and, although complex, they do not show the visible differentiation occurring among some cells of higher organisms.

Conjugation. Under the right conditions, paramecia of different mating type conjugate and carry out reciprocal fertilization. This is summarized in simple outline form in Figure 8-9. The essential events involve in the first place a close adherence of a pair of individuals, the members of the pair

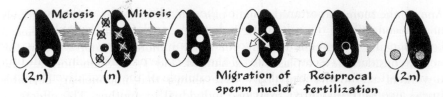

Figure 8-9. *Reciprocal fertilization occurs when Paramecia conjugate.* (*After Sonneborn; Baitsell, Science in Progress, Seventh Series, Yale University Press, 1951, p. 175.*)

being of different mating type. Then the nuclei of the conjugants undergo meiosis. In each member of the conjugating pair, three of the four products of meiosis disintegrate. The remaining nuclei divide mitotically, so that each of the conjugants contains two genetically identical haploid nuclei. From each conjugant, one of the nuclei migrates into the opposite member and fuses with the nucleus that has remained behind. Thus the diploid condition is restored. The conjugants move apart and may reproduce through fission.

Autogamy. The life history of Paramecium quite regularly includes a particular kind of nuclear reorganization with which you are perhaps not familiar. This is *autogamy,* a peculiar sort of self-fertilization that the investigators of Paramecium genetics can utilize to good advantage. In autogamy, the nuclei of unpaired animals undergo meiosis. As at conjugation, only one of the meiotic products persists. This residual nucleus divides mitotically, giving rise to a pair of identical haploid nuclei. Here the resemblance to conjugation ends. (See Fig. 8-10.) Because no mate is at hand, the nuclear migration and reciprocal fertilization described in the section above cannot take place. Instead, there is a fusion between members of the pairs of haploid nuclei occurring in single cells. You should perceive that this results in homozygosity within each of the newly formed diploid nuclei.

Cytoplasmic Transfer. Sometimes in the life history of Paramecium a special circumstance occurs which is of considerable genetic interest and

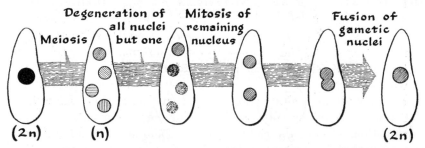

Figure 8-10. *Autogamy in Paramecium is self-fertilization within a single cell. See also Figure 8-11.* (*After Sonneborn; Baitsell, Science in Progress, Seventh Series, Yale University Press, 1951, p. 177.*)

importance. Members of a conjugant pair usually separate after a relatively short period of time. Occasionally, however, a cytoplasmic bridge connecting conjugant individuals remains for thirty minutes or more. When this occurs, considerable cytoplasm is exchanged, and T. M. Sonneborn and his co-workers at Indiana University have shown that nonnuclear, heritable entities can be transmitted from one individual to another. The effects on the behavior and functioning of individuals involved in this kind of situation may be profound.

Genetic Applications. Some of what we have to say about the genetics of Paramecium comes better under the general heading of "Extranuclear Inheritance," the subject of Chapter 13. It is at least worth emphasizing at this time, however, that the occurrence of autogamy in Paramecium provides a useful and perhaps a rather unusual tool for genetic investigation. The most significant feature of autogamy is the fusion of sister haploid nuclei, which in a single step brings about homozygosis for all genes.

Since autogamy takes place rather regularly in most strains, recessive genes cannot long remain masked by dominant alleles. Following mating in Paramecium, the occurrence of autogamy greatly facilitates an investigator's attempts to resolve the genetic constitution of the hybrids. This is because the result of autogamy in heterozygotes is that each allelic pair segregates into the two possible homozygous classes in the simple ratio of 1:1. Figure 8-11 diagrams the basis of the typical result.

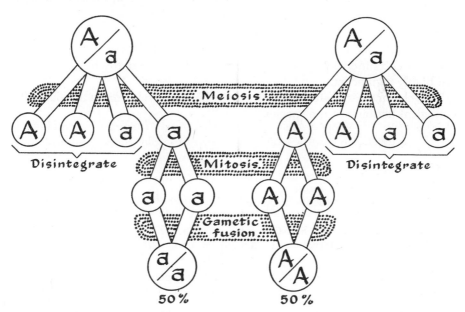

Figure 8-11. *Autogamy in heterozygous paramecia leads to homozygosity. Relate this figure to Figure 8-10. (After Sonneborn,* Advances in Genetics, *1:290, 1947.)*

General Aspects of Reproduction

Two additional points should be made before we leave the subject of life cycles. These are so apparent that there is some danger of their being neglected in our thinking. First, reproductive processes are basically physiological processes. Biologists and biochemists have already accumulated a vast store of information about the physiology of reproduction. Second, the specific processes of reproduction characteristic of particular organisms form an integral part of the genetic heritage of these organisms. Geneticists are already able to relate information about reproduction, including the physiology of reproduction, to the activities of particular genes. We can expect that future research will provide us with a clearer and more complete picture of the genetic bases of this vital function.

Keys to the Significance of This Chapter

Certain general aspects of reproduction are common to a great many living forms. But the details of the processes by which organisms reproduce may differ markedly from one kind of organism to another.

Geneticists must be familiar with the details of life cycles of organisms with which they work. Both the interpretation of genetic results and the development of techniques of investigation must be related to the life cycle of the plant or animal being studied.

From the genetic point of view, the activities and behavior of chromosomes at certain critical phases in the life cycle, particularly during meiosis, are highly significant.

The characteristic attributes of particular life cycles are a fundamental biological heritage of the species.

References

Allen, C. E., "The Genetics of Bryophytes." *Botan. Rev.*, 1:269–291, 1935. (A general review of genetic studies in mosses and liverworts.)

————, "Haploid and Diploid Generations." *Am. Naturalist*, 71:193–205, 1937. (Discussion of the alternation of gamete-producing and spore-producing generations at various levels in the plant kingdom.)

Beadle, G. W., "Genetics and Metabolism in Neurospora." *Physiol. Revs.*, 25:643–663, 1945. (Pages 643 to 651 are the most pertinent to the purposes of this chapter.)

Cooper, D. C., "Macrosporogenesis and Embryology of Melilotus." *Botan. Gaz.*, 95:143–155, 1933. (Details of embryo sac development and embryology of sweet clover. Well illustrated with camera lucida drawings.)

Kiesselbach, T. A., "The Structure and Reproduction of Corn." *Univ. Nebr. Agr. Exp. Sta. Res. Bull. No. 161,* 1949. (Detailed, abundantly illustrated, and has extensive bibliography.)

Lindegren, C. C., "The Genetics of Neurospora—II. Segregation of the Sex Factors in the Asci of *N. crassa, N. sitophila,* and *N. tetrasperma." Bull. Torrey Botan. Club,* **59:**119–138, 1932. (Segregation in Neurospora analyzed on the basis of different spore arrangements within asci.)

Randolph, L. F., "Developmental Morphology of the Caryopsis in Maize." *J. Agr. Research,* 53:881–916, 1936. (Definitive article on the development of the corn kernel.)

Sharp, L. W., *Fundamentals of Cytology.* New York: McGraw-Hill Book Co., 1943. (The chapters on the cytology of reproduction in animals [Chap. 9], in angiosperms [Chap. 10], and in plants other than angiosperms [Chap. 11] are directly pertinent to the consideration of life cycles.)

Sonneborn, T. M., "Recent Advances in the Genetics of Paramecium and Euplotes." *Advances in Genetics,* 1:263–358, 1947. (An authoritative and detailed review. See especially pp. 265–295.)

Questions and Problems

8- 1.   What do the following terms signify?

aleurone	dioecious	micronucleus
ascospore	embryo sac	microspore
autogamy	endosperm	monoecious
binary fission	first-division segregation	pericarp
chromosome cycle	gametophyte	second-division segregation
conidia	life cycle	self pollination
cross-pollination	macronucleus	sporocyte
	megaspore	sporophyte

8- 2.   List particular advantages of the following organisms for genetic research: corn, Drosophila, Neurospora, Paramecium, Sphaerocarpos.

8- 3.   What are some of the advantages for genetic analysis of haploid organisms as compared with diploids?

8- 4.   What genetic phenomena important in diploids cannot ordinarily be investigated in haploid organisms?

8- 5.   In corn the haploid number of chromosomes is 10. How many chromosomes would you normally expect to find in (a) the nucleus of an aleurone cell, (b) the tube nucleus, (c) a microsporocyte nucleus, (d) a root tip nucleus, (e) a polar nucleus, (f) an egg nucleus?

8- 6.   What are the major differences between the life cycle of a liverwort (e.g., Sphaerocarpos) and of an angiosperm (e.g., corn)?

8- 7.   What is some of the evidence that chromosome cycles as such do not regulate the alternation of generations found in many plant groups?

In corn, three of the allelic pairs concerned in aleurone pigmentation are *A-a, I-i,* and *Pr-pr.* For pigment to develop, at least one *A* allele must be present and no *I* allele may be present. Aleurone pigment is purple when *Pr* is present but is red under a genotype homozygous for *pr*.

8- 8. Suppose that in an isolated experimental corn plot seeds of the genotype *AaprprII* are planted in even-numbered rows and seeds of the genotype *aaPrprii* are planted in odd-numbered rows. When the plants grow up, natural pollination is permitted. What aleurone colors might you expect to find in ears of corn formed on plants in the even-numbered rows? In the odd-numbered rows?

8- 9. With reference to the preceding question, would you expect the aleurone colors to fall into Mendelian ratios? Justify your answer.

8-10. Designate all the possible genotypes of aleurone that might occur within ears formed on plants of the odd- and even-numbered rows of corn referred to in Question 8-8. (Remember that aleurone is part of the endosperm and therefore is triploid.)

8-11. Starting with the two kinds of seed described in Question 8-8, outline in detail the steps you would take to develop, in the most efficient way possible, a strain of corn that would breed true for purple aleurone color.

8-12. Which do each of the following ascospore arrangements in Neurospora indicate, first-division segregation or second-division segregation?

$$+ \ + \ c \ c \ + \ + \ c \ c$$
$$c \ c \ + \ + \ + \ + \ c \ c$$
$$c \ c \ c \ c \ + \ + \ + \ +$$
$$+ \ + \ c \ c \ c \ c \ + \ +$$

8-13. Suppose that you dissected an ascus of Neurospora, and after germinating the spores found the following spore arrangement to be indicated:

$$+ \ + \ c \ + \ c \ + \ c \ c$$

What would be anomalous about such an arrangement?

8-14. What possibilities can you think of that might explain the result indicated in the preceding question?

8-15. For various reasons, ascospores of Neurospora sometimes fail to germinate. Suppose that you have made a cross between a strain with wild-type pigmentation (+) and an albino strain (*al*). You wish to determine the frequency with which the *al* gene segregates at the second division of meiosis. What is the minimal number of spores out of a set of eight that must germinate in order for you to tell whether first- or second-division segregation has occurred within an ascus?

8-16. Suppose that you are still working with a cross where the allelic pair +/*al* is segregating. Assume equal viability of wild-type and *albino* ascospores. If only one spore from an ascus germinates, what is the probability that it will produce a wild-type culture? If two spores from an ascus germinate, what is the probability that both will produce wild-type cultures? That you will obtain a wild-type and an albino culture?

8-17. In a laboratory experiment by a student at Cornell University, an albino strain of Neurospora was crossed with a wild-type strain. After isolations of ascospores *at random*, 2018 albino cultures and 1996 salmon-pink (wild-type color) cultures were obtained. Apply the chi-square test to determine whether the result is consistent with expectation.

8-18. The *polycladous* race of *Sphaerocarpos donnellii* is characterized by frequent branching in the gametophyte. C. E. Allen has found consistently that, after the cross polycladous × nonpolycladous, sporophytes are formed that produce tetrads of spores with the following characteristics: Two of the spores give rise to polycladous gametophytes; the other two give rise to nonpolycladous gametophytes. Are these results consistent with the hypothesis that polyclady is determined by two independent genes? Justify your answer.

8-19. Two races of Sphaerocarpos differ in that one produces spores adherent in tetrads and the other has separate spores. Whenever crosses involving a difference in this character are made, the genetic character of the mother, irrespective of the inheritance of the father, determines whether the sporophyte the mother bears will produce adherent or separate spores. Suggest an explanation for these results.

8-20. In variety 1 of *Paramecium aurelia*, some stocks are pure type I (one-type condition). Others (two-type condition) contain both types I and II, and, at uniparental nuclear reorganization, individuals irrespective of their mating type can give rise to lines of each type. Sonneborn has found that when matings are made between pure type I individuals and type II individuals the F_1 is entirely of the two-type condition. In F_2, $\frac{3}{4}$ are of the two-type condition and $\frac{1}{4}$ are pure type I. A backcross of F_1 individuals to the type I parental line gives $\frac{1}{2}$ of the one-type condition and $\frac{1}{2}$ of the two-type condition. Interpret these results.

8-21. On the basis of your interpretation of results in the preceding problem, tell what would be expected if F_1 individuals were permitted to undergo autogamy.

8-22. Suppose that you have a single paramecium that has resulted from the process of autogamy. Compare the genetic results of (a) this animal undergoing fission with (b) its undergoing further autogamy.

8-23. The macronuclei of Paramecium regularly disintegrate at stages in the life cycle where nuclear reorganization occurs. At the time of their disintegration, macronuclei break up into as many as 40 or more pieces, which, normally, are resorbed. However, under particular circumstances a single such fragment of a macronucleus is able to regenerate a complete macronucleus which can control the normal functioning of a paramecium, even when micronuclei are not present. What do these findings imply about the genetic structure of the macronucleus?

CHAPTER 9

Linkage, Crossing Over, and Chromosome Mapping

THE PRINCIPLE of independent assortment of members of different allelic pairs at the time of germ-cell formation is one of the cornerstones on which an understanding of genetic systems has been built. You have met with and utilized this principle repeatedly, both in reading and in problem solving. Now you need to learn that independent assortment is not a rule without exceptions. When certain different allelic pairs are involved in crosses, deviations from independent assortment regularly occur. Study of the basis of these deviations has added much to our present detailed knowledge of the structure of germ plasm.

Linkage

Deviation from Independent Assortment Seen in a Testcross Ratio. For an initial example of systematic deviation from independent assortment we may return to the already familiar frizzle fowl. In an experiment conducted by F. B. Hutt, colored frizzle females were crossed with a White Leghorn male. The male was homozygous for gene *I*, a dominant which acts as an inhibitor for melanin pigmentation, and for the normal, recessive allele of frizzle. The hens were *iiFF*; that is, they did not have the dominant white gene but were homozygous frizzles. F_1 females obtained from the cross of colored, frizzle females × white, normal males were testcrossed. The crosses and their results are tabulated below:

P:　*iiFF* (colored, frizzle) ♀♀ × *IIff* (white, normal) ♂
F_1: *IiFf* (white, frizzle) ♀♀ and ♂♂
Testcross: *IiFf* ♀♀ × *iiff* ♂

white, frizzle	18
colored, frizzle	63
white, normal	63
colored, normal	13
	157

(Data from F. B. Hutt, *Genetics*, **18**:84, 1933.)

You see at once that the results are markedly different from the 1:1:1:1 ratio we have learned to expect from testcrosses of dihybrid individuals. If frizzle and normal feathering are considered alone, however, the proportion of 81 frizzles to 76 normals fits closely the expected 1:1 ratio. Likewise, the count of 76 colored to 81 white shows no greater deviation from expectancy than might reasonably be accounted for by chance. The real deviation from expectancy is therefore not in the behavior of either allelic pair alone, but in their behavior with respect to each other.

At this point the value of the testcross is conspicuous. Since the male parent in the testcross was homozygous recessive, the respective frequencies of the different kinds of egg cells formed by the dihybrid females can be determined directly by inspection of the phenotypes of the testcross progeny. Clearly, the F_1 females gave rise to egg cells in the following proportions: 63If, 63iF, 18IF, and 13if. The two classes of gametes found in unexpectedly great numbers have the same allelic combinations as were present in the gametes formed by the two parents of the F_1 dihybrids. The new combinations (IF and if) make up only 19.7 per cent ($^{31}\!/_{157}$) of the total.

The Meaning of Linkage. The tendency of parental combinations to remain together, which is expressed in the relative infrequency of new combinations, is the phenomenon of linkage. Genes show linkage because they are in the same chromosome. New combinations of linked genes are called *recombinations*.

For some of you who have been thinking independently about various aspects of segregation, an introduction to linkage will be the beginning of an answer to a troublesome question. We have said earlier that independent assortment of members of different allelic pairs depends upon independent assortment of members of homologous chromosome pairs at meiosis. But there are many more different genes than there are chromosome pairs in an organism, so that at least some chromosomes must carry many genes. How, then, you may have asked, can all genes segregate independently of one another? The answer is that they do not. You have just seen one illustration of this fact. The rest of the chapter will be an elaboration of the phenomenon of linkage, in the course of which you will find ample evidence that linked genes are indeed genes in the same chromosome.

The Method of Notation for Linked Genes. The crosses summarized on page 150 can now be shown in more meaningful fashion:

$$\text{P: } \frac{i\,F}{i\,F} \text{ (Colored, frizzle) } ♀♀ \times \frac{I\,f}{I\,f} \text{ (white, normal) } ♂$$

$$\text{Eggs: } i\,F \qquad\qquad \text{Sperm: } I\,f$$

$$\text{F}_1\text{: } \frac{i\,F}{I\,f} \text{ ♀♀ and ♂♂}$$

(concluded on next page)

$$\text{Testcross:} \frac{i\,F}{I\,f} \, \female\female \, \times \, \frac{i\,f}{i\,f} \, \male$$

sperm:

$$i\,f$$

eggs:		
$I\,F$	white, frizzle	(18)
$i\,F$	colored, frizzle	(63)
$I\,f$	white, normal	(63)
$i\,f$	colored, normal	(13)

Pay particular attention to the way of representing linked genes. For instance, the genotype of colored, frizzle females in the parental generation is written as $\dfrac{i\,F}{i\,F}$. This is a simplification of $\dfrac{i\ F}{i\ F}$, where the two horizontal lines represent the homologous chromosomes in which genes i and F are situated. The designation of F_1 individuals as $\dfrac{i\ F}{I\ f}$, then, indicates that genes i and F are in one homologue and genes I and f are in the other.

Examination of this new summary of the crosses will make it clear to you that the colored frizzles and the white normals occurring in the testcross progeny are determined by egg cells having the same allele-in-chromosome combinations as found in the different gametes of the P generation, and also in the chromosomes of the F_1 females used as parents in the testcross. Egg cells giving rise to colored normals or to white frizzles in the testcross progeny show recombination of the original parental arrangement of alleles.

Results of Another Testcross Involving Frizzle and Dominant White. Your understanding of the effects of linkage may be amplified if we consider another cross carried out in the course of Hutt's investigations. In this instance also, females heterozygous for the F and I genes were testcrossed to a double recessive male. The results showed:

white, frizzle	15
colored, frizzle	2
white, normal	4
colored, normal	12
	33

(Data from F. B. Hutt, *Genetics,* 18:85, 1933.)

Superficially, these results appear to represent an exact reversal of the tendency noted in the earlier cross. Here, colored frizzles and white normals make up the least frequent classes, whereas previously they were most frequent. The explanation of the apparent discrepancy in result is simple, however, and helps to substantiate what we have said about the chromosomal basis of linkage. In the experiment presently under consideration, the dihybrids being testcrossed were of a genetic constitution $\dfrac{I\,F}{i\,f}$ instead of

$\dfrac{i\,F}{I\,f}$. The greater frequency of $I\,F$ and $i\,f$ gametes in the second testcross is accounted for by the fact that they represent the arrangement of alleles in the dihybrid parent.

Observe that the 2 colored frizzles and the 4 white normals of the second cross make up 6 recombinations in the total of 33 progeny, or 18.2 per cent recombinations. This value for recombinations is very near the 19.7 per cent nonparental combinations found in the first experiment. The conclusion would seem warranted that the tendency of linked genes to recombine is equally strong whether the arrangement of alleles is both dominants in one chromosome and both recessives in the other, or whether it is a dominant and a recessive in each homologue. These different kinds of allelic arrangements in a double heterozygote are designated by the terms *coupling*, for the arrangement $\dfrac{AB}{ab}$, and *repulsion*, for the situation where alleles are associated as $\dfrac{Ab}{aB}$.

Linkage and F_2 Ratios. The typical Mendelian dihybrid ratio in F_2 results from the formation by F_1 individuals ($AaBb$) of equal numbers of gametes of the four possible genotypic combinations (AB, Ab, aB, ab). Linkage of the segregating genes of a dihybrid leads to deviations from a 9:3:3:1 ratio of phenotypes just as it leads to deviations from the corresponding testcross ratio of 1:1:1:1. The magnitude of such deviations depends upon the frequency with which recombinations occur. Another way of expressing the same idea is to say that the magnitude of such deviations depends upon the strength of the linkage.

For particular pairs of linked genes, recombination frequencies are remarkably stable. Once established, they may be used as a basis of prediction for genotypic and phenotypic ratios to be obtained from future crosses involving those gene pairs. Let us consider an example of how a recombination frequency derived from the results of a testcross can be made the basis for forecasting an F_2 ratio.

In tomatoes, gene O, for round fruit, is dominant over its allele o, for fruit of elongate shapes. Gene S, a gene for simple inflorescence, is dominant over s, which determines compound inflorescence. The simple type of inflorescence arises from successive third internodes; the *compound* arises from successive sixth nodes and is much branched. A cross was made between Yellow Pear tomatoes, characterized by elongate fruit and simple inflorescence ($ooSS$), and Grape Cluster tomatoes, having round fruit and compound inflorescence ($OOss$). The F_1 consisted of plants having nearly round fruits in simple clusters. A testcross of the F_1 gave the results shown below.

$$\frac{Os}{oS} \times \frac{os}{os}$$

round, simple (OS) 23
long, simple (oS) 83
round, compound (Os) 85
long, compound (os) 19

(Data from J. W. MacArthur, *Genetics*, **13**:414, 1928.)

Linkage is obviously indicated by the data. The two recombination types, round, simple and long, compound, make up only 42 out of 210, or 20 per cent of the total progeny. This means that of gametes formed by the dihybrid $\frac{Os}{oS}$, 80 per cent are types Os and oS, while 20 per cent are OS and os. Since the two recombination types are formed in about equal numbers, and since the two nonrecombination (parental) types seem also to be formed in equal numbers, we are justified in supposing that of 100 gametes formed by the hybrid, the following average frequency of genotypes will maintain:

$$\frac{Os}{oS}\quad \left.\begin{array}{l} oS \quad 40 \\ Os \quad 40 \end{array}\right\} 80 \text{ parental types}$$

$$\left.\begin{array}{l} OS \quad 10 \\ os \quad 10 \end{array}\right\} 20 \text{ recombination types}$$

Having these values in mind, we are in a position to make a prediction about what would happen if individuals $\frac{Os}{oS}$ were carried into an F_2 generation rather than testcrossed. The necessary calculation requires no difficult alteration in methods we have frequently employed in computing Mendelian ratios. In fact, a checkerboard square can be utilized again, with the qualification that we must now take into account that the gametic types are not equally frequent. Weighting the gametic frequencies is simple for the example at hand, since the gametes OS, Os, oS, and os are expected to occur in a proportion of 10:40:40:10. If the terms of this proportion are converted into decimal fractions (0.1, 0.4, 0.4, and 0.1), the probabilities for given gametic unions may be calculated in the way shown in Figure 9-1. A summation of phenotypes in this checkerboard square is:

round, simple (OS) 0.51
long, simple (oS) 0.24
round, compound (Os) 0.24
long, compound (os) 0.01
                                  $\overline{1.00} = 100\%$

		$\dfrac{Os}{oS} \times \dfrac{Os}{oS}$ pollen:		
		0.1 OS	0.4 Os	0.4 oS	0.1 os
eggs: 0.1 OS	0.01 OS/OS	0.04 OS/Os	0.04 OS/oS	0.01 OS/os
0.4 Os	0.04 Os/OS	0.16 Os/Os	0.16 Os/oS	0.04 Os/os
0.4 oS	0.04 oS/OS	0.16 oS/Os	0.16 oS/oS	0.04 oS/os
0.1 os	0.01 os/OS	0.04 os/Os	0.04 os/oS	0.01 os/os

Figure 9-1. *Prediction of F_2 genotypes when the F_1 is $\dfrac{Os}{oS}$ and the recombination frequency is 20 per cent.*

The corresponding values on the basis of independent inheritance (a 9:3:3:1 ratio) are approximately 0.56, 0.19, 0.19, and 0.06.

Now let us compare our prediction for an F_2 with actual counts of F_2 individuals segregating from an experimental cross of the kind we have outlined. In the actual F_2, 259 individuals were classified. From our checkerboard prediction, we would expect 51 per cent of these to be round, simple (OS), 24 per cent long, simple (oS), 24 per cent round, compound (Os), and 1 per cent long, compound (os). The comparison of real F_2 values with those expected on the basis of recombination frequency obtained from the testcross is shown in Table 9-1.

TABLE 9-1. Comparison of Actual F_2 Segregants with Those Predicted on the Basis of Testcross Results. (Data for actual F_2 from J. W. MacArthur, Genetics, 13:414, 1928.)

PHENOTYPES		NUMBER OF ACTUAL F_2 SEGREGANTS	NUMBER OF PREDICTED F_2 SEGREGANTS
Round, simple	(OS)	126	132
Long, simple	(oS)	66	62
Round, compound	(Os)	63	62
Long, compound	(os)	4	3

Examination of these values will convince you that the correspondence of actual segregants to predicted segregants is very good.

The F_2 progeny from a hybrid ($OoSs$) can fall into quite different proportions of phenotypes, depending on whether the alleles are in a repulsion or a coupling phase. Suppose that instead of F_1 hybrids of the combination $\dfrac{Os}{oS}$, we were to consider individuals of the constitution $\dfrac{os}{OS}$. Utilize again the recombination value of 20 per cent derived from the testcross data, and see whether you can predict the relative frequencies of F_2 phenotypes under this condition of coupling in the F_1. (On the basis of a progeny of 100 the answer to the problem is 66:9:9:16.)

Calculating Strength of Linkage from F_2 Data. It is easier to estimate linkage values on the basis of testcross data, from which the totals of recombination and nonrecombination types of gametes can be read directly, than on the basis of F_2 data like those shown in the first column of numbers in Table 9-1. Calculations of recombination frequency can, in fact, be made from such F_2 data, and sometimes investigators in genetics find it practical to utilize F_2's for establishing the strength of a linkage. The methods of calculation, however, are relatively devious. Since they add little to one's understanding of genetics in general, we will mention them only to say that they exist, and that the procedure for the necessary mathematical manipulations is readily available in the literature of genetics. (See "References" at the end of this chapter.) Later in the chapter, you will find that under special circumstances certain F_2 populations can be utilized in a direct way for the estimation of linkage strength.

Crossing Over

It has been implied, though not stated, in the first part of this chapter that recombination is accomplished through some process by which homologous chromosome strands exchange segments. Such a process does occur, and is called *crossing over*. To orient the discussion to follow, we shall list briefly at the outset certain points concerning the nature of crossing over which will be substantiated and amplified in the course of subsequent treatment.

1. The genes in chromosomes occur in linear order, somewhat like beads on a string.
2. When a gene (A) and its allele (a) are present in different members of a pair of homologous chromosomes, the gene and its allele occupy corresponding places in the homologues.
3. In order to be effective in producing recombinations between two different allelic pairs situated in the same chromosome pair, crossing over must occur between the locations (*loci*) of the genes involved.
4. Crossing over characteristically occurs in the first division of meiosis. It is

this kind of crossing over which concerns us most. However, somatic cross ing over is also known to occur.

5. Meiotic crossing over takes place at the time during the nuclear reproduc tive cycle when four chromatids are present for each pair of chromosomes

On this basis, we may initially visualize crossing over as occurring be tween chromatids in the manner indicated in Figure 9-2.

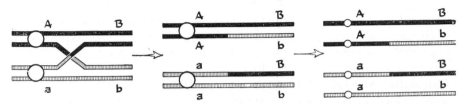

Figure 9-2. *Crossing over is the interchange of corresponding segments between chromatids of homologous chromosomes.*

Cytological Detection of Crossing Over. Before considering crossing over in more detail, let us be assured that recombination actually does result from a physical interchange of parts of homologous chromosome strands. To demonstrate this fact unequivocally is not so easy as might be imagined. The difficulty is that under ordinary circumstances members of a pair of homologous chromosomes are not visibly distinguishable, even by close microscopic examination. Only under unusual circumstances, when the ends of homologous chromosomes are somehow "labelled," can the recombination of linked genes be related to physical exchange of parts between the homologues. Curt Stern has exploited a set of unusual circum stances of this kind to fashion one of the classical experiments in genetics. His proof of a cytological basis for crossing over is summarized in Figure 9-3. Other investigators have utilized corn to demonstrate in equally elegant ways that recombination of linked genes is accompanied by interchange of chromosome material. The clear results obtained both in corn and Droso phila strengthen impressively the conviction that recombination has a defi nite physical basis.

Crossing Over in the 4-Strand Stage. If crossing over occurs at some time during the close association of homologous chromosomes at meiosis, two significant alternatives would seem to be possible. Crossing over might occur either when only two strands are present or it might occur after these have doubled.

A consideration of the life cycle of Neurospora makes it plain that this organism is tailor-made for resolving the question of whether crossing over occurs at a 2- or at a 4-strand stage. As a matter of fact, in the chapter on "Life Cycles" we have already indicated in a preliminary way how first- and second-division segregations in Neurospora relate to this question. The con sideration of chief importance is that all the products of a single meiosis

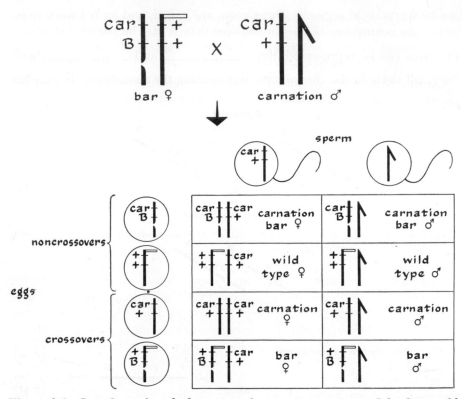

Figure 9-3. *Curt Stern found aberrant X-chromosomes in Drosophila that could be utilized for cytological demonstration of crossing over. One was an X-chromosome to which a portion of a Y-chromosome (shown in outline) was attached. The other was a broken X-chromosome whose acentric portion was attached to chromosome 4. Under a microscope, both kinds of aberrant chromosomes could be easily distinguished from each other and from normal X-chromosomes. Female Drosophila carrying these abnormal chromosomes and heterozygous for carnation (a recessive eye-color variant) and for bar (dominant) were crossed with carnation males. Examination of the chromosomes of progeny whose phenotypes indicated genic recombination revealed that the genic recombination was accompanied by appropriate exchange of identifiable chromosome segments. (After Stern, Biol. Zentr., 51:586, 1931.)*

can be recovered, since they are retained for a time within the ascus. With reference to the question posed above, it is only necessary to determine whether linked gene pairs may give rise to both parental and recombination types within a single ascus or whether only one type or the other is recovered after a meiotic division.

For an example, we may look at one kind of result obtained after the cross of an albino (*al*) strain, producing white conidia, with a strain (*ag*), unable to synthesize the amino acid arginine. The wild-type allele of the *al* gene conditions orange-pigmented conidia; and that of the *ag* gene permits the biosynthesis of arginine. These genes are linked, and ag is known to be nearer the centromere of the chromosome than is al. The parental strains in this cross can be represented, then: $\underset{\text{O}}{\_\_\_}\overset{+}{\rule{0pt}{0pt}}\quad\overset{al}{\_\_\_}$ and $\underset{\text{O}}{\_\_\_}\overset{ag}{\rule{0pt}{0pt}}\quad\overset{+}{\_\_\_}$, with the small circle in the chromosome representing the centromere. Remember

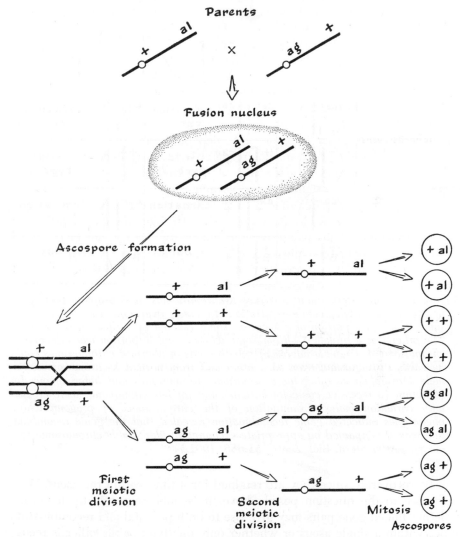

Figure 9-4. *Types of ascospores produced within an ascus of Neurospora in which a crossover has occurred between two linked genes. Gene ag determines an inability to synthesize arginine; al determines nonpigmented spores. The fact that ascospores are produced that give rise to parental-type mycelia in addition to ones that give double mutant and wild-type mycelia shows that crossing over occurs at a 4-strand stage.*

that Neurospora is haploid. Crossover types in the progeny of a mating between the two strains would be $\underline{\quad_o\overset{+\quad+}{\rule{2cm}{0.4pt}}}$ (wild type) and $\underline{\quad_o\overset{ag\quad al}{\rule{2cm}{0.4pt}}}$ (double mutant). These crossover types are recovered from certain asci dissected in order, but along with them, in the same asci, are parental types. Figure 9-4 shows the analysis of a typical ascus dissected in order. Observe that the allelic pair nearest the centromere shows first-division segregation, while the *al* pair segregates in the second meiotic division. Verify that this ascospore distribution could not be formed unless four discrete chromatids were already present when the exchange occurred. In short, crossing over in Neurospora occurs at a 4-strand stage. (Would the same sort of analysis be possible in Sphaerocarpos? In corn?)

Crossing over in the 4-strand stage has been demonstrated in Drosophila equally satisfactorily but in not quite so simple a manner as is possible in Neurospora. One proof in Drosophila depends upon the existence of attached-X female flies that are heterozygous for a sex-linked gene, such as that for vermilion eyes (*v*). Females of this kind are phenotypically wild type for eye color, inasmuch as the vermilion gene is recessive. Since the attached-X complex is inherited as a unit, one might expect these females to give rise only to wild-type daughters. Vermilion daughters do occur, however, in individuals where detachment of the X's has not taken place. This becomes understandable on the basis that crossing over occurs between the locus of *v* and the centromere of its chromosome at a time when four strands are closely associated during meiosis. Figure 9-5 diagrams the effects of crossing over at the 4-strand stage in attached-X females. Verify that, if crossing over occurred at a 2-strand stage, the effect would be merely to exchange *v* and its allele on the two arms of the attached-X, and that parental type gametes would still be produced.

Evidence for crossing over at a 4-strand stage in other organisms in addi-

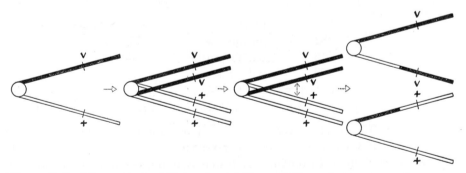

Figure 9-5. *When attached-X females of Drosophila are heterozygous for a sex-linked gene, homozygous egg cells may be produced if crossing over occurs between the gene locus and the centromere. This is another way of demonstrating that crossing over occurs at a 4-strand stage.*

tion to Neurospora and Drosophila suggests that this aspect of the mechanism of meiosis is widespread among living things.

Chiasmata and Crossing Over. In Chapter 7, the description of the prophase of the first meiotic division included a reference to chiasmata, cross-shaped figures whose appearance suggests a breaking and rejoining of chromatids. Whether chiasmata do in fact indicate the exchange of material which accounts for recombination is debatable. At present a number of troublesome facts seem to preclude any simple interpretation of the relationship, if any, between chiasmata and crossing over. One of these is the fact that in male Drosophila, chiasmata have been frequently observed, but crossing over occurs only as an exceptional event.

Absence of Crossing Over in Drosophila Males. An unusual feature of Drosophila genetics is that for the most part no recombinations among linked genes are found in the sperm cells of Drosophila males. This can be seen, for example, when males with purple eyes are crossed to females with black body color. In the F_1, members of both sexes are wild type. This is to be expected, since *purple* and *black* are autosomal recessives. But if the F_1 flies are used to make reciprocal testcrosses, quite different results are obtained, depending on whether the heterozygous parents in a testcross are males or females. Results of reciprocal testcrosses of this kind are diagrammed below.

$$P: \quad \frac{b \quad +}{b \quad +} \female \text{ (black)} \times \frac{+ \quad pr}{+ \quad pr} \male \text{ (purple)}$$

$$F_1: \quad \frac{b \quad +}{+ \quad pr} \female\female \text{ and } \male\male \text{ (wild type)}$$

Testcrosses:

$$\frac{b \quad +}{+ \quad pr} \female \times \frac{b \quad pr}{b \quad pr} \male \qquad \frac{b \quad pr}{b \quad pr} \female \times \frac{b \quad +}{+ \quad pr} \male$$

353	black	74
382	purple	71
16	black, purple	0
22	wild type	0

(Data from Morgan and Bridges, "Contributions to the Genetics of *Drosophila melanogaster*," *Carnegie Inst. Wash. Pub. 278,* pp. 184, 185, 1919.)

The data from each testcross give evidence for linkage between black and purple. But whereas 4.9 per cent recombination types were found in the progeny when an F_1 female was testcrossed, no recombination whatever was evidenced when an F_1 male was mated with a double recessive female. Results like these, while astonishing when first encountered by investigators, are now known to be perfectly typical for Drosophila. The males of certain other species of Diptera and female silkworms also fail to show recombination. However, in most species that have been studied, recombination occurs in both sexes, although it may not be equally frequent in males and females.

F$_2$ Ratios Involving Linked Genes in Drosophila. The absence of crossing over in male Drosophila affects F$_2$ ratios as well as testcross ratios involving linked genes. That this should be the case is now obvious, and you may wonder why we linger on a circumstance not typical of organisms in general. Actually some very instructive applications of genetic principle can be based on this unusual circumstance. One of the most useful of these applications has to do with establishing the linkage relations of newly found mutant genes in Drosophila.

In Drosophila, with only four pairs of chromosomes, the problem of establishing linkage relationships is a much simpler task than in corn, with ten pairs of chromosomes. Even in Drosophila, however, the task might not be easy, since different genes in the same chromosome may show widely differing recombination values, some of which may be so high that random assortment is reached. Thus, crosses are sometimes made involving genes in the same chromosome, but the fact of linkage does not appear from the results of the crosses.

It turns out that in Drosophila, however, because of the absence of recombination in the male, crosses involving two linked gene pairs in *repulsion* characteristically give rise to ratios of 2:1:1:0 in the F$_2$ generation. This readily identified ratio can be made the basis of a simple test for linkage.

Consider the series of matings diagrammed below.

$$\text{P:} \quad \frac{+ \quad a}{+ \quad a} \; ♀ \, (\text{arc}) \; \times \; \frac{b \quad +}{b \quad +} \; ♂ \, (\text{black})$$

$$\text{F}_1\text{:} \quad \frac{+ \quad a}{b \quad +} \; ♀♀ \text{ and } ♂♂ \; (\text{wild type})$$

F$_2$:

eggs:	sperm: $\dfrac{+ \quad a}{}$	$b \quad +$
$\dfrac{+ \quad a}{}$	arc	wild
$\dfrac{b \quad +}{}$	wild	black
$\dfrac{+ \quad +}{}$	wild	wild
$\dfrac{b \quad a}{}$	arc	black

These crosses were made by C. B. Bridges in an attempt to establish a linkage for a type of wing variant called *arc*. Arc was already known to be autosomal and recessive, and in crosses with the variant-type *pink* eyes it had given a ratio of 9:3:3:1 in F_2. In a cross with black, however, F_2 data were obtained as follows:

wild type	923
black	401
arc	387
black, arc	0

If you study the diagram, you will see why double-recessive type progeny cannot be formed in F_2, and why the ratio approximates 2:1:1:0. Since there is no crossing over in male Drosophila, sperm cannot be formed having both of the different recessive alleles, and double-recessive (black, arc) progeny cannot be produced. Moreover, as the checkerboard reveals, no matter what the degree of linkage between b and a, the phenotypes wild, black, and arc should occur in a ratio of 2:1:1 in the F_2. You can readily convince yourselves of this by noting that the four squares in the top half of the checkerboard represent progeny deriving from *parental-type* gametes from the mothers and that the bottom half of the checkerboard summarizes progeny deriving from *crossover-type* gametes from the mothers. In both these halves of the checkerboard, wild is represented twice as often as either black or arc. The over-all relationship, then, must also be 2:1:1.

Now demonstrate that the 2:1:1:0 ratio in F_2 is characteristic only when the linked gene pairs are in the repulsion rather than the coupling phase in F_1. This can be accomplished by redoing the diagram on p. 162 on the basis that the parents in the original cross are wild $\left(\dfrac{+\quad+}{+\quad+}\right)$ and black, arc $\left(\dfrac{b\quad a}{b\quad a}\right)$.

The Manifestation of Linkage in F_2 Ratios Involving Sex-Linked Characters. Earlier in the chapter it was said that under certain special circumstances estimates of linkage strength can be made quite simply on the basis of F_2 results. One of these circumstances occurs in the case of sex-linked genes. Since every male normally derives from his father a Y-chromosome that is virtually empty of genes, the sons in an F_2 population constitute what is, in effect, a testcross progeny insofar as sex-linked genes are concerned. This situation is revealed in the diagram below and on the next page, which outlines through the F_2 generation crosses involving the sex-linked genes y (yellow body) and cv (crossveinless wings).

$$\text{P:} \quad \frac{+\quad+}{+\quad+} \; ♀♀ \;\times\; \frac{y\quad cv}{} \; ♂♂$$

$$\text{F}_1\text{:} \quad \frac{+\quad+}{y\quad cv} \; ♀♀ \;\times\; \frac{+\quad+}{} \; ♂♂$$

F_2:   sperm:

		+ +	_____
eggs:	+ + ⎯⎯	wild ♀	wild ♂
	y cv ⎯⎯	wild ♀	yellow crossveinless ♂
	+ cv ⎯⎯	wild ♀	crossveinless ♂
	y + ⎯⎯	wild ♀	yellow ♂

Actually, if the F_1 males were double recessive for the linked genes, the entire F_2 population, males and females, could be treated in the same way as testcross segregants for analysis of recombination frequency. Verify this by diagramming a sequence of crosses through F_2 where the P generation is the reciprocal of the one shown in the text.

Chromosome Mapping

The Basis for Chromosome Mapping. In Drosophila, the genes for the mutant characters *white eyes, yellow body,* and *cut wings* are all sex-linked. Appropriate matings reveal that the white and yellow genes consistently show about 1 per cent crossing over. But white and cut give around 20 per cent crossing over. Results of this kind are typical for Drosophila and for other organisms where studies of linked genes have been carried out. The generalization can be made that crossing over between particular pairs of linked genes occurs at quite characteristic and stable frequencies, but that these frequencies may differ rather widely, depending upon the gene pairs involved. This might lead to, or at least is consistent with, the conclusion that each gene has a particular and well-defined locus in its chromosome. Such a conclusion is supported by the fact that crossover values can be utilized to demonstrate a definite serial order for the genes in a chromosome and even as a basis for mapping "distance" relations among linked genes.

Map Distance. The results of crosses involving linked genes provide no basis for estimating the distances between these genes in terms of standard linear measurements. However, chromosomes can be mapped effectively in terms of percentages of crossing over obtained from genetic experiments. Under this system, one unit of map distance between linked genes is the space within which 1 per cent crossing over takes place. Thus 5 per cent crossing over between genes A and B is taken to mean that they are situated 5 units of map distance apart in their chromosome.

$$A \longleftarrow 5 \text{ units} \longrightarrow B$$

The Orderly Arrangement of Genes in a Chromosome. The kind of reasoning utilized in chromosome mapping can be illustrated if we now assume that gene A, above, and a third linked gene, C, give 7 per cent crossing over, and that B and C are shown by crossover data to be 12 units apart. In such an instance, we can deduce that A is situated between C and B in its chromosome.

$$C \longleftarrow \overset{\text{7 units}}{\hspace{2cm}} \longrightarrow A \longleftarrow \overset{\text{5 units}}{\hspace{1.5cm}} \longrightarrow B$$
$$\longleftarrow \overset{\text{12 units}}{\hspace{3cm}} \longrightarrow$$

On the other hand, if B and C were to have given 2 per cent crossing over, the results would make sense only if we concluded that B lies between A and C.

$$A \longleftarrow \overset{\text{7 units}}{\hspace{2.5cm}} \longrightarrow C$$
$$\longleftarrow \overset{}{\hspace{1.5cm}} \longrightarrow B \longleftarrow \longrightarrow$$
$$\overset{\text{5 units}}{\hspace{1cm}} \qquad \overset{\text{2 units}}{\hspace{1cm}}$$

The situations just presented are hypothetical, but they have been repeatedly paralleled by real genetic situations in which the crossover relationships among three or more linked genes attest to a precise linear order of genes in chromosomes.

Double Crossing Over. Before proceeding to the analysis of actual crossover data, we need to consider a major pitfall to be avoided in the mapping of chromosomes. This pitfall is revealed by close examination of the relationship between recombinations and crossovers, which, although closely related, are not quite the same things. Recall that *recombinations* are new combinations of linked genes. *Crossing over*, the process which produces recombinations, is the interchange of corresponding segments between chromatids of homologous chromosomes. *Crossovers* are the chromatids resulting from such interchanges. Ordinarily we recognize a crossover by a recombination, and testcross data, at the same time that they give us recombination frequencies, provide a measurement of frequency of crossing over. This measurement is not always accurate.

Let us suppose that crossing over occurs more or less at random up and down the length of a chromosome. Relatively greater distance between two genes, then, should mean relatively better chances for simultaneous occurrence of two or more instances of crossing over between these genes. If two genes, A and B, are rather far apart in their chromosome, two exchanges between a pair of chromatids will have the effect shown in Figure 9-6. You

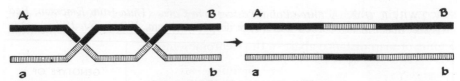

Figure 9-6. *If only two allelic pairs in the same chromosome are available as "markers," a double crossover between two chormatids is not genetically detectable, since the gene combinations produced are the same as in parental-type chromatids.*

can see that the *double crossover* chromatids do not show recombination of the marker genes, and, in fact, are indistinguishable from *noncrossover* chromatids. Since the concept of map distance is based on the number of actual physical interchanges, recombination values may give far too low an estimate of the distance between genes, if double crossing over has frequently occurred.

How may this difficulty be obviated? Double crossing over usually does not occur within distances under 5 map units, or, for certain chromosome segments, within distances up to 15 or 20 units. Therefore, data for chromosome mapping should be taken from linked gene pairs that are quite close together, so that the recombination values provide an accurate measure of crossing over.

Geneticists have found that an efficient way to obtain good recombination data is to employ so-called *three-point* testcrosses, involving three different genes situated within a relatively short segment of a chromosome. One of the advantages of the three-point testcross can be seen if you refer again to Figure 9-6. What if between genes *A* and *B* in this figure a third gene pair *C-c* were segregating? Then double crossing over between *A* and *B* might be detected genetically by the alteration of relationships of the middle allelic pair, *C-c*, as shown in Figure 9-7.

A Three-Point Testcross in Corn. Now, starting with the experimental data shown in Table 9-2, let us apply some of these principles to the specific problem of mapping genes in a chromosome. The data are testcross values from studies by G. W. Beadle, and involve the segregation of three mutant recessives in corn. These are: *v* = *virescent* seedling (of the type already described in Chap. 5); *gl* = *glossy* seedling (leaves have a particularly shiny

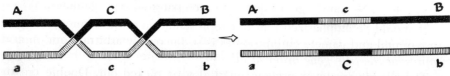

Figure 9-7. *Double crossing over between two allelic pairs is genetically detectable if a third allelic pair is situated in the segments exchanged. Under such circumstances, chromatids with new genic combinations are produced. Compare with Figure 9-6.*

TABLE 9-2. A Three-Point Testcross in Corn. (Data from Emerson, Beadle, and Fraser. Cornell Univ. Agr. Exp. Sta. Mem. 180, p. 59, 1935.)

I PHENOTYPES OF TESTCROSS PROGENY	II NUMBER OF INDIVIDUALS	III GENOTYPE OF GAMETE FROM HYBRID PARENT		
Normal	235	+	+	+
Glossy, variable sterile	62	gl	va	+
Variable sterile	40	+	va	+
Virescent, variable sterile	4	+	va	v
Virescent, glossy, variable sterile	270	gl	va	v
Glossy	7	gl	+	+
Virescent, glossy	48	gl	+	v
Virescent	60	+	+	v

appearance); and $va = variable\ sterile$ (characterized by irregular distribution of chromosomes at meiosis). In conformity with the usage of the investigator, the normal allele of each mutant gene is indicated by a "+."

Beadle's testcross data are shown in columns I and II of the table. Column III will be referred to in detail later, but its significance should already be apparent to you.

Parental and Double Crossover Types. In analyzing the progeny from a three-point testcross, it is well to work from the known toward the unknown. An obvious point of attack on the data is to identify the classes of progeny that represent parental (nonrecombination) type gametes from the hybrid parent. This parent, in the cross being considered, was of the genotype $\dfrac{+\quad +\quad +}{gl\quad va\quad v}$ having all the dominants in one chromosome and all the recessives in its homologue. Therefore, normal progeny and virescent, glossy, variable sterile individuals are the two classes among the testcross segregants that represent parental-type gametes. Reference to the table will show you that these classes include by far the largest numbers of individuals. Even if the allelic arrangement in the heterozygous parent were unknown, we might deduce, on the basis of relative frequency of types, that $+\quad +\quad +$ and $gl\quad va\quad v$ are parental-type gametes. Why?

It should be emphasized that our representation of the sequence of genes in parental and gamete chromosomes is so far purely arbitrary and *may not represent the true gene order at all.*

The double-crossover progeny may also be picked out. Double crossing over is the simultaneous occurrence of two relatively improbable events, and double-crossover gametes make up the least frequent type. Glossy plants, represented only 7 times, and virescent, variable steriles, of which there are but 4, clearly are the double-crossover progeny. Notice that when one member of a type, such as the double crossovers, is established, the other member can be written down automatically. If *gl*   +   + (glossy) represents one double-crossover type, its partner must be of complementary allelic constitution, in this case,   +   *va*   *v.*

Determining Gene Order.   Once the parental- and double-crossover type chromosomes have been established, the relative order of genes in the chromosome may be deduced. The reasoning here is based on the consequences of double crossing over as shown in Figure 9-7. Reaffirm that double crossing over in such an instance has the effect of changing the associations of the members of the middle allelic pair.

In a case of unknown gene order, therefore, if we note from three-point testcross data which allelic pair is transposed in order to make double crossover from parental-type chromosomes, that allelic pair must be situated between the other two. For ease of reference, we can write down again the parental and double-crossover types indicated by the data from the linkage study in corn.

PARENTAL TYPES				DOUBLE CROSSOVERS		
+	+	+		*gl*	+	+
gl	*va*	*v*		+	*va*	*v*

You can now see that if *gl* and its wild-type allele are transposed in their allelic associations, double crossovers can be obtained from parental types. Therefore, in the actual linear order of genes in the chromosome, *gl* must be situated between *va* and *v*. The heterozygous parent in the testcross can now be designated correctly, both for gene order and association of alleles in the homologous chromosomes, as follows:

$$\frac{+\quad\quad+\quad\quad+}{v\quad\quad gl\quad\quad va}$$

If we diagram double crossing over between chromatids of the parental type as written correctly, it is readily demonstrated that the gametic types so derived correspond to those indicated by the data from the testcross.

Looking at the correct hybrid parental type shown at the left above, you will observe that a single crossing over between the loci of *v* and *gl* gives rise to chromatids *v*   +   + and +   *gl*   *va* . This region of the chromosome between *v* and *gl* may be called, for convenience, Region I.

Also, single crossing over between *gl* and *va* gives rise to chromatids that are
+   +   *va* and *v*   *gl*   + . These chromatids may be said
to result from crossing over in Region II. According to genetic convention,
crossover regions are arbitrarily designated by numbers in sequence, with I
indicating the interval between the first two genes at the left, as the chromatid or chromosome is represented.

We are now in a position to resummarize our three-point testcross data
in meaningful fashion. Showing gametic frequencies of different chromosome types, the data are:

+	+	+	235	parental types
v	*gl*	*va*	270	
+	*gl*	+	7	double crossover types
v	+	*va*	4	
v	+	+	60	single crossovers, Region I
+	*gl*	*va*	62	
+	+	*va*	40	single crossovers, Region II
v	*gl*	+	48	
	Total		726	

Map Distance. Distances in this chromosome map under construction
may be computed in the usual way. You will remember that crossover frequencies can be translated directly into units of map distance. In the present
instance, crossing over in Region I is represented by gametes of the following chromosome types, which have derived from chromatids of the heterozygous parent.

v	+	+	60
+	*gl*	*va*	62
+	*gl*	+	7
v	+	*va*	4
	Total		133

Out of 726 chromosomes recovered in gametes, 133 represent interchanges
of chromatid material between the loci *v* and *gl*. One hundred thirty-three
is 18.3 per cent of 726. The map distance between *v* and *gl* is 18.3 units.

Similarly, crossing over between the loci of *gl* and *va* is represented by
these types:

+	+	*va*	40
v	*gl*	+	48
+	*gl*	+	7
v	+	*va*	4
Total			99

The instances of crossing over in Region II are 99 in 726 chromatids, or 13.6 per cent of the total. The map distance between *gl* and *va* is 13.6 units. The segment of chromosome we have charted may be represented as:

v		*gl*		*va*
	18.3 units		13.6 units	

The concept of map distance is based on total frequency of crossing over in a region of a chromosome. In calculating map distances from three-point testcross data, do not forget to add the numbers of double crossovers to each of the sets of single crossover figures. Remember that each instance of double crossing over represents single crossing over in both Regions I and II. If double crossovers are neglected in the computation of map distance, the computed values will indicate smaller distances than are actually shown by the genetic results.

Interference and Coincidence. Once a portion of a chromosome map is established, it provides the geneticist with what amounts to a table of rather specific probability values. For instance, the map distance of 18.3 units between *v* and *gl* really means that we can expect 18.3 per cent of gametes to represent crossing over between the loci of these genes. The value 13.6 for distance between *gl* and *va* has similar significance.

If, in the portion of a corn chromosome we have just mapped, crossing over in Region I is independent of crossing over in Region II, the probability of simultaneous crossing over in the two regions can be arrived at by applying a familiar principle which we first encountered in Chapter 3.

> When two events are independent, the probability of their simultaneous occurrence is the product of their separate probabilities.

In other words, if crossing over in the two regions is independent, $0.183 \times 0.136 = 0.025 = 2.5$ per cent double crossovers might be expected. Actually only $\frac{11}{726} = 1.5$ per cent doubles occurred.

In a single instance, a deficiency in the expected number of double crossovers might not worry us very much, since deviations from the expected are to be looked for simply as the effects of chance. It is fairly characteristic, however, that double crossovers do not appear as often as the frequency of crossing over in individual regions might lead us to expect. This seems to mean that once crossing over occurs the probability of another crossing over in an adjacent region is reduced. The phenomenon is called *interference*.

Interference may vary from one portion of a chromosome to another, and also among different chromosomes. For a chromosome map to function with all possible effectiveness, as a table of probabilities, interference in various portions of the map needs to be designated. Strengths of interference are commonly summarized as *coefficients of coincidence*. These are no more than ratios between observed and expected frequencies of double crossing over, and are calculated as $\dfrac{\text{actual frequency of doubles}}{\text{expected frequency of doubles}}$. For the portion of the chromosome map of corn we have been studying, the coincidence can be computed as $\dfrac{1.5}{2.5} = 0.6$.

Coincidence varies inversely as interference varies, and you may expect coincidence values to vary from 0 to 1. Complete interference gives a coincidence value of 0; a coincidence of 1 indicates no interference whatsoever.

How to Make Predictions from Chromosome Maps. Making predictions as to a segregating progeny on the basis of an established chromosome map is essentially the mapping process in reverse. Suppose that we have a portion of a chromosome map reading $a \qquad\qquad 20 \qquad\qquad b \quad 10 \quad c$, with the coincidence for that portion of the chromosome being 0.5. Out of 1000 individuals in a progeny, what proportions of phenotypes could be expected after the testcross $\dfrac{A \ B \ C}{a \ b \ c} \times \dfrac{a \ b \ c}{a \ b \ c}$?

First of all, what phenotypes may be expected in the progeny, and how do they relate to crossing over? Clearly, ABC and abc are parental types, and AbC and aBc would be double crossovers. Single crossing over in Region I would give rise to gametes detected as phenotypes Abc and aBC. Crossing over in Region II would give rise to individuals ABc and abC.

Now let us consider the frequencies with which the various phenotypes should occur. How many double crossovers may be expected? If there were no interference, double crossovers should occur $0.10 \times 0.20 = 0.02$ or 2 per cent of the time. The coincidence, however, is 0.5, which means that our prediction as to doubles must be modified to a figure half that which would occur if crossing over were at random. Half of 2 per cent is 1 per cent, so $1000 \times 0.01 = 10$ double crossovers can be predicted on the basis of the map. Dividing these 10 equally among the two types of double crossover progeny gives 5 of each.

How many crossovers of the Region I type? The map says 20 per cent total crossing over between a and b, which is 200 out of 1000 gametes. Of the 200, however, 10 are detected as double crossovers. Therefore, $200 - 10 = 190$ are to be expected as singles. This leaves 95 apiece for each of the Region I type single crossovers.

How many crossovers of the Region II type? Ten per cent total crossing over is recorded for the region b to c. This means crossing over in this region in 100 out of 1000 gametes. Again, 10 of the 100 gametes show up as double crossovers, leaving 90 as singles between b and c. Parentals may be arrived at by subtracting the sum of all other types from the total, in this case 1000, used as a basis for prediction. The completed prediction follows:

Parental Types	ABC	355
	abc	355
Region I Singles	aBC	95
	Abc	95
Region II Singles	abC	45
	ABc	45
Doubles	AbC	5
	aBc	5
		1000

Chromosome Mapping on an Extensive Scale.

Linkage Groups. A gene in a given chromosome shows linkage relations with other genes in the same chromosome but is inherited independently of genes in other chromosomes. As a result, each gene is the member of some one *linkage group,* composed of numbers of genes that are bound together by the physical continuity of a chromosome. The number of linkage groups for members of a particular species corresponds to the number of different kinds of chromosomes (the haploid number) characteristic of the species. Thus *Drosophila melanogaster* has a haploid number of 4, and has 4 linkage groups. Its relative *D. virilis* has 6 different kinds of chromosomes; 6 linkage groups are known for this species. Correspondingly, corn, with a haploid chromosome number of 10, has been found to have 10 different linkage groups. We can expect that some day 24 linkage groups will be identified in man. A chromosome map for all the genes of an organism is, then, a multipartite sort of chart, with as many parts as there are different kinds of chromosomes in the organism.

Extending Three-Point Testcross Data. Analysis of the results of a single three-point testcross obviously provides only a very small start toward mapping a chromosome. Even when four, five, or more points are studied at one time in a testcross—and this is possible if stocks of appropriate genotype are available—the mapping process is slow and laborious. However, as numerous testcrosses involving different genes in a chromosome are analyzed, and their results correlated on the basis of overlapping loci involved, an outline map of the chromosome takes shape in the form of an established sequence of known genes. Most chromosome maps are being added to and revised rather frequently, as new genes come to the attention of investigators and are fitted into place, and as additional data are brought to bear on relationships already studied.

Length of Individual Chromosome Maps. Different chromosomes which have been mapped differ as to map units of total length. This is expected, since there are wide differences in the physical size of chromosomes.

CHROMOSOME 1				CHROMOSOME 2				CHROMOSOME 3			
0.0	y	(yellow)	B	0.0	net	(net)	V	0.0	ru	(roughoid)	E
0.0+	ac	(achaete)	H	0.0	al	(aristaless)	B	0.2	ve	(veinlet)	V
0.0+	sc	(scute)	H	0.3	ds	(dachsous)	W	19.2	jv	(javelin)	H
0.8	pn	(prune)	E	1.3	S	(Star)	E	25.0±	be-3	(benign tumor	
0.9	gt	(giant)	B	6.0±	E-S	(Enhancer of				in 3)	B
1.5	w	(white)	E			Star)	E	26.0	se	(sepia)	E
3.0±	fa	(facet)	E	11.0	ed	(echinoid)	E	26.5	h	(hairy)	H
5.5	ec	(echinus)	E	13.0	dp	(dumpy)	W	37.5	app	(approx-	
6.9	bi	(bifid)	V	16.0	Sk	(Streak)	B			imated)	V
7.5	rb	(ruby)	E	16.5	cl	(clot)	E	40.4+	D	(Dichaete)	W
13.7	cv	(crossvein-		31.0	d	(dachs)	B	44.0	st	(scarlet)	E
		less)	V	41.0	J	(Jammed)	W	47.0	in	(inturned)	H
15.0	rux	(roughex)	E	44.0	ab	(abrupt)	V	48.0	p	(pink)	E
18.9	cm	(carmine)	E	48.5	b	(black)	B	48.7	by	(blistery)	W
20.0	ct	(cut)	W	48.7	j	(jaunty)	W	50.0	cu	(curled)	W
21.0	sn	(singed)	H	50.0	el	(elbow)	W	52.0	kar	(karmoisin)	E
27.7	lz	(lozenge)	E	54.5	pr	(purple)	E	58.5	ss	(spineless)	H
32.8	ras	(raspberry)	E	54.7±	rh	(roughish)	E	58.8	bx	(bithorax)	B
33.0	v	(vermilion)	E	54.9	Jag	(Jagged)	W	62.0	sr	(stripe)	B
36.1	m	(miniature)	W	55.0±	tri	(trident)	B	63.1	gl	(glass)	E
36.2	dy	(dusky)	W	55.1	stw	(straw)	B	69.5	H	(Hairless)	H
41.9	wy	(wavy)	W	57.1	buo	(burnt		70.7	e	(ebony)	B
44.4	g	(garnet)	E			orange)	E	88.0±	mah	(mahogany)	E
45.2	na	(narrow		57.5	cn	(cinnabar)	E	91.1	ro	(rough)	E
		abdomen)	B	65.0±	Bkd	(Blackoid)	B	93.8	Bd	(Beaded)	W
51.6	Bg	(Bag)	W	67.0	vg	(vestigial)	W	100.7	ca	(claret)	E
56.7	f	(forked)	H	72.0	L	(Lobe)	E				
57.0	B	(Bar)	E	75.5	c	(curved)	W		CHROMOSOME 4		
59.4	Bx	(Beadex)	W	93.3	hy	(humpy)	B	0.0	ci	(cubitus inter-	
59.5	fu	(fused)	V	100.5	px	(plexus)	V			ruptus)	V
62.5	car	(carnation)	E	104.5	bw	(brown)	E	0.2	gvl	(grooveless)	B
64.0	sw	(short-wing)	W	107.0	sp	(speck)	B	1.4	bt	(bent)	W
66.0	bb	(bobbed)	H	107.4	ba	(balloon)	W	2.0	ey	(eyeless)	E
								3.0	sv	(shaven)	H

Figure 9-8. *Map distance relationships for certain genes of* Drosophila melanogaster. *The capital letter to the right of the name of each mutant type designates the part of the Drosophila primarily affected by the mutant gene—B, body; E, eyes; H, bristles or hairs; V, wing venation; W, wings. The figures at the left specify the locus of each gene listed. The symbols* +, −, *or* ± *indicate uncertainties as to the position of the gene. (Information for chromosomes 1, 2, and 3 from Bridges and Brehme, Carnegie Inst. Wash. Pub. No. 552, 1944; information for chromosome 4 from Sturtevant, Proc. Nat. Acad. Sci., 37:407, 1951.)*

Whether the total length of any chromosome has yet been represented in a genetic map is not known, since it is difficult to be certain that the two terminal loci for any given chromosome have yet been identified. Additional genes are continually being found, even in the organisms that are best

CHROMOSOME 1

0	sr	(striate leaves)
15	ga_6	(gametophyte factor)
25	ms_{17}	(male sterile)
27	ts_2	(tassel seed)
28	P	(Pericarp color)
30	zl	(zygotic lethal)
53	as	(asynapsis)
59	hm	(Helminthosporium resistance)
75	br	(brachytic plant)
79	vg	(vestigial glumes)
80	f_1	(fine striped leaves)
102	an_1	(anther ear)
123	kn	(knotted leaf)
129	gs_1	(green striped leaves)
152	Ts_6	(Tassel seed-6)
156	bm_2	(brown midrib)

CHROMOSOME 2

0	ws_3	(white sheath)
4	al^*	(albescent)
11	lg_1	(liguleless)
30	gl_2	(glossy leaves)
49	B	(Anthocyanin booster)
56	sk	(silkless)
68	fl_1	(floury endosperm)
74	ts_1	(tassel seed)
83	v_4	(virescent)
128	Ch	(Chocolate pericarp)

CHROMOSOME 3

0	cr_1	(crinkly leaves)
18	d_1	(dwarf plant)
32	rt	(rootless)
38	Lg_3^*	(Liguleless leaf-3)

40	Rg	(Ragged leaves)
47	ts_4	(tassel seed-4)
64	ba_1	(barren stalk)
75	na_1	(nana plant)
103	a_1	(anthocyanin)
115	et	(etched aleurone)
121	ga_7	(gametophyte factor)

CHROMOSOME 4

0	de_1	(defective seed)
35	Ga_1	(Gametophyte factor)
56	Ts_5	(Tassel seed-5)
66	sp_1	(small pollen)
71	su_1	(sugary endosperm)
74	de_{16}	(defective endosperm)
84	zb_6	(zebra stripe)
100	Tu	(Tunicate)
105	j_2	(japonica stripe)
111	gl_3	(glossy leaves)

CHROMOSOME 5

0	a_2	(anthocyanin)
6	bm	(brown midrib)
7	bt_1	(brittle endosperm)
10	v_3	(virescent)
12	bv	(brevis plant)
31	pr	(red aleurone)
40	ys_1	(yellow stripe)
72	v_2	(virescent)

CHROMOSOME 6

0	po	(polymitotic)
13	Y	(Yellow endosperm)
33	pg	(pale green)
44	Pl	(Purple plant color)
45	Bh	(Blotched aleurone)
54	sm	(salmon silk color)

64	py	(pigmy plant)

CHROMOSOME 7

0	o_2	(opaque endosperm)
4	in	(intensifier)
8	v_5	(virescent)
22	ra_1	(ramosa ear)
26	gl_1	(glossy leaves)
36	Tp	(Teopod)
40	sl	(slashed leaves)
42	ij	(iojap stripe)
60	Bn	(Brown aleurone)
96	bd	(branched silkless)

CHROMOSOME 8

0	v_{16}	(virescent)
14	ms_8	(male sterile)
28	j_1	(japonica stripe)

CHROMOSOME 9

0	Dt	(Dotted)
7	yg_2	(yellow green)
26	C	(Aleurone color)
29	sh	(shrunken endosperm)
31	bz	(bronze anthocyanin color)
44	bp	(brown pericarp)
59	wx	(waxy endosperm)
71	v_1	(virescent)

CHROMOSOME 10

0	Rp	(Resistance to Puccinia)
16	Og	(Old gold stripe)
28	li	(lineate stripe)
38	l_8	(luteus)
43	g_1	(golden plant)
57	R	(Anthocyanin)

* The location of genes marked with the asterisk is only approximate.

Figure 9-9. *Map distance relationships for certain genes of corn.* (*After Rhoades,* J. Heredity, *41:64, 1950.*)

known genetically. However, certain chromosomes, already mapped, have proved to be over 100 units in length. In the map of the second chromosome of *D. melanogaster*, the genes for *net* veins and *speck* wings are designated as being 107 map units apart.

Chromosome Maps for Specific Organisms. Chromosome maps are available for a number of plants and animals, including several Drosophila species, corn, chickens, peas, tomatoes, and Neurospora. Of these, maps for *D. melanogaster* and corn may be used to represent those which are most thoroughly worked out. Portions of the maps are shown in Figures 9-8 and 9-9.

The Significance of Chromosome Maps. What good are chromosome maps? How seriously should we take them? One of the most meaningful answers to these questions came from T. H. Morgan, who with his co-workers spearheaded the Drosophila research that forms the basis for so much of our present understanding of genetics. In his opinion, the fundamental significance of chromosome mapping is the opportunity for "giving evidence as to the arrangement of the fundamental units of heredity, the genes, into systems of a higher order, the chromosomes." A great deal of our insight into the relationships of genes to chromosomes has come out of the development and application of mapping procedures.

Chromosome maps also have an immediately useful aspect. Occasions frequently arise when it is desirable to introduce particular combinations of genes into certain plants or animals. Linkage may strongly affect the probability of obtaining a given combination out of a population of segregants. This makes it desirable that the geneticist have a basis for predicting the probabilities of obtaining such genotypes. Chromosome maps furnish this kind of basis for prediction, and hence serve as guides to experimentation. For example, chromosome maps may be useful in helping a geneticist plan how large an experimental population need be.

Map distances based on frequencies of crossing over should not necessarily be taken to bear a direct and fixed relation to physical linear distance. In Drosophila, for example, frequency of crossing over seems to be affected by temperature, age of the mother flies, and by other environmental factors. Different chromosomes and various regions in the same chromosome may also show variations in frequency of crossing over. Therefore, the same physical distance may be represented by different frequencies of crossing over. Likewise, similar frequencies of crossing over may represent somewhat different physical distances. These facts emphasize that conditions for making crosses for mapping purposes need to be carefully controlled and standardized.

An additional complication in interpreting the quantitative relationships among recombination and crossing over and map distance has recently emerged. It now appears, at least in Drosophila, that crossing over may take place during mitosis in the nuclei of gonial cells. If gonial crossing over occurs frequently, a number of consequences and implications follow. Important among such consequences would be a lack of constant proportionality between recombinations and instances of crossing over.

Keys to the Significance of This Chapter

Genes situated in the same chromosome tend to be inherited in blocks rather than to assort independently. This is the phenomenon of *linkage*.

Linkages are broken when homologous chromatids exchange corresponding parts at meiosis, a process called *crossing over*. It is through crossing over that *recombinations* among linked genes occur.

Frequencies of crossing over between particular gene loci can be used as the basis for mapping chromosomes, with these frequencies corresponding to units of map distance between the genes.

The analysis of frequencies of crossing over proves that the different genes within a chromosome are situated in a definite serial order and that their loci are fixed. Thus chromosome mapping reveals a high degree of organization in the germ plasm, which is of extreme importance in our understanding of genetic systems.

Extensive chromosome maps for a number of organisms attest to the general occurrence of this kind of organization of germ plasm.

Chromosome maps may be used as probability tables for the quantitative prediction of results to be obtained from crosses involving linked genes that have been mapped.

References

Bridges, C. B., and Brehme, K. S., "The Mutants of *Drosophila melanogaster*." *Carnegie Inst. Wash. Pub.* 552, 1944. (An extensive compilation of the descriptions of Drosophila mutants. Chromosome maps are found on pp. 238–252.)

Cooper, K. W., "The Cytogenetics of Meiosis in Drosophila. Mitotic and Meiotic Autosomal Chiasmata without Crossing over in the Male." *J. Morphol.*, 84:81–122, 1949. (Important paper bearing on the subject of chiasmata and crossing over.)

Creighton, H. B., and McClintock, B., "A Correlation of Cytological and Genetical Crossing Over in *Zea mays*." *Proc. Nat. Acad. Sci.*, 17:492–497, 1931. (A landmark in experimental genetics.)

Emerson, R. A., Beadle, G. W., and Fraser, A. C., "A Summary of Linkage Studies in Maize." *Cornell Univ. Agr. Exp. Sta. Mem. No. 180*, 1935. (Gives a brief description of many of the known genes in corn, summarizes linkage data to 1935, and presents a chromosome map.)

Houlahan, M. B., Beadle, G. W., and Calhoun, H. G., "Linkage Studies with Biochemical Mutants of *Neurospora crassa*." *Genetics*, 34:493–507, 1949. (Presents data which have enabled at least 35 of the gene loci of Neurospora to be placed into five different linkage groups.)

Hutt, F. B., and Lamoreux, W. F., "Genetics of the Fowl: II—A Linkage Map for Six Chromosomes." *J. Heredity*, 31:231–235, 1940. (Gives a pictorially illustrated chromosome map showing approximate locations of 21 genes in six linkage groups of the fowl.)

Immer, F. R., "Formulae and Tables for Calculating Linkage Intensities." *Genetics*, 15:81–98, 1930. (The calculation of linkage intensities from F_2 data.)

————, and Henderson, M. T., "Linkage Studies in Barley." *Genetics*, 28:419–440, 1943. (Gives an analysis of data involving linked genes in barley, and presents tables which facilitate the calculation of recombination frequencies from F_2 data.)

Lindegren, C. C., "The Genetics of Neurospora—III. Pure Bred Stocks and Crossing-Over in *N. crassa*." *Bull. Torrey Botan. Club*, 60:133–154, 1933. (Analysis of linkage and crossing over in Neurospora. Pages 145 and 146 discuss the relationship of frequency of second-division segregation to map distance from the centromere.)

MacArthur, J. W., "Linkage Groups in the Tomato." *J. Genetics*, 29:123–133, 1934. (Presents a tentative chromosome map for the tomato, giving approximate locations for 20 genes in ten of the twelve pairs of chromosomes.)

Mather, K., *The Measurement of Linkage in Heredity*. New York: Chem. Pub. Co. of N. Y., Inc., 1938. (A general treatment of problems of measuring linkage.)

Morgan, T. H., *The Theory of the Gene*. New Haven: Yale University Press, 1926. (A classic by a geneticist who received a Nobel prize for his work. The first chapter is pertinent here. Note the "theory of the gene" formulated on p. 25.)

Owen, A. R. G., "The Theory of Genetical Recombination." *Advances in Genetics*, 3:117–157, 1950. (Suitable for the student who is mathematically inclined.)

Stern, C., "Somatic Crossing Over and Segregation in *Drosophila melanogaster*." *Genetics*, 21:625–730, 1936. (A very extensive analysis of mosaic formation in Drosophila resulting from somatic crossing over.)

Warren, D. C., "Linkage Relations of Autosomal Factors in the Fowl." *Genetics*, 34:333–350, 1949. (Adds valuable data to those presented in the reference by Hutt and Lamoreux.)

Whittinghill, M., "Consequences of Crossing Over in Oögonial Cells." *Genetics*, 35:38–43, 1950. (The possible effects of premeiotic crossing over in gonial cells upon recombination phenotypes. Discussion accompanied by a useful diagram.)

Questions and Problems

9-' 1. What do the following terms signify?

chromosome map
coincidence
coupling
crossing over
crossovers
double crossing over
double crossover chromatid
gonial crossing over

independent assortment
interference
linkage
locus
map distance
parental type gamete
recombinations
repulsion
three-point testcross

9- 2.   In your study of genetics thus far, what evidence has been presented that genes are situated in chromosomes?

9- 3.   Why has considerable time and effort been spent in the mapping of chromosomes?

9- 4.   How do undetected double crossovers affect estimates of map distance? Explain.

9- 5.   What are the cytological and genetic conditions necessary for a straightforward demonstration that the recombination of linked genes results from a physical interchange of appropriate parts of homologous chromosomes?

9- 6.   In tomatoes, round fruit shape (*O*) is dominant over elongate (*o*), and smooth fruit skin (*P*) is dominant over peach (*p*). Testcrosses of F₁ individuals heterozygous for these pairs of alleles gave the following results, reported by MacArthur:

smooth, round	smooth, long	peach, round	peach, long
12	123	133	12

In the F₁, were the two pairs of alleles linked in the coupling or the repulsion phase? Calculate the percentage of recombination.

9- 7.   In the fowl, gene S determines silver-colored plumage; its recessive allele *s* determines gold. Gene *Sl* determines slow feathering; its allele *sl* determines rapid feathering. Both allelic pairs are sex-linked. D. C. Warren crossed a Brown Leghorn ♂ (gold plumage, rapid feathering) with Silver Penciled Rock ♀♀ (silver plumage, slow feathering). F₁ ♂♂ were mated to ♀♀ carrying the recessive alleles of both genes. Among the progeny of this cross were:

	gold, rapid	silver, rapid	gold, slow	silver, slow
♀♀	156	28	7	117
♂♂	127	40	7	94

Diagram the crosses made by Warren and designate crossover and noncrossover types among the testcross progeny. What is the percentage of recombination?

9- 8.   In Neurospora, the frequency of second-division segregations of a gene is a function of the distance between the gene and the centromere of its chromosome. Explain this statement.

9- 9.   In order to calculate *map distance* between gene and centromere in Neurospora it is necessary to divide the percentage of second-division segregations by two, if the map units are to be comparable to those utilized, for example, in chromosome maps of Drosophila. Why is the division by two necessary? (If you are unable to reason out the answer, look up the reference to Lindegren at the end of this chapter.)

9-10.   A summary of data revealing segregation of the mating type alleles, *A* and *a*, in Neurospora has been made by Barratt and Garnjobst. Out of 755 asci analyzed, 117 second-division segregations have been observed. Calculate the percentage of second-division segregations and the distance of the mating type locus from the centromere of its chromosome.

9-11.   Two mutant genes (*ag* and *thi*) in Neurospora are known to interfere, respectively, with the syntheses of the amino acid arginine and the vitamin thiamine. After a cross in which these genes were segregating, the following spore arrangements were found in the frequencies noted. (Only one member of each pair of spores is indicated.)

Pair 1	Pair 2	Pair 3	Pair 4	
ag thi	*ag thi*	+ +	+ +	42
+ *thi*	+ *thi*	*ag* +	*ag* +	40
+ +	+ +	*ag thi*	*ag thi*	39
ag +	*ag* +	+ *thi*	+ *thi*	42

How are the *ag* and *thi* genes located in the chromosomes with respect to their centromeres and with respect to each other?

9-12. Suppose that in a Neurospora cross genes x and y are segregating. If the following spore arrangements were found, what would you conclude as to the locations of x and y?

+ +	+ +	x y	x y	57
x y	x y	+ +	+ +	60

9-13. Bridges and Morgan report a series of crosses in Drosophila beginning with a mating between a *dachs* ♂ and a *black* ♀. In F_2 there were obtained 186 wild type, 71 dachs, 93 black, and 0 dachs, black. Do these results indicate that the loci of genes d and b are very closely linked? Explain your answer.

9-14. *Curled wings* (*cu*) and *spineless bristles* (*ss*) are autosomal recessive characters in Drosophila. The genes giving rise to these characters are both in chromosome 3. Starting with a wild-type ♀ and a curled, spineless ♂, prepare a diagram showing parents and progenies through an F_2 generation. Remember that there is no crossing over in male Drosophila.

9-15. Suppose that after the crosses indicated in the preceding question, the following were obtained in F_2:

wild	292
curled	9
curled, spineless	92
spineless	7
	400

Remembering again the special circumstance of no crossing over in male Drosophila, is there some reasonably straightforward way in which you can arrive at an estimate of the map distance between *cu* and *ss*? Explain your method and calculate the distance.

9-16. Assume in Drosophila three pairs of alleles, +/x, +/y, and +/z. As shown by the symbols, each mutant gene is recessive to its wild-type allele. A cross between ♀♀ heterozygous at these three loci and wild-type ♂♂ gives the following results:

♀♀:	+ + +	1010
♂♂:	+ + +	30
	+ + z	32
	+ y +	441
	+ y z	1
	x + +	0
	x + z	430
	x y +	27
	x y z	39

How were members of the allelic pairs distributed in the members of the appropriate chromosome pair of the heterozygous ♀♀? What is the sequence of these linked genes in their chromosome? Calculate the map distances between the genes and the coefficient of coincidence. In what chromosome of Drosophila are these genes carried?

9-17. In Drosophila, assume three pairs of alleles, $+/n$, $+/o$, and $+/p$. Genes n, o, and p are all recessives and sex-linked. They occur in the order n-o-p in the X-chromosome, with n being 12 map units from o, and o being 10 units from p. The coefficient of coincidence for this region of the X-chromosome is 0.5. From a cross between ♀♀ of the genotype $\dfrac{+\ +\ p}{n\ o\ +}$ and wild-type ♂♂, predict the kinds and frequencies of phenotypes that would be expected to occur in a progeny of 2000 individuals.

9-18. In corn, the following allelic pairs have been identified in chromosome 3:

$+/b$ = plant color booster *vs.* nonbooster
$+/lg$ = liguled *vs.* liguleless
$+/v$ = green plant *vs.* virescent

A testcross involving triple recessives and F_1 plants heterozygous for the three gene pairs gave in the progeny the following phenotypes:

+	v	lg	305
b	+	lg	128
b	v	lg	18
+	+	lg	74
b	v	+	66
+	+	+	22
+	v	+	112
b	+	+	275
			1000

Give the gene sequence, the map distances between genes, and the coefficient of coincidence.

9-19. In corn, the genes *an* (*anther ear*), *br* (*brachytic*), and *f* (*fine stripe*) are all in chromosome 1. From the data of R. A. Emerson, summarized below, determine the sequence of genes in their chromosome, the map distances, and the genotypes of the homozygous parents used to make the heterozygote.

Testcross Progeny

+	+	+	88
+	+	f	21
+	br	+	2
+	br	f	339
an	+	+	355
an	+	f	2
an	br	+	17
an	br	f	55
			879

9-20. *Curved wing* and *brown eye* are recessive characters in Drosophila. The genes for these characters are located about 30 units apart in chromosome 2. Suppose that you wish to obtain a double mutant stock curved, brown. You have available for breeding purposes a single mutant stock having brown eyes, and a double mutant stock homozygous for curved and also true-breeding for *yellow body*, a sex-linked recessive.

Outline the steps you would take in obtaining as efficiently as possible a true-breeding stock for curved wings and brown eyes.

For each step show the genotypes of the parents to be used in the cross, the genotypes of progeny that will be useful in succeeding steps, and the probability of obtaining such progeny.

9-21. In Figure 7-11 (p. 122), it is suggested that, of the four sperm produced by a primary spermatocyte in a trihybrid, two are alike and of one kind, and the other two are alike and of another kind. Show how a single exchange between the locus of *a* and the centromere, for example, would result in the formation of four kinds of sperm from a single primary spermatocyte.

CHAPTER 10

Chromosomal Aberrations and Position Effects

ON VIEWING chromosomes for the first time, the student frequently remains unimpressed. This is because chromosomes are usually seen as inert things—fixed, artificially colored, and laid out motionless on a microscope slide. Actually an amazing amount of genetic and cytogenetic knowledge has come out of studies of "dead" material of this kind. But to think of chromosomes correctly, it is necessary to realize that living chromosomes are the quintessence of biological dynamism. As carriers of genes, chromosomes are the seat of constant and myriad biochemical activity—activity which is the basis of life. The precise movements of chromosomes at mitosis and meiosis and their astonishing powers of reproduction are other evidences of extreme vitality. In some ways, we get an even more striking picture of the liveliness of chromosomes when we consider them in their aberrant behavior. Chromosomes do not always behave according to rule. Their irregular behavior may have important genetic results for organisms, and may help us to appreciate better the meaning and consequences of their usual, predictable action.

Breakage-Fusion-Bridge Cycles. Chromosomes are structures of definite organization. They are not unchangeable, however, and through various means they may be broken and their normal structure disrupted. X-rays, atomic radiations, and various chemicals are among the agents that can cause breaks in chromosomes. Breaks also sometimes occur under natural conditions. Some of these breaks may be attributed to mechanical accidents in the usual system of chromosome reduplication and distribution. In many cases the origin of breakage is as yet unknown. As an introduction to the exceptional behavior of chromosomes, let us see how a single deviation from the normal can give rise to a whole series of unusual cytological events.

In the gametophyte and endosperm of corn, ends of chromosomes that have recently been broken behave as though they were "sticky," as is shown by their tendency to adhere to one another. Extensive studies of broken chromosomes in corn have been made by McClintock. She finds that follow-

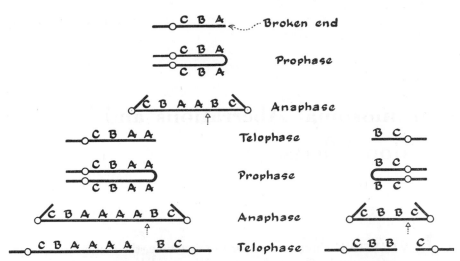

Figure 10-1. A breakage-fusion-bridge cycle in corn. The chromosome at the top has been recently broken, near gene A. (From McClintock, Genetics, **26**:235, 1941.)

ing reduplication of a broken chromosome the two sister chromatids may adhere at the point of previous breakage. This situation and some of its possible consequences are diagrammed in Figure 10-1. You will note that the fused sister chromatids are unable to separate readily. In effect, they constitute a single chromatid with two centromeres, a *dicentric* chromatid. As the centromeres move to opposite poles at anaphase, the dicentric chromatid stretches out, forming a chromatin bridge from one pole toward the other. This bridge eventually breaks, but the break does not always occur at the point of previous fusion. Therefore, chromosomes may be formed which show duplications or deficiencies with respect to an original type.

Thus if an original chromosome is —o——$\frac{C\ B\ A}{}$——, the type —o——$\frac{C\ B\ A\ A}{}$ is a *duplication* type, since region A is twice represented. A type —o——$\frac{C\ B}{}$ is a *deficiency*, since region A is absent.

When a chromosome bridge such as we have described breaks, perhaps as the result of tension caused by the movements of the centromeres of the dicentric chromatid, two new broken ends are provided. Each of these has the same qualities of adhesiveness which gave rise to the original fusion. This situation permits a repetition, in cyclic series, of more events like those diagrammed in Figure 10-1. Spontaneous production of chromosome aberrations through breakage-fusion-bridge cycles may occur in this manner for some time. But when a broken chromosome is introduced into the sporophytic generation, such cycles cease, for in the zygote the broken ends heal.

The Visual Detection of Chromosomal Aberrations. Not all chromo-

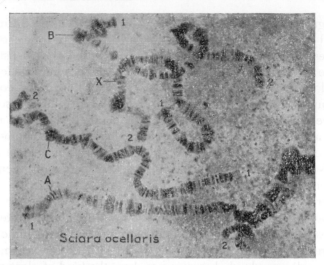

Figure 10-2. *The salivary gland chromosomes of fungus flies show distinct longitudinal differentation, so that particular chromosomes and particular parts of chromosomes are readily identified. The entire chromosome complement of a salivary gland cell is shown, with the sex chromosome being labelled X, and the autosomes A, B, and C. The different ends of each chromosome are designated 1 and 2.* (*Courtesy of C. W. Metz,* J. Heredity, 23:176, 1935.)

somes are equally well suited for detailed microscopic examination, at least by methods presently available. The chromosomes of corn are exceptionally favorable cytological material. Especially in the first prophase of meiosis, knobs, chromomeres, and other distinguishing features of the chromosomes can be clearly observed, and they stand out as landmarks for the orientation of the cytologist. For particular chromosomes, the relative sizes and spacing of these landmarks provide constant patterns in linear arrangement. Absence or reduplication of chromomeres, or their unusual arrangement as compared to the typical topography of a particular chromosome, is visible evidence of aberration. Probably the chromosomes of all organisms possess longitudinal differentiation in the sense that we have described it for the chromosomes of corn. But the suitability of an organism for cytological investigation depends rather directly on the ease of detecting visually the longitudinal differentiation of its chromosomes.

Salivary Gland Chromosomes. Chromosomes at meiosis in Drosophila happen to be small and difficult to work with. Despite this fact, which once was discouraging to genetic investigators, Drosophila provides extraordinary facilities for cytological study. Nuclei of cells in the salivary glands of larvae of Drosophila and other Dipterans have remarkably large chromosomes with distinct longitudinal differentiation. In fact, these salivary gland chromosomes may be up to 200 times the size of corresponding chromosomes at meiosis or in the nuclei of ordinary somatic cells.

A photograph of salivary gland chromosomes of Sciara (a fungus fly) is reproduced in Figure 10-2. Note particularly the appearance of the *cross bands*. These are very striking when stained with basic fuchsin or other appropriate dyes, but are also obvious in unstained living nuclei. The salivary gland chromosomes are thought to be multiple units, composed of many reduplicated chromonemata in close longitudinal association. A widely accepted interpretation of the cross bands is that they represent a fusion, or at least a juxtaposition, of corresponding chromomeres of the multiplied chromonemata. In any case, for a given chromosome the various cross bands show a constancy of relative size and spatial arrangement which permits them to serve as reliable landmarks.

A further advantage of the salivary gland chromosomes for cytological study is that they appear constantly to be in a prophaselike state. For practical purposes, this means that the chromosomes are at all times in a condition appropriate for effective staining and detailed observation. Moreover, homologous salivary gland chromosomes show the kind of close pairing you have learned to associate with the zygotene stage of meiosis. Differences between the homologous chromosomes, therefore, become relatively easy to detect. The size of salivary gland chromosomes together with the fact that they show *somatic pairing* have facilitated the explanation of certain puzzling phenomena characteristic of aberrant chromosomes at meiosis.

Deficiencies

Cytological Properties of Deficiencies.   The ease of detection of a deficiency depends largely on how obvious in a corresponding normal chromosome are the chromomeres, knobs, or other landmarks that may be missing in the aberrant member. Long deficiencies are, of course, likely to be more readily detectable than are short ones. The cytologist is aided in finding deficiencies and in establishing their length by the very strong tendency of pairing chromosomes to achieve an exact apposition of homologous parts. In *deficiency heterozygotes,* where one member of a pair of homologues is

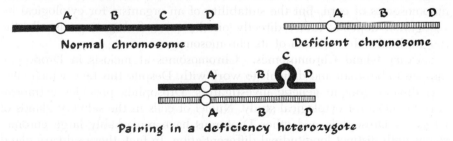

Figure 10-3. *In this deficiency heterozygote, region C of the normal chromosome bulges out in an unpaired loop when the homologues synapse, since this region has no corresponding part in the deficient chromosome.*

normal and the other has a nonterminal deficiency, this tendency results in a bulging out as an unpaired loop by the portion of the normal chromosome homologous to the deficient segment. This situation is diagrammed in Figure 10-3. An unpaired loop is characteristic of deficiency heterozygotes, either in meiotic cells at synapsis or in somatic cells if chromosome pairing occurs.

Genetic Effects of Deficiencies. When a segment of a chromosome is absent, the genes normally situated in the missing segment also are absent. The consequences for the organism may be more or less severe, depending on the physiological importance of the gene-controlled processes involved. Usually, if a chromosome is deficient in any considerable number of gene loci, lethality results, even in the presence of a complete homologous chromosome. Deficiency homozygotes are still less likely to be viable than are deficiency heterozygotes. This is understandable, since in the homozygotes important functions of absent genes may be entirely lost to the organism.

The same principles hold in general for the viability of deficiency gametes and gametophytes of plants. For a particular chromosomal deficiency in a higher plant, the effects on viability of the male and female gametophytes may be quite different. Ordinarily in such instances, female gametophytes are the more likely to survive. In animals, gametes with sizable chromosomal deficiencies are frequently able to function.

Nonlethal deficiencies may give rise to unusual phenotypic effects. In an organism heterozygous for any allelic pair (Aa), loss of a chromosome segment carrying the dominant allele (A) permits the recessive allele (a) to express itself phenotypically. For example, corn aleurone of the genotype Ccc is colored, provided that other genes necessary for the development of pigmentation are present in addition to the dominant C. If a chromosome carrying C acquires a broken end, so that it goes through breakage-fusion-bridge cycles, the chromosomal segment in which C is situated may be lost from certain cells. The phenotypic result is a variegated aleurone—that is, an aleurone having patches of both colored and colorless tissue. Figure 10-4 shows how such variegation may come about. This kind of unexpected expression of a recessive trait, which is caused by the absence of a dominant allele, is called *pseudodominance*.

In corn, a series of very small, nonlethal deficiencies has been studied by McClintock. These deficiencies, when homozygous, produce phenotypic effects similar to those obtained after "gene mutations" which presumably did not involve chromosomal loss. Particular deficiencies give rise, for example, to the characters *white seedling, pale yellow seedling,* and *brown midrib.* In the case of brown midrib, the phenotypic effect produced by the appropriate deficiency resembles in every way the effect of a mutant gene, bm_1. The locus of this gene is known to be in the very chromosomal segment which was deficient in McClintock's material. Similarly, the mutant character *yellow body* is produced in Drosophila that are homozygous deficient

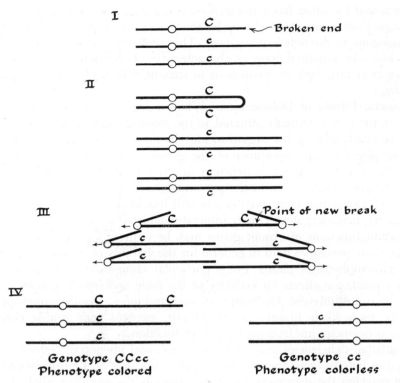

Figure 10-4. *The origin of variegated aleurone color in corn through the operation of breakage-fusion-bridge cycles. Gene C is essential for the development of aleurone color; its allele, c, when homozygous, gives rise to colorless aleurone. Aleurone nuclei are triploid (3n). I. A nucleus of the genotype Ccc; the chromosome carrying gene C has a recently broken end fairly near the locus of C. II. Prophase in this nucleus, showing fusion of the chromatids carrying gene C. III. Anaphase, showing a bridge formed by the dicentric chromatid; the other chromatids can separate in regular fashion. IV. Sister telophase nuclei; the bridge has broken in such fashion that one nucleus has a duplication CC, and the other is deficient for the C locus. The former can give rise to a colored phenotype, the latter to colorless. Breakage-fusion-bridge cycles may continue throughout the development of the aleurone tissue.*

for a particular very small portion of the X-chromosome. The segment of chromosome involved is that which has been established as the locus of gene *y*.

Utilization of Deficiencies in the Physical Mapping of Chromosomes. We have already emphasized in Chapter 9 that linkage-map distances between genes do not necessarily relate in any fixed way to physical linear measurements. Special cytological techniques must be used to determine the physical location of a gene in a chromosome. Localization is accomplished by identifying a gene locus with relation to some visible landmark such as a chromomere or cross band. In this process of *cytological mapping,* deficiencies have been particularly useful.

You will recall how, in an originally heterozygous individual, recessive genes may show pseudodominance as a consequence of deficiencies involving the loci of their dominant alleles. In suitable chromosomal material, the positions of deficiencies may be visually identified, as we have just shown. The geneticist therefore has means not only for the genetic detection of loci involved in a deficiency but also for the cytological delimitation of deficiencies of appreciable size. If, for a particular deficiency, certain genes can be shown to be absent, and a particular chromosomal segment is also seen to be missing, the inference is reasonable that the loci of the absent genes are in the missing segment. In order to locate genes as accurately as possible, it is necessary in cytological mapping either to study short deficiencies, involving as few cross bands and gene loci as are feasible to detect, or to study a series of more extended deficiencies that overlap one another in varying degree.

Figure 10-5 illustrates the use of deficiencies to localize genes in the salivary gland chromosomes of Drosophila. Diagram A shows the nondeficient left-hand tip of the X-chromosome as it usually appears in the salivary glands. Because of exceedingly close pairing, what is actually a pair of homologous chromosomes appears to be single. Diagrams B and C show different deficiency heterozygotes, also with strong pairing. The complete

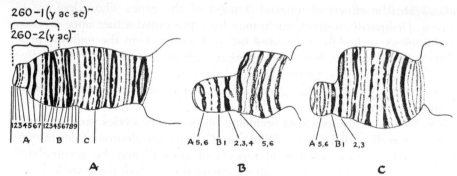

Figure 10-5. *Utilization of deficiencies to localize genes in the salivary gland chromosomes of Drosophila. The left-hand tip of the X-chromosome is shown in A. The pointer lines A 1, 2, 3, etc., and B 1, 2, 3, etc., serve to identify cross bands in the chromosome, and may be used as points of reference. The bracketed region 260–1 designates that portion of the X-chromosome absent in the deficiency heterozygote shown in drawing B. Similarly, 260–2 defines the limits of the deficiency in the heterozygote shown in C. The larger deficiency includes the loci for* yellow, achaete, *and* scute, *the smaller includes only the loci for* yellow *and* achaete. *Therefore, the* scute *locus must be in the narrow band of chromosome material that differentiates the two deficiencies. (After Demerec and Hoover, J. Heredity,* **27:**206, *1936.)*

complement of cross bands in the nondeficient member may be used as an index for identifying the missing bands in the deficient homologue. Since both deficiencies shown are terminal deficiencies, no unpaired loop is formed by the nondeficient chromosome. Instead, the tip of the deficient chromosome looks as if it were chipped off. Genetic tests show the deficiency chromosome represented in B to be lacking in the loci for *y* (*yellow*), *ac* (*achaete*), and *sc* (*scute*). The deficiency chromosome in diagram C lacks the loci for *y* and *ac*. Since the *scute* locus is absent in the first deficiency chromosome but is present in the second, it must be situated in the narrow chromosomal segment which differentiates the second deficient chromosome from the first.

Duplications

Occasionally a nucleus is found to be aberrant in that it has extra material beyond that found in the normal chromosomal complement. Special terms, to be introduced in the next chapter, are usually applied to instances of extra whole chromosomes or extra sets of chromosomes. Extra parts of chromosomes are called *duplications*. Various kinds of duplications have been observed. Some exist attached to the chromosome whose segments are "repeated"; some are attached to different chromosomes; others may exist as independent fragments.

One reason duplications are interesting is that they make it possible to investigate the effects of unusual dosages of the genes whose loci are involved. Ordinarily, a given allele may be represented either once or twice in a nucleus, although, as pointed out in Chapter 8, in the endosperm an allele may occur one, two, or three times within a nucleus. With duplications, an allele may be present three or more times; hence duplications may be utilized in studying the effects of various quantitative ratios between members of an allelic set.

You have already seen that breakage-fusion-bridge cycles produce duplications as well as deficiencies. When the *C* locus, for aleurone color in corn, is involved, various numbers of repeats of gene *C* may be accumulated. Variegated endosperm arising out of circumstances like those indicated in Figure 10-4 may show colored patches that vary from quite intense to extremely light coloration. Presumably the color intensity depends upon the number of dominant alleles present. This situation correlates well with the fact that in the normal aleurone one dose of *C* gives lighter color than two *C* alleles, whereas triple dosage (*CCC*) conditions the darkest coloring of all.

Duplications and Suppressor Effects. A *suppressor* is a gene that reverses the effects of another, nonallelic gene. For example, a mutant gene in the third chromosome of Drosophila has the effect of producing wild-type eye color in individuals homozygous for purple eyes (*pr pr*). And in Neurospora the effect of a gene mutation that results in defective pyrimidine metabolism can be suppressed by a quite different mutant gene situated at another locus.

Suppressor phenomena are sometimes simulated by the effects of duplications. Phenotypically wild-type Drosophila that were homozygous recessive for the mutant characters *speck* (body), *balloon* (wings), and *plexus* (wings) were studied by C. B. Bridges. He found that the "suppressor" of the mutant characteristics was a duplicating fragment of the second chromosome, which was attached to chromosome 3 and carried wild-type alleles for the mutant genes whose usual effects were nullified. Interesting dominance relationships were revealed by differences in degree of suppression. One wild-type allele in the duplicating segment was dominant over the two recessive speck genes. But the two plexus genes in the presence of their wild-type allele gave a phenotype of "weak plexus," a condition of abnormal wing venation distinguishable both from wild type and from standard plexus. Thus the unexpected presence of a duplication sometimes gives rise to genetic results that at first sight appear to be quite anomalous.

Translocations

We have just referred to a situation where a piece of chromosome 2 of Drosophila was attached to chromosome 3. This kind of aberration, where a fragment of one chromosome becomes attached to a nonhomologous chromosome, is called a *translocation*. Nonhomologous chromosomes may interchange parts in *reciprocal translocation*. If two normal nonhomologous chromosomes have a sequence of regions designated ABCDE and LMNO, reciprocal translocation might give rise to the aberrant types ABCNO and LMDE. The segments involved in reciprocal translocation may or may not be equal in size.

The nature of the translocation process is imperfectly understood. But the general situation resulting in translocation can be said to be one where chromosome breaks are followed by unions in new ways among the broken ends of chromosomes. X-ray treatment of nuclei, which induces chromosome breakage, is known to give rise to increases in translocation frequency.

A number of students of chromosomal behavior have been impressed by the resemblances between the translocation process and crossing over. Whether these resemblances are fundamental or superficial is not clear. But in the literature of genetics, translocations have sometimes been said to arise as a consequence of "illegitimate crossing over," that is, exchanges between nonhomologous chromosomes.

The Cytology of Translocations. The cytology of translocations is a large and complicated subject in itself, and we can deal only with its simplest manifestations. In the following discussion, we shall confine ourselves to *reciprocal translocations,* since these seem to be the most frequent and

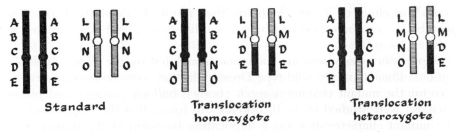

Standard

Translocation
homozygote

Translocation
heterozygote

Figure 10-6. *If the chromosome pairs at the left have the standard arrangement of chromatin material for a species, those in the center represent a possible arrangement in nuclei homozygous for a reciprocal translocation. The pairs at the right show heterozygosity for the same type of translocation.*

important in genetic systems. You should keep in mind from the outset three basic chromosomal types: (1) the *standard,* untranslocated types; (2) translocation homozygotes; (3) translocation heterozygotes. All these are illustrated in Figure 10-6.

Translocation homozygotes may have no obvious cytological peculiarities. Their pairing at meiosis is often regular, and the transmission of chromosomes from one nuclear generation to another may be as uncomplicated as in the original untranslocated types. In fact, when translocated pieces are about the same size, cytological observation of translocation homozygotes may not reveal the aberration at all, although suitable genetic experiments will. Naturally, if outstanding chromosomal landmarks are involved, trans-

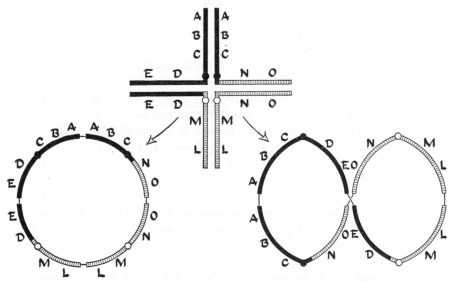

Figure 10-7. *Chromosome pairs heterozygous for a reciprocal translocation characteristically conjugate in a crosslike configuration at pachytene in meiosis (center). Later, this configuration may open out into a ring (left) or a figure-eight (right). For simplicity, the figures are not shown with doubled strands.*

location is disclosed by the change in their physical relationships with one another.

In translocation heterozygotes, the chromosomes get into various awkward situations, to a large extent occasioned by the complications of attaining close pairing of homologous parts at meiosis. To achieve conjugation in a translocation heterozygote, the chromosomes characteristically assume a crosslike configuration at pachytene. Later, as terminalization (see p. 118) of chiasmata in the arms of the cross nears completion, the figure may open out into a four-membered ring. Or, as a fairly frequent variation, the crosslike configuration of pachytene may be transformed into a "figure-eight." The basic configurations are diagrammed in Figure 10-7.

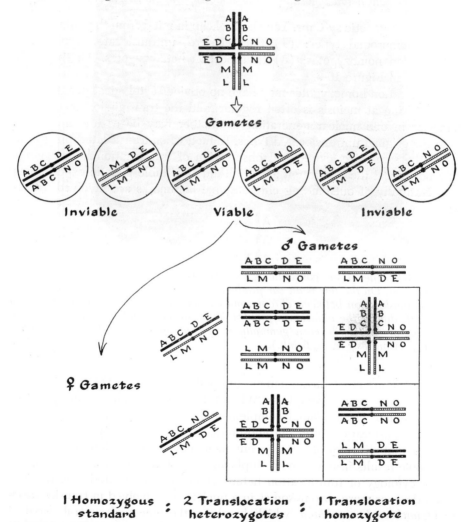

Figure 10-8. *Gamete formation and the results of self-fertilization of a plant heterozygous for a translocation.*

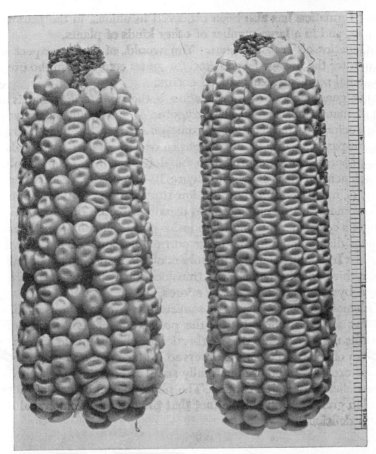

Figure 10-9. *Phenotypic consequences of semisterility in corn. On the right is a normal ear. On the left is an ear produced on a plant heterozygous for a reciprocal translocation between chromosomes 1 and 7. Note the gaps in the ear on the left, due to the abortion of ovules. Why, do you think, are the kernels on the ear of semisterile corn generally somewhat larger and of more irregular shape? (Courtesy R. A. Brink.)*

In the "figure-eight" arrangement, alternate members of the configuration go to the same pole at anaphase. When this is the case, the resulting nuclei have complete chromosomal complements, with half of them carrying reciprocal-translocation type chromosomes. Looking at the plain ring, you will see that distribution of adjacent members of the configuration to the same pole results in nuclei with duplications and deficiencies.

The cytology of translocation heterozygotes is complicated considerably when three or more chromosomes in a nucleus are involved in translocation. In *Oenothera lamarckiana*, which has been the object of several classical studies in cytogenetics, multiple reciprocal translocation results in all but 2 of the 14 chromosomes forming a single ring at meiosis. More or less complex ring formation has also been observed in onions, in the Jimson weed, in Paeonia, and in a large number of other kinds of plants.

The Genetics of Translocations. You would, of course, expect translocation to alter the linkage associations for genes contained in the exchanged chromosomal segments. This indeed occurs.

Another genetic effect of translocation is the *semisterility* that is characteristic of many translocation heterozygotes. If, in a plant heterozygous for a single reciprocal translocation, chromosomes from the meiotic translocation figure pass two by two at random to opposite poles, two-thirds of the resulting spores can be expected to be defective because of duplications and deficiencies. This is shown in Figure 10-8. Actually, random separation by twos, of members of a translocation ring, appears to be relatively rare. The centromeres of the chromosomes usually separate disjunctionally, with homologous centromeres going to opposite poles. Therefore, of the six types of gametes diagrammed in the upper portion of Figure 10-8, the two at the left are less frequently found. In numbers of plant species, about half rather than two-thirds of the gametes of translocation heterozygotes seem to be produced by duplication-deficiency spores.

The phenotypic consequences of semisterility are easily observed. Figure 10-9 shows an ear produced after the pollination of semisterile corn. The gaps in this unfilled ear are due to abortion of about half the ovules.

If pollen of semisterile corn is observed under the microscope, about half the grains are seen to be of abnormally small size. Staining tests reveal that they are deficient in starch content. The physiological defects of these aberrant pollen grains are due to the fact that they carry chromosomal duplications and deficiencies.

Inversions

The validity not only of chromosome maps but of many of our broad concepts of genetics as well depends upon the assumption that the linear order

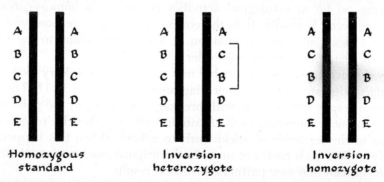

Figure 10-10. *Comparison of a pair of chromosomes having the standard arrangement of chromatin material with a pair of chromosomes heterozygous for an inversion and with a pair of homologues homozygous for an inversion.*

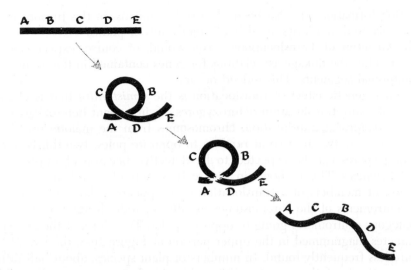

Figure 10-11. *A possible manner of origin for inversions.*

of the genes in a chromosome is well fixed. This assumption has survived many tests, and in general must be taken to be true. However, a given portion of a chromosome occasionally provides genetic results indicating a gene order just the reverse of one already found for others of the same kind of plant or animal. If there are appropriate visible landmarks for the portion of the chromosome in question, these too can be seen to occur in inverted order. The term *inversion* is given to this kind of aberration in which a chromosomal segment exists in reverse relationship to the rest of its chromosome.

Just as with translocations, organisms may be homozygous for an inversion, heterozygous for an inversion, or they may be homozygous for the standard order of parts in the chromosome. (See Fig. 10-10.) The *standard* chromosome order is the generally established order within the group of organisms. So far as cytological activities go, inversion homozygotes may behave perfectly normally. If in the course of time an inversion type gains numerical ascendancy in a population, it has a better claim to the title of "standard" than does the original order.

How do inversions arise? Probably in a variety of ways. Very likely some inversions originate in the manner diagrammed in Figure 10-11. That is, a chromosome may form a loop, with breakages occurring at the point where the chromosome intersects itself. A single unit may then be reconstituted because of the tendency of sticky ends to adhere. When this happens the recently broken ends need not unite in the original combination. If they do not, but instead find new partners, inversion results.

Pairing in Inversion Heterozygotes. Inversion heterozygotes have no special difficulties in mitosis. At meiosis they have the same general sort of troubles as those in which translocation heterozygotes get involved; inver-

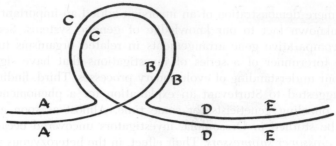

Figure 10-12. *Pairing in an inversion heterozygote.*

sion heterozygotes cannot achieve a true synapsis by simple linear pairing. Where direct conjugation must fail, however, circuitous means accomplish very nearly the same purpose. The characteristic way in which inversion heterozygotes synapse is by forming a looped configuration such as is shown in Figure 10-12.

Inversion loops offer a ready means of detecting the kind of aberration they represent. In salivary gland chromosomes and other favorable material, a loop makes it possible to determine with precision the extent of an inversion. This is illustrated in Figure 10-13. However, loop formation does not occur in every inversion heterozygote. Sometimes an inverted segment and the portion of a normal chromosome homologous to it simply fail to pair.

Inversions as Crossover Suppressors. In 1921, part of the research activities of A. H. Sturtevant were being devoted to the study of corresponding genes in the related species *Drosophila melanogaster* and *D. simulans*. A comparison of maps for chromosome 3 in each of these species disclosed a most interesting fact. The corresponding genes for *scarlet*, *peach*, and *delta* had a gene order *st-p-△* in *D. melanogaster* but existed in the sequence *st-△-p* in *simulans*. Sturtevant's discovery was significant in several ways.

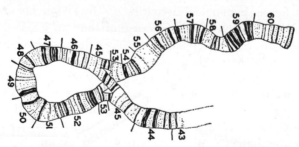

Figure 10-13. *An inversion loop seen in the salivary gland chromosomes of an inversion heterozygote of* Drosophila azteca. *In this favorable material for cytological observation, it is possible to determine that the inversion involves the segments labelled 45 to 53. (From Dobzhansky and Socolov,* J. Heredity, **30:**9, 1939.)

First, the mere demonstration of an inversion added an important and previously unknown fact to our knowledge of genetic systems. Second, the
study of comparative gene arrangements in related organisms turned out
to be the forerunner of a series of investigations that have significantly
enlarged our understanding of evolutionary processes. Third, finding the inversion suggested to Sturtevant an explanation for a phenomenon which
had been puzzling geneticists for some time. Almost as soon as linkage
began to be studied in Drosophila, investigators uncovered occasional instances of *crossover suppressors*. Their effect, in the heterozygous state, was
to reduce markedly crossing over as it is measured by recombination.

The nature and mode of action of crossover suppressors was at the outset
entirely obscure. With his discovery of an inversion, however, Sturtevant
perceived that synapsis along an inverted segment would necessarily be
abnormal in inversion heterozygotes, perhaps even absent. He predicted
that, as a result of abnormal conjugation, crossing over would probably be

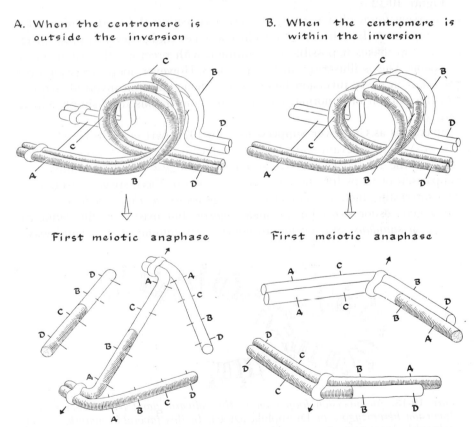

A. When the centromere is outside the inversion

B. When the centromere is within the inversion

First meiotic anaphase

First meiotic anaphase

Figure 10-14. *Crossing over within the inversion loop of an inversion heterozygote leads to the formation of aberrant chromatids with duplications or deficiencies.*

considerably reduced. Subsequent experimentation saw the prediction ful-filled, and also made it clear that many of the mysterious crossover suppres-sors of earlier studies were actually chromosomal inversions.

Why should recombination be suppressed by an inversion? You will find it enlightening to draw out what happens when a single exchange occurs *within the inversion loop* of an inversion heterozygote. We have done this for you in Figure 10-14, but for practice try it yourself. Remember that cross-ing over occurs at a four-strand stage. Notice that the results of crossing over differ somewhat, depending upon whether or not the inverted segment includes the centromere of the chromosome. But in either case, the end effects are the same: Aberrant chromatids with duplications and deficien-cies are produced. If the centromere is outside the inverted segment, a *di-centric* chromatid and an *acentric* (lacking a centromere) fragment are formed. The dicentric chromatid forms a chromatin bridge, which may break. The acentric fragment has an uncertain future, but it usually is lost rather quickly because it has no means for systematic orientation at the time of nuclear division. On the other hand, where the centromere is included in the inverted segment, a single exchange gives rise directly to duplication and deficiency in each of the chromatids involved.

Inversions, then, do not necessarily suppress cytological crossing over. However, genetic recombinations in the inversion segment are very ef-fectively suppressed, because single crossover chromatids carrying such recombinations are of a duplication-deficiency type, and either fail to func-tion in fertilization or fail to produce viable zygotes. But this is not a com-plete accounting for the suppression of recombinations, since the presence of an inversion is often a powerful influence for reducing recombination immediately outside the inverted segment as well as within it. Doubtless, unsatisfactory pairing in inversion heterozygotes leads in some instances to interference with the crossing over process. We may say, then, that the "suppression of crossovers," as detected phenotypically, probably involves both nonappearance of crossover types and actual reduction in the fre-quency of the process of crossing over.

Position Effects

Probably you find it easy enough to understand how either absence of genes or their presence in abnormal quantity should have detectable effects on an organism. What about genes that simply are transferred to new neighborhoods within the chromosome complement? We have seen that translocation and inversion lead to changed linkage relationships for genes and to disruptions of normal chromosomal mechanics in the aberration het-erozygotes. Apart from these effects, does the mere relocation of a gene change its activities or the results of its activities? *The fact is that a given*

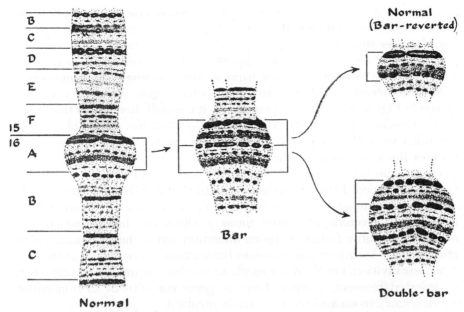

Figure 10-15. *Portions of X-chromosomes from salivary glands of* D. melanogaster, *showing the bar region. Notice the segment that is duplicated in bar and triplicated in* double-bar. (*From Bridges,* Science, *83:210, 1936.*)

gene may have different phenotypic effects as a function of its location in the chromosome complement. These are called position effects.

Position Effect on Bar Eye in Drosophila. The discovery that genes may show position effects was by Sturtevant, in 1925. He utilized unusual properties of *bar-eyed* Drosophila to demonstrate that the effect of a gene may depend upon its position in relation to its neighbors.

Close cytological examination of the appropriate region in salivary gland chromosomes of *D. melanogaster* discloses that bar eye is not due to an instance of ordinary gene mutation but is associated with reduplication of a chromosomal segment (Fig. 10-15). Homozygous stocks of bar flies do not breed quite true, since about 1 in 1600 offspring is a reversion to wild type. In the same proportion, a new mutant type, called *double bar*, also arises out of homozygous bar strains. The effect of double bar is to reduce the eye even more than does bar. If a double-bar chromosome is examined cytologically, the cross bands which are duplicated in bar are found now to exist in triplicate. Figure 10-16 indicates how homozygous bar females might produce normal and double-bar gametes as a consequence of *unequal crossing over.*

The existence of normal, bar, and double-bar chromosomes provides an opportunity for study of the different effects of the bar segments in various

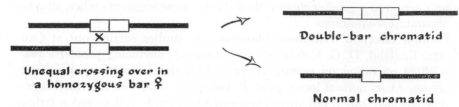

Unequal crossing over in
a homozygous bar ♀

Double-bar chromatid

Normal chromatid

Figure 10-16. *Schematic representation of how unequal crossing over might account for the appearance of normal and double-bar individuals in bar stocks of Drosophila. For simplification, only the two strands involved in the crossing-over process are shown.*

numerical and positional combinations. Keeping in mind that a particular chromosomal segment is represented once in a normal chromosome, twice in bar, and three times in double bar, you can see that both in homozygous bar females and in double-bar/normal heterozygotes there is a total of four of these segments per chromosome complement. In terms of quantity of basic hereditary material these flies are equivalent for the loci we have been considering. However, the two situations prove not to be equivalent physiologically. As shown in Figure 10-17, eyes of the heterozygous female are smaller than those of the comparable homozygote. The difference in phenotypic expression can be ascribed to position effect. For it is clear that segments lying side by side in a single chromosome somehow reinforce each

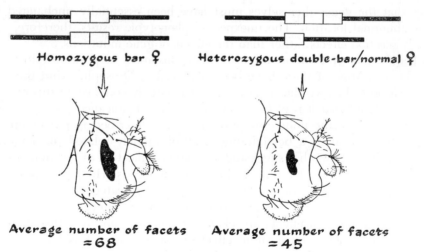

Homozygous bar ♀   Heterozygous double-bar/normal ♀

Average number of facets   Average number of facets
≈68   ≈45

Figure 10-17. *In homozygous bar females, a particular segment of the X-chromosome is represented four times, twice in each homologue. In heterozygous double-bar normal females, this same segment is also represented four times, once in the normal X-chromosome and three times in the double-bar chromosome. Eye size in the two kinds of females, however, is appreciably different. This is an instance of position effect.*

other's action to a greater degree than do the same segments when situated in separate chromosomes.

Position Effect in *Oenothera blandina*. In studies carried out at Cambridge, England, D. G. Catcheside has obtained convincing proof for position effect operating on certain genes in *Oenothera blandina*, an evening primrose. At its normal locus, gene P^s governs a condition in which flower bud sepals have broad red stripes separated by narrow yellow-green stripes. Gene S, which is linked to P^s, gives rise to *yellow* as distinct from *sulfur-colored* (*ss*) petals.

When, following X-ray treatment, a chromosomal segment containing the P and S loci was translocated to another chromosome, various striking phenotypic anomalies appeared in translocation heterozygotes. For example, in plants of the genotype $P^s P^s$ the red pigmentation of the sepals is broken up into irregular patches of varying size. Variegation of petal color may also occur. In plants homozygous for normal chromosomal arrangement, Ss individuals have uniformly yellow petals. But in the translocation heterozygotes the petals of Ss plants are a mosaic of sulfur and yellow, if the s allele is carried in the normal chromosome. The genotype Ss does not give variegation in translocation heterozygotes where s is in the aberrant chromosome.

Catcheside was able to transfer genes P^s and S from the translocation chromosome to a normal chromosome by crossing over. Subsequently these genes produced normal phenotypes, and showed no instability. This indicates that the genes themselves must have been essentially unchanged in their abnormal location. The unexpected phenotypic results, therefore, are clearly position effects rather than the effects of gene mutations.

Classification of Position Effects. Many instances of position effect are now known. Most of these have been observed in Drosophila, but there is little reason to believe that position effect is largely confined to this organism or to doubt that it is of fundamental genetic significance.

In many ways, the numerous position effects described in the literature of genetics appear as a bewildering array of vaguely related phenomena. However, E. B. Lewis has suggested a broad classification of position effects which brings some order out of this apparent chaos. He points out that known position effects can be placed into one of two categories: (1) stable-type position effects; or (2) variegated-type position effects.

Stable-type position effects are characterized by a uniform alteration of normal gene action. The position effect on bar eye is of this kind. Variegated-type position effects, on the other hand, result in somatic instability of gene action. Among such position effects in Drosophila is the effect of chromosomal rearrangements involving the locus for white eyes. Heterozygotes having the *w* gene on a normal chromosome and its "+" allele on a rearrangement chromosome show mosaicism for eye color. The variegated eyes may have scattered red or pink patches on a light background, light patches on a red background, or any of several variations on these color schemes, depending upon the modifying influences of genotype and environment. All of the variegated-type position effects in Drosophila seem to occur when genes normally situated in euchromatin are transferred near to heterochromatin. So far as is known, the position effects in Oenothera resemble closely the variegated-type position effects in Drosophila.

Explanations of Position Effect. Various interpretations of position effect have been proposed. All of these are as yet so speculative that in this general text we are justified in pointing out only the main trends of thought. One set of hypotheses takes the line that reversible alterations in the physical structure of genes may be involved in position effects. Another approach is based on the idea that chemical reactions among substances produced through genic activity may be affected by the proximity of particular genes. Quite possibly, different kinds of position effects will require different explanations.

The Spreading Effect. When one gene shows mosaic expression as an accompaniment of rearrangements between heterochromatin and euchromatin, other loci between the gene and the heterochromatin are also affected, and in increasing degree with the nearness of the loci to heterochromatin. This "spreading effect" strongly suggests activity on the part of some kind of diffusible substance originating in heterochromatin. Spreading phenomena appear to offer geneticists unique opportunities for investigating the fundamental nature of position effects.

Keys to the Significance of This Chapter

Ordinarily, chromosomes behave regularly and predictably at mitosis and meiosis, and the genes carried in chromosomes reproduce themselves with accuracy at definite times in the nuclear cycle. Genetic systems are essentially conservative and stable. If this were not true, there would be none of the familiar genotypic and phenotypic ratios that attest so impressively to regular patterns of inheritance and that facilitate our study and understanding of genetics. Even more important, life would be quite different than we now know it.

But suppose that genes always reproduced other genes exactly like their originals, and suppose that the vehicles of heredity always followed the paths diagrammed so simply in Chapter 7. Then, also, life would be somewhat different than it is. Variation is characteristic of life, and you will learn —if you are not already aware—that it is at the basis of the evolution of life. One source of variation is gene mutation, which will be discussed at length in Chapter 12. Another continuing source of variation is chromosomal aberration.

Translocations, inversions, deficiencies, duplications, and other aberrant chromosomal phenomena may affect organisms in a variety of ways. Fertility and other phenotypic characteristics may be affected. Whole cycles of extraordinary chromosomal behavior may be set in motion. Vital components in the genetic system, such as synapsis and crossing over, may be interfered with. The rearrangement of genes as a result of chromosomal aberration may result in position effects. All of these consequences of aberration help to account for the variety we find in life.

Yet even when chromosomal aberrations occur, genetic systems hold to an over-all organization and a conformity to design. If we know the nature of a particular aberration, its effects are usually very near what might be predicted on the basis of our knowledge of normal chromosomal behavior. Conversely, the nature of an aberration may often be deduced from the nature of its effects on the organism.

References

Bouricius, J. K., "Embryological and Cytological Studies in Rats Heterozygous for a Probable Reciprocal Translocation." *Genetics*, **33**:577–587, 1948. (Description of the phenotypic characteristics of the abnormal progeny of rats heterozygous for a spontaneous translocation.)

Cleland, R. E., "Some Aspects of the Cyto-Genetics of Ocnothera." *Botan. Rev.*, **2**:316–348, 1936. (A clear and compact review of the cytogenetic complexities of the evening primroses, which have furnished material for many classical investigations.)

Dobzhansky, Th., "Position Effects on Genes." *Biol. Rev.*, **11**:364–384, 1936. (A thorough review of the earlier literature on this subject.)

Gates, W. H., "A Case of Non-Disjunction in the Mouse." *Genetics*, **12**:295–306, 1927. (To follow a fascinating experimental trail leading to the first establishment of a case of chromosomal deficiency in a mammal, read this and then the reference to Painter, 1927.)

Koller, P. C., "Segmental Interchange in Mice." *Genetics*, **29**:247–263, 1944. (The experimental induction of semisterility in mice, and the evidence that this reduced fertility is the effect of chromosomal translocation.)

Lewis, E. B., "The Phenomenon of Position Effect." *Advances in Genetics*, **3**:73–115, 1950. (A penetrating review which served as a basis for interpretations given in this chapter.)

McClintock, B., "The Association of Mutants with Homozygous Deficiencies in *Zea mays*." *Genetics*, **26**:542–571, 1941. (The production of homozygous minute deficiencies through the aberrant behavior of ring chromosomes and the phenotypic effects of these deficiencies are described.)

———, "The Stability of Broken Ends of Chromosomes in *Zea mays*." *Genetics*, **26**:234–282, 1941. (An admirable paper in experimental cytogenetics. Gives a detailed discussion of breakage-fusion-bridge cycles.)

Painter, T. S., "The Chromosome Constitution of Gates' 'Non-Disjunction' (*v-o*) Mice." *Genetics*, 12:379–392, 1927. (Read this article after reading Gates' paper referred to above.)

————, "Salivary Chromosomes and the Attack on the Gene." *J. Heredity*, 25:464–476, 1934. (A well-illustrated, general discussion of the use of salivary gland chromosomes in localizing genes in Drosophila.)

Rhoades, M. M., and McClintock, B., "The Cytogenetics of Maize." *Botan. Rev.*, 1:292–328, 1935. (A general treatment of the fundamentals of corn cytogenetics by two leaders in the field.)

Sturtevant, A. H., and Beadle, G. W., *An Introduction to Genetics*. Philadelphia: W. B. Saunders Co., 1939. (Chaps. 8, 9, and 11 give an excellent introduction to the basic cytogenetics of chromosomal aberration.)

Questions and Problems

10- 1.   What do the following terms and phrases signify?

acentric	reciprocal translocation
chromosomal ring	semisterility
chromosome bridge	somatic pairing
cross band	spreading effect
crossover suppressor	standard chromosome type
deficiency	sticky chromosome
deletion	suppressor
dicentric	translocation homozygote
inversion loop	translocation heterozygote
physical mapping of chromosomes	variegated type position effect

10- 2.   Describe some of the ways in which chromosomal aberrations may arise.

10- 3.   Explain how breakage-fusion-bridge cycles may give rise to phenotypic variegation.

10- 4.   In contrast to the normal gait for mice, certain individuals execute bizarre steps, and are called "waltzers." The difference between normals and waltzers is genetic, with waltzing being a recessive characteristic. W. H. Gates crossed waltzers with homozygous normals and found among several hundred normal progeny a single waltzing ♀. When crossed to a waltzing ♂, she produced all waltzing offspring. Crossed to a homozygous normal ♂, she produced all normal progeny. Certain ♂♂ and ♀♀ of this normal progeny, when intercrossed, never gave waltzing offspring. Painter examined the chromosomes of waltzing mice that were derived from some of Gates' crosses and that showed a breeding behavior similar to that of the original, unusual waltzing ♀. He found that these individuals had 40 chromosomes, just as in normal mice or the usual waltzing mice. In the unusual waltzers, however, one member of a chromosome pair was abnormally short. Interpret these observations, both genetic and cytological, as completely as possible.

10- 5.   Grüneberg states that the observations detailed in the preceding question represent "the only case where a mammalian gene has been localized in a particular autosome." Amplify this statement.

10- 6. Why is it easier to localize the genes carried in the sex chromosomes than it is to localize the genes carried in particular autosomes?

10- 7. Would it be appropriate to say that the exceptional waltzing ♀ described in Question 10-4 represents an instance of *pseudodominance?* Explain.

10- 8. Give reasons why it is generally easier in Drosophila than in mice to localize genes in particular regions of particular chromosomes.

10- 9. There is some evidence that many so-called "recessive mutations" are actually minute deletions, so that the loci of the genes involved are lost rather than merely altered. What kinds of experiments and observations could be made to investigate this problem?

10-10. C. R. Burnham, working with a semisterile line of corn, found that crosses with normal gave progeny in a ratio of 1 normal to 1 semisterile. Further genetic tests showed *semisterility* giving 4.1 per cent recombinations with gene *an* (*anther ear*) and 1.1 per cent recombination with *ra* (*ramosa tassel*). From linkage studies carried out with standard chromosomal lines of corn, it is known that *an* is in chromosome 1, and *ra* in chromosome 7. How can you account for this failure of semisterility to recombine at random with members of two separate linkage groups?

10-11. Do you think it likely that the semisterility in Burnham's line of corn is due to gene mutation? Elaborate.

10-12. What unusual cytological configuration might you expect to see if chromosomes of the semisterile line of Question 10-10 were examined at pachytene?

10-13. Koller and Auerbach X-rayed mice and thereby produced three individuals that had semisterile offspring. In each of the lines derived from these individuals, it was possible to find associations of four chromosomes at meiosis. What appears to have been the effect of X-rays on germ plasm that accounts for the semisterility?

10-14. In corn, a plant *pr/pr*, having standard chromosomes, was crossed with a plant homozygous for a reciprocal translocation between chromosomes 2 and 5, and for the *Pr* allele. The F_1 was semisterile and phenotypically *Pr* for aleurone color. A backcross to the parent with standard chromosomes gave: 764 semisterile, *Pr;* 145 semisterile, *pr;* 186 normal, *Pr;* and 727 normal, *pr*. What can you say about the location of gene *pr* with reference to the translocation point?

10-15. Summarize the crosses outlined in the preceding question with a series of diagrams, showing both the genes and the chromosomes involved for all parents and progenies. When homologous chromosome pairs are shown at meiosis, represent them at a four-strand stage. To make the diagrams clearer, you might draw chromosomes 2 with colored pencil and chromosomes 5 with ordinary pencil. (The locus of *pr* is in chromosome 5.)

10-16. In the *standard* arrangement of genes in chromosome 3 of *D. melanogaster, sr* (*stripe*), *e* (*ebony*), and *ro* (*rough*) occur in the order named. One strain of Drosophila has been found to have a gene sequence *sr—ro—e*. Name the type of aberration shown in this strain. How, besides different gene order as indicated by linkage tests, might the aberration be demonstrated?

10-17. One strain of a plant has an order of regions *l m n o p q r s t u v* in chromosome 3. Another strain of the same species has a chromosome 3 order of *l m n r q p o s t u v*. Diagram the configuration of synapsing chromosomes 3 in an F_1 hybrid between these different strains.

10-18. Single crossovers within the inversion loop of inversion heterozygotes give rise to chromatids with duplications and deficiencies. Diagram what happens when, within the inversion loop, there is a *double exchange* involving the same two strands and when the centromere is outside the inversion loop. (Remember that crossing over occurs at a four-strand stage.) Are aberrant chromatids produced?

10-19. What may be an important role of chromosomal duplications in evolution?

10-20. Devise an experiment to substantiate that the emergence of wild types and double-bar types out of bar stocks of Drosophila is an event associated with crossing over.

10-21. What criteria might be used to distinguish position effects from gene mutations?

CHAPTER 11

Variations in Chromosome Number

YOU ARE doubtless aware that there are different kinds of cultivated wheat, each kind suited to particular purposes and growing conditions. But you may not realize the full extent of diversity within the genus Triticum, to which wheats belong. To indicate this diversity we can mention three examples. Plants of *einkorn* wheat are small, yielding comparatively little grain, which threshes out with the glumes attached. Today, einkorn is planted chiefly for experimental purposes and is of minor agricultural importance. *Durum* wheat, grown largely in the Dakotas and Minnesota, has thick heads and large, hard grains. Because of its high gluten content, durum flour is utilized for macaroni and other pastes. Probably most familiar to you is *common,* or *bread,* wheat, which occurs in many varieties and is more widely grown than any of the other wheats.

If einkorn is examined cytologically, the chromosome number in the nuclei of somatic cells is found to be 14, whereas durum has 28 chromosomes, and common wheats have 42. These wheats represent the three groups into which different species of the genus Triticum naturally fall, on the basis of their chromosome numbers. A grouping of Triticum species is summarized in Table 11-1.

In oats, also, 14-, 28-, and 42-chromosome species can be distinguished. Different species of the genus Chrysanthemum are found to have chromosome numbers of 18, 36, 54, 72, and 90. Note that in wheat and oats the chromosome numbers exist as different multiples of the number 7, and in

TABLE 11-1. Grouping of Triticum (Wheat) Species According to Chromosome Number.

14 CHROMOSOMES	28 CHROMOSOMES	42 CHROMOSOMES
T. monococcum (einkorn)	T. dicoccum (emmer)	T. vulgare (common wheat)
	T. durum (durum wheat)	T. compactum (club wheat)
	T. polonicum (Polish wheat)	T. spelta (spelt)
	T. turgidum (poulard wheat)	
	T. dicoccoides (wild emmer)	

207

Chrysanthemum of the number 9. In a great many groups of related plants, similar progressions of chromosome number have been observed. What is their significance?

To answer this question, we can return to the situation in wheat. Each *genome*, or full complement of the different kinds of chromosomes, in einkorn consists of 7 members; in other words, the basic chromosome number (*n*) is 7. Somatic cells of einkorn have the diploid (2*n*) number of 14. It is an easily drawn inference that the higher multiples of *n* among wheats may have arisen through reduplications of genomes. Thus durum, with 28 chromosomes, may be thought of as a *tetraploid* (4*n*) and bread wheat, with 42, as a *hexaploid* (6*n*).

As early as 1917, a Danish geneticist, Ö. Winge, observed the frequent occurrence of different multiples of a single basic chromosome number among related groups of higher plants. On the basis of this observation, he suggested that reduplication of chromosome complements may occur rather frequently in the evolution of taxonomic series. More recently, variations in the number of genomes per nucleus have been found to occur occasionally among members of the same species. Figure 11-1 pictures mitoses

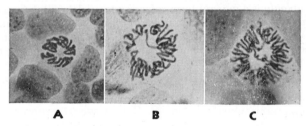

A   B   C

Figure 11-1. *Nuclei of haploid* (A), *diploid* (B), *and triploid* (C) *salamanders seen at mitotic metaphase.* (*Courtesy of R. B. Griffiths,* Genetics, **26:76, 1941.**)

in epidermal cells of the tail tips of salamanders, *Triturus viridescens*, that differ from one another in having 1, 2, or 3 genomes per nucleus.

At about the same time that Winge's publications were serving to focus attention on problems of genome reduplication, A. F. Blakeslee and J. Belling, in the United States, were concerned with another aspect of the relationship of variation in chromosome number to genetic diversity. They found that Jimson weeds (*Datura stramonium*) do not invariably have their normal diploid chromosome number of 24. Instead, occasional plants have 25 chromosomes, with one of the 12 kinds occurring in triplicate, the others in duplicate. This type of aberrant condition is called *trisomic*. Over a period of years, each of the 12 different chromosomes which make up a genome in Datura was observed one or more times in the trisomic condition. All of these trisomics are characterized by separate and recognizable phenotypic effects. For example, the so-called *Globe* phenotype is typical of plants trisomic for the particular chromosome that Datura geneticists have labelled

21·22. Globe plants differ from normal in that their leaves are broader and less indented, and their seed capsules are more globular and have stout spines.

The Terminology of Ploidy. We have just considered, in the introduction to this chapter, two sorts of exception to the rule that somatic nuclei contain two of each kind of chromosome characteristic of the species, and germ-cell nuclei one. An organism may have an unusual number of full chromosome complements (as in tetraploidy) or an unusual number of chromosomes involving an incomplete genome (as in trisomics). Distinguishing these as different kinds of situations is in a way arbitrary, since from one point of view all variations in chromosome number are matters of duplication and deficiency. Variations in the presence or absence of *parts of chromosomes*, or of *whole chromosomes*, or of *whole sets of chromosomes* form an almost continuous series of situations having to do with gene dosage. The number of different possibilities for duplication and deficiency in this larger sense is so vast, however, that there is real need for breaking down the total into some sort of working classification. Our aim is to introduce you to a reasonable minimum of this necessary terminology.

1. *Aneuploidy* is a general term referring to nuclei containing chromosomes whose numbers do not exist as true multiples of the basic number in the genome or genomes involved. In other words, *aneuploid* plants or animals are characterized by incomplete genomes. An organism lacking one chromo-

TABLE 11-2. *Examples of Basic Types of Chromosome Complements.*

I. IN EUPLOIDY		
Name of Type	Shorthand Formula	Chromosome Complement Where C, B, A, and S Are Nonhomologous Chromosomes
Monoploid	n	(CBAS)
Diploid	$2n$	(CBAS) (CBAS)
Triploid	$3n$	(CBAS) (CBAS) (CBAS)
Autotetraploid	$4n$	(CBAS) (CBAS) (CBAS) (CBAS)
Allotetraploid	$4n$	(CBAS) (CBAS) (C'B'A'S') (C'B'A'S')
II. IN ANEUPLOIDY†		
Monosomic	$2n - 1$	(CBAS) (CBA)
Trisomic	$2n + 1$	(CBAS) (CBAS) (C)
Tetrasomic	$2n + 2$	(CBAS) (CBAS) (C) (C)
Double Trisomic	$2n + 1 + 1$	(CBAS) (CBAS) (CA)

† Examples of aneuploidy in this table are based on a diploid complement. Chromosome complements that are polyploid may show analogous aneuploid variations, as (CBAS) (CBAS)(CBAS)(C), for example.

some of a diploid complement is called a *monosomic*. A *trisomic* has two complete genomes plus a single extra chromosome, as previously illustrated in Datura. *Tetrasomics* carry a chromosome in quadruplicate; the remaining chromosomes are present twice. If there are two extra chromosomes that are different members of the genome, the organism is called *double trisomic*. There are other types of variations of aneuploidy described by a nomenclature similar to that just indicated.

2. *Euploidy* is a term covering situations where the total chromosome number involves complete genomes. Among *euploids*, a *monoploid* organism has but a single genome per nucleus. A *triploid* has 3, a *tetraploid* 4, a *hexaploid* 6, an *octaploid* 8 genomes per nucleus, and so on. Multiple genomes including three or more sets of chromosomes per nucleus (in other words triploids and above) are frequently designated by the term *polyploid*. Polyploids are sometimes differentiated into *autopolyploids* and *allopolyploids*.

Autopolyploids are those in which the multiple genomes are identical, or very nearly so. Genome reduplication within a normally diploid species gives rise to autopolyploidy.

Allopolyploids are those in which the genomes making up a multiple set are not alike. You will see later on that in particular instances it may be difficult to tell whether a polyploid organism should be called auto- or allopolyploid.

A guide to the terminology of ploidy is summarized in Table 11-2.

Aneuploidy

Monosomics. Monosomics have a good deal in common with the deficiencies we discussed in the chapter on chromosomal aberrations. You will recall that deficiencies of any considerable length usually result in lethality. It is not surprising, then, that monosomics are rather rarely found. However, viable monosomics have been studied in Drosophila, tobacco, and elsewhere.

Monosomics at meiosis behave much as you might expect. Being of a chromosome constitution $2n - 1$, they produce two kinds of gametes, n and $n - 1$. The odd chromosome, which has no pairing partner, tends to pass at random to either pole at meiosis. Frequently, however, it acts as a laggard at anaphase and is not included in either of the daughter nuclei. For this reason, n gametes occur less frequently than the $n - 1$ type. In plants, nuclei with a missing chromosome seldom survive the gametophytic generation, presumably because the complete absence of certain genes means that fundamental biochemical functions cannot be carried on. This fits well with what we learned about deficiencies.

Perhaps the best known monosomic is the *haplo*-IV type of *D. melanogaster*. Flies of this kind lack one of the fourth chromosomes, to be remembered as by far the smallest in the *D. melanogaster* chromosome complement. Bridges described haplo-IV flies as differing from normals by having pale body color, shortened wings, roughish eyes, slender bristles, reduced fertility, and high mortality.

Haplo-III and haplo-II types have not been found in Drosophila. Apparently the absence of a second or a third chromosome results in the drastic physiological difficulties we expect to follow from any sizable deficiency. XO flies do occur, however, and they turn out to be scarcely distinguishable from normal males (XY), except that XO flies are sterile.

Trisomics. Trisomics are a complementary type to monosomics. The latter have one chromosome too few; the former have a single extra chromosome. These two types of aneuploidy may have exactly the same origin. Sometimes at the first division of meiosis, homologous chromosomes fail to pair properly or to orient themselves in regular fashion at metaphase. If both members of a pair of homologues go to the same pole (*nondisjunction*), half of the eventual products of meiosis will have one chromosome too many, and the other half will be one chromosome short of a full complement.

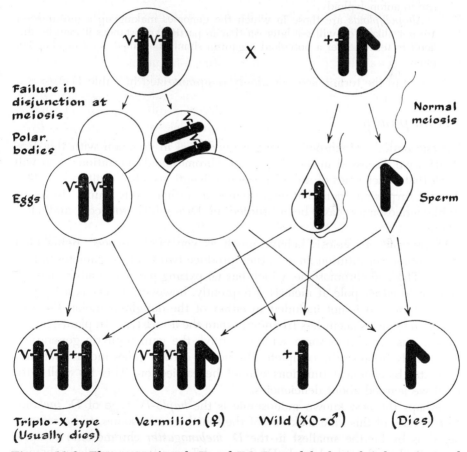

Figure 11-2. *The origin of triplo-X and XO Drosophila through failure of normal disjunction of the X-chromosomes at meiosis. The usual two meiotic divisions are assumed but not shown in the figure. (After Bridges, Genetics, 1:10, 1916.)*

Union of the first type of abnormal meiotic product with a normal gamete of the opposite sex produces a trisomic. Meiotic products with a missing chromosome can give rise to monosomics. A possible origin for triplo-X and XO Drosophila is given in Figure 11-2.

We can expect genetic segregation after crosses involving trisomics to fall into patterns different from those observed among normal diploids. But to make meaningful generalizations about patterns in trisomic inheritance is difficult. A consideration of sources of this difficulty will be instructive.

If disjunction in trisomics were such that two chromosomes always went to one pole, and the third chromosome went to the opposite pole, and if the distribution of individual chromosomes under this condition were random, then predictions as to phenotypic ratios might be made for crosses involving organisms of known genotype. Take, for example, a triplo-IV Drosophila having the genotype $+ + ey$ for the recessive character *eyeless*. Assume absence of crossing over between the locus of eyeless and the centromere. As noted in Figure 11-3, random segregation would give the following gametes in the designated frequencies: $2+ey : 2+ : 1++ : 1ey$. In a cross to ordinary eyeless flies (*ey ey*), the resulting phenotypic ratio would be 5 normal to 1 eyeless, a proportion closely approached when actual crosses of this kind are made. In tomatoes, Datura, corn, and other plants, however analogous crosses do not give these results. And different types of trisomic matings (e.g., $AAa \times AAa$) often fail also to yield results conforming to expectancy as based on the conditions that account for the 5:1 ratio just described.

There are various reasons for these deviations from the expected. First of all, the assumption of no crossing over between the locus of the segregating gene and the centromere of its chromosome may not hold. Moreover, although a trisomic is expected to give rise to equal numbers of $n + 1$ and n gametes, $n + 1$ types may not be formed as frequently; and even if they

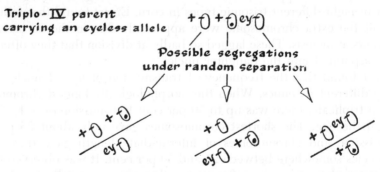

Triplo-IV parent carrying an eyeless allele

Possible segregations under random separation

Summary of gametic types: 1++, 2+, 2+ey, 1ey

Figure 11-3. *The gametic types produced by a triplo-IV Drosophila carrying an eyeless gene. The dot in one of the chromosomes is utilized to distinguish it from its homologue, which also carries a wild-type allele.*

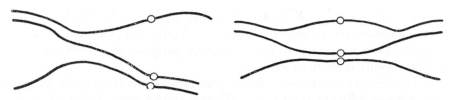

Figure 11-4. *Two trivalent configurations at pachytene. Note that at any given place along the chromosomes, pairing occurs between only two of the homologues.*

are, $n + 1$ pollen may not function as effectively in fertilization. For instance, Buchholz and Blakeslee found in trisomics of Datura that $n + 1$ pollen grows considerably more slowly down the style. In a study involving the trisomic type *cocklebur*, where the 11 · 12 chromosome is present in triplicate, $n + 1$ pollen grew at an average rate of 1.9 mm per hour as compared to 2.6 mm per hour for n pollen.

In the female gametophyte of corn, also, $n + 1$ nuclei fail to reach the theoretical transmission frequency of 50 per cent. This failure seems to be not an effect of poor viability of $n + 1$ female gametes, since trisomic corn plants often give perfectly filled ears. Work carried out by J. Einset, of the New York State Agricultural Experiment Station at Geneva, indicates that the relative infrequency of transmission of the extra chromosome of corn trisomics is due to the frequent loss of this chromosome at meiosis.

When a chromosome exists in triplicate, regular meiotic segregation of two homologues to one pole and one to the other depends on all three homologues pairing in a single *trivalent* configuration. Such a configuration is diagrammed in Figure 11-4, where you will note that at any given place pairing is between two chromosomal segments only. If, instead of a trivalent being formed, two homologues form a *bivalent* configuration and the other homologue exists as a *univalent,* the univalent may be lost altogether during meiosis, as often happens with monosomics. Studying the cytogenetic behavior of eight different trisomic types in corn, Einset found that failures to transmit the extra chromosome were apparently due to the occurrence of univalents at meiosis. These lagged so badly at division that they often were not incorporated into the daughter nuclei.

Einset found that the frequency of transmission of $n + 1$ nuclei varied among different trisomics. When the morphologically longest chromosomes were in triplicate, there was up to 50 per cent transmission of $n + 1$ nuclei through the egg. The shortest chromosomes gave only about 25 per cent transmission, and chromosomes of intermediate length gave transmission frequencies somewhere between 25 and 50 per cent. It was observed that in the shorter chromosomes configurations that were originally trivalent frequently underwent "desynapsis," to form a bivalent and a univalent. With the longer chromosomes, desynapsis was a much less common occurrence. Einset has suggested that these rather curious results may be interpreted in relation to chiasma formation. Assuming that chiasmata tend to prevent the separation of synapsed homologues, longer chromosomes, because they offer greater opportunity for chiasma formation, might be expected to show less frequent desynapsis of the trivalents.

Tetrasomics. It is possible for aneuploid nuclei to have chromosomes occurring in quadruplicate or even to be further reduplicated. Phenotypic expression of the tetrasomic condition may take the form of accentuation of the effects found for the corresponding trisomic. Or, sometimes, the extra chromosomes of a tetrasomic give rise to no obvious consequences. For example, a closely analyzed tetrasomic in wheat, obtained by self-fertilizing a trisomic, was phenotypically indistinguishable from normal.

The four homologues of a tetrasomic often tend to form a quadrivalent figure at meiosis. If disjunction is regular by twos, a fairly stable genetic system can be maintained. But quadrivalents are not always formed, and disjunction is not always regular. On the whole, however, tetrasomics and other even-numbered extra-chromosome types behave in more stable and regular fashion at meiosis than do odd-numbered types.

Euploidy

Monoploidy. In a monoploid organism, each kind of chromosome is represented but once in a nucleus. This is the typical condition in eggs, sperm, and in the gametophytic generation of plants; but to describe nuclei having a *gametic* chromosome number the term *haploid* is generally used. There is a valid reason for this distinction in terms, since polyploid organisms may regularly produce gametes having two or more genomes. The gametic chromosome number of a polyploid may be *haploid* with reference to the chro-

Figure 11-5. *Monoploid and normal (diploid) Marglobe tomatoes. Monoploidy in tomatoes is characterized not only by smaller, relatively weak plants, but, as shown in the photograph, the size of the fruits is also much reduced. Moreover, monoploids produce very few seeds. (Courtesy of Ferry-Morse Seed Co., J. Heredity, 27:432, 1936.)*

mosome number characteristic of the adult organism but not *monoploid* in terms of number of genomes.

As illustrated in Figure 11-5, monoploids are usually smaller and less vigorous than their diploid prototypes. Nevertheless, monoploids hold a certain amount of interest for plant breeders. This is because doubling the chromosomes of a monoploid can give rise to diploid individuals homozygous for all the gene pairs in the organism. The practical advantages in having such genetically "pure lines" for the accurate reproduction of superior germ plasm are obvious. So far, monoploids have not been extensively exploited in crop improvement programs, but work is being done with monoploids of corn, and they may one day be utilized to great benefit.

Characteristically, monoploid plants are highly sterile. The reason for this is that the chromosomes have no regular pairing partners during meiosis. At the first division, some of the chromosomes may go to one pole and some to the other, so that nuclei are formed that are deficient in one or more chromosomes. This leads to the production of large numbers of nonfunctional spores or gametes. Occasionally, by chance, all the members of the genome pass to one pole at the first meiotic division. Then a normal spore or gamete is produced. Union of two "complete" gametes of this kind gives rise to a diploid organism.

If the distribution of chromosomes to the poles is at random in the meiosis of a monoploid, we can make predictions as to the probability of a daughter nucleus receiving the entire genome. The probability of any chromosome going to a given pole is $\frac{1}{2}$ under conditions of random distribution. In the monoploid tomato (12 chromosomes) pictured in Figure 11-5, the probability of all the chromosomes passing to a given pole at meiosis would then be $(\frac{1}{2})^{12}$, or one in 4096 times. Small wonder that monoploids show low fertility and are seldom found in nature.

Triploidy. Triploids have three complete genomes per nucleus. Our discussion here will deal with *autotriploids,* where the genomes have been derived by reduplication within one species of organism and, cytologically at least, are essentially identical.

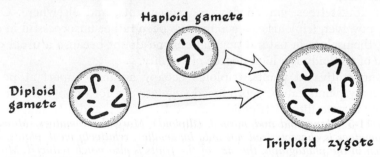

Figure 11-6. *The origin of a triploid, showing two genomes coming from one gamete, and one genome from the other.*

Triploids doubtless can arise in several ways. In general, however, they originate by the fusion of a monoploid gamete with a diploid gamete, a situation that is simply diagrammed in Figure 11-6. Diploid gametes occur sporadically as *unreduced* germ cells in a diploid organism. They are also produced by meiosis in tetraploid organisms or in segments of otherwise diploid organisms where doubling of the somatic chromosome number has taken place. *Somatic doubling* is sometimes spontaneous, but it may also be induced by certain experimental treatments.

In considering the genetics of triploids, you may find it helpful to think of a triploid nucleus as one having a complete set of trisomics. You will immediately realize, then, that the triploid state is highly unstable when it comes to sexual reproduction. The difficulties of triploids, like those of trisomics, arise from the fact that at meiosis there is no way in which the centromeres of three homologous chromosomes can orient themselves to give equivalents at the two poles of the division figure. As a result, if out of every three homologues two go to one pole and one to the other, a meiotic product may contain either n or $2n$ chromosomes, or any number in between. This is generally true whether three homologues originally align themselves as a trivalent or whether they exist as a bivalent and a univalent. Therefore, many of the gametes arising from a triploid have unbalanced genomes. In fact, the probability of getting gametes that are complete in the sense of being either n or $2n$ is relatively small. If you wish to calculate this probability, on the basis that segregation of each set of three chromosomes is independent of the other sets, you may use a procedure similar to that employed in computing the probability for obtaining a complete genome after meiosis in a monoploid. In other words, the probability of a nucleus obtaining a complete genome and no more is $(\frac{1}{2})^n$. (What is the probability that a nucleus will obtain two complete genomes?)

Examples of triploidy in animals are rather rare but cover a range of forms including Drosophila, salamanders, and the land isopod Trichoniscus. Recently, in a Swedish laboratory, triploid rabbits have been produced following a chemical treatment of rabbit eggs at the time of fertilization. Triploidy is somewhat more common and widespread in plants; it has been found in grasses, forest trees, garden flowers, crop plants, and elsewhere. On the whole, however, triploids as a group have been rather unsuccessful in establishing themselves in natural populations, no doubt because a usual consequence of triploidy is a high degree of sterility.

Among cultivated plants, triploids occupy a fairly important position. Since many plants can be reproduced vegetatively, for example by grafts or cuttings, the sterility of triploids can be by-passed, and advantage can be taken of their sometimes superior qualities. A number of important varieties of fruits are triploids, like the Gravenstein and Baldwin apples. The Keizerskroon tulip, which has unusually large flowers, is a triploid, and so are a good many other ornamental plants.

Experimental Techniques for Inducing Polyploidy. Techniques for inducing polyploidy involve creating disturbances in the normal synchronization of the processes of nuclear division. The same general effects may be achieved in a variety of ways. For example, if tomato plants are decapitated, some of the new shoots that arise may turn out to be tetraploid. Also, shoots arising near the point of union in certain graft combinations are not infrequently of a doubled chromosome constitution. L. F. Randolph, at Cornell University, has induced chromosome doubling in corn by surrounding the ear-shoot regions of growing plants with a heating pad. Cold shock has been used to similar effect in Drosophila.

A number of chemical agents induce polyploidy, among which are chloral hydrate, acenaphthene, sulfanilamide, ethyl-mercury-chloride, hexachloro-cyclohexane, and colchicine. Of these, colchicine, an alkaloid obtained from the autumn crocus Colchicum, has been most widely and effectively used. Colchicine is water soluble, and has the added advantage of being almost nontoxic to plant cells at concentrations that are effective in producing a high proportion of polyploid nuclei. Treatments with this substance are also effective on animal cells, and were utilized to produce the triploid rabbits mentioned in the preceding section.

Certain aspects of the action of colchicine on dividing nuclei, especially in plants, are well understood. At critical concentrations of colchicine, spindle fibers do not form, so that the normal process of mitosis is modified to

I Normal mitosis in a nucleus with 2 pairs of chromosomes

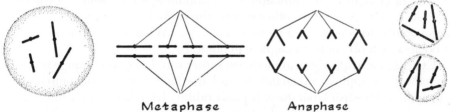

Metaphase   Anaphase

II Mitosis in the same kind of nucleus treated with colchicine

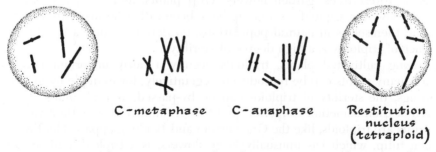

C-metaphase   C-anaphase   Restitution
                                nucleus
                                (tetraploid)

Figure 11-7. *Normal mitosis compared with mitosis in a nucleus treated with colchicine (C-mitosis).*

a sequence of events called *C-mitosis*. In the absence of a functioning spindle, chromosomes fail to move into an equatorial plate but remain scattered in the cytoplasm (a stage called C-metaphase). However, the chromosomes eventually separate at the centromeres, and a C-anaphase is initiated. (See Fig. 11-7.) Following this, the distributed and reduplicated chromosomes go through regular telophasic transformations, with a membrane finally developing around a nucleus which has the doubled chromosome number. If the effects of the colchicine are dissipated, this new polyploid cell may regenerate a bipolar spindle and produce daughter nuclei that are polyploid like their immediate progenitor. But if critical concentrations of colchicine remain, additional C-mitoses may follow, resulting in further reduplications of the chromosome complement. More than 1000 chromosomes have been found in onion root tip nuclei left in colchicine for four days. However, when the reduplication of genomes exceeds octoploidy, the regeneration of a regular spindle mechanism does not readily take place.

Phenotypic Consequences of Autopolyploidy. Many of the phenotypic effects of polyploidy are of practical importance in plant improvement work. These will be considered in Chapter 22, and the following discussion will be confined to a general characterization of the effects of polyploidy.

Effects on Fertility. From the standpoint of evolution, one of the most important effects of autopolyploidy is that it often reduces fertility, sometimes to an extreme degree. A great deal of evidence indicates that sterility in autopolyploids is only partly due to irregular chromosome distribution following multivalent associations at meiosis. The addition of genomes seems frequently to result in disturbances of gene-controlled physiological processes, and thus to alter a variety of conditions essential to normal fertility.

Morphological Effects. Polyploids are sometimes huskier and rather more vigorous than corresponding diploids. In fact, the phenotypic differentiation of polyploids often has led to their first being recognized as unusual types worthy of study. Triploid aspen trees owe their discovery to exceptionally large leaves, which attracted the attention of investigators. Subsequently, triploid aspens were produced experimentally by crossing diploids with tetraploids. Analysis of the triploids revealed that the striking "gigantism" of their leaves was due to appreciably larger cell size. Pollen grains, stomatal cells, and wood cells of the xylem also were found to be larger in the triploids than in the diploids.

G. Fankhauser, of Princeton University, has found that the nuclei and cells of triploid salamanders are consistently larger than those of diploids. The number of cells in most body organs of the triploids is somewhat reduced, however. Through this kind of compensation, the size of organs and over-all body size, as between many diploids and polyploids, remain approximately the same.

The effects of chromosome doubling may differ for various genotypes within a species. In the grass *Stipa lepida* certain autotetraploids have broader leaves than the diploids from which they are derived, but other diploids produce tetraploids that have narrower leaves.

Physiological Effects. The difficulty in drawing general conclusions from morphological comparisons between diploids and polyploids is a reflection of the lack of obvious pattern in physiological differences. For example, the ascorbic acid content has been reported to be higher in tetraploid cabbages and tomatoes than in the corresponding diploids. On the other hand, an investigation of the riboflavin and pantothenic acid in grapes showed diploids and tetraploids to have about the same content of these vitamins.

In summation, we can say that the phenotypic consequences of polyploidy may be expressed in a variety of ways, depending on the species of organism, its particular genotype, the characteristics observed, and no doubt also on the circumstances under which the organism lives.

General Genetic Aspects of Autotetraploidy. Autotetraploids have four similar genomes per nucleus. We have already considered how tetraploidy arises in certain nuclei through somatic doubling. The simplest way in which tetraploidy can occur and be maintained in entire plants is through a fusion of diploid gametes.

At meiosis in autotetraploids, pairing usually takes place in quadrivalent groups, as illustrated in Figure 11-8. Sometimes, however, two pairs of bivalents or a trivalent and a univalent occur. In these cases the products of meiosis are irregularly formed; incomplete genomes find their way into gametes, and sterility often results.

Where quadrivalents are regularly formed, and where disjunction from the quadrivalents is two by two, the chromosomal basis for a stable system of sexual reproduction is at hand. Even then, however, the genetics of tetraploids is far more complex than the genetics of diploids. Considering a given pair of alleles, *A–a*, in an autotetraploid, there are two possible homozygous states, *AAAA* and *aaaa*, and in addition three possible states of heterozygosity, *AAAa*, *AAaa*, and *Aaaa*.

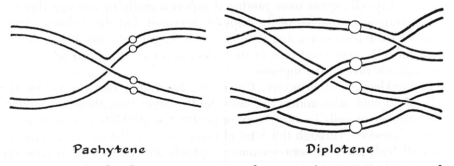

Pachytene   Diplotene

Figure 11-8. *Quadrivalent association in early stages of meiosis in an autopolyploid.*

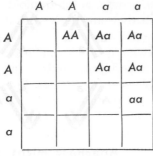

Figure 11-9. *Prediction of the assortment of alleles into gametes in an autotetraploid of the genotype AAaa. The prediction is based on the assumptions that gene a is near the centromere of its chromosome, and that at the first meiotic division the four homologous chromosomes separate at random by twos.*†

Summation of Gametes: 1AA : 4Aa : 1aa

† The checkerboard is a simple device for arriving at the various possible allelic combinations in gametes under these assumptions. Since the horizontal and vertical series outside the checkerboard are merely two different representations of the same meiotic complement, only the portion of the checkerboard that has been filled in needs to be utilized for arriving at all the *different combinations by twos.* The squares on the diagonal from upper left to lower right cannot be utilized; filling in any square on the diagonal would not mean a combination of two different representatives of the meiotic complement but could only mean taking the same representative twice. The other unfilled squares represent duplications of combinations already shown.

Let us first look at a simple instance of segregation in an autotetraploid plant of the genotype *AAaa. If the locus with which we are concerned is close to the centromere of the chromosome,* then assortment of the genes into gametes can be predicted by a summation of random separation of the four chromosomes by twos. Such an assortment is predicted in Figure 11-9, which utilizes the checkerboard square to predict combinations. You see that the gametes can be expected in a proportion of 1AA:4Aa:1aa. Self-fertilization of a plant producing this frequency of gametic types should result in a phenotypic ratio of 35:1, if gene A is dominant over one, two, and three a alleles. Figure 11-10 summarizes the basis of the 35:1 ratio.

Remember, however, that a tetraploid has 8 chromatids at diplotene instead of 4, as occur in a diploid. *If the locus of the gene with which we are concerned is sufficiently distant from the centromere that crossing over*

	gametes		
	1AA	4Aa	1aa
1AA	1 AAAA	4 AAAa	1 AAaa
gametes 4Aa	4 AAAa	16 AAaa	4 Aaaa
1aa	1 AAaa	4 Aaaa	1 aaaa

Figure 11-10. *Results of self-fertilization of an autotetraploid AAaa. The gametic frequencies are those derived under the assumptions noted for Figure 11-9.*

Summation of Phenotypes 35A : 1a

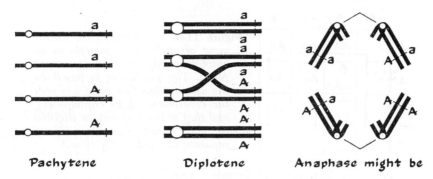

Pachytene   **Diplotene**   **Anaphase might be**

Figure 11-11. *The prediction of the frequency of gametic combinations pro-*
duced in autotetraploids is complicated by crossing over between the centro-
mere and the gene locus involved in the prediction. When such crossing over
occurs, the assortment of genes into gametes cannot be predicted by a mere
summation of random separation of the four chromosomes by twos, which is the
basic assumption in Figure 11-9. The situation pictured above is only one of
many that are possible. A simple variation would occur, for example, if the
centromeres were so oriented that different pairs migrated together at anaphase.

	A	A	A	A	a	a	a	a
A		AA	AA	AA	Aa	Aa	Aa	Aa
A			AA	AA	Aa	Aa	Aa	Aa
A				AA	Aa	Aa	Aa	Aa
A					Aa	Aa	Aa	Aa
a						aa	aa	aa
a							aa	aa
a								aa
a								

Summation of Gametes: 6AA : 16Aa : 6aa

Figure 11-12. *Prediction of the assortment of alleles into gametes in an autotet-*
raploid AAaa where there is "random assortment of chromatids." The predic-
tion is based on the assumption that gene a is located far enough from the cen-
tromere of its chromosome so that chromatid segments containing the a locus
assort at random at meiosis. The use of the checkerboard in making the pre-
diction follows the principle described for Figure 11-9 (see p. 220).

gametes

	3AA	8Aa	3aa
3AA	9 AAAA	24 AAAa	9 AAaa
gametes 8Aa	24 AAAa	64 AaAa	24 Aaaa
3aa	9 AAaa	24 Aaaa	9 aaaa

Figure 11-13. *Results of self-fertilization of an autotetraploid* AAaa *when conditions of "random assortment of chromatids" prevail. The gametic ratio of 6:16:6 shown in Figure 11-12 can be reduced to 3:8:3.*

Summation of Phenotypes: 187A : 9a
(approximately 21:1.)

occurs between them, segregation is immediately complicated (Fig. 11-11). In such an instance, the simplest prediction can be made if we assume that the gene is far enough from the centromere, i.e., 50 map units or more, that these points on the chromosome assort independently. If this condition holds, assortment is said to occur by *chromatids* rather than by *chromosomes. Chromosome assortment* is the situation we dealt with previously, where loci are very near the centromere.

When assortment among appropriate chromatid segments is at random, the gametic combinations of segregating alleles from an organism *AAaa* may be predicted as shown in the checkerboard of Figure 11-12. The proportion of types of gametes so derived is *3AA:8Aa:3aa,* and self-fertilization should give rise to a phenotypic ratio of approximately 21:1 (see Fig. 11-13).

In Table 11-3 are summarized the results to be expected on the basis of "chromosome" and "chromatid" segregation after selfing autotetraploids of different genotypes. *The two columns of values shown in this table, and similarly computed values for other matings, represent limits within which*

TABLE 11-3. *Expected Phenotypic Ratios After Selfing Autotetraploids of Different Genotype.*

PARENTAL GENOTYPE	EXPECTED RATIOS	
	Under "Chromosome" Segregation	Under "Chromatid" Segregation
AAAA	All A	All A
AAAa	All A	783A:1a
AAaa	35A:1a	20.8A:1a
Aaaa	3A:1a	2.4A:1a
aaaa	All a	All a

TABLE 11-4. Chromosome Numbers Indicating Polyploidy in Genera That Include Representative Agricultural Plants.

GENUS AND SPECIES		COMMON NAME	n
Sorghum	versicolor	———	5
	vulgare	Sorghum	10
	halepense	Johnson Grass	20
Gossypium	arboreum	Asiatic treecotton	13
	hirsutum	Upland cotton	26
Trifolium	hybridum	Alsike clover	8
	repens	White clover	16
	medium	Zigzag clover	40 (?)†
Medicago	hispida	Bur clover	8
	sativa	Alfalfa	16
Avena	brevis	Short oat	7
	Abyssinica	Abyssinian oat	14
	sativa	Common cultivated oat	21

† Different chromosome numbers have been reported for this species.

autotetraploid ratios may vary. Many genes show some crossing over with their centromere but still are close enough to it that random assortment of neither chromosomes nor chromatids can be said to maintain. Since this is true, and since occasional separations other than by twos do occur at meiosis, genetic analysis of tetraploids is often difficult.

Application of Principles of Polyploid Genetics. As indicated in Table 11-4, genera which include many of our important crop plants have polyploid members. Plant breeders, then, are constantly confronted with the difficulties inherent in dealing with polyploidy on a genetic basis. Some of these are already apparent to you. Others can be readily seen in polyploid ratios of the kind you have just been studying. For example, you saw from Table 11-3 that in autotetraploids the recessive phenotype often appears relatively infrequently as compared to the 3:1 relationship found in the F_2 progeny of a diploid hybrid. If a breeder is looking for recessive phenotypes in a population involving the segregation of more than one gene, the difficulties of working with polyploids are accentuated. Suppose that a dihybrid *AAaa BBbb* is selfed. The phenotypic ratio expected on the basis of random assortment of chromosomes is:

Phenotype	Frequency
AB	1225
Ab	35
aB	35
ab	1

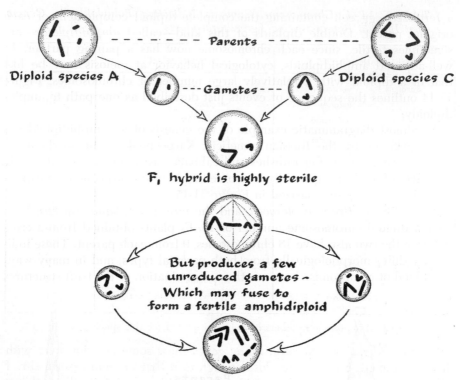

Figure 11-14. *The typical sequence of events leading to amphidiploidy.*

Recall that the corresponding diploid ratio from selfing *AaBb* is 9:3:3:1. In an autotetraploid trihybrid, if random "chromosome assortment" occurs, the chance of obtaining an individual showing all three recessive characters is somewhat lower than 1 in 45,000. From a practical standpoint, this means that plant breeders sometimes need to grow immense populations, and do some very close looking, to have a reasonable chance of finding particular combinations they want. Notice that we have not introduced into our examples such complications as linkage and incomplete dominance!

Origin of Allopolyploids: The Genesis of an Amphidiploid. When certain crosses are made between members of distinct taxonomic groups, the first-generation hybrid is highly sterile, because the genomes are so different that each kind of chromosome lacks a homologue to act as its pairing partner at meiosis. Because of sterility, such hybrids face extinction unless they are able to reproduce vegetatively. Even with unsystematic distribution of the chromosomes at meiosis, however, some unreduced gametes can be expected to occur merely by chance. The situation is comparable to the formation of unreduced gametes in monoploids. Or, somatic doubling in the hybrid may result in the regular formation of gametes containing one complete genome of each of the parental types. A fusion of such gametes gives rise to a fertilized egg cell containing the complete diploid complement of each original parent. Double diploids of this kind—called *amphidiploids*—are sometimes fertile, since each chromosome now has a pairing partner. In well-adjusted amphidiploids, cytological behavior at meiosis may be like that of a diploid with a relatively large number of chromosomes. Figure 11-14 outlines the sequence of events just described as one path to amphidiploidy.

An almost diagrammatic example of the genesis of an amphidiploid has been given us by the Russian geneticist Karpechenko, who made intergeneric crosses involving radishes and cabbages as parents, and ultimately obtained a fertile and generally true-breeding hybrid. Karpechenko's experimental results are summarized in Figure 11-15.

The cabbage, *Brassica oleracea,* and the radish, *Raphanus sativus,* both have a diploid chromosome number of 18. F_1 plants obtained from a cross between the two also have 18 chromosomes, 9 from each parent. These individuals differ morphologically from both parental types, and in many ways are a kind of compromise between them. Examination of the fruit structures

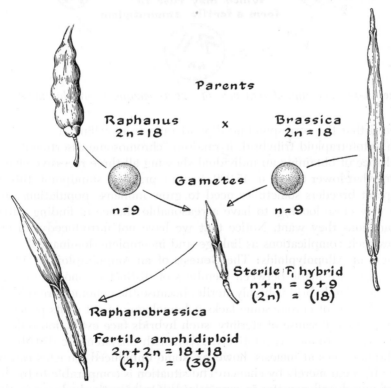

Parents

Raphanus   x   Brassica
2n = 18   2n = 18

Gametes

n = 9   n = 9

Sterile F_1 hybrid
n + n = 9 + 9
(2n) = (18)

Raphanobrassica

Fertile amphidiploid
2n + 2n = 18 + 18
(4n) = (36)

Figure 11-15. *The origin of the Raphanobrassica, showing chromosome numbers and characteristic fruit structures for the different plants involved. (After Karpechenko, Z. Indukt. Abst. Vererb., 48:27, 1928.)*

of the different kinds of plants, parents and progeny, shows this particularly well. The F_1 plants are highly sterile because of failures in pairing at meiosis. They do produce a few seeds, however, and some of the plants arising from these seeds turn out to be fertile. Cytological examination reveals 36 chromosomes in the nuclei of somatic cells. Chromosomal behavior is regular, even at meiosis, where pairing takes place in such fashion that 18 bivalents are formed. It is apparent that the fertile F_2 plants have arisen from a fusion of unreduced gametes from F_1 individuals, and that these F_2 plants contain the full diploid complements of the original cabbage and radish progenitors. Morphologically, the amphidiploids are a good deal like the F_1 hybrids. But the fruits of the amphidiploids are characteristically somewhat larger, with the plants as a whole possessing a good deal of the robustness which sometimes is a consequence of reduplication of genomes. This stable new form of plant may be considered a distinct taxonomic entity. In recognition of its hybrid origin, it has been given the name *Raphanobrassica*.

Diverse Forms of Allopolyploidy. The Raphanobrassica was chosen to introduce you to allopolyploidy because it offers a simple and straightforward example. Among naturally and experimentally produced allopolyploids there are many variations on the theme we have introduced. Some of these variations can be seen among plant types obtained following crosses of members of the genus Rubus. The European raspberry, *R. idaeus*, has 14 chromosomes, and we can represent its two genomes by the symbols I and I. The dewberry, *R. caesius*, is a tetraploid having 28 chromosomes; its genomes can be designated $C_1C_1C_2C_2$. Hybridization of the European raspberry and the dewberry produces sterile F_1 individuals (IC_1C_2) that are triploids with 21 chromosomes. Chromosome doubling in the F_1's has given rise to hexaploid amphiploids. Backcrosses to the parents designated above have given rise respectively to tetraploids and pentaploids. These results can be summarized:

	Genomes	Chromosome Number
F_1 is	IC_1C_2	21
Backcross to *R. idaeus* gives	IIC_1C_2	28
Backcross to *R. caesius* gives	$IC_1C_1C_2C_2$	35
Amphiploid (*R. maximus*) is	$IIC_1C_1C_2C_2$	42

(After Clausen, Keck, and Hiesey, "Experimental Studies on the Nature of Species," *Carnegie Inst. Wash. Pub.* 564, p. 111, 1945.)

Apparently only unreduced gametes of the triploid F_1 function in these crosses.

Difficulties of Distinguishing Between Auto- and Allopolyploidy. Autopolyploidy and allopolyploidy are not entirely separate phenomena, and to distinguish between the two is often difficult. In the first place, a given individual may combine characteristics of both auto- and allopolyploidy. This is the case, for example, with any redoubled amphidiploid. Moreover, there is no simple answer to the question of *how different* genomes must be in order to make an individual an allo- rather than an autopolyploid. Within species, genic constitution and structural arrangement of chromosomes may vary considerably among individuals. On the other hand, in the widest possible crosses the parents may have a good many genes in common, and between the parents there may be numbers of homologous chromosome segments. In short, genomes show innumerable shades of difference.

Attempts have been made to distinguish kinds of polyploidy on the basis of chromosome homologies as indicated by pairing affinities at meiosis. The principle here is that autopolyploids should show multivalent associations at meiosis and allopolyploids should not. This criterion breaks down, however, in many instances. A well-known example involves members of the Primrose family. *Primula kewensis* arose at Kew, in England, as a result of somatic doubling in a sterile hybrid plant obtained from a cross between *P. floribunda,* a native of Afghanistan, and *P. verticillata,* an Arabian species. Two facts about chromosome pairing in *P. kewensis* are worth noting. First, pairing in the diploid F_1 was almost regular (an indication that not all hybrid sterility is due to failures in pairing). Second, some quadrivalent formation occurs in the tetraploid. Thus, if *P. kewensis* were not known to have arisen as a species hybrid, criteria of chromosome pairing might lead to its classification as an autopolyploid. Conversely, in some undoubted autopolyploids, of which there are examples in the tomato, conjugation may occur largely as bivalents. Here classification on the basis of chromosome pairing would probably lead to an autoploid being designated as an alloploid. As a final complication, over a period of time autopolyploids may shift from a multivalent to a bivalent type of synapsis. Cytological examination has been made of autotetraploid corn that originated following heat treatment in 1937 and has been propagated every year since. Plants grown from seed of the 1937 harvest showed more quadrivalents and fewer bivalents at meiosis than did plants grown from seed of the 1947 harvest.

Unless the origin of a polyploid is specifically known, or unless it is a rather extreme or "typical" example of one of the two types, there is no foolproof way of telling whether an unknown type should be called auto- or allopolyploid. Perhaps the most useful rule of thumb that can be employed is one suggested by G. L. Stebbins, cytogeneticist at the University of California, who discusses this problem in the article in *American Naturalist* cited at the end of this chapter. He proposes that "an autopolyploid is a polyploid of which the corresponding diploid is a fertile species, while an allopolyploid is a polyploid containing the doubled genome of a more or less sterile hybrid." (See whether you can outline the general argument on which such a definition would be based.) Very often, however, a variety of criteria need to be invoked in the analysis of polyploids, including studies of chromosome morphology and conjugation, and of cytological and morphological relationships with other members of the taxonomic groups involved.

Polyploidy and Evolution. Some authorities estimate that a third or more of the species of angiosperms are polyploids. And polyploidy is common, although not everywhere found, in the rest of the plant kingdom. This argues strongly for the evolutionary significance of polyploidy.

To leap immediately to judgment of the importance of polyploidy in evolution may lead to precarious conclusions, however. Autoploidy as such adds no new genes to the chromosome complex. The phenotypic effects of autoploidy are frequently seen largely as exaggerations of characteristics already present in the diploid. Only seldom do significantly divergent characters appear. Allopolyploids are sometimes strikingly different from any of their progenitor types; but also they may be nearly indistinguishable from one of the parental species, and they are most often intermediates. Stebbins has expressed the view that allopolyploidy "has probably involved chiefly the production of new combinations of characters, rather than the origin of the characters themselves." †

What, then, is the role of polyploidy in evolution? A few of the concepts that have emerged from the voluminous work of many investigators appear in the following paragraphs.

Polyploidy and the Sudden Emergence of Species. In Chapter 21 of this book you will learn that in many of its aspects evolution moves slowly and involves gradual processes by which many differences in organisms arise and are accumulated. In contrast to these time-consuming forces, at least one mechanism operates by which species may originate in what has been termed "cataclysmic" fashion. This mechanism is polyploidy. You have seen in the case of the Raphanobrassica how a new taxonomic entity can be produced in a relatively few simple steps. There is little reason to doubt that the experimental synthesis of Raphanobrassica followed steps that have led to the formation of many naturally occurring amphiploids.

More or less direct observations of this kind of evolution in action have been made with reference to *Spartina townsendii,* which has been called "probably the only amphiploid which is known to have arisen spontaneously in historic times." *Spartina townsendii,* a kind of cord grass, was first collected in England in 1870. By 1907 it had spread over thousands of acres on the south coast of England, and now it is established on the coast of France as well. The fascinating history of *S. townsendii* is summarized in a paper by Huskins cited among this chapter's references.

There is a good deal of evidence for the amphiploid origin of *S. townsendii.* First, it combines several of the distinctive characteristics of *S. stricta,* a European species, and *S. alterniflora,* a species thought to be American in origin but transferred to Europe via shipping. Natural populations of *S. stricta* and *S. alterniflora* meet in precisely the locality in which *S. townsendii* appeared. Huskins' cytological studies showed that *S. townsendii* has 63 pairs of chromosomes, the sum of the chromosome numbers of its puta-

† *Advances in Genetics,* 1:427, 1947.

tive parents. S. *alterniflora* has 35 pairs of chromosomes, and S. *stricta* 28 pairs.

Polyploidy as a Conservative Force in Evolution. A diploid that can give rise to polyploids is flexible in the evolutionary sense because of its possibility for rapid production of new types. This is especially important in the event of sudden environmental changes unfavorable to previously existing members of the group.

Polyploidy, once developed, makes for inflexibility. Mutations to the recessive form of a gene have relatively little chance of expressing themselves phenotypically in polyploids. The discussion of autotetraploid ratios as contrasted with diploid ratios should have given you preliminary indication that this holds true.

Allopolyploidy has much the same general effect with reference to the phenotypic expression of mutant recessive genes. At least the effect is the same for loci in common among the diverse genomes of an allopolyploid. Let us take any amphidiploid and designate its different genomes as *1* and *2*. If a gene *A* occurs in both genomes, the genotype for a homozygous dominant individual might be written $A^1A^1A^2A^2$. Suppose now that gene A^1 mutates to a recessive form a^1. Reproduction of the mutant allele followed by recombination may produce individuals of the genotype $a^1a^1A^2A^2$. But dominant alleles are still present, and the dominant phenotype will be preserved.

Assuming the amphidiploid to behave cytogenetically like a diploid, no normal recombination can give rise to completely homozygous recessive individuals under the conditions we have outlined. If such homozygous recessives are to occur, independent mutation of the *A* gene must take place in genome 2. On the basis that mutations are random events, the probability of simultaneous mutations in the two different genomes would be something like the square of the probability for one mutation. Of course, a recessive mutation occurring in one of the different genomes might be reproduced at length until a corresponding mutation of the wild-type allele took place in the other kind of genome. But even this possibility scarcely argues for the genetic flexibility of polyploids. Some experimental results obtained by L. J. Stadler are pertinent. In studies of the frequencies of visible mutations induced by X-rays, he found that significantly fewer mutations appeared in tetraploid wheats than in diploids. In a hexaploid wheat, he observed no mutations at all.

The visible effects of recessive gene mutation tend, then, to be suppressed by polyploidy. The result is that polyploids have largely lost one of the important sources of variability available to diploids. Since inherited variability is essential for evolution, one of the evolutionary disadvantages of polyploidy becomes apparent.

Polyploidy in Relation to Asexual Reproduction. The frequency of occurrence of polyploidy within plant groups has been found to be positively correlated with the occurrence of means for asexual reproduction, which takes many forms in the plant kingdom. Both the reasons for this association and its consequences have been objects of active investigation accompanied by fruitful debate. We cannot detail this debate here. It seems clear, however, that polyploidy can become established more readily where means for asexual reproduction are at hand. This is because one of the frequent immediate consequences of polyploidy is reduction in sexual fertility.

Continued asexual reproduction has the important consequence that genetic variation is lost. Here, then, is another aspect of the lack of genetic flexibility so often characteristic of polyploidy.

Polyploidy and Geographical Distribution. When polyploids and their diploid prototypes show physiological and morphological differences, they can be expected to show adaptation to different environmental conditions. And in fact, polyploids and their diploid relatives frequently have different geographical distributions.

For an example we can turn to the genus Crepis, which belongs to the family of plants called the composites. Races of Crepis which occupy the Mt. Hamilton range in California appear to be allopolyploids. The climate of their habitat is essentially the combination of a hot, dry summer and a mild winter. This is not a climate typical of the regions inhabited by any of the diploid species of Crepis. Indications are, however, that the allopolyploids of the Mt. Hamilton region arose from diploid progenitors, one of which is adapted to a cold, dry climate and the other to rather mild, relatively moist conditions. The implication is that the tolerance of dryness on the one hand and tolerance of a mild winter on the other comes about in the allopolyploids as a result of the combination of different genomes.

We can generalize to say that polyploids, through the accumulation of diverse genomes, have the ability to acquire wide ranges of environmental tolerance. This, plus the fact that different polyploid forms may be *rapidly* evolved, has served to make polyploids expert colonizers, especially when environmental change opens new areas to plant invasion. For any given instance, however, the success or lack of success of polyploidy as an evolutionary mechanism depends on a variety of factors. In the higher northern latitudes, the proportion of polyploids is particularly great. Stebbins has emphasized that the "success" of polyploidy in these regions is partly attributable to the prevailing growth habit among arctic plants. Arctic flora include a great many perennials with means for asexual reproduction, a condition which favors the establishment of polyploidy.

Keys to the Significance of This Chapter

Additions and losses of chromosomes and of whole sets of chromosomes are important sources of heritable variability. Since aneuploidy and euploidy result in altered numbers of genes, and sometimes in altered genic proportions or even genic composition, they lead to physiological and morphological variations in the organism.

Aneuploidy gives rise to alterations of physiological balance which may or may not be deleterious. For the most part, an aneuploid state does not breed true, and irregularities at meiosis occurring in aneuploids often result in sterility as well as in genetic instability. The consequences of aneuploidy are therefore not likely to lead to evolutionary success.

The implications of euploidy, at least in the light of present knowledge, appear to be different. Reduplication of complete genomes does not unbalance the organism so drastically as do alterations in number of individual chromosomes. Some polyploids are able to behave quite regularly at meiosis and to undertake sexual reproduction, thereby avoiding the penalties of sterility.

By means of various forms of auto- and allopolyploidy, taxonomic groups within the plant kingdom have been able to elaborate a variety of new forms whose fitness for survival is tested by their environments. The relative rapidity with which this process of elaboration can take place is doubtless of the utmost importance under circumstances of sudden change in environment. Thus many plant groups are constant participants in an unconscious experimentation to provide types better adapted to altering conditions and to the different ecological circumstances occurring at the boundaries of the original locale of the group.

The importance of polyploidy in evolution has as yet scarcely been measured. But it must be remembered that there is no evidence that polyploidy as such is effective beyond giving new combinations or new emphases of principles already established in organisms. There is some reason to believe that the major role of polyploidy is the exploitation rather than the origination of trends in evolution. Polyploid forms tend to lack plasticity, and therefore they appear chiefly to describe the byways rather than the main tracks of evolutionary progression.

References

Blakeslee, A. F., "New Jimson Weeds from Old Chromosomes." *J. Heredity*, 25:80–108, 1934. (A readable summary of the most extensive investigation of trisomics carried out in any plant. This article has many useful diagrams and photographic illustrations.)

Clausen, J., Keck, D. D., and Hiesey, W. M., "Experimental Studies on the Nature of Species. II. Plant Evolution through Amphiploidy and Autoploidy, with Examples from the Madiinae." *Carnegie Inst. Wash. Pub.* 564, 1945. (Contains brief summaries of our knowledge of the origin of many allopolyploids. For example, the origin and history of the loganberry, pp. 112–115, is likely to be of interest to many students.)

Clausen, R. E., and Cameron, D. R., "Inheritance in *Nicotiana tabacum*. XVIII. Monosomic Analysis." *Genetics*, 29:447–477, 1944. (Describes the complete set of monosomics which have now been isolated from tobacco. Includes discussion of methods for obtaining monosomics and of uses to which monosomics may be put, for example, in the location of genes in particular chromosomes.)

Einset, J., "Chromosome Length in Relation to Transmission Frequency of Maize Trisomes." *Genetics*, 28:349–364, 1943. (The details of work referred to in the discussion of trisomics in this chapter.)

Gustafsson, A., "Some Aspects on Variation and Evolution in Plants." *Evolution*, 5:181–184, 1951. (A brief review of Stebbins' book noted below. Can serve to point out some of the highlights of this work to the genetics student.)

Huskins, C. L., "The Origin of *Spartina townsendii*." *Genetica*, 12:531–538, 1930. (Describes the natural origin of a new amphidiploid species.)

Leslie, J. W., "Trisomic Types of the Tomato and Their Relation to the Genes." *Genetics*, 17:545–559, 1932. (Describes and pictures certain tomato trisomics.)

Little, T. M., "Gene Segregation in Autotetraploids." *Botan. Rev.*, 11:60–85, 1945. (Summarizes autotetraploid ratios and discusses their basis.)

Müntzing, A., "The Evolutionary Significance of Autopolyploidy." *Hereditas*, 21:263–378, 1936. (An exhaustive treatment replete with examples.)

Stebbins, G. L., "The Significance of Polyploidy in Plant Evolution." *Am. Naturalist*, 74:54–66, 1940. (A general essay on the subject, including the example of geographical distribution of Crepis cited in this chapter.)

———, *Variation and Evolution in Plants*. New York: Columbia University Press, 1950. (Chaps. 8, 9, and 10 deal with aspects of polyploidy important in evolution. A scholarly and vigorous treatment.)

Stephens, S. G., "The Internal Mechanism of Speciation in Gossypium." *Botan. Rev.*, 16:115–149, 1950. (Deals with interspecific hybridization among cottons, emphasizing the significance of small structural differences between genomes.)

Sturtevant, A. H., and Randolph, L. F., "Iris Genetics." *Am. Iris Soc. Bull.*, No. 99: 52–66, 1945. (Includes an elementary discussion of autotetraploid ratios and the practical problem of recovering recessive types from autotetraploids.)

Questions and Problems

11- 1.   What do the following terms signify?

amphidiploid	genome
aneuploid	somatic doubling
chromatid assortment	trivalent
chromosome assortment	univalent
euploid	unreduced gamete

11- 2.   In corn, how many chromosomes would be typical of the root tip nuclei in (a) a monosomic, (b) a trisomic, (c) a monoploid, (d) a triploid, (e) a tetrasomic, (f) an autotetraploid?

11- 3.   What is the basis of distinction between *haploid* and *monoploid*?

11- 4. What are the criteria for distinguishing between auto- and allopolyploids? How reliable are these criteria?

11- 5. In corn, R is a gene for red aleurone; its recessive allele r determines colorless. McClintock and Hill made a cross between a diploid rr and a trisomic Rrr, using the diploid as the female parent. There were 1282 red kernels and 2451 colorless in the progeny. Confirm that this approximation of a 1:2 ratio is expected, if the $n + 1$ pollen grains are nonfunctional.

11- 6. On the basis of the result noted in the preceding question, what ratio of colored to colorless would be expected from the cross rr ♀ × RRr ♂ ? (Actually McClintock and Hill obtained 646 red kernels and 355 colorless after making such a cross.)

11- 7. Assume that gene x is a new mutant in corn. An x x plant is crossed with a triplo-10 individual (trisomic for chromosome 10) carrying only dominant alleles at the x locus. Trisomic progeny are recovered and crossed back to xx ♀♀. What ratio of dominant to recessive phenotypes is expected if the x locus is not in chromosome 10? If it is in chromosome 10?

11- 8. Assuming that you had a complete set of trisomics in maize, how could you utilize the type of experiment indicated in the preceding question to determine which of the chromosomes of corn was the site of any new gene mutation you happened to discover?

11- 9. What advantages would this trisomic method for determining the linkage group of a new mutant have over the familiar method of utilizing testcrosses involving the new gene and known members of already established linkage groups?

11-10. A gene A is situated very near the centromere of its chromosome. What phenotypic ratio of A to a is expected if $AAaa$ plants are testcrossed against $aaaa$ individuals? (Assume that the dominant phenotype is expressed whenever at least one A allele is present.)

11-11. What would be the answer to Question 11-10 if the locus of A were far enough from the centromere to permit "random assortment of chromatids"?

11-12. In tetraploid irises, the *plicata* pattern and *tangerine beard* are both recessive characters. Suppose that you have lines true breeding for each of these characters and wish to obtain a plicata with tangerine beard. You cross these lines and obtain an F_2, but none of the desired individuals appear. This failure would not be too unlikely unless you had an immense population. What would you do next? Obtain another F_2, or carry your original crosses to F_3? Why? (Various ramifications of this problem are discussed in the reference by Sturtevant and Randolph, pp. 61–63.)

11-13. What would you estimate to be the probable frequency of fertile pollen in a monoploid plant derived from a diploid with five pairs of chromosomes?

11-14. Why in plants is the transmission of unbalanced genomes in general less frequent through male than through female gametes?

11-15. Experimentally induced chromosome doubling has led to production of tetraploid lines of corn many of which are more vigorous than corresponding diploids. From your knowledge of the genetics of autotetraploids, what might you anticipate as a difficulty in utilizing these tetraploid lines of corn in agricultural production?

11-16. Is polyploidy more readily established in plant groups *with* means for asexual reproduction or in groups *without* such means? Why?

11-17. What are some of the reasons that polyploids are often relatively "inflexible," or conservative, in the evolutionary sense?

11-18. The American cultivated cotton *Gossypium hirsutum* has 26 pairs of chromosomes. The Asiatic cotton *G. arboreum* has 13 pairs of chromosomes, as does an American cotton, *G. thurberi*. When *hirsutum* and *arboreum* are crossed, the resulting triploids have 13 pairs of chromosomes and 13 singles at meiosis. Thirteen pairs and 13 singles are also observed in triploids derived from the cross *hirsutum* × *thurberi*. When *thurberi* and *arboreum* are crossed, the F₁ individuals are highly sterile, with chromosome pairing being very irregular. What do these observations suggest about the possible origin of American cultivated cotton?

11-19. What steps might an investigator take to produce experimentally from diploid species a cotton chromosomally equivalent to American cultivated cotton?

11-20. How may amphidiploids arise other than through chromosome doubling of a sterile F₁ interspecific hybrid?

CHAPTER 12

Mutations

IN THE SPRING of 1937 an unusual fox was born on a ranch in Wisconsin. His parents were ordinary standard silver foxes, and there was nothing remarkable in his ancestry. But he himself was remarkable; he was symmetrically spotted with white, and the parts of his fur that were colored were a silvery blue. He was an attractive fox—a "platinum silver" (Plate II, facing p. 6).

In 1939, "Hillcrest Chief," as the platinum fox was called, mated with an ordinary silver female and sired a litter of four pups—two ordinary silver and two platinum like himself. During the years since 1938, platinum has been shown to be inherited as a simple dominant characteristic. Since it is dominant, and since the parents, grandparents, and great grandparents of Hillcrest Chief are known to have been nonplatinum, a change from the normal allele to the dominant allele for platinum must have occurred in the germ line of one of Chief's parents. The sperm or the egg that gave rise to the platinum fox contained the allele for platinum, but the somatic tissues of both parents were nonplatinum. Such sudden, heritable changes are called *mutations.*

Had the Wisconsin mutation to platinum occurred only a few years earlier, it would probably have been discarded, rather secretly and guiltily, by the breeder. Fox and mink breeders, together with other animal breeders and plant breeders generally, had a horror of new and unusual types appearing in their herds, kennels, fields, and flocks. These variations were considered an indication of "impurity" in the breeding stock. And indeed there were and are sound reasons, in many instances, for such an opinion. An undesirable recessive may be carried as a hidden "impurity" for generations, only to crop out as a visible indication of that impurity through mating of unsuspected heterozygotes. The basis for distinguishing between the sudden appearance of new forms through simple recombinations of hidden recessive alleles on the one hand, and, on the other, through the appearance of mutations, could not be expected to be available to most breeders even if the distinction were appreciated as a necessary one.

But for the platinum fox the economic aspects of a new type had by 1937 been shown to be opposite from those prevailing in most other lines of plant and animal breeding. However greatly an off-color variant on his ranch might irritate the esthetic standards of a breeder of "pure" fox strains, the ladies who bought or accepted furs evidently prized natural colors that were different from those worn by their neighbors. A mutation to platinum had occurred in Norway in 1933, and another independent mutation, apparently of the same gene, in 1934. By 1937, buyers were paying as much as $500 for a single platinum pelt; breeding stock was at a premium, and breeders were spending $1000 for the privilege of mating an ordinary silver female to another breeder's platinum male. In 1939, one Norwegian platinum skin sold for $11,000 on the New York market. The Norwegian breeders had placed an embargo on the export of platinum breeding stock, and efforts had been made to secure international patents on the characteristic.

Perhaps fortunately for American fox breeders, at least three independent mutations to platinum occurred in America. The new form of the gene was widely disseminated, and with the decline in its novelty the platinum characteristic lost much of its premium value. Because platinum pelts are attractive, however, they still command respectable prices on the market. And fur breeders have learned a valuable lesson; today almost any new color mutation is exploited for its novelty instead of being hidden as an indication of impurity.

Characteristics of Spontaneous Mutation

Repeated Occurrences of the Same Mutation. Besides illustrating the fact of spontaneous mutation, the platinum fox exemplifies an important general characteristic of changes in germ plasm. Any particular gene change is usually *recurrent;* if we wait and search long enough we can expect to observe the same change again. And any particular change that we observe today is likely to have occurred many times before in the history of the species.

The frequency with which specific changes occur varies from one gene to another. The normal allele of platinum, for example, seems to be a relatively labile gene; it was observed to change to its allele for platinum at least five times independently during the decade of the 1930's. Other genes affecting color in foxes are apparently much more stable. Similarly, in human beings, the normal allele of the sex-linked recessive gene for hemophilia is an example of a relatively unstable gene; it has mutated to its defective allele many times in human history, and estimates indicate that about one normal allele of the gene for hemophilia in 31,000 mutates to its defective allele in each generation. On the other hand, the normal allele of the gene for Huntington's chorea, a severe nervous disorder appearing relatively late in life, seems to be a fairly stable gene. In the United States almost all the carriers of the dominant allele for Huntington's chorea can be

TABLE 12-1. Summary of Estimates of the Rate of Mutation of Human Genes. (After Neel and Falls, Science, 114:421, 1951.)

CLASSIFICATION OF GENE	CHARACTER PRODUCED BY GENE†	AVERAGE NUMBER OF MUTATIONS OF STANDARD ALLELE PER MILLION GAMETES
Autosomal dominant	Epiloia	10
	Chondrodystrophy	45
	Pelger's nuclear anomaly	80
	Aniridia	10
	Retinoblastoma	23
Autosomal recessive	Microphthalmos and anophthalmos	15
	Albinism	28
	Congenital total color blindness	28
	Infantile amaurotic idiocy	11
	Ichthyosis congenita	11
Sex-linked recessive	Hemophilia	32

† Most of these characteristics are described in *Medical Genetics*, by L. H. Snyder, Duke University Press, 1941.

traced back through their pedigrees to three brothers who came to New England in the 17th Century. No mutations in the normal allele since the time of this country's colonization have been noted, in contrast to the several changes known to have occurred in the normal allele of the gene for hemophilia during the same interval.

Table 12-1 gives a summary of mutation-rate determinations for human genes. Most of those whose rates have been measured appear to be relatively unstable.

It is difficult to get direct data on frequencies of particular gene changes (*mutation rates*) in human or large animal populations. Only very prolific forms under experimental control can be studied relatively easily in this regard. Even Drosophila require extensive and laborious experiments. The fact that much of what we know of mutation comes originally from work with Drosophila represents no easy accomplishment on the part of geneticists working with this form. Corn has also been useful in studies of mutation.

In recent years, organisms much more prolific even than Drosophila and corn have been shown to be of value in mutation studies. These include bacteria and molds, especially the mold Neurospora.

Reversibility of the Process of Mutation. The second general characteristic of mutation to be discussed is easily illustrated with Neurospora: Mutations are often reversible. That is, an allele that arose through mutation of a gene can in turn mutate back to the original form of the gene.

The techniques that have been developed for the analysis of reverse mutation ("back mutation") in bacteria and Neurospora, and in similar forms, are simple in principle and effective. They depend mainly on the use of biochemical mutations—mutations that involve specific failures in biochemical syntheses that the wild type can perform. For example, a particular strain of Neurospora cannot grow unless *adenine* is added to the medium in which it is growing. Wild-type Neurospora can grow very well without being provided with adenine, because it can make enough for its needs from other sources in the medium. The difference between this particular adenineless strain and wild type is controlled by a single pair of alleles. Apparently, one gene controls a specific step in the synthesis of adenine by wild-type Neurospora, and an allele of this gene fails in this step. The defective allele was picked up as a mutation from wild type.

If conidia of the adenineless strain are placed in a medium lacking adenine, they will not grow as long as they have the mutant allele. But if this allele back-mutates to the wild-type form of the gene, the ability to grow on the unfortified medium is restored. By testing a known very large number of conidia, and observing what proportion of these regain their ability to produce their own adenine and therefore to grow on unfortified medium, a measure of the rate of back-mutation is easily obtained (see Fig. 12-6A).

The scheme has its drawbacks. Each of the conidia has several nuclei, and the back-mutation rate is therefore difficult to put on a precise "per-gene" basis. Sometimes, changes in genes at other loci ("suppressors") can produce the same apparent end-result as a back-mutation. On the other hand, the development of wild-type back-mutants is in some cases inhibited by the presence of large numbers of non-wild-type cells in the culture with them. And it is sometimes difficult to be sure how many of the apparent back-mutations are really independent and how many represent cellular descendants of a single primary reverse mutation. But when allowance is made for all these and other difficulties, it remains clear that a technique of this kind is a very productive method for large-scale study of mutation rates.

The essential characteristics of spontaneous mutation so far discussed can be summarized by means of a simple diagram:

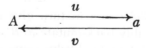

in which A and a are alleles, and u and v represent the mutation rates in the two directions. The diagram implies that:

1. Genes spontaneously change to allelic forms, at rates generally constant for any particular gene but varying from one gene to another. A sample of mutation rates in corn is given in Table 12-2.

2. Mutation is often reversible; the rates in the two directions are usually different.

TABLE 12-2. Frequency of Spontaneous Mutation in Corn. (After Stadler, Spragg Memorial Lectures, Third Series, p. 13. Michigan State College, 1942.)

GENE	NUMBER OF GAMETES TESTED	NUMBER OF MUTATIONS OBSERVED	FREQUENCY PER MILLION GAMETES
R	554,786	273	492
I	265,391	28	106
Pr	647,102	7	11
Su	1,678,736	4	2
C	426,923	1	2
Y	1,745,280	4	2
Sh	2,469,285	3	1
Wx	1,503,744	0	0

Multiple Alleles. As you might expect, a number of different mutational possibilities exist for any particular gene. When, for example, the R gene in Table 12-2 mutates, it may change to any one of a large number of mutant alleles. Alleles at this locus may be classified into four main groups, depending on how they affect aleurone color and certain pigments (not including chlorophyll) of the plant:

R^r = colored aleurone, pigmented plant—red or purple.
R^g = colored aleurone, unpigmented (therefore, green) plant.
r^r = colorless aleurone, pigmented plant—red or purple.
r^g = colorless aleurone, unpigmented (green) plant.

These groups may again be subdivided; there are, for example, at least 22 different alleles that fall within the R^r class but which differ among themselves in such characteristics as the amount and distribution of pigment they produce. (*See* Stadler, L. J., in References.)

The various mutational possibilities for a particular gene are not equally likely to occur. For example, when an allele of the R^r class mutates, it is much more likely to change to one of the R^g or of the r^r class than to an r^g allele.

Similarly, the mutant alleles can in turn give rise by mutation to new alleles, or they can presumably back-mutate to R^r. Here again, the different possible mutations are not equally likely; some of the changes that you might expect to occur have in fact never been observed.

Different mutations at the same locus give rise to *multiple allelic series*. These series are symbolized in terms of a basic designation for the locus, and the different alleles are usually distinguished by superscripts. Thus in Drosophila, the sex-linked white-eye locus (w) is represented by a large number of different alleles. These include eosin (w^e) and apricot (w^a), as well as white (w) and the wild-type allele (w^+) (Plate III, facing p. 7).

A male may have any one of these alleles on his X-chromosome, a female any two, one on each X. The w^+ allele is dominant to all others, and w is the ultimate recessive in the series. Intermediate alleles can be arrayed in order of their effects on color or in order of their relative dominance to each other. In series that affect more than one phenotypic character, the orders of effects in the series or the orders of dominance of the alleles may be different for one character affected than for another.

We will be concerned with multiple allelic series at several later points in this book.

Lethals. The allele for platinum color in the fox, used to introduce the concept of mutation, has another characteristic of interest. No fox homozygous for this allele has been known to live past weaning age. Genes whose action results in death in a standard environment, as the allele for platinum does when homozygous, are called *lethal genes*, or *lethals*. This class of alleles was discussed briefly in Chapter 5.

A very large number of lethal genes are known. Different ones cause death at different stages of development; some act very early, while others, like the dominant human gene for Huntington's chorea, produce their lethal effects only late in life. In the case of the platinum fox, it appears that the homozygous platinum usually dies near the time of its birth—sometimes shortly before, sometimes as much as four or five weeks after birth. The homozygotes (PP) are pure white in color (Fig. 12-1 and Plate II).

Figure 12-1. A *white fox pup, from platinum × platinum mating, rarely lives beyond birth. This one died at about five weeks of age. (From Cole and Shackelford, Am. Naturalist, 77:300, 1943.)*

The lethality of platinum could not be detected as long as breeders were trying to disseminate this dominant gene as rapidly as possible. Matings were regularly *platinum* × *silver;* generation after generation, heterozygous platinum and homozygous silver progeny appeared, as expected, in 1:1 ratios under this mating system. But when breeders tried to get true-breeding platinums through mating *platinum* × *platinum,* they ran into trouble. Average litter sizes dropped in these crosses to about three-fourths the usual number of pups. No true-breeding platinums were obtained, but occasionally a pure white pup would appear, only to die (and usually to be eaten by its mother) before it could be weaned. The genetic situation was clear:

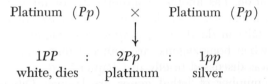

Platinum (Pp) × Platinum (Pp)

1PP : 2Pp : 1pp
white, dies   platinum   silver

This kind of result—litter size reduced by one-fourth, a 2:1 ratio (phenotypic and genotypic), and the absence of the true-breeding (homozygous) class—characterize the segregation of a lethal factor in the progeny of heterozygotes.

In most plants and animals, lethals are recognized only if they have some dominant phenotypic effect in the heterozygous condition and if they are lethal only when homozygous. Their *lethality* therefore behaves as a recessive, whereas in other phenotypic effects they are at least partially dominant. Two general exceptions to this rule occur, however:

1. A few known genes may be called *dominant* lethals because they result in the death of the organism even when heterozygous. All such genes to persist must produce their lethal effects on heterozygotes relatively late in life, after the individual has had an opportunity to reproduce. A mutation that in the heterozygous condition kills its bearer before he can reproduce is automatically lost the generation it appears. Such mutations cannot be studied by ordinary Mendelian methods, although their frequencies can be estimated and they can be investigated through the use of more complex and less direct techniques.

2. Many genes are known that have no detectable phenotypic effect other than their lethality when homozygous. Here, there is no phenotypic "giveaway" to make the detection of heterozygotes possible, and these lethals are evidenced only through the death at some stage in development of a quarter of the progeny of matings between heterozygotes and a 2:1 genotypic ratio among the survivors.

The biochemical mutations of Neurospora referred to earlier in this chapter serve to emphasize an important point made in Chapter 5: A given gene may be lethal in one environment and may have no detectable effect in another. The adenineless allele in Neurospora, for example, is lethal when the mold is grown on a medium lacking adenine—a medium on which the wild type thrives. But on a medium containing adequate adenine, the mutant strain grows as well as wild type.

Sex-Linked Lethals. If a recessive lethal is located on the X-chromosome, it can survive only in the heterozygous condition in the sex having two X-chromosomes. In Drosophila, for example, the inheritance of a sex-linked lethal (*l*) follows the pattern illustrated in Figure 12-2.

The lethal is therefore carried only by the female, from generation to generation; and the sex ratio observed in crosses with heterozygous females, instead of being 1:1, is 1 ♂ : 2 ♀♀ .

The effect of sex-linked lethals on the sex ratio makes them relatively easy to detect. For this reason, much of the work on mutation in Drosophila has utilized this particular kind of mutation. Special techniques have been worked out to make the detection of new sex-linked lethal mutations easy and objective; we will describe one of these methods in a later section.

It has been pointed out that if the same lethal mutation frequency *per unit time* prevailed in man as in Drosophila, an average of almost two lethals would arise on each human X-chromosome in each generation. This would make men rather scarce. As far as human mutation rates are known, however, it would appear that it is the mutation rates *per generation* that agree fairly well with Drosophila rates, also on a per-generation basis, and not the rates per unit time. Drosophila, with their 15-day life cycle, show about the same over-all mutation rate per generation as do other organisms with much longer generation times.

Data collected by Muller on some 200,000 Drosophila X-chromosomes tested for spontaneous lethals showed that the mutation rate must be much higher at some stages in the life of a fly than in others. A large fraction of

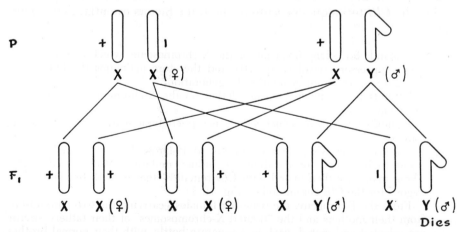

Figure 12-2. *The progeny of a female heterozygous for a sex-linked lethal show a 2:1 sex ratio.*

the spontaneous lethal mutations that occur in a male appear in sperm accumulated during his pupal period. Muller's data also suggest that sperm stored in the female after insemination show greatly increased frequencies of mutation. The latter point may well be pertinent to observations in poultry, pigeons, and doves that embryonic death increases in frequency in fertile eggs laid some time after a hen has been separated from cocks. Hens "store" sperm from a single insemination over periods of two or three weeks; possibly, during such storage, mutations occur in many of the stored sperm such that, although the sperm are still able to fertilize eggs, the resulting embryos are genetically inviable.

Induced Mutations

Our discussion up to this point has been limited to the spontaneous origin of new alleles. Geneticists have long hoped that the process of mutation could be brought under experimental control, so that new hereditary qualities could be induced at will in an experimental population. This hope has been in part realized, but only to the extent that spontaneous mutation rates can be enormously "speeded up" by a variety of external agents. With a very few notable exceptions, this increase in mutation rate is a general one, and it is still impossible to single out particular genes and make them mutate at will.

The ClB Method for Detecting Sex-Linked Lethals. The first clear evidence for the successful induction of mutations was reported in 1927 by H. J. Muller, who is now at Indiana University. Muller's demonstration that X-rays induce mutations was made possible through the development of an efficient technique for the easy and objective identification of new lethal mutations in the X-chromosome of Drosophila. The technique has been called the *ClB* technique, because of the three factors essential to its operation:

> *C* stands for a long inversion of the X-chromosome, which acts as a crossover suppressor (recall Chap. 10) and therefore maintains the integrity of the chromosome from generation to generation.
> *l* stands for a known recessive lethal on the X-chromosome carrying the inversion.
> *B* stands for bar eye, which serves as a phenotypic marker for this chromosome.
> The technique is simple in operation: Male Drosophila are treated with the agent to be tested for its ability to induce mutation. Muller used X-rays. These males are then mated with *ClB* females—that is, with females heterozygous for the *ClB* chromosome (Fig. 12-3).
> From the F_1 progeny, the wide-bar females (carrying the *ClB* chromosome from their mothers and the "treated X-chromosomes" of their fathers' sperm) are selected and mated, each in a separate bottle, with their normal brothers (almost any male Drosophila can be used in this mating). Figure 12-4 shows the result of this cross.

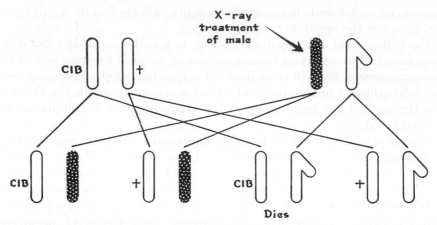

Figure 12-3. *The first step in the ClB method for detecting sex-linked lethals is to mate the treated males with females heterozygous for the ClB chromosome.*

The advantage of this method is that it depends for its interpretation only on noting whether or not males appear in F_2 of any mating. The investigator can simply look through the side of the glass bottle in which the flies are grown; if he sees males, he can conclude that no lethal was induced in the treated X, whereas if he sees no males, he can check more carefully and, if they are really absent, he can conclude that a lethal was present in the treated X.

The total spontaneous mutation rate for all lethals on the X-chromosome is about two per thousand X-chromosomes per generation (0.2%). Observed

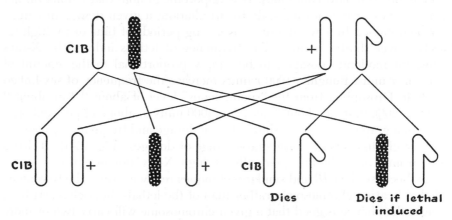

Figure 12-4. *The bar-eyed female progeny of the cross in Figure 12-3 are heterozygous for the ClB chromosome (from their mothers) and the "treated X-chromosome" (from their fathers). If a lethal was induced on the treated X, these females, mated to normal males, will have no sons. If they have sons, no lethal was induced.*

frequencies significantly in excess of this figure indicate that the agent tested has increased the mutation rate.

The *ClB* method has contributed greatly to genetic knowledge. But it has been found to have certain limitations, chiefly because the inversion of the X-chromosome in the *ClB* stock does not completely suppress crossing over, and misleading or inaccurate observations occasionally result. For this reason, the method has been improved by relatively minor modifications also devised by Muller.

Induction of Mutations by Ionizing Radiations. X-ray is representative of *ionizing radiations,* a group including the α, β, and γ radiation of radioactive substances, protons, and neutrons, in addition to X-rays. The atomic bomb is now a familiar and terrible source of this kind of radiation.

As almost everyone knows nowadays, an atom is made up of a positively charged atomic nucleus and a surrounding constellation of negatively charged electrons, the charges so balanced that normal atoms are electrically neutral. When ionizing radiations pass through matter, they dissipate their energy in part through the ejection of electrons from the outer shells of atoms, and the loss of these balancing, negative charges leaves atoms that are no longer neutral but positively charged. Such charged particles are called *ions.* When an atom becomes ionized, the molecule of which it is a part probably undergoes chemical change; when this changed molecule is a gene or a part of a gene, and when the modified gene duplicates its new pattern, the result of the change is a mutation. Probably X-rays induce mutations in other ways as well.

The amount of X-ray treatment is measured in *Roentgen units* (*r* units), which are calibrated in terms of the number of ionizations per unit volume of air under standard conditions. It is important to note that *r* units do not in themselves involve a time-scale for irradiation; a given dosage in *r* units may be obtained by low intensities over long periods of time or by high intensities over shorter periods. The frequency of lethals induced by X-rays seems, for moderate dosages, to be simply proportional to the amount of X-rays in *r* units. Roughly, 1000 *r* units increase the frequency of sex-linked lethals in Drosophila from the "spontaneous" level of about 0.2 to about 3 per cent; 2000 units to about 6 per cent; 4000 units to about 12 per cent, and so on. In a graph, this relationship between dosage and frequency appears to be a straight line, over a considerable range of dosages (Fig. 12-5). It drops away from a straight line markedly at high X-ray dosages; this may be mainly because the *ClB* and similar techniques really measure the frequency of lethal-bearing chromosomes rather than of the lethals themselves. At high dosages the chance is good that a given chromosome will carry two or more induced lethals. This chromosome would be counted as only a single induction by the *ClB* technique. There is, however, current debate on the question of whether the shape of the curve may have some further significance beyond this simple relationship.

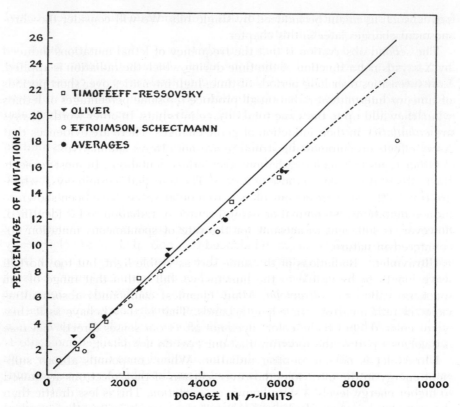

Figure 12-5. *As the dosage of X-ray (in r units) increases, the percentage of mutations rises. Points on the graph represent the observations of investigators as shown with regard to the induction of sex-linked lethals by X-rays. For low dosages, the relationship is approximately linear; the solid line is calculated from this linear relationship at low dosages. At higher dosages, the observed data fall away from this line. The dotted line is based on a calculation recognizing the probability that more than one lethal may be induced on any particular chromosome. (After Sturtevant and Beadle,* An Introduction to Genetics, *W. B. Saunders Co., 1940, p. 211. From Timoféeff, Zimmer, and Delbrück.)*

If the essentially straight-line relationship between dosage and effect can be accepted as fact, at least two interesting conclusions are indicated. The first is that a specific effect is produced by a single "hit." If two or more independent hits were required to produce a lethal mutation, then the relationship between density of ionization and percentage of lethals would plot as a curve, not as a straight line. It is with this question that some of the debate over the true shape of the curve is concerned. Some of the effects of X-radiation on chromosome structure clearly require two "hits." The question is whether the X-ray-induced lethal mutations may involve these same kinds of changes in chromosomes, or whether they are mostly specific, single-gene changes involving perhaps chemical changes in the genes themselves, such as might be induced by single hits. We will consider the chromosomal changes later in this chapter.

The second observation is that the frequency of lethal mutations induced by X-rays is not a function of the time during which the radiation is applied. Low intensities over long periods of time, high intensities over short periods of time, or intermittent radiation all produce the same percentages of lethals when they add up to the same total dosage in *r* units. In other words, X-rays are *cumulative* in their induction of genic changes. There are evidences that X-ray effects on chromosome structure are not always cumulative.

Other types of ionizing radiations also induce mutations. In most respects their effects are similar to those of X-rays. The so-called "cosmic rays," which are constantly bombarding our planet from outer space, have been shown to induce mutations. No normal or natural source of radiation so far identified, however, is sufficient to account for the rate of spontaneous mutation encountered in nature.

Ultraviolet. Radiations of the same sort as visible light, but too short in wave length to be visible to the human eye, fall within that range of the spectrum called the *ultraviolet*. Many chemical compounds absorb ultraviolet in rather narrow wave-length bands. That is, they behave as if they were "colored," but their "color" does not affect our senses directly because it involves a part of the spectrum that our eyes do not detect.

Ultraviolet is not an ionizing radiation. When compounds absorb sufficient energy in the ultraviolet, however, certain of their electrons are raised to higher energy levels, a state known as *excitation*. This is less drastic than the complete ejection of electrons, but it does result in greatly increased reactivity on the part of the affected molecules. This may be the direct effect of ultraviolet involved in its mutation-producing (*mutagenic*) activity.

In contrast to X-ray, ultraviolet penetrates tissues only very slightly. It is difficult, for example, to irradiate a male Drosophila sufficiently with ultraviolet to affect the sperm in his body. For this reason, most of the work with ultraviolet has been done with other forms—bacteria, molds, and the pollen of higher plants—although the first work with ultraviolet was done by irradiating Drosophila eggs. When male flies are compressed between quartz plates, to bring their testes close to the surface, and their ventral sides are irradiated, some ultraviolet can penetrate to the sperm. Properly used, ultraviolet is a very effective mutagenic agent.

Other Mutagenic Agents. Several other kinds of agents are now believed to induce mutations. These include:

Extreme Temperatures. Heat definitely increases mutation rates, but generally so little as to make the increase difficult to detect. A reasonable estimate of the order of magnitude of the over-all temperature effect seems to be about a doubling of the spontaneous mutation rate per generation for every 10°C rise in temperature above normal. Some types of mutation also increase in frequency toward extremes of *low* temperature.

TABLE 12-3. Chemicals Behaving as Mutagens in E. coli. (From Demerec, Bertani, and Flint, Am. Naturalist, 85:134, 1951.)

Boric acid	Formaldehyde	Neutral red, light
Ammonia	Phenol	Neutral red, dark
Hydrogen peroxide	Alpha-dinitrophenol	Acriflavine
Copper sulfate	Trinitrophenol	Caffeine
Acetic acid	Carbamate, ethyl	Necrosin
Lactic acid	" n-propyl	
Formic acid	" n-butyl	
	" isoamyl	

Chemical Agents. Several chemical agents are now known to be mutagenic. Chief among these are mustard gas, a material of chemical warfare; certain organic peroxides; urethane, β-propiolactone, and diazomethane. Table 12-3 lists a variety of other chemicals that appear, from the experiments of Demerec and his colleagues at Cold Spring Harbor, to be mutagenic in the bacterium *Escherichia coli*. Somewhat similar lists might be cited for other systems in which the chemical induction of mutation has been studied extensively: lethals and other mutations in Drosophila, chromosome breaks in certain plants, and back-mutation in Neurospora. Figure 12-6 illustrates the last-named system.

Irradiated Media. A group of investigators at the University of Texas observed that bacteria and Neurospora grown in ultraviolet irradiated media showed significant increases in mutation rate. The effect seemed fantastic, since the organisms were not irradiated themselves, and since no lingering radioactivity could be invoked to explain such a result. It now seems clear that the irradiation of an organic medium results in the formation of short-lived and very reactive chemicals, and that these chemicals act as effective mutagens. Indications point to organic peroxides, whose mutagenic activity has been independently demonstrated, as at least in part responsible.

Transforming Principles in Pneumococcus and Other Microorganisms. The organism causing lobar pneumonia, a diplococcus, is known to occur in a considerable variety of types, distinguished by their different reactions to antibodies. These types are designated by numbers, as Type I, Type II, Type III, and so on. Another sort of variation in pneumococcus involves the presence or absence of a capsule, secreted around the organisms. "Rough" forms, so called because the colonies they form on media in the laboratory have rough surfaces, lack a capsule. They are incapable of producing disease. "Smooth" forms have capsules and are generally pathogenic.

The type specificity of a strain depends on the chemical makeup of its capsules. Rough forms can be derived from smooth forms by mutation; having no capsule, they have no type specificity, but when they back-mutate spontaneously to smooth forms again, they regain their original type. When

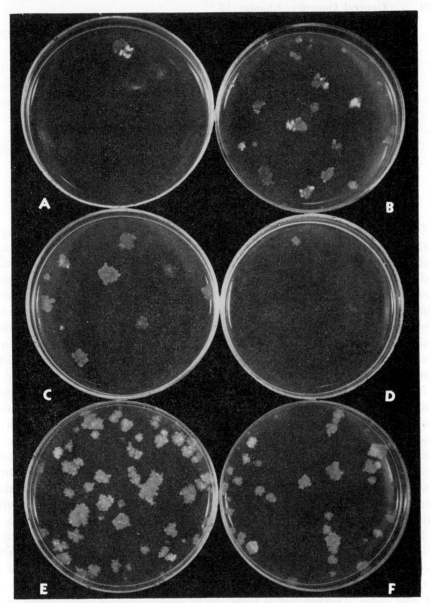

Figure 12-6. *Spontaneous and induced back-mutation in Neurospora is studied by plating out about 600 million living conidia of a colonial form of the adenine-less mutant on each dish of minimal medium. Since this strain cannot grow without added adenine, in the absence of a genetic change the plate remains clear. A, the untreated control shows a single colony descended from a spontaneous back-mutation. B, conidia treated with ultraviolet radiation for 60 seconds display an increased frequency of back-mutation. Treatments in the remaining plates were as follows: C, hydrogen peroxide, 0.2M, 40 minutes. D, as in C, but with an anti-oxidant, nor-di-hydro guaiaretic acid. E, hydrogen peroxide (0.02M) and formaldehyde (0.03M), 30 minutes. F, as in E, but with anti-oxidant as in D. (From Jensen, Kirk, Kölmark, and Westergaard,* Cold Spring Harbor Symposia Quant. Biol., **16:**247, 1951.)

rough forms of pneumococcus, derived by mutation from smooth forms of a particular type, are grown in media containing extracts from smooth forms of another type, under certain conditions these rough forms are induced to form capsules. The surprising thing is that the capsules formed are not the same type as the original smooth type from which the rough was derived. They agree in type *with the extract that induced the change back to capsule formation.*

This change is inherited and will continue in the new strain indefinitely unless it is lost or modified by spontaneous mutation. In this case, then, we are clearly dealing with a specific, directed, hereditary change. Similar observations of type transformation have been made on *E. coli,* and have been suggested by work with other bacteria.

The ingredient in the extract that induces the directed hereditary change is known as a "transforming principle." It appears to be a nucleic acid, and the transformed strain goes on to make its own transforming principle, which can then be used to transform other rough forms to the same type. The nucleic acid, of a specific type, acts as if it had become incorporated into the genic material of the organism and were directing its own self-reproduction. The actual basis for the activity of transforming principles is, however, unknown. In fact, any discussion of changes in pneumococcus in terms of gene mutation must be to some degree insecure, since in the absence of demonstrated sexual reproduction the evidence for genes in a Mendelian sense is indirect.

Other Genes. Mutation, like other processes occurring in living cells, is itself affected by genes. Different strains within a species sometimes differ in general mutation rate, and sudden changes in mutation rate have occasionally appeared within stocks. It has been reported that a hybrid between two species of Drosophila has shown a significantly greater mutation rate than was found in either parent species. Perhaps, in such a case, a normal mechanism for the control of gene stability is disrupted by an incompatibility or imbalance of the two different chromosome complements combined in the hybrid.

The most specific kind of genic control of mutation is illustrated by the "dotted" gene in corn. We will discuss this in connection with somatic mutation.

Chromosomal Changes and Gene Mutations. Throughout most of this chapter we have been speaking of mutations as though they involved only changes in genes. Your recollection of Chapters 10 and 11, however, will convince you that "sudden heritable changes," as we described mutations, also include changes in the number and structure of chromosomes. The material of Chapters 10 and 11 need not be reviewed here, but we should emphasize that it is often very difficult to distinguish genic and chromosomal mutations. In Drosophila, where the precise evidence of the salivary gland chromosomes can be brought to bear, any but minute changes in chromosomal structure can be expected to be detectable. It would seem easy to decide whether a given sudden inherited change is the result of a deletion, or a duplication, or a position effect connected with an inversion or a translocation, or is indeed a gene mutation.

But how minute can a chromosomal aberration be? If it is small enough, its detection will be difficult or impossible even in the salivaries. There is direct visual evidence, for instance, that about 30 to 40 per cent of the *lethal* mutations induced by X-rays in Drosophila are in fact deletions; perhaps many of the remaining ones are also deletions, too small to detect. Stadler has argued, from his work with corn, that X-rays produce predominantly chromosomal mutations, while ultraviolet induces mainly true gene mutations due to chemical changes within genes. It was once thought that all recessive mutations were simply "losses" of the genic material of the dominant alleles.

Now it may be unlikely that even X-rays produce their effects on germ plasm exclusively through inducing deletions and similar chromosomal changes. In the first place, the loss of a fragment of a chromosome is not likely to be reversible, as certain mutations have been shown to be. And, second, only one gene of a multiple allelic series—the ultimate recessive in the series—could involve the loss of a locus; the intermediate alleles must be something else, if the locus is a unit.

But we are left with the likelihood that what we have called "gene mutation" is a rather heterogeneous collection of things. We can explain some hereditary changes in terms of demonstrable changes in the structure of chromosomes. The "gene mutations" generally constitute the unexplained, Mendelizing residue. Probably a part of this heterogeneous class represents true chemical changes in genes. There is no way of knowing how large a part this is.

Within the residual class that we call gene mutations, a "spectrum" can be distinguished in terms of the severity of phenotypic effect of the individual changes. These range from extreme effects (lethals), through all degrees of visible effects (visibles), to very slight modifications detectable only through their small but consistent statistical effects on survival, or on sex ratios, or on the expression of other genes. Of these three classes of change, it seems clear that the "visibles" are by far the least frequent; probably, gene changes with slight effects occur most frequently.

Somatic Mutations. Mutations of any type are not limited to the germ plasm but can in general occur at any time and in any tissue. Those occurring in somatic tissue of course reach a dead end with the death of the individual, unless they can be propagated asexually or unless they involve sexual tissues secondarily.

The occurrence of a mutation in somatic tissue results in patches of tissue that are genetically distinct from the rest of the individual. "Sectors" due to chromosomal losses often occur in fruits, for example. Crossing over and segregation of genes occasionally occur in somatic tissues, and Huskins, at Wisconsin, has illustrated "somatic reduction" in the roots of some plants. We referred to other examples of somatic variations in chromosome number in Chapter 7.

Outside of these known chromosomal effects, again a large residue of apparent *gene changes* in somatic tissues remains. Rarely, these can be subjected to ordinary genetic tests. A mutation in the tassel of corn, for instance, may give rise to a sector that produces mutant pollen, which can be tested by ordinary Mendelian methods. Or a "bud mutation" on a tree may be propagated asexually and produce a whole new line of distinct individuals. Some of our best varieties of fruits are believed to have arisen originally in this way.

"Mosaics," having patches of genetically distinct somatic tissues, occur in animals as well. Chickens and pigeons, for example, have occasionally shown large patches of feathers colored differently from the rest of the bird, and similar mosaics have been observed in mice, rabbits, and other animals. A recent study by W. F. Hollander, now at Iowa State College, constitutes a caution against classifying all such mosaics as examples of mutation; he has demonstrated conclusively that they sometimes result from the participation of more than one sperm in fertilization. Part of the tissue of the resulting individual therefore has a set of genes from one sperm, and part a different set from another sperm. There is no easy way of being sure how common this *polyspermy* may be.

The frequency of somatic mutation can be increased by some of the same agents that increase germinal changes. X-rays, for instance, induce flecking in pigeon feathers, and these induced changes are transmitted through successive "somatic generations" of regenerated feathers after intermittent plucking.

The most specific and regular kind of somatic mutation is illustrated by

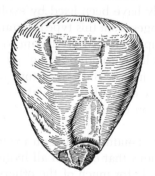

Figure 12-7. *The aleurone of a corn kernel homozygous for a is colorless* (left), *unless it also carries* Dt *("dotted," right). The* Dt *gene promotes the somatic mutation of a to A, and in kernels of appropriate genotype, color therefore develops in the mutant areas.*

the "dotted" gene in corn. This gene acts as a dominant to its normal allele; its effect is to cause the frequent mutation of one of the genes for colorless aleurone (a) to its dominant allele (A). In plants that are $aaDt-$, therefore, there are "dots" of color in the aleurone resulting from the mutation of a to A in this tissue (Fig. 12-7). Since the tissue involved is triploid (endosperm), several "doses" of the "dotted" gene can be compared for their effect (*cf.* Problem 12-19). This specific control of the mutation of gene a on the third chromosome by a gene on another chromosome (*dotted* is on chromosome 9) has been the subject of much interesting work.

Mutation and Important Problems in Biology, Medicine, and Agriculture

It is not surprising that genes should sometimes change, or that such changes can be increased in frequency by certain external agents. On the contrary, it is most remarkable that such changes should be on the whole so very rare. And it is remarkable, too, that the modified gene, after its sudden change, continues to reduplicate the new form. When we can understand these facts, we will have gone some way toward understanding some of the most fundamental aspects of life.

Mutations provide what has been called "the raw material of evolution." They are the ultimate source of inherent variation on which evolutionary change depends. Similarly, the improvement of plants and animals is based ultimately on the genetic variation provided by mutational changes. Many of these have occurred in the past and are stored as potential variability in present domestic populations. Other genic and chromosomal changes are occurring in the present.

Most mutations observed in the present can be classed as "undesirable" ones. This is understandable, since mutation is a random and generally uncontrollable recurrent process; the most "desirable" changes, having occurred many times in the past, will already have been fixed by evolution as the wild type of any species. Random changes from this type are much more likely to impair than to improve this complex and nicely balanced system, just as the things that a ten-year-old boy is likely to do in "fixing" a television set are likely to impair the quality of the image. But the history of plants and animals under domestication shows clearly that populations can be shaped toward desired ends by the selection of hereditary variants present in the population through mutation.

We have indicated that known sources of natural radiation explain only a small fraction of the spontaneous mutations that occur in all living forms. Chemical mutagens are probably responsible for much of the otherwise unexplained residue of spontaneous mutations. Certain of these mutagens are doubtless elaborated during the normal course of metabolism. They may sometimes reach the germ plasm, and induce mutations there.

Human beings subject themselves to unnatural sources of ionizing radiations in excess of the natural "background." This is true:

1. In the industrial use of X-ray, for example, to check flaws in materials or in the utilization of fluoroscopic devices for fitting shoes and for similar purposes.

2. In the growing use of radioactive materials in research and industry, as in uranium mines, atomic energy plants, and laboratories investigating and utilizing the particles of modern physics.

3. In medical diagnosis and therapy, where X-ray technicians and physicians particularly require protection against long-continued exposure to stray radiation. From the patients' point of view it is of course advisable that any dosage of X-ray in excess of medical necessity be avoided.

In all these connections, it is imperative that equipment be designed, and all possible precautions be observed, to keep unnecessary radiation to a minimum. This is particularly important in view of the known cumulative effects of low dosages over long periods of time. A daily dosage of 0.1r per working day, for example, adds up to about 300r in a decade—calculated to be enough to increase the mutation rate to about 150 per cent of the spontaneous level. In view of the generally low spontaneous rates, this need not be alarming as a statistic. In terms of individual human suffering, however, even the induction of a single unnecessary hereditary abnormality is of inestimable significance. It is reassuring to note that the arbitrary industrial "tolerance dose" of 0.1r permitted per working day is in fact considerably in excess of the average radiation actually experienced in the pertinent industries and laboratories, and that continued effort is being made to reduce the uncontrolled radiations.

A fourth source of ionizing radiation, the military use of radioactive material, is in a class by itself. Depending on the nature of the explosion (overhead or underwater, for example) an atomic bomb releases or produces various large amounts of ionizing radiations. These radiations differ in their intensities at given distances from "ground zero," in their ability to penetrate tissues, and in the times at which they are liberated and over which they persist. Both the "immediate" and the "lingering" radioactivity are of genetic significance. For discussions of these and related matters, see the references cited at the end of this chapter.

Keys to the Significance of This Chapter

Sudden, heritable changes occur in living things; these changes are called *mutations*. They may involve gross changes in chromosome quantity and quality, or they may in other instances be specific chemical changes in genes.

The two primary qualities of spontaneous mutations are that they are generally *recurrent* and *reversible*. The mutation rate typically differs in the two directions, $A \rightleftarrows a$, and varies from one gene to another. At many loci, a number of different mutations have occurred. These constitute *multiple allelic series*.

Lethals represent a common class of mutations. They are particularly useful in studies of mutation rates.

The rate of spontaneous mutation can be speeded up by a variety of agents. These include ionizing radiations, ultraviolet, heat, and certain chemicals. With very rare exceptions, the agents that increase mutation rates are not specific for particular genes. The exceptions to this statement include the *transforming principles* observed in certain microorganisms (which may in fact represent a kind of "gene transfer" rather than induced mutation), and the specific effect of the *dotted* gene in corn on the somatic mutation of gene *a* in another chromosome.

Over the broad sweep of evolution, and in connection with the controlled development of new and different kinds of plants and animals, mutation provides the raw material for progress. But mutation is generally a random process, and as such it usually results in deleterious rather than desirable changes in germ plasm. Defective human germ plasm must therefore be considered among the recognized hazards of atomic warfare, since the ionizing radiations increase mutation rates. Similarly, X-ray and other ionizing radiations must be handled with all possible caution.

References

Auerbach, C., "Chemical Mutagenesis." *Biol. Rev.*, **24**:355–391, 1949. (A competent and extensive review.)

Catcheside, D. G., "Genetic Effects of Radiations." *Advances in Genetics*, **2**:271–358, 1948. (A comprehensive review; note particularly the effects of mutagens on chromosomes.)

Cole, L. J., and Shackelford, R. M., "White Spotting in the Fox." *Am. Naturalist*, **77**:289–321, 1943. (Describes mutations to platinum and to other kinds of white spotting, with an historical account on which our introduction to this chapter was based.)

Demerec, M., Bertani, G., and Flint, J., "A Survey of Chemicals for Mutagenic Action on *E. coli*." *Am. Naturalist*, **85**:119–136, 1951. (Source of Table 12-2, and illustrates the use of the streptomycin technique.)

Ephrussi-Taylor, H., "Genetic Aspects of Transformations of Pneumococci." *Cold Spring Harbor Symposia Quant. Biol.*, **16**:445–456, 1951.

Genetics Conference, Committee on Atomic Casualties, National Research Council, "Genetic Effects of the Atomic Bombs in Hiroshima and Nagasaki." *Science*, **106**:331–333, 1947. (A summary of the status of the problem in 1947.)

Grigg, G. W., "Back-Mutation Assay Method in Micro-organisms." *Nature*, **169**:98–100, 1952. (Reports research results that suggest serious reservations in the use of certain back-mutation methods.)

Herskowitz, I. H., "A List of Chemical Substances Studied for Effects on Drosophila, with a Bibliography." *Am. Naturalist,* **85:**181–199, 1951. (Both the list and the bibliography are extensive.)

Ives, P. T., "The Importance of Mutation Rate Genes in Evolution." *Evolution,* **4:**236–252, 1950. (A critical evaluation, with a good bibliography.)

Jensen, K. A., Kirk, I., Kölmark, G., and Westergaard, M., "Chemically Induced Mutations in Neurospora." *Cold Spring Harbor Symposia Quant. Biol.,* **16:**245–246, 1951.

Kölmark, G., and Westergaard, M., "Induced Back-Mutations in a Specific Gene of *Neurospora crassa." Hereditas,* **35:**490–506, 1949. (Description of methods of study, and results using various mutagens.)

Lea, D. E., *Actions of Radiations on Living Cells.* New York: Macmillan Co., 1947. (A good source book on numerous aspects of this subject.)

Lederberg, J., ed., *Papers in Microbial Genetics.* Madison: University of Wisconsin Press, 1951. (Intended as a collection of papers to be read for a course in the genetics of microorganisms, this valuable selection has many inclusions relevant to mutation.)

Lerner, I. M., "Lethal and Sublethal Characters in Farm Animals." *J. Heredity,* **35:**219–224, 1944.

Levan, A., "Chemically Induced Chromosome Reactions Studied in *Allium cepa* and *Vicia faba." Cold Spring Harbor Symposia Quant. Biol.,* **16:**233–243, 1951.

Muller, H. J., "The Production of Mutations." *J. Heredity,* **38:**259–270, 1947. (Nobel prize lecture delivered in Stockholm in 1946. Available from American Genetic Assoc., 1507 M. St., N.W., Washington 5, D. C. 20¢.)

———, "Radiation Damage to the Genetic Material." *Am. Scientist,* **38:**33–59, 126, 399–425, 1950. (Based on material presented in a Sigma Xi National Lectureship, this is a broad and interesting review.)

Pontecorvo, G., "The Problem of Dominant Lethals." *J. Genetics,* **43:**295–300, 1942.

Rhoades, M. M., "The Genetic Control of Mutability in Maize." *Cold Spring Harbor Symposia Quant. Biol.,* **9:**138–144, 1941. (Includes discussion of the "dotted" gene and its effects.)

Russell, W. L., "X-ray Induced Mutations in Mice." *Cold Spring Harbor Symposia Quant. Biol.,* **16:**327–336, 1951.

Schrödinger, E., *What Is Life?* New York: Macmillan Co., 1946. (A short and well-written book illustrating a physicist's wonder at the remarkable stability of genes.)

Stadler, L. J., "Spontaneous Mutation at the *R* Locus in Maize. I. The Aleurone-Color and Plant-Color Effects." *Genetics,* **31:**377–394, 1946.

———, "Spontaneous Mutation in Maize." *Cold Spring Harbor Symposia Quant. Biol.,* **16:**49–63, 1951.

Stern, C., *Principles of Human Genetics.* San Francisco: W. H. Freeman and Co., 1949. (Chaps. 21 and 22 are excellent summaries of the subject of mutation, with particular regard to human genetics.)

Stone, W. S., Wyss, O., and Haas, F., "The Production of Mutations in *Staphylococcus aureus* by Irradiation of the Substrate." *Proc. Nat. Acad. Sci.,* **33:**59–66, 1947.

Wagner, R. P., Haddox, C. H., Fuerst, R., and Stone, W. S., "The Effect of Irradiated Medium, Cyanide and Peroxide on the Mutation Rate in Neurospora." *Genetics,* 35:237–248, 1950.

Questions and Problems

12- 1. What do the following terms signify?

adenineless Neurospora	mutation rate
chromosomal mutation	polyspermy
ClB	recurrent mutation
excitation by ultraviolet	reversible mutation
gene mutation	*r* unit
induced mutation	somatic mutation
ionizing radiation	somatic mosaic
lethals	spontaneous mutation
multiple alleles	"tolerance dose of X-ray"
mutagenic	transforming principle

12- 2. In experimental plants and animals most of the mutant genes known are recessive to the wild type. In man, however, most of the simple autosomal abnormalities known depend on dominant alleles, and only among sex-linked characteristics are recessive mutations common. Can you offer explanations for this apparent difference between human and experimental populations?

12- 3. When seed corn subjected to atomic radiation in atom bomb tests was planted, the seedlings' first leaves showed many fine light stripes among normal green tissues. The amount of striping was related to the distance the seed had been from "ground zero" for the bomb. Can you explain these facts? (Note that a well-formed embryo, complete with several leaf primordia, is present in the kernel.)

12- 4. A dwarf bull calf is born to apparently normal parents in a herd of cattle. How might you decide whether the dwarf is the immediate result of a mutation, or a segregant resulting from the chance mating of "carriers" of a recessive dwarfism, or the result of a nongenetic (environmental) modification?

12- 5. In certain systematic inbreeding programs, dairy bulls are regularly bred to their own daughters. Suppose that a bull is heterozygous for a recessive lethal, and that the cows to which he is originally bred are all homozygous for the normal allele of this lethal. What will be the outcome of sire-daughter matings in the next generation with regard to this particular lethal?

12- 6. A dairy cattle inbreeding program at the University of California started with six bulls, the progeny of which were systematically inbred. It turned out that two of the bulls were carrying recessive lethals, and each of the other four was carrying at least one clear, simple, major anomaly in the heterozygous condition. What does this suggest about the frequency of simple recessive anomalies and lethals in cattle generally?

In mice, the following are members of an autosomal, multiple allelic series:

$$A^Y = \text{lethal yellow}$$
$$A = \text{agouti (wild type)}$$
$$a = \text{non-agouti (black)}$$

The agouti/non-agouti alternative was utilized in Problems 4-2 to 4-9. The A^Y allele when heterozygous produces a clear yellow coat color; it is dominant to both A and a. Embryos homozygous for A^Y die. (There are other alleles in this series not listed here.)

12- 7. What phenotypes, and in what proportions, would result from the following matings:

a. $A^Y a$ (yellow) $\times$ $A^Y a$ (yellow)
b. $A^Y a$ (yellow) $\times$ $A^Y A$ (yellow)
c. $A^Y a$ (yellow) $\times$ aa (black)
d. $A^Y a$ (yellow) $\times$ AA (wild type)
e. $A^Y a$ (yellow) $\times$ Aa (wild type)

Example: In (a), zygotes will be $A^Y A^Y$, $A^Y a$, $A^Y a$, and aa in equal numbers. The first class will die as embryos, so the phenotypic ratio would be 2 yellow: 1 black.

12- 8. Assuming an average litter size of eight mice born per litter for many matings of type (e) above, what would you expect to be the average litter size for many matings of type (b) under the same conditions?

12- 9. You would never expect both wild-type agouti and non-agouti mice among the progeny of a single lethal yellow male mated to non-agouti females. Why?

12-10. Suppose that you wanted to study the induction of additional mutant alleles at the A locus in mice. What techniques might you use to induce and to detect such mutations most efficiently?

12-11. The attached-X ($\widehat{XX}$) Drosophila stock described in Chapter 6 is useful for the detection of new, visible sex-linked recessive mutations. Assume that in studying mutation in the progeny of an X-rayed adult male you are dealing mainly with mutations induced in the sperm the male has formed at the time of treatment. If you contrast the result of mating such a male to an $\widehat{XX}$ female with the result of using a normal female, you will see why the $\widehat{XX}$ technique offers advantages in detecting sex-linked recessive visibles. (Ignore for the present the few $XX\widehat{X}$ progeny that survive in $\widehat{XX}$ matings.)

12-12. What would be the effect of a sex-linked recessive lethal induced in a treated male on the progeny of his mating to an $\widehat{XX}$ female? Contrast the ClB technique and the $\widehat{XX}$ technique with respect to the types of mutations they are best adapted to detect.

12-13. How would you distinguish between an autosomal dominant and a sex-linked recessive visible mutation in the $\widehat{XX}$ technique (Problem 12-11)?

12-14. If you assume that sex-linked dominant lethals are induced rather frequently in the sperm of X-rayed males, how would the sex ratio in the progeny of treated males mated to $\widehat{XX}$ females be affected? If the males were mated to ClB females? Wild-type females?

12-15. In the *ClB* technique, assume a recessive lethal induced on the X-chromosome of a sperm that has fertilized a *ClB* egg. Now this zygote has a recessive lethal on both X-chromosomes. Why does it not die?

12-16. How might a particular somatic mutation be established in a large population of cultivated plants? Is this likely in animals? Why?

In pigeons, a sex-linked, multiple allelic series includes:

$$B^A = \text{ash-red}, \quad B = \text{wild type (blue)}, \quad b = \text{chocolate}.$$

Dominance may be considered complete, in the order listed. Remember that in birds the male is XX, the female XY.

12-17. Male pigeons of genotype *Bb* are blue but sometimes have "flecks" of chocolate areas in certain of their feathers. Offer two explanations (chromosomal and genic, respectively) of this phenomenon.

12-18. When flecks occur in female pigeons of genotype $B^A(-)$, the flecks are usually chocolate, but blue flecks have also been observed in such birds. How might this bear on the respective likelihoods of your two explanations in Problem 12-17?

12-19. In corn, Rhoades found that when homozygous $\dfrac{Dt}{Dt}\dfrac{a}{a}$ plants were crossed with $\dfrac{dt}{dt}\dfrac{a}{a}$ plants, the number of mutations in the aleurone of the resulting kernels depended in large part on which way the cross had been made. When the $\dfrac{Dt}{Dt}\dfrac{a}{a}$ plant had been the pollen parent, there were an average of 7.2 dots per kernel, representing somatic mutations $a \rightarrow A$. But in the reciprocal cross there were 22.2 mutations per seed. Why?

12-20. In Drosophila, *Dichaete* (*D*), a dominant wing-and-bristle characteristic lethal when homozygous, and *Glued* (*Gl*), a dominant eye characteristic also lethal when homozygous, are so close together on the third chromosome that crossing over between the two loci is effectively absent. Given a stock of type

$$\frac{D \quad Gl+}{D+ \quad Gl}$$

what types of progeny, and in what proportions, would survive matings within the stock? Can you discern the advantages of such "balanced lethals" in the maintenance of "true-breeding" heterozygous strains?

12-21, 12-22, 12-23. Several different techniques have been useful in identifying, selecting, and studying mutant and mutantlike bacteria and other microorganisms. The following three problems list the essential bases of three of these. Given these minimal facts, can you work out methods for using them in studying bacterial mutation?

Certain strains of bacteria are sensitive to particular bacteriophages, so that when phage and bacterial suspensions are mixed, the bacteria are killed. Occasionally, however, a bacterium will mutate to a state of "phage resistance." Such a bacterium will then form a colony of living, phage-resistant organisms on an agar plate even when many phage particles are present.

Many bacteria are killed by streptomycin. Certain mutant strains, however, are not only "resistant" to streptomycin but actually require it, and will not grow when it is absent from the medium. When a suspension of organisms of such a mutant strain is grown on a medium lacking streptomycin, only back-mutant individuals, no longer streptomycin-dependent, can establish colonies.

In certain bacteria, penicillin kills growing, actively metabolizing organisms, but quiescent, nongrowing individuals may be treated with penicillin, then washed, and be unaffected by the treatment. On a "minimal" medium containing penicillin, the wild-type organisms will begin to grow, then be killed by the penicillin. Mutant individuals that have lost an essential biosynthetic function, however, are unable to grow on the "minimal" medium and are therefore not usually killed by the penicillin.

12-24.   Assume two mutant strains of bacteria, one unable to synthesize an amino acid X, the other unable to grow without a vitamin Y. On minimal medium, lacking both X and Y, neither strain would grow. Suppose that you mixed the two strains, plated the mixture on minimal medium, and observed that several colonies were growing. How might (a) recombination resulting from a type of sexual reproduction, (b) mutation, or (c) a transforming principle explain the occurrence of these colonies? How might you distinguish these possibilities by further experimentation?

CHAPTER 13

Extranuclear Inheritance

THROUGH CAREFUL and extensive inbreeding and selection, lines of mice have been developed that differ markedly in their incidence of mammary cancer. In certain lines, almost all of the female mice, generation after generation, die of this disease. In other lines, the mice die from other causes, rarely from this type of cancer. Once stabilized at a high or a low level, the mammary cancer incidence is transmitted as a characteristic of the line.

It is of interest to investigate the inheritance of this difference between lines. When reciprocal crosses are made, the outcome of a cross in the first and later generations seems to depend largely on the characteristic of the *female* parent. No matter which way the cross is made, the male makes little immediate contribution to the incidence of this cancer in his descendants. No chromosome or other known element in the nucleus follows this pattern in inheritance. This suggests that an inherited predisposition to mammary cancer in mice may depend on some nonchromosomal, or extranuclear, element for its transmission. Furthermore, since the differences introduced by a female in a cross are transmitted for an indefinite number of generations, the responsible element seems to be capable of perpetuating itself, just as genes are.

The hypothesis that an extranuclear element is involved in the transmission of mammary cancer in mice can be tested in other crosses—backcrosses, for example. Extensive tests have given results consistent with the hypothesis.

This raises an important question relevant to our study of heredity. We can take it as adequately established that a great variety of inherent individual differences are controlled by genes in chromosomes. These differences obey the laws of Mendelian inheritance. But they do not by any means prove that the chromosomes are the sole vehicles of inheritance, or even necessarily the most significant ones. We now need to ask: *Are there other bases of biological inheritance besides the chromosome-borne genes? If so, how important are they, and what kinds of laws do they obey?*

Milk Factors and Placental Transmission. The explanation of the transmission of mammary cancer in mice came when baby mice from lines showing respectively high and low incidence of the cancer were taken from their mothers at birth and allowed to nurse on "foster mothers" of the opposite type. It soon became evident that mother mice from lines showing a high incidence of the disease transmit *through their milk* an agent that later causes mammary cancer to develop in mice that have nursed from them. This agent, called a "milk factor," acts like an infective particle, and meets at least in some respects the criteria for a filterable virus. A female mouse that as a baby has been infected by nursing from an infected mother can in turn transmit the factor through her milk to her progeny.

So defined, the "maternal inheritance" of mammary cancer in mice loses much of its mystery. Medicine has encountered similar situations before, in the form of diseases that can be contracted by embryos or infants through infections carried by their mothers. Syphilis is a familiar example. It has long been emphasized that such *congenital* diseases are not truly *inherited;* they are never part of the germ plasm, but are acquired through agents external to the developing individual. The distinction is an important one, and we were evidently wrong in speaking of the "inheritance" of mammary cancer in mice in connection with the results presented.

These results represent only a small part of the extensive work that has been done with mammary cancer in mice. The case is not as simple as we shall leave it here; a full discussion would be qualified in some respects and extended to the consideration of other conditions affecting the incidence of the disease. It should be emphasized that we have been discussing *mouse* mammary cancer only; there is no present indication that human breast cancer is similarly transmitted.

Whether we call the regular transmission of a quality like mammary cancer from mother to child through milk *inheritance,* or *milk transmission,* or something else, it is a biologically important consideration, and we need to evaluate it and to discuss related examples.

One somewhat similar situation has been reported in horses. Breeders of horses have for a long time been bothered by the fact that an occasional stallion and mare seemed to develop a queer kind of incompatibility in reproduction. The mare, after having had three or more foals, would begin to have repeated difficulties rearing her young, and valuable foal after foal, apparently normal when born, would develop severe jaundice about 96 hours after birth, and die. Two facts have helped to define the situation. First, if the potentially jaundiced foal is prevented from nursing on its own mother and is given a foster mother, the foal does not get sick at all, but develops normally. And second, if the mare is bred to a different stallion, she commonly has no difficulty rearing his foals.

The effect of fostering will remind you of the milk factor in mice. But the fact that the particular male used has an immediate effect on the character of the young shows that the situation is different. And there is another im-

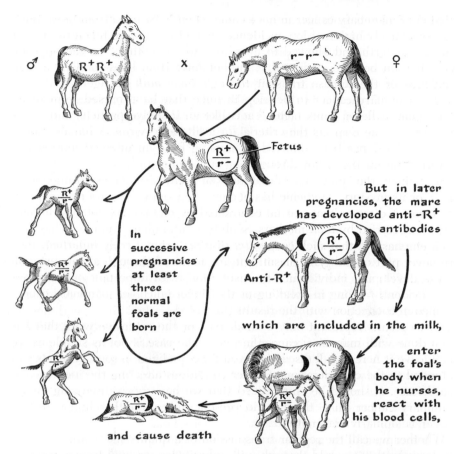

Figure 13-1. *A foal sometimes dies because antibodies that react with his blood cells are contained in his mother's milk.* (*Based on Bruner, Hull, Edwards, and Doll,* The Blood Horse, **53**:24–25, 52, 1948.)

portant difference: There is no indication that the element in mare's milk responsible for the incompatibility is transmitted to later generations by an affected individual when such an individual recovers and lives to reproduce. This element, in other words, is not a specifically self-duplicating particle, as the infective agent causing mammary cancer in mice seems to be.

The basis of the incompatibility in horses, which depends in large part on ordinary gene differences, is illustrated in Figure 13-1. A foal inherits from his sire the ability to make a particular substance absent in his dam. This substance acts as a foreign material when it reaches the mother's circulation from the fetus, and she elaborates *antibodies* capable of reacting specifically with the substance. For the first three or more pregnancies, the antibodies, if they are present at all, are apparently too weak to cause any serious damage. In later pregnancies, however, the antibodies in the milk that the foal gets from his mother may react with the substance he makes by virtue of a gene inherited from his father, and this reaction is often fatal to the foal. The substance is part of his blood cells, and jaundice, a yellow coloring of tissues by the hemoglobin and derived pigments of the destroyed red cells, is one of the early symptoms of the disorder.

The severe reaction in the foal, then, depends on a two-component system. One of these components is a direct result of ordinary Mendelian inheritance: The foal inherits the ability to form an *antigenic* (antibody-inducing) substance from his sire. The other component of the system is an indirect result of the same Mendelian situation: When the mare lacks the antigenic substance present in the foal, she may elaborate antibodies against it. These antibodies, transmitted not through germ plasm but through milk, comprise the second component necessary for incompatibility between mare and foal.

The interpretation of this incompatibility in horses was relatively easy, because an essentially similar situation in human beings was already widely known. This was the Rh factor, causing in human infants the disease *erythroblastosis fetalis* (hemolytic anemia of the newborn). The condition is comparable to the severe jaundice of the foal described above, with one major exception: Instead of being transmitted primarily through milk, Rh antibodies are transmitted from mother to fetus primarily across the placenta (Fig. 13-2). A human fetus may inherit from its father a gene governing the ability to produce a substance absent in the mother. The mother may then elaborate antibodies against the foreign substance, and these antibodies, which in the human diffuse back across the placenta to the fetus, react with the developing fetal blood to cause its destruction.

Rh incompatibility apparently has serious consequences in about one human birth in 200 or 300 (in North America). Through the development of a transfusion technique for replacing the reactive blood of an affected baby with nonreactive blood, and through other recently developed techniques, medicine can now save the potentially erythroblastotic children that are

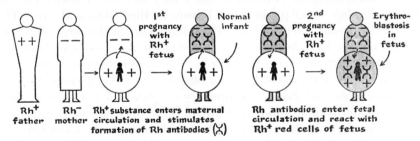

Figure 13-2. *Second or later Rh-positive babies of Rh-negative mothers are sometimes severely anemic, because antibodies that react with the baby's blood cells may be developed by the mother and passed across the placenta to the fetus.*

born alive. The genetic aspects of Rh are more complicated than this brief presentation might suggest. We will return to the subject in Chapter 19.

Situations comparable to Rh are now known in a number of other species: chickens, dogs, cats, mice, rabbits, mules, and guinea pigs, for example. The case in chickens poses a nice distinction. Hens can store in their eggs antibodies capable of reacting in Rh-like fashion with the developing chick. Here the antibody component of the incompatibility system is part of the egg but cannot be considered an integral part of the germ plasm.

Maternal Influence. In the examples previously discussed, the elements passively transferred from mother to child through milk or across the placenta, or even in the egg in the case of "chicken Rh," were not properties produced under the direct control of the mother's own genotype. They were more directly the result of influences external to the mother as an individual —the viruslike agent in mouse mammary cancer, the foreign fetal antigens in the antibody-mediated incompatibilities. But a basic function of a mother is to provide, through the egg or across the placenta, materials of her own elaboration for use by the embryo. A few individual differences are known to depend on the extranuclear transmission of this kind of material.

Perhaps the clearest example is concerned with the color of larval skin and eyes in the meal moth, Ephestia. The basic difference here is a simple Mendelian alternative, such that

$$A = \text{pigment}$$
$$a = \text{no pigment.}$$

These are ordinary, chromosome-borne alleles. The A allele controls the production of a diffusible, hormonelike substance of known chemical composition (*kynurenin*) involved in pigment synthesis. When the a allele is homozygous, this "hormone" is not elaborated.

A female of genotype Aa forms eggs, half of which carry the A allele, and half the a. If the female is mated with an aa male, the progeny are of two genotypes, equal in frequency: Aa and aa. Now the aa offspring have no means of elaborating the A hormone, since they lack the A allele. They do, however, develop some pigment, as larvae, in their skin and eyes. They "fade" as they grow older, and the effect disappears in the next generation.

The Aa mother includes in her eggs some of the A hormone elaborated in her own body. This substance, present by "maternal influence" in the a eggs as well as the A ones, enables the aa offspring to develop some pigment. But, being unable to elaborate a continuing supply of the hormone for themselves, the aa individuals dilute and use up the supply passively transmitted to them from their mother, and the effect is therefore only a transient one.

A presumably similar but less concrete example is provided by the direction of coiling in the shells of certain snails. Snail shells may coil in either of two directions, clockwise or counterclockwise. These are commonly distinguished by the terms *dextral* and *sinistral;* if you hold a shell so that the opening through which the snail's body protrudes is facing you, this orifice may be either on your right (dextral) or on your left (sinistral). The difference is the same as that between a "right-handed" and a "left-handed" screw. Different species may be either dextral or sinistral, and within some species, races may differ in this regard. The race difference may be investigated

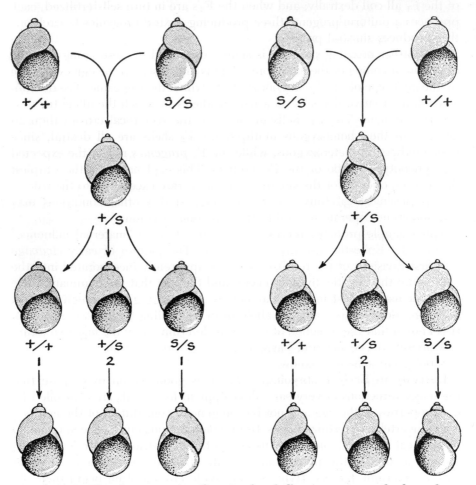

Figure 13-3. *The direction of coiling in the shells of certain snails depends on the mother's genotype, rather than on the genotype of the individual itself. Left, eggs produced by a homozygous dextral snail, fertilized by sperm from a homozygous sinistral individual, develop into dextral progeny. These heterozygous progeny, when self-fertilized, produce only dextral progeny in turn. But the three genotypes in this generation are reflected in the progenies produced in the next generation, again after self-fertilization. Right, the reciprocal cross is different, in ways that confirm the maternal influence on direction of coiling. (After Sturtevant and Beadle,* An Introduction to Genetics, *W. B. Saunders Co., 1940, p. 330.)*

through routine genetic techniques; the investigation has been facilitated by the fact that the particular species most studied (*Limnaea peregra*) is monoecious and can reproduce either by crossing or by self-fertilization (Fig. 13-3).

When reciprocal crosses are made, the F_1 progeny show the same direction of coiling as did their mothers. But F_2's produced by self-fertilization of the F_1 all coil dextrally; and when the F_2's are in turn self-fertilized, each produces a uniform progeny, three producing dextral progenies to each one that produces sinistral progeny.

This rather puzzling situation is simply explained by postulating that the direction of coiling of the embryonic shell is impressed on the egg cytoplasm by the genotype of the diploid oöcyte from which the egg came. The dextral-sinistral alternative depends on a pair of alleles in which the allele for dextral is dominant. The F_1 shells in either of the reciprocal crosses then all agree with their homozygous mothers; the F_2 shells are all dextral, since their mothers are heterozygous; while the F_3 *progenies* reflect the expected 3:1 "phenotypic" ratio of the F_2 mothers. This explanation is the simplest that can be offered for the situation, although rare exceptions to the rule in the species most carefully investigated suggest that other conditions may also sometimes operate to modify the direction of coiling.

This example probably represents the same type of "maternal influence" as does the Ephestia case discussed above. The pattern of early *cleavage* (the first divisions of the fertilized egg) is apparently incorporated into the egg before the meiotic divisions occur, and the fact that the dominant allele of a pair may be lost in the polar bodies as the egg goes through meiosis, therefore, does not prevent this allele from controlling the cleavage pattern. It is known that the direction of coiling is determined by the first two cleavage divisions. The material basis of the egg's organization responsible for this behavior remains unknown.

Heredity in Early Embryology. There is good reason to suppose that the major directions of very early development in animals are controlled by the properties of the egg and not by the genetic constitution of the embryo. Some invertebrate fertilized eggs, from which the nucleus has been removed by surgical methods, may nevertheless go through cleavage in fairly normal fashion, as though this process and the life of these early embryos involved only cytoplasmic factors. Hybrids from wide crosses often begin their development as though they were identical with the maternal species. Later in development, the nuclei of the embryo itself begin to exert their specific effects and take over the direction of differentiation.

It seems probable, therefore, that the egg may have incorporated in its structure a large part of the plan of very early development. But it is also evident that these characteristics of the egg may be controlled very specifically by the genes of the female that produced the egg.

We have posed the problem for this chapter: Are there other bases of biological inheritance besides the chromosome-borne genes? Let us pause for a moment to take stock of what we have learned of this subject so far.

It is clear that the characteristics of a developing individual may be influenced by factors other than its own genetic constitution. We have come to recognize that among these "other factors" are materials and patterns of organization incorporated into the egg itself, or transmitted across the placenta or through the milk from mother to offspring. With regard to the immediate character of the offspring, such extranuclear transmission may be of considerable significance. On a long-term, generation-to-generation basis, however, it is of secondary rather than primary consequence. This is because it is transient in nature; it depends ultimately either on genes (in the case of maternal influence), or on factors outside the inherent germinal material of the individual (in the case of the milk factor), or on some combination of these (as in the case of the antibody-mediated incompatibilities).

In order for an extranuclear element to play a true and stable role in biological inheritance, it must have one characteristic, above all others, in common with genes. It must be capable of specific self-duplication from generation to generation. If it does not have this property, it is likely to be transient and of secondary consequence.

It is true that the viruslike agent called the milk factor has this essential property. But here we appear really to be considering the reproduction of a virus, not an essential of the reproduction of mice.

We must return, then, to our original question, rephrased: *Are there specifically self-duplicating elements outside the nuclei of cells responsible for the extranuclear transmission of inherent qualities?* The examples we have considered up to this point are now seen to be largely irrelevant to this problem.

The Inheritance of Plastid Characteristics. Almost everyone is familiar

TABLE 13-1. Progeny of a Variegated Four-o'clock.

POLLEN FROM BRANCH OF TYPE	POLLINATED FLOWERS ON BRANCH OF TYPE	PROGENY GROWN FROM SEED:
Pale	Pale	Pale
	Green	Green
	Variegated	Pale, green, and variegated
Green	Pale	Pale
	Green	Green
	Variegated	Pale, green, and variegated
Variegated	Pale	Pale
	Green	Green
	Variegated	Pale, green, and variegated

with variegated plants—plants that have areas of pale green or white in their otherwise normally green leaves. Sometimes the variegation is quite symmetrical and uniform; in other cases it is irregular, and whole branches may carry normal green leaves, while others are entirely pale or white, or mixtures of pale or white and dark-green areas.

In the four-o'clock, *Mirabilis jalapa,* controlled pollination of flowers borne on these three kinds of branches of the same plant has given the provocative results summarized in Table 13-1.

You will notice that the type of pollen used is not important; pollen grains from pale, green, and variegated branches behave the same. The determining factor is the female's contribution. Seeds borne on pale branches produce only pale plants; those borne on green branches produce green plants, while those borne on variegated branches segregate in irregular ratios of pale, green, and variegated.

The results can be interpreted on the basis of two different elements, transmitted only through the female and distributed in a variegated plant as follows:

Types of Branches	*Types of Elements Maternally Transmitted*
Pale	Pale
Green	Green
Variegated	Pale and Green

Now the "elements" involved in leaf variations of this sort are very well known and are easily visible under the microscope. They are the *chloroplasts.* There is evidence that these bodies develop from smaller cytoplasmic particles included in the seed, and that they have a demonstrable continuity of their own from generation to generation, multiplying only through the duplication of these formative particles. Seeds borne on a pale branch would therefore include only the pale plastid primordia; those on a green branch only the green; and those borne on a variegated branch might include either pale or green or a mixture of the two plastid types. Neither the constitution of the male gametophyte nor the nuclear constitution of the fertilized egg would be involved in the control of this type of inherent variation. Here, then, is straightforward evidence of a cytoplasmic self-duplicating particle, a "vehicle of heredity" that is extranuclear.

The cytoplasmic primordia of chloroplasts can mutate, and the mutant particles reproduce their own kind just as do mutated genes. In fact, the process of plastid mutation can be influenced by specific genes. In corn, for example, Rhoades has reported a gene (*iojap*) that when homozygous greatly increases the mutation rate of the plastid primordia from normal to defective. The primordia do not appear to back-mutate under the influence of any allele at the iojap locus.

This effect of a gene on plastid behavior may recall to your mind the fact that many genes are known to affect the greenness of plants (e.g., Fig. 5-2).

How can this be consistent with our present observation that the chloroplasts develop from self-duplicating cytoplasmic particles?

It is clear that the plastid primordia are not independent of their environment in producing their phenotypic effects, any more than are genes. Just as other genes can often affect the expression of any particular pair of alleles, so the nuclear elements, through controlling in large part the specific environment in which plastids multiply and develop, can affect the end result of that development. This does not minimize the significance in inheritance of these self-reproducing cytoplasmic particles, any more than it makes genes less generally important to observe that one gene can influence the mutation rate of another, or that the mutation rate of genes can be affected by external agents, or that many genes require the provision of specific materials upon which to act in order to produce their specific effects. All of these things are true of plastids, too.

Other Evidences of Persistent Cytoplasmic Properties in Plants. The four-o'clock and corn examples are representative of a rather large number of essentially similar situations. There can be little doubt that plastids provide an important vehicle of extranuclear inheritance in plants. Besides the variety of instances in which plastids have been clearly identified as the basis for extranuclear transmission, however, there are several additional examples of cytoplasmic inheritance in plants in which no definite cytoplasmic particle has as yet been clearly implicated. In each of these the cytoplasm seems to have some degree of self-perpetuating autonomy.

By way of illustration, we may consider another example briefly. Different species and races of the fireweed, Epilobium, sometimes give different results in reciprocal crosses. For example, E. hirsutum (race 4) ♀ × E. parviflorum ♂ gives hybrids that grow no more than a few inches tall; their leaves are rippled, and they are almost entirely sterile. Hybrids of the reciprocal cross grow about four feet tall, have normal leaves, and bloom generously. Such differences in reciprocal crosses, in the absence of an obvious chromosomal basis like the sex chromosomes, usually suggest cytoplasmic differences between the parent forms. The major difference between male and female contributions to the hybrid may reside in the very limited cytoplasmic contribution of the male in contrast to the large contribution of the female parent. A tentative explanation of the difference in reciprocal crosses described above might be: The hybrid nucleus is unable to work properly with cytoplasm that is primarily E. hirsutum 4, but the hybrid nucleus is compatible with the cytoplasm of E. parviflorum.

Now, to what extent is this postulated character of E. hirsutum cytoplasm, in contrast to E. parviflorum cytoplasm, a stable and independent quality? One way of testing this is to backcross repeatedly to one of the parents, using the original male parent type as the male in each backcross (Fig. 13-4). In terms of nuclear constitution, the effect of this continued backcrossing is to approach quite rapidly a condition in which the nucleus is

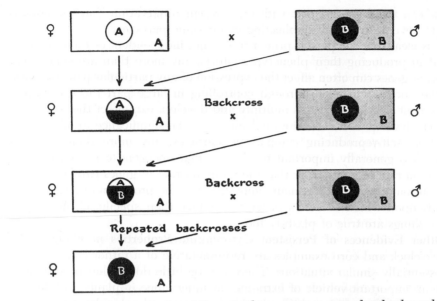

Figure 13-4. *If characteristics of the cytoplasm are transmitted only through the egg, and are independent of the nucleus, then repeated backcrossing according to the pattern illustrated should ultimately give a B nucleus in A cytoplasm.*

virtually identical with that of the recurrent parent. If the cytoplasmic character with which we are concerned is derived from the genic constitution of the nucleus, then the cytoplasm also should show increasing influence of the recurrent male parent. But if the cytoplasmic character is autonomous, the character of the original female parent should persist and be transmitted maternally all down the line of the repeated backcrosses.

Extensive work along this line has shown that in Epilobium the second alternative prevails. The characteristics of the cytoplasm responsible for its incompatibility with a foreign nucleus in this genus of plants is transmitted, to a large degree, independently of nuclear control.

The situation is complicated by somewhat contradictory results of different workers, by evidence that Mendelian genes also affect the incompatibility reaction, and by indications that the small amount of cytoplasm contributed to a hybrid by the male parent may also affect the result. Students wishing to explore this rather complex field will find references to more detailed discussions at the end of this chapter.

Again, the Epilobium example is only one of several that we might consider. Somewhat similar situations have been extensively studied in mosses, for example; yeasts under certain circumstances transmit important biochemical characteristics through asexual reproduction according to cytoplasmic patterns; particular types of *male sterility* in corn, onions, sugar beets, thistles, and flax sometimes depend to a considerable degree on cytoplasmic control. In any or all of these, plastids may be, but are not surely known to be, involved. Nuclear genes, too, may be capable of modifying the cytoplasmic reaction, just as they are in plastid inheritance. In a male-sterile corn, for example, the male sterility appeared to be transmitted through the cytoplasm. When all of the chromosomes of the male-sterile line were replaced with chromosomes of normal plants, the line remained male-sterile, but the degree of male sterility became less pronounced in successive generations.

Other types of male sterility, in corn and in other plants, are known to be under straightforward gene control. The characteristic is often useful in plant breeding, because the inherently emasculated plants cannot self-fertilize, and controlled cross-pollination is therefore made easier.

Killer Paramecia. Some strains of paramecia produce a substance that kills other strains. In a brilliant series of investigations, Sonneborn and his co-workers at Indiana University have demonstrated that this characteristic involves a kind of extranuclear inheritance.

Paramecia that produce the lethal material are called *killers*. The individuals that are killed are called *sensitives*. Two different pairs of alternatives are concerned in the killer *versus* sensitive system:

In the Nucleus		*In the Cytoplasm*
A gene K for *killer*		A self-duplicating cytoplasmic particle (kappa)
or	and	or
Its allele k for *nonkiller*.		No kappa.

Combinations of these alternatives have the characteristics shown in Figure 13-5.

Kappa, the cytoplasmic particle, is directly responsible for the production of the killing substance. But the continued reproduction of kappa in a paramecium depends on the presence of the gene K in the nucleus of the cell; without this gene, kappa is soon lost. Even in the presence of the gene K, proper manipulation of the culture can cause the paramecia to reproduce more rapidly than does kappa. Once kappa is lost, it cannot be regained unless more kappa is introduced from another cell; in other words, gene K is important in the maintenance of kappa, but cannot initiate its production. In this way, a stock having the killer gene but free of kappa can be developed. Some very neat reasoning based on the number of generations required to lose kappa in this fashion resulted in an estimate of the number of kappa particles originally present. This figure was confirmed as an order of magnitude when it was found possible by means of a special technique to stain the kappa particles and to count them directly. There were as many as 1000 per animal in a strong killer stock.

Some biologists suppose that kappa is a parasite of paramecia and not a natural and inherent cytoplasmic particle at all. In some respects, the killer

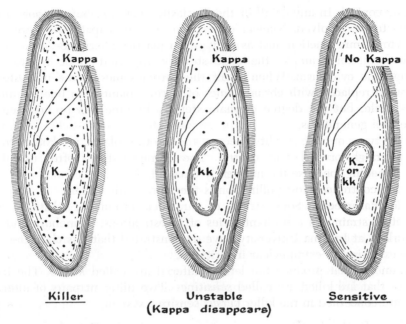

Figure 13-5. *The "killer" characteristic in certain paramecia depends on self-duplicating cytoplasmic particles (kappa). These particles are maintained only when allele K is present in the nucleus. K, however, cannot initiate the production of kappa.*

characteristic behaves like a disease, with which uninfected individuals can be infected under proper conditions. Kappa, then, could be regarded as a very small microorganism that is pathogenic to some strains of paramecia but capable of indefinite self-perpetuation, without evident damage to its host, in others.

If kappa is indeed a parasite, it is a most interesting one; chronic infection with it confers a kind of immunity to its otherwise lethal product. It is transmitted through reproduction of its host and not by casual contact, and its multiplication in a cell depends on the presence of a particular allele in the nucleus of that cell. The *K* gene may be concerned with the production of a specific biochemical factor necessary to the growth and multiplication of this "parasite."

It is impossible at present to decide between the "parasite" theory and the "natural, self-duplicating cytoplasmic particle" theory relative to kappa. In any case, kappa is capable of specific self-duplication; it resides in the cytoplasm of the cell; it is normally transmitted from generation to generation; and it is basic to an inherited quality of present-day paramecia. Kappa has been shown to mutate, and it contains desoxyribonucleic acid, a kind of compound also important in the chemical structure of chromosomes.

Intracellular Symbionts. Many insects normally have yeasts or other microorganisms included within certain of their cells. These microorganisms contribute to their hosts growth factors that the hosts are unable to synthesize for themselves. The relationship between the microorganism and its insect host is therefore mutually beneficial; their life together is *symbiotic*.

Steinhaus has recently summarized the great variety of methods through which the "infection" of successive generations of insects with these beneficial, intracellular symbionts is assured. Here there can be no doubt that the association between host and organized cytoplasmic particle is a secondary, evolutionary adjustment. The germ plasm of host and symbiont remain distinct from each other, but they are so associated in inheritance that they pass together from generation to generation.

Comparable examples might be cited in many other organisms. A classic case is that involving the lichens, long familiar to botanists. And one can conceive of situations in which virus particles, for example, have become so well adjusted to their hosts that they play an integral part in the host metabolism and are transferred to new generations of hosts through the eggs. In such cases it would be very difficult to distinguish between these particles and the normal, self-duplicating cytoplasmic particles elaborated by the higher organism itself and responsible for true extranuclear inheritance.

Other Evidences of Cytoplasmic Transmission in Animals.   Besides the killer characteristic in Paramecium, with its clear-cut particulate basis in kappa, a few other indications of cytoplasmic transmission in animals have been studied. The *basal granules* of the Ciliate protozoa in general, for example, are visible, self-reproducing cytoplasmic bodies from which the cilia are formed. Lwoff has summarized, in the interesting book cited at the end of this chapter, the evidence for precise cytoplasmic transmission of these particles and associated parts of the locomotor system. Other characteristics of Paramecium have also been shown by Sonneborn and his collaborators to involve some degree of cytoplasmic control.

Among higher animals, perhaps the clearest example of cytoplasmic transmission is found in Drosophila. Normally, Drosophila can be anesthetized by carbon dioxide, and the flies tolerate high concentrations of this gas without apparent injury. A strain is known, however, that is killed by relatively low concentrations of CO_2. This characteristic, called *carbon dioxide sensitivity*, is normally transmitted almost exclusively through the egg and behaves in inheritance as though it were dependent on some specifically self-duplicating property of the cytoplasm. In certain respects, the controlling element acts like an infectious particle. For example, a fly can be rendered sensitive by injecting him with hemolymph from an affected individual. But the condition is not spread by simple contact.

True cytoplasmic transmission from one sexual generation to another is as yet not certainly known among the vertebrates. There is, however, some reason to suspect that during development the somatic cells of an individual may become different from each other as a result of the establishment of different stable, self-perpetuating cytoplasmic systems. No definite cytoplasmic particles have been identified with these differences, although there are in the cytoplasm of cells bodies that seem to enjoy a continuity and a degree of autonomy of their own. The possible significance of self-duplicating cytoplasmic particles in inheritance and development among higher animals represents at present a controversial subject.

General Aspects of Extranuclear Inheritance. Our review of extranuclear inheritance in this chapter has now completed something like a circle. Beginning with the maternal transmission of the milk factor in mice, which might be described as depending on an infective particle, we turned to the transmission through milk and across the placenta of the inanimate particles called antibodies, and then to maternal influence through the inclusion in the egg of passive materials and hormones elaborated by the mother's body under the influence of her own genotype. We then considered the visible, particulate basis of the cytoplasmic inheritance of plastid characteristics; several other indications of persistent cytoplasmic properties in plants, and finally the kappa particles in paramecia, the intracellular symbionts of insects, and other evidences of cytoplasmic transmission in animals. Several of these later examples brought us back to the possibility that infective foreign elements may be transmitted from generation to generation. We should now pause to evaluate the significance of the kind of inheritance enclosed within the circle that we have described.

The most powerful technique for the identification of inherited characteristics transmitted in extranuclear fashion is the comparison of reciprocal crosses. The egg regularly contributes much more cytoplasm to the next generation than does the sperm. If this is a valid indication that cytoplasmic inheritance will show differences, either quantitative or qualitative, in reciprocal crosses, then we can generally limit our search for extranuclear inheritance to cases in which the reciprocal crosses differ. But evidently on this basis, extranuclear inheritance must be the exception, whereas nuclear inheritance is the almost universal rule. Identity of the progeny of reciprocal crosses is far more common than is a consistent difference. Furthermore, the majority of examples in which there is a difference in reciprocal crosses are explained in straightforward fashion on the basis of sex chromosomes or similar chromosomal mechanisms. And, finally, the existence of maternal influence, dependent on the passive transfer from mother to offspring of materials elaborated under strict gene control, serves to qualify the evidence from reciprocal crosses. Only in the relatively small residue of cases, therefore, are we justified in suspecting the existence of independent determinants of heredity outside the nucleus.

Probably the main weakness in this logical sequence is the assumption that the sperm must contribute less significantly than the egg to cytoplasmic inheritance. It is true that the male's contribution is a nucleus almost naked in the sperm head. But the *almost* may represent a critical qualification, and there is in fact evidence that in certain cases the extranuclear parts of the sperm contribute elements controlling precise cytoplasmic characteristics. On this basis, we should be cautious in accepting the assertion that only crosses that differ in reciprocal can involve extranuclear inheritance. We are in no position at present to be dogmatic in refusing to recognize the possible significance of extranuclear transmission.

The idea seems to have gained some credence, particularly during the past decade, that geneticists are the jealous custodians of the "gene theory," and are unwilling or unable to accept extranuclear elements as established determinants of heredity. This idea insults the scientific open-mindedness of geneticists as a group. Many students of heredity search eagerly for evidence of extranuclear inheritance in their experimental materials. When such evidence is established, it is accorded the attention and respect it deserves.

When you consider the care and thorough objectivity with which the reality of genes has been established, and the critical checking and counterchecking and confirmation upon which our knowledge of genes is based, it is only to be expected that postulated cytoplasmic elements in heredity must be subject to similar careful scrutiny. We can only say, today, that the nucleus and the Mendelian factors it contains seem on the basis of presently available fact to be of overwhelmingly greater significance in biological inheritance.

From another point of view, it is plausible that this should be so. The behavior of the chromosomes in mitosis and meiosis provides an elegant system for assuring progeny a balanced, complete, and workable set of hereditary elements. No similarly precise mechanism has been suggested for the distribution of cytoplasmic factors. The cytoplasm would therefore seem in general to provide a rather risky basis for the transmission of important, independent elements of heredity.

Plastid inheritance of course constitutes a frequent and important exception to the above generalizations. Furthermore, as we have previously pointed out, it seems possible that plastids may be involved in the determination of other characters not obviously related to them.

Keys to the Significance of This Chapter

Materials of importance to the developing individual, transmitted from the preceding generation, include not only the nuclear genes but also a variety of extranuclear substances. For the most part the latter appear to be only passive materials, transient in their effects, and not vehicles of continuing heredity in the sense in which we have applied this phrase to the chromosomes.

There are, however, examples of self-reproducing autonomous elements in the cytoplasm that are concerned with the transmission of inherent qualities from generation to generation. In some cases these are clearly normal and essential qualities of the organism. In others it is debatable whether they are original parts of the organism or represent secondary, well-adjusted "infections." When present, these factors commonly interact in specific ways with their gene-controlled environment in the cell.

References

Altenberg, E., "The 'Viroid' Theory in Relation to Plasmagenes, Viruses, Cancer and Plastids." *Am. Naturalist*, **80**:559–567, 1946. (Interesting speculation on the possible significance of intracellular symbionts.)

Caspari, E., "Cytoplasmic Inheritance." *Advances in Genetics*, **2**:1–66, 1948. (A review, with many references.)

Correns, C., "Vererbungsversuche mit blass (gelb) grünen und buntblättrigen Sippen bei *Mirabilis Jalapa, Urtica pilulifera* und *Lunaria annua*." *Z. Ind. Abst. Vererb.-lehre*, **1**:291–329, 1909. (Classic study of plastid inheritance.)

Darlington, C. D., "Mendel and the Determinants," in *Genetics in the 20th Century*, pp. 315–332. New York: Macmillan Co., 1951. (An historical evaluation, with particular reference to cytoplasmic factors.)

Ephrussi, B., "Remarks on Cell Heredity," in *Genetics in the 20th Century*, pp. 241–262. New York: Macmillan Co., 1951. (Presents studies of apparent cytoplasmic transmission in yeasts, and a general evaluation of "cell heredity.")

————, and Hottinguer, H., "On an Unstable Cell State in Yeast." *Cold Spring Harbor Symposia Quant. Biol.*, **16**:75–85, 1951.

Hagberg, A., "Genotype and Phenotype in Alkaloid Content in Lupines." *Hereditas*, **36**:228–230, 1950. (A short discussion of maternal influence on the sweet-bitter alternative.)

Knudson, L., "Permanent Changes of Chloroplasts Induced by X Rays in the Gametophyte of *Polypodium aureum*." *Botan. Gaz.*, **101**:721–758, 1940. (Source of the promising material upon which Problem 13-18 is based.)

L'Heritier, P., "The CO_2 Sensitivity Problem in Drosophila." *Cold Spring Harbor Symposia Quant. Biol.*, **16**:99–112, 1951.

Lwoff, A., *Problems of Morphogenesis in Ciliates. The Kinetosomes in Development, Reproduction and Evolution.* New York: Wiley & Sons, 1950. (Brief, brilliant, and highly interesting analysis of cytoplasmically controlled cell patterns.)

Michaelis, P., "Interactions Between Genes and Cytoplasm in Epilobium." *Cold Spring Harbor Symposia Quant. Biol.*, **16**:121–129, 1951.

Owen, F. V., "Cytoplasmically Inherited Male-Sterility in Sugar-Beets." *J. Agr. Research*, **71**:423–440, 1945. (Detailed discussion of this subject, and a review of general aspects of the inheritance of male sterility in plants.)

Provasoli, L., Hutner, S. H., and Pintner, I. J., "Destruction of Chloroplasts by Streptomycin." *Cold Spring Harbor Symposia Quant. Biol.*, **16**:113–120, 1951.

Rhoades, M. M., "Plastid Mutations." *Cold Spring Harbor Symposia Quant. Biol.*, **11**:202–207, 1946. (A good review and bibliography, with particular reference to the *iojap* gene in corn. This is perhaps the most revealing study available of relationships among genes and plastids.)

Sonneborn, T. M., "Beyond the Gene." *Am. Scientist,* **37**:33–59, 1949. (A clear and well-organized evaluation of extranuclear inheritance.)

——, "The Role of Genes in Cytoplasmic Inheritance," in *Genetics in the 20th Century,* pp. 291–314. New York: Macmillan Co., 1951. (Somewhat more technical than the above.)

Questions and Problems

13- 1. What do the following terms signify?

antibody	killer, kappa, and *k*
antigen	maternal influence
erythroblastosis	milk transmission
extranuclear inheritance	

13- 2. A mother who has been severely infected with German measles during the first three months of pregnancy sometimes gives birth to a child with one or more anomalies. These anomalies may include deafness, cataract or other eye defects, abnormality of the heart, liver defect, or abnormal smallness of the head. Other virus diseases in a pregnant woman— mumps, chicken pox, and ordinary measles—also may sometimes affect her developing child. Why is it important to distinguish between *inheritance* and *prenatal effects* of this sort?

13- 3. Consider the diagram in Figure 13-2. Why do you suppose that a first-born child almost never has erythroblastosis?

Assume that the Rh-positive/Rh-negative alternative is controlled by an allelic pair such that

$$R- = \text{Rh-positive (having the Rh substance on}$$
$$\text{red blood cells)}$$
$$rr = \text{Rh-negative (lacking the Rh substance).}$$

Further assume that erythroblastosis may occur only in an Rh-positive baby of an Rh-negative mother who has had at least one previous Rh-positive baby.

13- 4. An Rh-positive father and an Rh-negative mother have a first born, Rh-negative son. What is the chance that the next child will be Rh-positive? That it will be erythroblastotic?

13- 5. Among Rh-positive children of Rh-negative mothers who have had at least one previous Rh-positive child, erythroblastosis actually occurs in only about one child in twelve. In other words, erythroblastosis does not often occur even under conditions optimal for its development. Now suppose that the second child in Question 13-4 was a normal, Rh-positive girl. What would be the approximate chance that a third child born to these parents would be erythroblastotic?

13- 6. Is erythroblastosis an inherited characteristic? Elaborate.

Hagberg, at the Institute of Genetics, Svalöf, Sweden, has studied the inheritance of bitterness and sweetness in lupines. (Different kinds of lupines are used as ornamental plants and as forage crops; wild lupines decorate our countryside.)

13- 7. When sweet and bitter lupines are crossed, with bitter as the pollen parent, and the plants grown from the seeds resulting from this cross are tested within a month after the seed is sown, all of the F_1 plants are sweet. F_1 plants from the reciprocal cross, grown and tested under similar conditions, are bitter. What might explain these results?

13- 8. Usually, the leaves of F_1 plants more than a month old, and always the ripe seeds of these plants, whichever way the parental cross was made, are bitter. Does this help to narrow down the possibilities suggested in your answer to Question 13-7?

13- 9. Hagberg observed that 40 mature F_2 plants from the cross ♀ sweet × ♂ bitter segregated as 12 sweet: 28 bitter, in terms of their ripe seed. Their leaves, however, had all been bitter until they were almost a month old. Diagram the reciprocal crosses of sweet × bitter through F_2, suggesting when in the life cycle of lupines the alternatives sweet and bitter are affected by the genes of each generation.

13-10. When bison bulls are bred to domestic cows, the hybrid calves are rarely born alive; a great excess of watery fluid is formed within the fetal membranes of the embryo, and the cows almost always abort. Crosses between domestic bulls and bison cows have no such consequences, and the hybrid calves are born alive and healthy. Could an Rh-like situation explain this difference between the reciprocal crosses? How? How would you test the explanation?

13-11. Diagram reciprocal crosses of AA × aa Ephestia (p. 265), showing parental phenotypes, genotypes, and gametes; F_1 phenotypes, genotypes, and gametes; F_2 genotypes and phenotypes, distinguishing phenotypes of larvae and adults in each generation.

13-12. Diagram meiosis, in both testes and ovaries, and self-fertilization in a snail heterozygous for the dextral-sinistral alternative. List genotypes and phenotypes of progeny, and indicate the phenotypes of the progeny of another generation of self-fertilization from each of these genotypes.

13-13. What was the phenotype of the heterozygous snail with which you started in Question 13-12? Explain.

13-14. It is possible to remove the ovaries of a mouse and to transplant in their place ovaries from another mouse. Such transplanted ovaries, in a high proportion of cases, become established and function normally, shedding eggs to be fertilized in their new host. How might this technique be used to distinguish between *transfer of materials from mother to fetus across the placenta*, and *egg transmission of cytoplasmic materials?*

13-15. Given consistent differences between two strains of mice in a particular characteristic, and a marked difference in the results of reciprocal crosses between the two strains, how might you distinguish ordinary sex linkage, maternal influence *via* egg or placenta or milk, or cytoplasmic inheritance as responsible?

In sugar beets, F. V. Owen has described a type of male sterility dependent on:

a. a stable, maternally transmitted cytoplasmic factor $\boxed{S}$, resulting in male sterility, in contrast to normal cytoplasm $\boxed{N}$ (male-fertile).

b. two different allelic pairs, X-x and Z-z.

Interactions of these factors appear to result in the following:

$\boxed{S}$ xxzz = completely male-sterile.

$\boxed{S}$ Xxzz or $\boxed{S}$ xxZz = almost entirely male-sterile.

$\boxed{S}$ XxZz, $\boxed{S}$ XXzz or $\boxed{S}$ xxZZ = partially male-fertile.

$\boxed{S}$ XXZz, $\boxed{S}$ XxZZ = practically male-fertile.

$\boxed{S}$ XXZZ = male-fertile.

$\boxed{N}$ with any relevant genotype = male-fertile.

(The male-sterile *vs.* male-fertile characteristic refers to the production of functional pollen. Owen did not report all of the combinations listed; we have "filled in" the table arbitrarily, and to this extent the scheme presented here is somewhat hypothetical.)

13-16. Given the existence of "tester stocks" of beets $\boxed{S}$ xxzz, $\boxed{S}$ XXZZ, $\boxed{N}$ xxzz, and $\boxed{N}$ XXZZ maintained when necessary by asexual propagation, how would you ascertain the cytoplasmic type and genetic constitution of a given male-fertile plant? What crosses would you make and what results would you expect?

13-17. Owen also described a type of male-sterile beet that, when fertilized with pollen from an $\boxed{N}$ xxzz line, gave a total of 70 completely male-fertile progeny, no male steriles. Do these beets fit the scheme given above? If not, how might they be explained? How would you check this explanation?

13-18. Knudson has reported various permanent changes in chloroplasts induced in the gametophyte of the hare's-foot fern, *Polypodium aureum,* when the haploid spores giving rise to these gametophytes were X-rayed. These plants can be propagated asexually. How would you ascertain whether changes in genes or in cytoplasmic plastid primordia were responsible for the mutant plastid characteristics?

13-19. In Problem 12-3, we referred to the stripes on seedling leaves of corn grown from kernels exposed to atomic radiation. You probably interpreted this in terms of genic changes induced in particular cells of the embryonic leaf primordia. Can you now suggest an alternative explanation? It is very difficult to get evidence bearing directly on the relative likelihoods of these two explanations. Why?

Ephrussi has studied a rather common type of mutation in yeasts involving the simultaneous loss of two important respiratory enzymes. The spontaneous "mutation rate" is greatly increased in the presence of certain chemicals (*acridines*). The interference with normal yeast physiology in the mutant is such as to result in dwarf colonies when mutant cells are plated on solid medium; the characteristic is called *petite*.

13-20. When a normal "mother cell" of yeast is permitted to reproduce asexually (by budding) in the presence of an acridine, some of the buds produced are enzymatically deficient, and others are normal. All mother cells, even after producing several mutant buds, remain capable of producing normal ones as well, and remain normal themselves. The mutant characteristic, when it occurs in an asexual line, is permanent for successive generations of budding. In sexual crosses, however, the mutants behave as though their genes are identical with those of the mother cell. Suggest an explanation of these results.

13-21. An acridine has been known for many years to inhibit selectively the duplication of the *kinetoplast,* a self-duplicating, autonomous cytoplasmic structure concerned with locomotion in a flagellate. Suggest a possible mechanism for the "mutagenic" action of the acridines in yeast.

13-22. Ephrussi also found a simple recessive mutation in yeasts, which resulted when homozygous in the absence of the same enzymatic functions missing in the "petite" mutants discussed above. He refers to the genic mutants as "segregational mutants," and to the mutants first described as "vegetative mutants." Crosses between "segregational" and "vegetative" mutants gave normal diploid cells, which segregated into two segregational mutants : two normals, as the four products of meiosis. Suggest an explanation of this result in terms of a relationship between the two types of mutants.

13-23. A group of related French families has experienced seventy-two female births and no male births over a period of three generations. The original female parent transmitted to all fourteen of her daughters and granddaughters the faculty of becoming a mother of daughters only, not a mother of sons. Assume that the faculty involved is that of producing eggs fertilizable only by X-bearing sperm. What is a simple explanation of the basis of this faculty?

13-24. The following chain of effects has been suggested as responsible for Mongolian idiocy in man:

Specific genetic constitution of mother

↘

    Formation of some cytoplasmically defective eggs, increasing in frequency as mother grows older

        ↘

        Mongolian idiocy in offspring resulting from defective eggs (about 0.1% of all births).

Consider how this hypothesis is consistent with the following facts:
a. *Identical* twins (two individuals arising from a single fertilized egg) are always alike with regard to this characteristic; they are either both normal or both Mongolian idiots.
b. When one of a pair of *fraternal* twins (twins from two separate fertilized eggs) is a Mongolian idiot, the other is almost always normal in this regard.

How does the scheme differ from the illustrations of maternal influence discussed in this chapter?

CHAPTER 14

Genetic Aspects of Sexuality and of Sex Determination

SEXUAL REPRODUCTION leads to the occurrence of a great variety of genetic combinations, and thus accounts for much of the heritable variation that is so typical of life and basic to evolutionary processes. It is significant, then, that sexual reproduction is widespread, occurring not only within the higher groups in the plant and animal kingdoms but also in lower plants and invertebrates. In 1946, J. Lederberg and E. L. Tatum, then working at Yale University, demonstrated that genetic recombination takes place among certain bacteria. Since recombination is a consequence of sexual reproduction, their experiments suggest that bacteria, too, have some kind of mechanism for sexual reproduction.

Even bacteriophage may show genetic recombination. Bacteriophage are viruses that live on bacteria. Electron microscope studies have shown them to be particulate entities, some of them with shapes curiously reminiscent of tadpoles. Numbers of heritable characteristics are known in bacteriophage. From time to time, these may be altered by mutation, so that bacteriophage have certain attributes which may be viewed as paired alternatives. As illustrated in Figure 14-1, when two genetically different strains of bacteriophage are added to a bacterium that both can attack, types of virus are produced that have the parental characteristics in new combinations. Here, as in the bacteria studied by Lederberg and Tatum, the results lead to the conclusion that a mechanism like sexual reproduction is in operation.

Differences in Sexual Reproduction. Although the most fundamental genetic aspects of sexual reproduction are the same at all levels of life, the organization and the mechanics of systems of sexual reproduction take various forms. What these are in bacteria and viruses have not yet been discovered. But among certain algae and fungi, for example, sexual reproduction is based on the fusion of morphologically similar gametes produced within undifferentiated cells. In man, sexual reproduction occurs on a much more specialized basis. Gametic fusion takes place between a small, motile sperm cell and a much larger, immotile egg. The sperm are produced in spe-

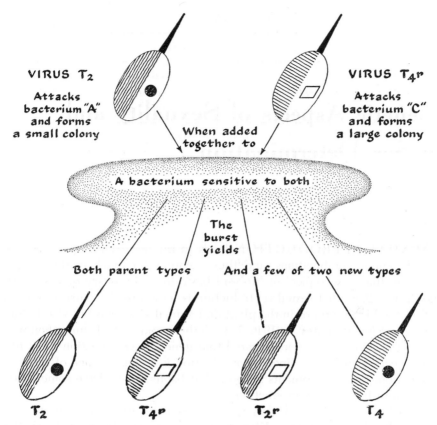

VIRUS T₂

Attacks
bacterium "A"
and forms
a small colony

When added
together to

VIRUS T₄ʳ

Attacks
bacterium "C"
and forms
a large colony

A bacterium sensitive to both

The
burst
yields

Both parent types   And a few of two new types

T₂   T₄ᵖ   T₂ʳ   T₄

Figure 14-1. *When certain bacterial viruses having different genetic characteristics are added to the same bacterium, some of the progeny show recombinations of the parental characters. This suggests sexual reproduction. These bacterial viruses are tadpole-shaped. The circles and squares and the vertical and horizontal lines symbolize the two sets of alternative characters that show recombination. (After Delbrück and Delbrück, Sci. Am., 179:50, April 1948.)*

cial organs by males of the species, and eggs are produced in different special organs by females. Between the high degree of specialization found in the sexual reproduction of some organisms and the complete lack of specialization in others, a variety of intermediate situations exists.

Sex Determination and Sex Differentiation. How is heredity related to the division of labor that so often characterizes sexual reproduction? Or, to put the question in more familiar terms: Why are some individuals males, and others females? For different groups of organisms, different answers need to be given.

You have already learned from Chapter 6 that in man, Drosophila, and in many other animals and some plants, sex determination traces back to the segregation of different members of a particular chromosome pair. But a sex-

TABLE 14-1. Typical Sex Differences in Man.

♀	PRIMARY DIFFERENCES	♂
Ovaries		Testes
Vagina, uterus, oviducts		Penis, scrotum, prostate, seminal vesicles
	SECONDARY DIFFERENCES	
Breasts well developed		Breasts rudimentary
Subcutaneous fat well developed		Subcutaneous fat poorly developed
High voice		Low voice
Body hair sparse		Body hair relatively well developed
Broad hips and pelvis		Relatively narrow hips and pelvis

determining mechanism like the XY, although very satisfactory for explaining some aspects of sexuality, may be misleadingly simple. Look back to Figure 6-4, on p. 88, which shows the cytological basis of sex determination. Ask yourself how much such a scheme does toward explaining sex differences in our own group, man. Remember that, besides the cytological differences already emphasized, men and women show considerable diversity at the physiological, structural, and psychological levels. In addition to so-called *primary* sex differences in the organs particularly concerned in reproductive processes, there are numerous secondary differences as well. A very few of these differences are indicated in Table 14-1. This table is not intended to summarize sex differences in man but only to suggest to you that knowledge of the functioning of the XY mechanism may be but a first step in understanding why some individuals are males and some are females.

As presently understood, the XY system is a mechanism that sets in motion alternative trains of events that more or less faithfully follow a pattern ultimately leading either to maleness or femaleness. According to this concept, sex is normally *determined* at the time of fertilization. Fusion of an egg with an X-bearing sperm cell determines that the zygote is a potential female; fusion with a Y-bearing sperm determines a male. But the realization of this potentiality, normally ordained at fertilization, is a slow and complex process—a matter of embryonic developmental physiology as well as postnatal development. In other words, processes of *differentiation* follow *determination* and translate determination into the practical reality of sex differences.

Embryological Aspects of Sex Differentiation. The structure of the young mammalian embryo is sexually "indifferent," or "neutral." This is the state even of the rudimentary gonads, which consist of a *cortex,* or outer tissue layer, and a *medulla,* or inner tissue mass. As differentiation proceeds, one

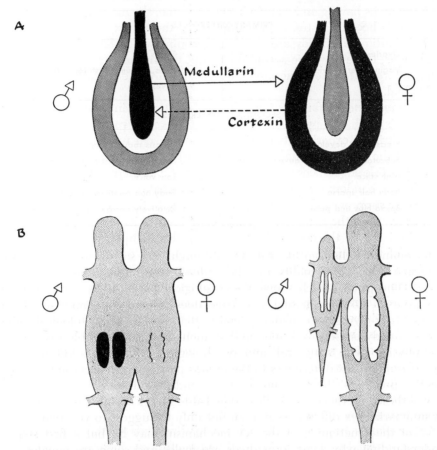

Figure 14-2. A. *In genetically determined male salamanders, the central medulla of the embryonic gonad becomes highly developed, while the cortex disappears. In females, it is the medulla that disappears, and the cortex that develops. The medulla produces a diffusible substance, "medullarin," which may act to suppress cortical development. The cortex produces "cortexin," which may act to suppress medullary development. The antagonistic effects of these substances are indicated by the arrows. Of the two, medullarin has the stronger suppressing effect. B. The antagonistic action of medullarin and cortexin is strikingly illustrated when male and female salamanders are grafted together in early embryonic stages. If the graft members are of equal size, the male effect dominates, and ovarian development in the female graft partner is often entirely suppressed. If the male is quite small compared to its graft partner, the female effect predominates, and the male gonads may be converted into ovaries. In the diagram, testes are shown in black and ovaries in white. (Based on Witschi, after Waddington,* An Introduction to Modern Genetics, *1939. By permission of George Allen & Unwin Ltd. and of the Macmillan Co.)*

part of the rudimentary gonads develops while the other largely disappears. In individuals having an X- and a Y-chromosome, the medulla increases, and the gonads become testes. In XX individuals, the cortex becomes dominant, and the ultimate gonads are ovaries. Accompanying these developmental alterations, the embryonic sexual ducts and the rudiments of external genitalia differentiate into structures appropriate to the determined sex of the individual.

Hormones and Differentiation. Sex differentiation in many groups of organisms is mediated by biologically potent chemical substances called hormones. Striking experiments carried out by Witschi with salamanders suggest that the cortex and medulla of the embryonic gonad produce characteristic diffusible substances which are antagonistic in their effects. If male and female salamanders are grafted together, the male substance (medullarin) ordinarily suppresses development of the ovary in the female graft member. However, when the male is very small compared to its female partner, processes initiated by the cortical hormone may get the upper hand, so that the gonads of the genetically determined male become ovaries. The basic situations in Witschi's experiment are diagrammed in Figure 14-2.

In man as well as in the salamander, differentiation, especially of secondary sexual characters, comes under hormonal influence. Fairly direct evidence on this point is provided by the effects of castration on males. When the testes are removed before puberty, an individual typically grows to adulthood having many qualities usually associated with femaleness, such as a high-pitched voice, relatively large hips, and lack of a beard or of much body hair. To a certain extent, the feminizing effects of loss of function or of absence of the testes can be counteracted by injections of the male hormone testosterone.

Other glands besides the sex glands are involved in the elaboration of secondary sexual characters. So closely interacting are members of the endocrine system, and so sensitive to one another's functions, that failure or alteration of function in one member leads to widespread consequences in many areas of the organism. For example, disturbances in the adrenal cortex are frequently associated with changes in secondary sexual characters. In males, such disturbances may lead to atrophy of the genitals, and to enlargement of the breasts and other tendencies toward femaleness. On the other hand, disturbances of adrenal function in women, which may be due, for example, to a tumor in the gland, sometimes lead to masculinization, as evidenced by more abundant facial hair, a lower register of the voice, and so on.

A final sample of the evidence for hormonal influence on sex differentiation is provided by one of those occasional biological "experiments in nature" so ingenious that any scientific investigator would have been proud to devise it. The male member of a pair of unlike-sexed twins in cattle is usually quite normal, but his female co-twin is often an anomalous sort of creature called a *freemartin.* The external genitals of freemartins are female; the internal sex organs and their accessories are more or less male, varying from one individual to another. Freemartins are sterile, and show considerable masculinization in a number of traits. Systematic probing into the background of these animals, particularly by Lillie, has led to the conclusion that they occur when there is fusion of the fetal membranes of unlike-sexed twins, so that cross-circulation of blood takes place between them. When fusion does not occur, the female develops normally—as does the male in any case. The current explanation is that cross-circulation, if established, carries hormones from the male into the body of the genetically determined female, where they affect her sex differentiation.

Gynandromorphism. One of the more important concepts to be derived from the preceding section is that genes and chromosomes carried in a particular organism may not be decisive in fixing its fate. You have seen that tissues genetically determined as female can differentiate in the direction of maleness if acted upon by male hormones. This situation arises, however, under a system of sex differentiation that is not universal for the animal kingdom. In insects, the key factors in sex differentiation are apparently intracellular rather than hormonal. Occasionally you can find Drosophila, for example, that show a sharp mosaic of sex characters. These individuals, typically male in certain portions of the body and typically female in others, are called *gynandromorphs.* The mosaic patterns often involve the sex combs, the color patterns of the abdomen, and body size. Some individuals have both male and female gonads and genitalia. These flies, when looked on as whole organisms, can scarcely be designated either as male or female. Their own state of confusion is shown vividly by the anomalies frequently displayed in their courtship patterns.

The origin of gynandromorphs in Drosophila has been successfully explained in relation to the XY mechanism for sex determination. You will remember that XX individuals are females, XY individuals are males, and that exceptional XO individuals are males, although sterile. You will recall, too, that once in a great while a chromosome gets lost at the time of nuclear division. If the chromosome lost is an X-chromosome in a somatic cell of a developing individual determined at fertilization as female (XX), the daughter cell missing the chromosome will be male in chromosomal constitution (XO), and the other daughter cell will remain female (XX). Assuming the divisions to be regular thereafter, nuclear progeny of the former will reproduce a male chromosome complement and descendants of the latter will continue XX. The *when* and *where* of the chromosome loss determine the size and position of the male sector in the mosaic.

Beautiful genetic demonstrations that chromosome loss is involved in gynandromorphism may occur when the original fertilized egg cell is heterozygous for one or more sex-linked characters. If the X-chromosome eliminated is one carrying the dominant alleles of heterozygous gene pairs, the

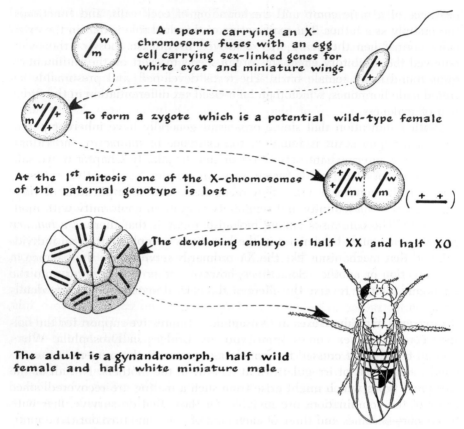

A sperm carrying an X-chromosome fuses with an egg cell carrying sex-linked genes for white eyes and miniature wings

To form a zygote which is a potential wild-type female

At the 1st mitosis one of the X-chromosomes of the paternal genotype is lost

The developing embryo is half XX and half XO

The adult is a gynandromorph, half wild female and half white miniature male

Figure 14-3. *The origin of gynandromorphism in Drosophila, and some of its possible phenotypic consequences. If the X-chromosome lost had been the one carrying the mutant alleles, the male portion of the adult would have been phenotypically wild type. If the chromosome elimination had occurred some time after the first mitotic division of embryonic development, a correspondingly smaller portion of the individual would have been male.*

recessive characteristics may be expressed in the male areas from which this chromosome is missing. A diagrammatic representation of the origin of gynandromorphism and of certain of its possible phenotypic consequences is found in Figure 14-3.

The Balance Concept of Sex. A number of lines of evidence indicate that in many groups of organisms, even where males and females are ordinarily separate, all individuals have genes for both sexes. One such indication comes from instances where genetically determined males are influenced by female hormones, or vice versa. In extreme instances, almost complete sex reversal may take place. A notable chicken, reported by Crew, began life as a female, climaxing her existence as a hen by laying fertile eggs. Subsequently, "she" took up another career, evidenced first by the appearance of a male comb and the sounding of cock calls, and functioned successfully as a father. The explanation of this dual role is that in the originally normal hen the ovary was destroyed by disease. Loss of the ovary removed the inhibitory effect this organ seems to exert on the rudimentary testis found in all female birds. The testis developed, and presumably secreted male hormones, which then influenced sex differentiation in the direction of maleness.

Another indication that single organisms generally have inherent potentialities for both sexes is found in the existence of *intersexes*, individuals more or less intermediate between male and female. In Chapter 6, we said that the Greeks had words for six sexes in people. No objective evidence bears out the number of sexes they recognized, but the implication of varying degrees of masculinity and femininity is quite in conformity with modern views. The consensus among biologists today is that there is a *balance* of male and female tendencies in the hereditary complement of an individual, and that mechanisms like the XY ordinarily serve to trip the balance in one direction or another. Sometimes, however, other factors enter onto the scales and alter or reverse the effect of the normal mechanism for sex determination.

Intersexes and Supersexes in Drosophila. Impressive support for the balance concept of sex comes from work by Bridges in Drosophila. When triploid females are crossed to normal males, some of the progeny are aneuploids, as a result of irregularities at meiosis in the mothers. Not all of the aneuploid types which might arise from such a mating are recovered, since many of the combinations are inviable. Of those that do survive, flies with two X-chromosomes and three of each kind of autosome turn out to be *intersexes*. They are variable in appearance, in general having complex mixtures of male and female attributes for the internal sex organs and external genitalia, without showing clear regional mosaicism.

The correlation of an unusual combination of X-chromosomes and autosomes with an unusual brand of sexuality provided Bridges with the foundation for a meaningful concept of the basis of sexuality in Drosophila. In brief summary, this concept may be developed as follows: Two sets of autosomes and one X-chromosome give a male. Two sets of autosomes and two X-chromosomes give a female. Three sets of autosomes and two X-chromosomes, however, give an intersex! Differences between the sexes would appear, then, to be based on proportions between X-chromosomes and autosomes. Y-chromosomes seem to be of little consequence in sex determination, since XO individuals are phenotypically male. Moreover, the unusual presence of Y's in female chromosome complements, for example in attached-X stocks, does not alter sex. A logical interpretation of sex determination in Drosophila is that X-chromosomes carry genes that are predominantly female-determining, while among genes in the autosomes the predominant tendency is toward maleness. Under normal circumstances the additional X-chromosome found

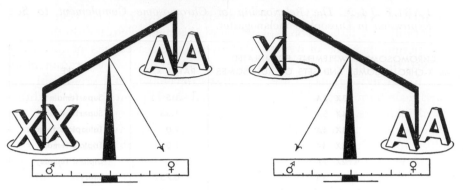

Figure 14-4. *In Drosophila, sexuality is a matter of balance between opposing factors toward maleness and femaleness. Under normal circumstances, the mechanism for sex determination is such that the additional X-chromosome in females tips the balance decisively toward feminine development. Where there is a single X-chromosome and two sets of autosomes, the balance is tipped toward maleness.*

in females is a decisive factor in tipping the balance toward feminine development. In individuals with one X-chromosome and two sets of autosomes the balance hangs in the direction of maleness. (See Fig. 14-4.)

For ease of summarization and analysis, the proportion between X-chromosomes and autosomes in a given individual can be formulated as follows: If X stands for an X-chromosome, and if A signifies a set of autosomes, the formula $2X\ 2A$ designates the chromosome complement of a normal diploid female. As a ratio of X-chromosomes to autosomes this can be expressed as $X/A = \frac{2}{2} = 1$. For males the derivation of the corresponding value is $X/A = \frac{1}{2} = 0.5$. The value for an intersex is $X/A = \frac{2}{3} = 0.67$.

The values 1.0, 0.5, and 0.67 doubtless have no deep intrinsic meaning with regard to sex determination. But by indicating proportionality between X-chromosomes and autosomes, they do serve as sex indices, thus pointing to femaleness, maleness, and the area in between. It is of particular interest to see whether still different X-chromosome/autosome relationships, and the sex types they determine, fall into an orderly scheme consistent with the sex index numbers already presented.

Triploid ($3X/3A$) and tetraploid ($4X/4A$) flies have been studied. The reduplication of chromosome sets has some phenotypic consequences, but sexually these polyploids are females. Now $4X/4A$ and $3X/3A$ both come to 1. Since each of these types appears to be female, the result conforms with what might be expected on the basis of the index number of a diploid female.

The same cross, triploid ♀ × normal ♂, that gives $2X/3A$ progeny also produces $3X/2A$ and $1X/3A$ offspring. You have already been introduced to $3X/2A$ Drosophila, since they are one of the types produced by crosses involving attached-X females (Chap. 6). The $3X/2A$ individuals are desig-

TABLE 14-2. *The Relationship of Chromosome Complement to Sex Expression in* Drosophila melanogaster.

CHROMOSOME COMPLEMENT, FORMULATED AS X-CHROMOSOMES AND SETS OF AUTOSOMES	RATIO X/A	TYPE
3X 2A	1.5	Superfemale
4X 3A	1.33	Superfemale
4X 4A	1.0	Tetraploid female
3X 3A	1.0	Triploid female
2X 2A	1.0	Diploid female
3X 4A	0.75	Intersex
2X 3A	0.67	Intersex
1X 2A	0.5	Male
2X 4A	0.5	Male
1X 3A	0.33	Supermale

nated as *superfemales,* the 1X/3A as *supermales.* These flies, unfortunately, scarcely live up to their glamorous names, and are weak, sterile, and poorly viable. In fact, their names are not intended to connote any particular kind of prowess, but were devised to indicate that the sex indices in each case, $3X/2A = 1.5$ and $1X/3A = 0.33$, lie outside the range of values for normal female and normal male.

A few other aneuploid types of Drosophila have been reported. Among these, 2X/4A individuals turn out to be males, and 3X/4A flies are inter-sexes, results which fit nicely into the series established by the sex indices already described. Table 14-2 summarizes the relations of sex to chromosomes in Drosophila.

The "Transformer" Gene in Drosophila. A recessive gene, *tra,* which is situated between 44.0 and 45.3 in the third chromosome of *D. melanogaster,* has the effect when homozygous of transforming diploid females into sterile males. Phenotypically the XX *tra/tra* flies are like normal males in that they have well-developed sex combs, normal male external genitalia, genital ducts and sperm pump, a male colored abdomen, and other of the masculine traits of Drosophila. The testes, however, are much reduced in size.

The *tra* gene, of course, may affect sex ratios quite drastically. For example, as seen in Figure 14-5, a cross between a heterozygous female and a homozygous male gives three males for every female in the progeny.

Out of an experimental cross involving *tra,* one individual was obtained that was superfemale in X-chromosome/autosome ratio and homozygous for the *tra* gene. This fly was a kind of intersex with strong tendencies toward maleness. If the single specimen is characteristic, superfemales would seem more resistant than ordinary females to modification to a male status by the *tra* gene. At least in this unusual situation, therefore, superfemales may be ultrafeminine indeed.

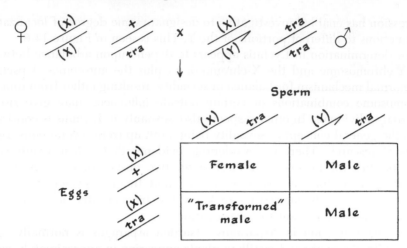

Figure 14-5. *A cross in Drosophila between a male homozygous for the* transformer *gene and a female heterozygous for* tra. *Note the sex ratio in the progeny.*

From our present point of view, the most significant thing about the *tra* gene is the demonstration that the normal chromosomal mechanism for sex determination can be nullified by a single gene substitution. The transformer effect is understandable when we remember that sexuality is a matter of balance, and that normal devices for sex determination are only means for weighting the scales in one direction or the other. The *tra* gene may be thought of as an extra counterweight introduced into the system for sex determination.

Balance and Sex Determination in Lychnis. In only one instance has sex determination in higher plants been studied with anything like the thoroughness applied to the corresponding problem in Drosophila. This is in the species of Lychnis, often called Melandrium. Lychnis belongs to the pink family. Its genetics and cytology, particularly with reference to sex determination, have been investigated by Westergaard in Denmark, by Warmke in the U. S. A., and by others.

The normal basis for sex determination in Lychnis is the distribution of members of an X-Y chromosome pair. As is true in all but a few of such instances known in higher plants (the strawberry is one exception), presence of the unequal pair in diploids determines *staminate* (pollen-bearing) plants; XX individuals are *pistillate* (egg-bearing) plants. Beyond analysis of the basic situation just described, sex expression in artificially induced polyploids and in their polyploid and aneuploid progeny has also been studied. Results show that the Y-chromosome in Lychnis is not a mere nonentity, as it appears to be in Drosophila. The Y in Lychnis is physically larger and more prominent than the X, and it definitely carries factors for maleness. Analysis of the effects of fragments of the Y-chromosome on sex expression has enabled investigators to designate some degree of localization of functions to different portions of the Y. This is seen in Figure 14-6.

Sex determination in Lychnis appears to depend upon a balance between the Y-chromosome and the X-chromosomes plus the autosomes. Upsets in the normal mechanism for balance in sexuality, resulting either from unusual chromosome combinations or certain outside influences, may give rise to bisexual individuals. In other respects also, sexuality in Lychnis is consistent with the general concept of sexuality being built up from several converging fields of research. There is considerable evidence that female plants carry potentialities for maleness. A most suggestive observation has been that pistillate plants infected by a particular smut fungus develop anthers. It would be especially interesting to know the biochemistry accounting for this response of the plant to parasitization.

Sex Determination in Asparagus. Garden asparagus is normally dioecious, with staminate and pistillate plants appearing in approximately equal numbers. But a tendency toward the monoecious state can be seen in the occurrence of rudimentary stamens in pistillate flowers and of rudimentary, usually nonfunctional, pistils in staminate flowers. Once in a great while, the pistils found in staminate flowers produce viable seeds, which almost undoubtedly arise from self-pollination. Rick and Hanna, at the University of California, planted seeds originating in this way and obtained 155 staminate plants and 43 pistillate plants. The results, which closely approximate a 3:1 ratio, suggest segregation of a single allelic pair. To test this interpretation, staminate plants from the progeny indicated above were crossed with nor-

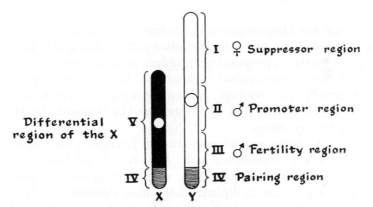

Figure 14-6. *Diagram of the sex chromosomes in Melandrium. Regions I, II, and III of the Y-chromosome do not have homologous segments in the X, and hence they make up the* differential *portion of the Y. Regions IV are homologous in the X and Y, and are pairing regions at meiosis. V is the differential portion of the X-chromosome. When I is lost from a Y-chromosome, a bisexual plant is produced. When II is lost, a female plant is produced. If III is absent, male-sterile plants with abortive anthers appear. (After Westergaard, Hereditas, 34:269, 1948.)*

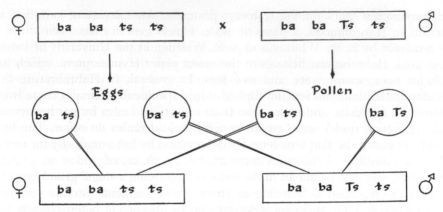

Figure 14-7. *Through the manipulation of mutant genes, corn can be transformed from a monoecious into a dioecious plant. With parents of the genotypes shown, equal numbers of pistillate and staminate plants would occur in the progeny.*

mal pistillate plants. One-third of the staminate parents produced all staminate offspring. The other two-thirds produced staminate and pistillate offspring in about equal numbers. This confirms the hypothesis of segregation at a single locus, the gene for staminate being dominant over its allele for pistillate. (As a review of Mendelian genetics, utilize gene symbols to diagram the crosses made by Rick and Hanna; verify in detail that the interpretation fits the results obtained.)

You have seen that chromosomal mechanisms for sex determination operate on the principle of the testcross, with homozygotes mating with heterozygotes to give equal numbers of two kinds of progeny. The widespread occurrence of this essentially simple sort of system testifies to its effectiveness. Precisely the same principle is utilized in asparagus, where the segregating germinal elements which determine sex are not whole chromosomes but members of a single allelic pair.

Transformation from the Monoecious to the Dioecious State. In contrast to asparagus, corn is monoecious. The tassel is staminate; the ear is pistillate. Among the many mutant genes known in corn are several that can be used to convert corn plants into individuals that are no longer monoecious but are either pistillate or staminate. For example, gene *ba* (*barren stalk*) when homozygous makes plants staminate by eliminating the ears. Gene *ts* (*tassel seed*) when homozygous converts the tassel into a pistillate inflorescence that produces no pollen. A plant *ba ba ts ts*, then, is effectively pistillate. It has no ears, but produces egg cells in the tassel. A plant *ba ba Ts Ts* is staminate. Figure 14-7 shows how one might manipulate genotypes to establish in corn a system of sex determination, complete with 1:1 ratio, analogous to that in asparagus. Such an experiment is perhaps not too far in principle from evolutionary processes that have actually taken place.

Sex Determination in Habrobracon. Not all genetic mechanisms for sex determination work on the testcross principle. An interesting variation is found in Habrobracon, a parasitic wasp whose genetics has been studied intensively by P. W. Whiting and A. R. Whiting, at the University of Pennsylvania. Habrobracon belongs to the insect order Hymenoptera, which includes bees, wasps, ants, and saw flies. In general, in Habrobracon, the males are haploid and females diploid. More specifically, females come from fertilized egg cells, and males arise from unfertilized eggs by parthenogenesis. However, under some circumstances, diploid males do occur. The fact now appears to be that femaleness is determined by heterozygosity for members of a multiple allelic series designated as xa, xb, xc, xd, and so on. (These are not thought to be alleles in the sense of occupying a single gene locus but rather are regarded as homologous chromosome segments perhaps containing several genes.) Maleness is determined by absence of heterozygosity for members of this multiple allelic series. Thus males may be haploid, having genotypes as xa, xb, or xc, or may be homozygous diploid, as $xa\ xa, xc\ xc$, or $xd\ xd$. Heterozygous combinations like $xa\ xb, xa\ xc$, or $xb\ xd$ determine females.

A possible general interpretation of the situation in Habrobracon is that members of the x series act in *complementary* fashion to produce femaleness. Support for this view comes from an exceptional kind of gynandromorph, called *gynandroid*, which now and then appears in Habrobracon. Gynandroids arise from binucleate eggs which have not been fertilized, and where the two nuclei have different x alleles. These mosaic wasps are haploid, and therefore male. However, in the region of the genitalia, at the frontier between tissues of different genotype for x, small female reproductive appendages develop. A possible interpretation is that gene products peculiar to one of the x tissue regions diffuse for a distance into the other region and interact there with locally produced substances to give rise to female differentiation.

The Major Role of Environment in Certain Systems of Sex Determination. In the genus Crepidula (boat-shell snails), each individual normally goes through a developmental sequence in which an early asexual stage is followed by a male phase, then a transitional phase, and finally a female phase. Studies of the duration of the male phase have revealed a significant phenomenon. When individuals in the male phase are suitably mated and sedentary, their transformation to the opposite sex is deferred. On the other hand, wandering "males" relatively quickly change over to a female phase. Thus the transformation from male to female appears to be strongly influenced by environment.

A related phenomenon occurs in the marine worm Bonellia. The free-swimming larval forms of this organism are sexually undifferentiated. Those individuals which settle down by themselves become females; some of the larvae attach to the bodies of adult females and differentiate as males. Here then, as in Crepidula, the direction of sex differentiation is not determined at fertilization by some genetic component that has segregated at a preceding meiosis. Instead, alternatives in sex differentiation are conditioned by environmental factors related either to association or to lack of association with other members of the species. Some plants, as well as animals, regularly rely on environmental influences to direct the course of sex differentiation. In the parasitic fungus Olpidium, for instance, environmental effects determine whether particular cells are to behave sexually or asexually in the life cycle. These examples do not imply an absence of a genetic basis for sexuality; they rather illustrate that sex, like other characteristics of developing organisms, is subject to threshold effects of the kind discussed in Chapter 5.

Compared to a mechanism like the X-Y, the Bonellia system of sex determination may seem to be excessively haphazard. However, as W. C. Allee has pointed out, it has the advantage of guarding against waste of the reproductive potential of isolated males. Isolated individuals in Bonellia become females. As females, they are able to determine that newcomers into their spheres differentiate as members of the opposite sex.

Complementary Genes for Sexual Fertility in Glomerella. Recently initi-

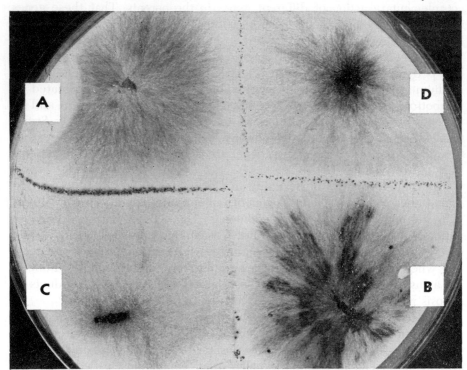

Figure 14-8. *Four different strains of Glomerella, with mating indicated by perithecial formation at the lines of juncture on the agar plate. Comparative fertility of the different crosses is indicated by the numbers of perithecia formed. For example, A × C is a more fertile combination than A × D. (Courtesy of C. L. Markert, Am. Naturalist, 83:228, 1949.)*

ated studies with Glomerella offer some insight into gene action as it relates to important aspects of sexuality. Glomerella belongs to the same general group of fungi as Neurospora, and is well known as a plant pathogen. Almost all strains of Glomerella will mate within themselves or with any other strain. However, among many strains, differences in fertility can be detected, for example by the experimental device illustrated in Figure 14-8. As you look at the picture you will see dotted lines which appear to divide the petri dish into four sections, like pieces of pie. The dividing lines are really rows of perithecia (fruiting bodies containing ascospores) formed at the lines of juncture of different strains of the mold being grown on agar. Mating has taken place along these lines, and the numbers of perithecia are a measure of fertility between the strains involved.

The figure illustrates what appears to be a general phenomenon in Glomerella: No single strain shows greater fertility than all others, in all possible crosses. For instance, strain D is more fertile than C in crosses with B; but in crosses involving A, many more perithecia are formed with C than with D. This kind of result implies that the fertility of a particular cross depends upon complementary action of different genes in the parents. That these genes may perhaps produce their effects by way of diffusible chemical substances has been demonstrated by C. L. Markert in the following way. Strains A and D normally show rather weak formation of perithecia when they are crossed. If a petri dish is prepared in such a way that there are two layers of agar medium separated by a cellophane membrane, and strain C is inoculated on the bottom layer and A and D are inoculated together on the top, A and D, in contrast to their normal indifference to each other, cross vigorously. Strain C itself cannot penetrate the membrane. The results indicate, therefore, that C produces a substance that can penetrate the membrane and enhance fertility between A and D.

The Genetic Control of Sexuality in Chlamydomonas. The most extensive studies of the biochemical genetics of sexuality have been carried out with the one-celled alga Chlamydomonas. The cells of this organism are normally haploid, and may reproduce vegetatively by fission. In certain species, every cell is potentially a gamete, with sexual reproduction occurring when motile cells of opposite sex unite to form diploid zygotes. Following a fusion of gametes, meiosis takes place. The four haploid products of meiosis may reproduce vegetatively to form more Chlamydomonas.

The German biologist Franz Moewus and his co-workers have reported that several functions involved in sexuality in Chlamydomonas are due to the action of specific hormonelike substances. One of these initiates the growth of flagella in nonmotile cells; other compounds, called gamones, control the conjugation of gametes; still others act to determine maleness or femaleness; and one substance has been found to hinder conjugation, and in this way to produce sexual sterility. All of these compounds are synthesized in the organism through chains of integrated chemical reactions, with

TABLE 14-3. Gene-Controlled Substances Which Influence Specific Functions in the Sexuality of Chlamydomonas. (After F. Moewus, Angew. Chem., 62:501, 1950.)

FUNCTION	SUBSTANCE
Growth of flagella	crocin
Conjugation of gametes	(gamones) *cis* and *trans*—crocetin-dimethylester
Sex determination	(female termone) isorhamnetin
	(male termone I) 4-oxy-β-cyclocitral
	(male termone II) peonin
Sexual sterility factor	rutin
Precursor of rutin	quercitin

each reaction being controlled by a particular identifiable gene. The compounds and their corresponding functions are listed in Table 14-3.

Perhaps even the ancient Greeks would have had trouble finding words for the sexes in Chlamydomonas. Moewus simply describes maleness and femaleness in Chlamydomonas as occurring in different potencies, or valences. There are five valences of maleness and five of femaleness, in each case ranging from very strong to very weak. A male of any valence is able to conjugate with a female of any valence. But certain males can also conjugate with other males, if their respective valences are sufficiently different. The same is true of females. Thus, sexuality in Chlamydomonas appears to be a relative matter.

The physiological basis of this relative sexuality is particularly interesting. Each valence depends upon the presence of a particular gamone, or conjugation-controlling substance. The various gamones are not different compounds, but consist of mixtures, in different proportions, of the *cis* and *trans* isomers of crocetin-dimethylester, a carotenoid substance. For example, the most extreme female valence is determined by the *cis* and *trans* isomers in a ratio of 98:2, the weakest female valence in a ratio of 65:35. On the other hand, a *cis-trans* ratio of 2:98 determines the strongest valence of maleness.

If sexuality appears to you to be complex in Chlamydomonas, you may at least be sure that it is no less so in higher organisms. All available evidence indicates that sexuality has multiple functional components, and that these are based on and integrated by the activities of many genes, with many of these activities being sensitive to environmental influence.

Keys to the Significance of This Chapter

Sexual reproduction is found among all kinds of plants and animals. Its chief distinguishing feature, and its advantage over asexual reproduction, is that it produces a variety of gene combinations.

In most organisms we find characteristic physiological and morphological differences in individuals that are able to cross. Very often such individuals can be simply classified as male or female. The determination of sex in such instances is frequently based on the segregation of simple alternatives at meiosis. These may be chromosomes, groups of genes, or single allelic pairs. In some genetic systems, however, environment may play the critical role in determining the direction of sex differentiation.

Sexuality is a complex phenomenon, embracing many functions. This means that the activities of many genes are involved in sexuality. Where individuals are ordinarily either male or female, exceptional circumstances, genetic or environmental, may lead to the expression of sexuality in unusual ways.

Among some organisms, sexuality is regularly expressed as a series of relative differences. These differences, like other aspects of sexuality, are fundamentally physiological in nature.

References

Allee, W. C., *et al.*, *Principles of Animal Ecology*. Philadelphia: W. B. Saunders Co., 1949. (The section on "Animal Aggregations and Sex," pp. 408–410, deals with relations of environment and sexuality, including the cases of Bonellia and Crepidula.)

Allen, C. E., "The Genotypic Basis of Sex-expression in Angiosperms." *Botan. Rev.*, 6:227–300, 1940. (An extensive summary of the field, including a large and useful bibliography.)

Allen, E., *Sex and Internal Secretions*. Baltimore: Williams & Wilkins, 1939. (A survey with different topics treated by specialists. See particularly Chap. 6, "Relation of Genic and Endocrine Factors in Sex," by C. H. Danforth, and Chap. 4, "Modification of Development of Sex," by E. Witschi.)

Bridges, C. B., "Sex in Relation to Chromosomes and Genes." *Am. Naturalist*, 59:127–137, 1925. (A classical paper on sex determination in Drosophila.)

Goldschmidt, R., "Lymantria." *Bibliographia Genetica*, 11:1–186, 1934. (An important monograph on the gypsy moth. Pages 10–105 are concerned with the analysis of intersexuality in Lymantria.)

Moewus, F., "Die Bedeutung von Farbstoffen bei den Sexualprozessen der Algen und Blutenpflanzen," *Angew. Chem.*, 62:496–502, 1950. (For the student who can read German, this summarizes work by Moewus and his collaborators on biochemical genetic aspects of sexuality in Chlamydomonas—some of the most exciting work in modern genetics, but currently subject to controversy in some respects.)

Rick, C. M., and Hanna, G. C., "Determination of Sex in *Asparagus officinalis L.*" *Am. J. Botany*, 30:711–714, 1943. (Reports the genetic mechanism for sex determination in asparagus.)

Tatum, E. L., and Lederberg, J., "Gene Recombination in the Bacterium *Escherichia coli.*" *J. Bact.*, 53:673–684, 1947. (The elegant genetic demonstration of a sexual phase in a bacterium.)

Warmke, H. E., "Sex Determination and Sex Balance in Melandrium." *Am. J. Botany*, **33**:648–660, 1946. (Concise. Graphically summarized with figures and tables.)

Whiting, P. W., "The Evolution of Male Haploidy." *Quart. Rev. Biol.*, **20**:231–260, 1945. (A review. Presentation at a high level.)

Questions and Problems

14- 1. What do the following terms and phrases signify?

bacteriophage	intersex
balance concept of sex	primary sex differences
freemartin	relative sexuality
gynandroid	sex
gynandromorph	supersex

14- 2. Distinguish between sex determination and sex differentiation.

14- 3. What are the evolutionary advantages of sexual reproduction over asexual reproduction?

14- 4. Give some evidence that the Y-chromosome in Drosophila carries few, if any, genes involved in sex determination.

14- 5. If through some aberrant circumstance chromosome doubling occurred in certain somatic cells of triploid Drosophila, would you expect these islands of hexaploid cells to differentiate as "male" or as "female" tissue?

14- 6. 2X 3A Drosophila are intersexes. The addition of duplicating fragments of X-chromosomes into 2X 3A nuclei shifts the balance of sexuality. Would this shift be in the direction of maleness or femaleness?

14- 7. Do you think it likely that gynandromorph human beings might occur that showed a sharp mosaicism for primary and secondary male and female characteristics? Explain your answer.

14- 8. What ratio of females and males would be expected in the progeny of a Drosophila cross between parents both heterozygous for the *tra* (*transformer*) gene?

14- 9. Assume a chicken that has undergone transformation from female to male, as reported by Crew. What would be the sex ratio of offspring from a mating between such a "male" and a normal female?

14-10. In corn, plants homozygous for gene *sk* (*silkless*) have abortive pistils, no silks, and thus are female-sterile. In addition, a gene Ts_3 is known that has much the same effect as the tassel seed gene described in this chapter, except that Ts_3 is dominant to its normal allele. Utilizing genes *sk* and Ts_3, show how genotypes could be manipulated to produce dioecious lines of corn with a heterozygous female system of sex determination.

14-11. There is some evidence that staminate plants of Asparagus outyield pistillate plants. Suggest a method by which seed could be obtained that would give all staminate plants.

14-12. Assume that in Habrobracon 25 per cent of the eggs a female lays are unfertilized, and that the rest are fertilized. What would be the sex ratio in a progeny from the mating *xa xb*♀ × *xc*♂? From the mating *xa xb*♀ × *xb*♂?

14-13. Making the same assumption about percentage of unfertilized eggs as in the last question, what would be the sex ratio in a progeny from the mating *xa xb*♀ × *xa xa*♂? From the mating *xa xb*♀ × *xc xc*♂? (Assume fertility in the diploid males, although in fact they are usually highly sterile.)

14-14. In Habrobracon, gene *vl* (*veinless*) is an autosomal recessive. When making experimental crosses, how could you utilize *vl* and its wild-type allele (+) so that haploid males could be readily separated from diploid males in the cross progenies?

14-15. Gene *fu* (*fused*) in Habrobracon affects the antennae, legs, and wings. It is in the same chromosome as the locus for the multiple allelic series concerned in sex determination, with the two loci showing about 10 per cent crossing over. From the cross $\dfrac{xa \quad +}{xb \quad fu} \times \dfrac{xa \quad fu}{}$, what ratio of nonfused to fused would you expect among the female offspring? Among the diploid male offspring? Among the haploid male offspring?

14-16. Answer Question 14-15 on the basis that the male parent in the cross is $\dfrac{xb \quad fu}{}$.

14-17. Answer Question 14-15 on the basis that the male parent in the cross is $\dfrac{xc \quad fu}{}$.

14-18. From the point of view of survival of the species, what advantages can you see to systems of sex determination, like the X-Y, where the production of relatively equal numbers of females and males is genetically assured?

14-19. From the point of view of survival of the species, what advantages are there to the system of sex determination found in Crepidula?

14-20. Having in mind the material in this chapter on sex determination, can you suggest any reason why polyploidy should become established much more frequently among the species of plants than of animals?

CHAPTER 15

Quantitative Inheritance

THOSE WHO ARE familiar with white-spotted breeds of dairy cattle, like the black-and-white Holstein-Friesians or the fawn-and-white Guernseys, have doubtless observed the great variation in amount of white from one individual to another. Two aspects of the hereditary control of this kind of spotting are significant. In the first place, whether or not an animal is spotted at all is controlled by a simple Mendelian alternative, in which the allele for solid color, or "self-color," is dominant to the allele for spotting (s). Secondly, given the gene s homozygous in a herd, numerous other genes influence the *amount* of spotting. These genes, which usually have no other known effect than to modify the expression of the s gene, are called *modifying genes*. There are so many of them, and they are so similar in their effects, that they cannot often be individually identified, symbolized, or mapped on chromosomes. They can only be treated collectively as "the complex of genes modifying the amount of white spotting."

Modifiers, working toward either more or less white, can be concentrated in a herd by appropriate breeding procedures. Thus a breeder who happens to like his Guernseys mostly solid in color, by selecting rather solid-colored bulls and keeping for breeding purposes calves that are rather solid-colored, can arrive in a few generations at a herd with only a little white. Or a Holstein breeder who likes his cattle almost white, with only a little black here and there, can progress fairly rapidly in this direction. Modifying genes, then, are real genetic entities, although elusive. They can often be quite specific in their pattern effects. "Belted" cattle and swine, for example, have uniform white and colored areas, giving the effect of "belts" around the body of the animal. Breeds of pigeons exist that have white wings but are otherwise colored; other breeds are like a photographic negative of these, and have colored wings but are otherwise white. There is no doubt about the general precision of these effects, although rumor has it that pigeon fanciers occasionally have to correct a minor slip by nature, and to pluck, judiciously, a colored or white feather here and there just before their birds are exhibited.

Modifying genes are known in many organisms, and for many different

302

characters. Very often, they account for much of the genetic heterogeneity in populations.

Penetrance and Expressivity. The complicating effects of modifying genes and of environmental impacts on the expression of particular genes often lead to confusion. A characteristic that seems to depend fairly regularly on a simple dominant gene, so that it is transmitted from one individual to another, generation after generation, may occasionally "skip" a generation, and be transmitted by an individual who carries the gene but does not evidence it phenotypically. Or, phenotypic expression may be so variable, from one individual to another, as not to look like a single characteristic at all. Irregularities of the first type, in which a known hereditary unit fails to come to expression in some of its carriers in a population, are said to show *incomplete penetrance* of the gene concerned. Variations in the *way* in which a gene expresses itself in different individuals are described as *variable expressivity* of the gene in question. By naming these phenomena we do not in any way explain them. Probably variations in penetrance and expressivity result from modifying genes, varying from one group and from one individual to another, and from fluctuations in the external and internal environment. It is usually difficult to identify these sources of variation concretely in any particular instance.

For a more detailed consideration of such complications, we can discuss briefly a gene causing bluish eye-whites (*blue sclera*) in human beings. In general, this gene behaves as a simple dominant to its normal allele. It segregates clearly in affected families and is typically transmitted by affected individuals to about half their children, as would be expected if these people are heterozygous for the dominant defective gene. Occasionally, however, an apparently unaffected individual in such a family, married to an unrelated person with normal eye-whites, has one or more affected children. In such cases, the aberrant gene has behaved as a recessive in one individual, but as a dominant in his children. This "irregular dominant" therefore occasionally "skips a generation" in pedigrees; to use the terminology to which you have just been introduced, the gene has *incomplete penetrance*.

About nine out of ten individuals that possess and transmit the gene for *blue sclera* show its effect phenotypically, in one way or another. The penetrance of the gene can therefore be expressed quantitatively as about 0.9, since it comes to some form of expression in about nine-tenths of the individuals carrying it. But its expressivity is variable; the eye-whites of affected individuals may be any shade of blue, ranging from pale, almost whitish blue to a blue so dark as to be nearly black. This variability encompasses much more than the relatively unimportant matter of how blue an affected individual's eye-whites happen to be. About three-quarters of the individuals possessing this gene suffer from marked fragility of their long bones. Affected babies may break their legs when they kick their covers; a boy may shatter his femur if he attempts to carry a pailful of water up an incline;

children may have twenty or thirty or more fractures of legs and arms before they are twelve years old. And about six out of ten affected individuals become deaf, through a kind of ear defect called *otosclerosis*.

Typically, the bone fragility is "outgrown" with puberty, and only the bluish eye-whites remain to mark the condition. But in some individuals, the bone abnormalities fail to appear until middle age or later. One case is known in which a man with blue sclera had no inkling of his potential fragility until he took a job manning a pneumatic hammer! Usually, only the long bones are fragile, but sometimes (as in the case cited) it is the vertebral column that yields first. This, then, is *variable expressivity* of a human gene, exemplifying a widely occurring genetic phenomenon.

Quantitative Characters. The expression of blue sclera has a fundamental resemblance to the expression of sex, as discussed in the preceding chapter with reference, for example, to Drosophila. Both of these genetic characters are strongly influenced by many genes in the organism. Sex, certainly, and blue sclera, almost certainly, are sensitive to environmental influence. *Both may take so many forms that it is impossible to categorize them in a qualitative way.* The initial analysis of the genetic basis of blue sclera is, however, relatively straightforward, since its mere *presence* depends upon a single "major" gene, which usually acts as a dominant; it is only the *form of expression* of blue sclera that depends upon minor genetic components, whose multiplicity makes them difficult to identify. Similarly, although sexuality has multiple genetic and environmental components, our approach to the genetic basis of sex differences is facilitated by the existence of a simple mechanism which usually tips the balance of these components toward one of two alternative states; it is only under extraordinary circumstances that sex differences present an unbroken array of quantitative variations.

In general, then, we can classify individuals either as male or female, although differences occur within the sexes. And we can tell whether or not people have blue sclera. But there is a large group of characteristics, also showing subtle variations from one individual to another, which offer no basis for classification into a small number of groups. The variations in these instances are best expressed in terms of some scale of measurement like inches, pounds, or bushels. These variations are *quantitative* in nature, and characteristics showing them are called *quantitative characters*. They cannot be identified with one or two major genes, but rather depend upon the action and interaction of several genes. Typically, they are subject to considerable phenotypic modification by environment.

Examples of quantitative characters include stature in man, egg-laying in chickens, yield of grain in cereal crops, and milk production by dairy cattle. Such characteristics are of great practical importance, and an understanding of their inheritance is a primary objective wherever useful application of genetic principles is a goal.

The Statistical Approach

The description and analysis of quantitative characters requires special tools provided by the branch of mathematics called statistics. We must turn briefly to this field before proceeding with the genetic analysis of quantitative characters.

The Arithmetic Mean. You are already familiar with, and often utilize, one of the central concepts of statistics. In describing phenomena subject to considerable variation, you commonly refer to things that are true "on the average," or to *mean* or *average* values. You have used such terms as "mean annual rainfall," and no doubt you have actually calculated your "grade-point average." You know that to compute your average grade in genetics to date, for example, you need only add up the individual grades and divide the sum by the total number of grades added. The resulting quotient is the arithmetic mean, or average. If the individual grades do not "count" equally, a weighted average is used. If your midterm examination grade is to be given three times the weight of a single short quiz, you simply add in three times the midterm grade, and count this as three grades in determining the weighted average.

You may also have had occasion to use a shortcut approximation to the arithmetic mean, when some large number of values was to be averaged. This involves first grouping the data into arbitrary classes and counting how many observations fall within each class. The mean is obtained by taking the sum of the products of these frequencies by their respective midclass values and then dividing by the total number of observations. The treatment of the values in Tables 15-1 and 15-2 illustrates this method of calculation.

TABLE 15-1.

3, 7, 11, 12, 13, 14, 15, 16, 17, 17, 18, 18, 18, 19, 19, 19, 20, 20,
21, 21, 21, 22, 22, 23, 23, 24, 24, 24, 25, 25, 25, 26, 26, 26, 26, 27,
27, 27, 28, 28, 28, 29, 29, 29, 29, 30, 30, 30, 30, 30, 30, 30, 30, 30,
30, 31, 31, 31, 31, 32, 32, 33, 33, 33, 33, 33, 34, 34, 34, 35, 35, 35,
36, 36, 36, 37, 37, 38, 38, 39, 39, 39, 40, 40, 41, 41, 41, 42, 42, 42,
43, 43, 44, 45, 46, 47, 48, 49, 53, 57

TABLE 15-2.

Midclass value (pounds), v	5	10	15	20	25	30	35	40	45	50	55
Frequency, f	2	2	6	13	15	23	16	13	6	2	2
(fv)	10	20	90	260	375	690	560	520	270	100	110

$$\text{Mean} = \frac{\Sigma(fv)}{N} = \frac{3005}{100} = 30.05 \text{ pounds}$$

In **Table 15-1,** the individual weight gains of 100 swine over a 20-day period are arranged in order of magnitude from the pig that gained only 3 pounds to the one that showed a gain of 57 pounds. In Table 15-2, these values are collected in a *frequency distribution,* representing eleven classes with a "class interval" of 5 pounds. The class midpoints (midclass values) are placed at successive multiples of 5 pounds. You should check this table carefully, and also the calculation of the mean gain in weight, to be sure you understand what has been done with the original measurements of Table 15-1. The values, slightly modified from experimental data, are from Snedecor's excellent and readable textbook, *Statistical Methods* (Iowa State College Press).

Other Measures of Central Values. The arithmetic mean is by far the most useful single statistic for describing the "central tendency" of a normal population. For certain purposes, however, two other central values are utilized: the *mode* and the *median.* The mode is simply the *most frequent value* in the population; thus the modal class in the population of weight gains we have been considering is 30 pounds. The median is the *middle item* in an array; in any sample there are as many values above the median as below it. For the weight gains we are considering, 30 pounds, again, is the median value. It is not an attribute of all populations that the mean, mode, and median coincide.

The *geometric mean* is an average value useful in special cases. You will have noticed that the arithmetic mean of two different numbers is midway between them on an additive scale. Thus the arithmetic mean of two and eight is five; it is the middle term in an arithmetic series (2, 5, 8) in which

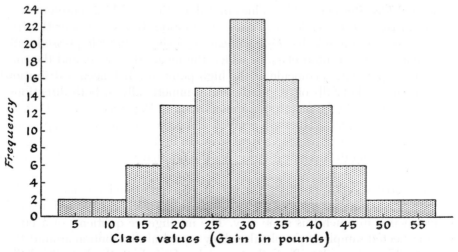

Figure 15-1. *A histogram of the weight gain values summarized in Table 15-2 shows the familiar bell-shape of a normal distribution. (After Snedecor. Statistical Methods, 4th ed., Iowa State College Press, 1946, p. 56.)*

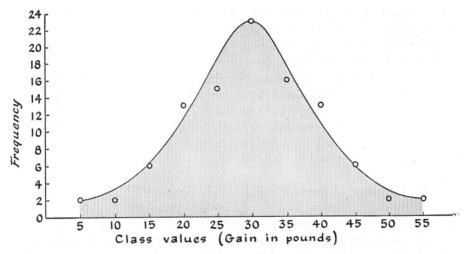

Figure 15-2. *If the frequency distribution in Table 15-2 is plotted as a smooth curve, one obtains a close approximation of a normal curve. (After Snedecor, Statistical Methods, 4th ed., Iowa State College Press, 1946, p. 56.)*

the difference between successive terms is three. The geometric mean is a similar midpoint, but on a multiplying (geometric) scale. The geometric mean of two and eight is four; it is the term between two and eight in a geometric series (2,4,8) in which there is a constant of multiplication rather than of addition. The geometric mean of two numbers is the square root of their product. We call attention to the geometric mean because it fits some of the data of quantitative inheritance better than does the arithmetic mean.

Normal Distributions. The values in Tables 15-1 and 15-2 represent well a kind of distribution called a *normal* distribution. If you consider the frequency distribution in Table 15-2, you can scarcely fail to be impressed with its symmetry. The central class, in which the mean, the mode, and the median of the population coincide, is the high point of a balanced distribution of frequencies that falls off regularly and symmetrically in both directions. This can most easily be pictured graphically, as in Figures 15-1 and 15-2. In these figures, the class values are arrayed along the baseline of a graph, and the frequencies placed on the vertical scale. In both the histogram of Figure 15-1 and the smooth curve of Figure 15-2 the familiar bell-shape of a normal distribution is evident.

The distribution is familiar because it is experienced commonly. The heights of a sample of boys of a given age are normally distributed around a mean value in much this same way. The intelligence quotients of a large and unselected sample of people also show a normal distribution around the average. A great number of similar examples, from both the living and the inanimate worlds, could be cited. Because of the common occurrence and regularity of normal distributions, their precise description in mathematical

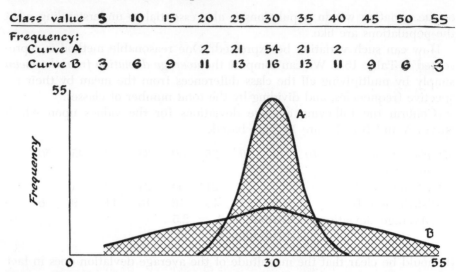

Class value	5	10	15	20	25	30	35	40	45	50	55
Frequency:											
Curve A				2	21	54	21	2			
Curve B	3	6	9	11	13	16	13	11	9	6	3

Figure 15-3. *Frequency curves for hypothetical populations more uniform (curve A) and more variable (curve B) than the population illustrated in Figure 15-2, but with the same mean values.*

terms is of great value in characterizing and comparing quantitative population data. We cannot approach this problem with mathematical rigor here, but we can and should consider those conclusions—the formulas—derived from rigorous mathematical treatment that are most important to statistical analysis.

The Standard Deviation. The average gain of 30 pounds that characterized the sample of swine we considered earlier might be quite closely approached in a sample taken from a different breed. But this second sample might be much more uniform than the first, and show a frequency curve concentrated much more closely around its mean. Or, it might be much more variable, with the curve spreading more broadly (Fig. 15-3). Mean values by themselves, then, give incomplete pictures of populations; some measure

TABLE 15-3.

Midclass value	5	10	15	20	25	30	35	40	45	50	55
Deviation, d	−25	−20	−15	−10	−5	0	5	10	15	20	25
Frequency, f	2	2	6	13	15	23	16	13	6	2	2
(fd)	−50	−40	−90	−130	−75	0	80	130	90	40	50

$$\frac{\Sigma(fd)}{N} = \frac{775}{100} = 7.75$$

(You will note that we ignored the "+" and "−" signs of the deviations in order to compute this average deviation; if this were not done, the positive and negative deviations would compensate for each other, and the average deviation, for this or any other normal distribution, would approximate 0.)

of the variation within populations is also essential to understanding what the populations are like.

How can such variation be expressed? One reasonable method is represented in Table 15-3. We can compute the *average deviation from the mean* simply by multiplying all the class differences from the mean by their respective frequencies, and dividing by the total number of classes.

(Confirm the following average deviations for the values upon which curves A and B in Figure 15-3 are based:

Midclass value	5	10	15	20	25	30	35	40	45	50	55
Frequencies of:											
Distribution A				2	21	54	21	2			
Distribution B	3	6	9	11	13	16	13	11	9	6	3

Average deviation: Distribution A = 2.5
Distribution B = 10.1

It should be clear that the magnitude of the average deviation does in fact reflect the variability within each sample.)

We have introduced the average deviation as a measure of variability, or "spread," because you can easily see how this statistic is related to the population characteristic it is supposed to measure. In practice, the average deviation is seldom calculated; another kind of average that you will now find relatively easy to compute and understand is used instead. This is the *standard deviation* (σ). It is essentially the *square root of the average squared deviation*. Expressed in symbols this would be

$$\sigma = \sqrt{\frac{\Sigma(fd^2)}{N}}$$

By reasoning more complex than we are prepared to detail, mathematicians can show that $(N - 1)$ is a more reasonable divisor to use in computing the standard deviation for a sample than is N. The key formula actually used to measure variation in a normally distributed sample, therefore, is

$$\sigma = \sqrt{\frac{\Sigma(fd^2)}{N - 1}}$$

Table 15-4 shows the computation of σ for the weight-gain values of Table 15-1.

(Verify that for distribution A (p. 308), $\sigma = 3.8$, and for distribution B, $\sigma = 12.5$.)

You should realize that the values in these illustrations permit maximal ease of calculation. Usually, the mean will not coincide with the midpoint of the central class, but will be some other value. It could be, for example, 28.5 or 31.1, for other samples of weight gains from the same population we have been considering. In such cases, the deviations are not nice even numbers

TABLE 15-4.

Midclass value	5	10	15	20	25	30	35	40	45	50	55
Frequency, f	2	2	6	13	15	23	16	13	6	2	2
Deviation, d	−25	−20	−15	−10	−5	0	5	10	15	20	25
d^2	625	400	225	100	25	0	25	100	225	400	625
(fd^2)	1250	800	1350	1300	375	0	400	1300	1350	800	1250

$$\sigma = \sqrt{\frac{(fd^2)}{N-1}} = \sqrt{\frac{10175}{99}} = 10.1$$

to be squared, and calculations become something of a chore. Again, there exist shortcut methods (and calculating machines) to make the computations somewhat easier, but we will leave such devices to your further experience with statistical methods.

The Standard Error. We have now realized a primary aim of practical statistics—the reduction of a mass of quantitative data to a few precise values that picture faithfully the original data and render them susceptible to comparison and analysis. Instead of the 100 separate figures for weight gains shown in Table 15-1, we now have, representing this sample,

$$N = 100; \quad \bar{x}(\text{the mean}) = 30.05; \quad \sigma = 10.1.$$

We have a better picture of the sample than we could have comprehended in the original array, and are in a much better position to compare the sample with others.

However, we must not lose sight of the fact that our statistical descriptions up to this point are largely matters of convenience. We have arrived at a shorthand way of describing a *sample,* by computing its mean and its standard deviation, but have not yet considered the main purpose for which the sample is taken. This is to get as reliable an idea as possible of the population which the sample represents. In almost any quantitative experiment, a certain limited number of observations is made as a sample of a general situation. These observations provide true values for the sample investigated. But the larger problem is: "What does the sample tell about the general situation which exists under the conditions investigated?" The values we have computed so far are *statistics;* their significance is that they are estimates, or more or less reliable samples, of true and stable values in much larger parent populations. It is because the statistics provide information about the larger population from which the sample was drawn that the experiment has meaning outside the sample it comprises.

How is the mean of a sample related to the mean of the population from which it was taken? If different samples are drawn from the same population, the means of these samples will not all be the same, but will vary around the population mean. Most of them may be near the population mean; a few will show considerable deviation from it. If we were to plot such sample mean values as a frequency distribution, we would find that they are normally distributed around the true mean. This kind of distribution is in turn subject to description in the terms now familiar to us: There is an average value for the means which coincides with the population mean, and there is a standard deviation of the means which is related to the amount of variation in the population and to the adequacy (size) of the samples.

Mathematical analysis establishes that the standard deviation of this distribution of means (called the *standard error* of the mean) can be estimated from the standard deviation of any sample as follows:

$$S.E. = \frac{\sigma}{\sqrt{N}}$$

where N is the size of the sample and σ is its standard deviation. The standard error gives an indication of how much the means of other similar samples drawn from the same population might be expected to vary. In any normal distribution (and this is true of the normal distribution of means to which the standard error applies), about two-thirds of the individual observations have values within one standard deviation above or below the mean of the distribution. About 95 per cent fall within two standard deviations, and over 99 per cent within three, above or below the mean (Fig. 15-4).

It is customary to describe any sample in terms of its *mean value plus or minus the standard error.* Thus in the sample of weight gains, we may summarize by noting that $N = 100$, $\bar{x} = 30.05$, $\sigma = 10.1$, and $S.E. = 1.0$, while 30.05 ± 1.0 gives an indication of the sample's reliability as a representation

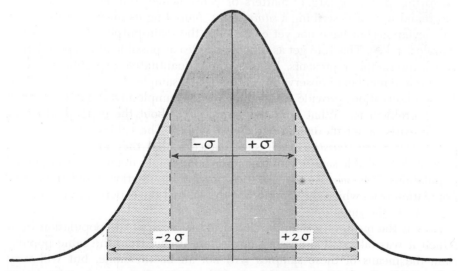

Figure 15-4. *A normal distribution, showing proportions of the distribution that are included between ±1σ, ±2σ, or ± more than 2σ, with reference to the mean.*

of 20-day gains in swine of the breed used and under the conditions of the experiment.

There are, of course, many other aspects of statistics that are important in biology and genetics. Tests for the significance of differences between samples, or between observation and hypothesis, are as useful in quantitative inheritance as they were in dealing with the ratios of qualitative characteristics. If you go on with advanced study in genetics or some other biological science, you will encounter more and more of these statistical techniques and will gain increasing appreciation of their utility. At present, equipped with a few simple statistical tools, we can proceed to a consideration of quantitative inheritance.

The Inheritance of Quantitative Characters

The frontispiece of this book shows several different endosperm and pericarp colors in corn. If you were to shell off the kernels of the ears illustrated, you would probably have little difficulty separating the kernels into sharply distinct color classes. Characteristics of this kind, which can be satisfactorily categorized on a qualitative basis, are called *qualitative* characters. Notice in the parents and in the F_1 generation how the kernels in each ear show great uniformity for these characters. The F_2 is highly variable. This is the result of segregation and recombination. But the effects of recombination are clean-cut, and the phenotypic classification of individual kernels is a simple matter.

In the same color plate, you can observe another genetic trait in corn, ear length. The differences in length among ears are of a kind that makes simple classification unfeasible, inasmuch as there is a more or less continuous variation from the shortest to the longest ear. This is the kind of variation typical of quantitative characters.

The Inheritance of Ear Length in Corn. Significant aspects of quantitative inheritance emerge when crosses between short-eared and long-eared parental lines of corn are carried to the F_2. An extensive study of this kind

TABLE 15-5. Data on Length of Ear in Maize. (After Emerson and East, Nebraska Research Bull. 2, 1913.)

	FREQUENCY DISTRIBUTIONS																				
	Length of Ear, cm																				
	5	6	7	8	9	10	11	12	13	14	15	16	17	18	19	20	21	N	$\bar{x}$	σ	S.E.
Parent 60:	4	21	24	8														57	6.632	.816	.108
Parent 54:									3	11	12	15	26	15	10	7	2	101	16.802	1.887	.188
F_1 (60 × 54):					1	12	12	14	17	9	4							69	12.116	1.519	.183
F_2 (60 × 54):			1	10	19	26	47	73	68	68	39	25	15	9	1			401	12.888	2.252	.112

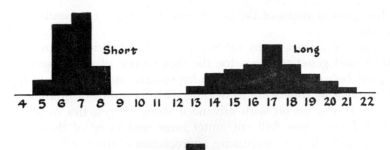

Figure 15-5. *Distributions of ear length of corn (in centimeters) in the parental lines and F₁ and F₂ generations studied by Emerson and East. The vertical axes represent percentages of the different populations. (From Sturtevant and Bea-dle,* An Introduction to Genetics. W. B. Saunders Co., 1940, p. 265.)

has been reported by Emerson and East, who for many years conducted brilliant investigations in plant genetics at Cornell and Harvard, respectively. Their data are found in Table 15-5. Your first glance at the data will confirm what was indicated in your examination of the frontispiece. Ear length is a quantitative character, in that measurements of individual ears, instead of falling readily into discrete classes, show continuous variation.

The pertinent difference between the parental types, Tom Thumb pop-corn (parent 60) and Black Mexican sweet corn (parent 54), can be seen most readily in a comparison of their respective means for ear length, which are 6.63 and 16.80 centimeters. Within each parental line, however, there is some variability in ear length. And this is also true of the F_1 and F_2 populations. Viewed as histograms, shown in Figure 15-5, all these different populations fall into rough approximations of normal distributions. If we assume each parental line to be homozygous for most genes affecting ear length, it would seem that a good deal of the variability within lines must be due to environment. Furthermore, members of the F_1 populations should be genetically alike. Here also, then, we must suppose that most of the variation around the mean is derived from outside influences. And, naturally, if ear length is subject to alteration by environment, there is no reason why the F_2 generation should be exempt. On the other hand, there is no *a priori* reason why the F_2 generation should be more susceptible to environmental influence than the parental generations or the F_1. The increase in variability in F_2, therefore, might be taken as preliminary evidence for genetic segregation and recombination.

With the complicating factor of environmental influence in mind, we can make several observations about these data which are typical of findings in many similar studies.

1. The mean of the F_1 is approximately intermediate between the means of the long- and short-eared parents.
2. The mean of the F_2 is similar to the mean of the F_1.
3. The F is appreciably more variable than the F_1, as shown by the σ values in Table 15-5 and also by the "spread" of the histograms in Figure 15-5.
4. The extreme measurements in the F_2 overlap well into the distributions of parental values.

Now, do these basic observations make sense in terms of genetics as we presently understand it? Obviously, no simple genetic situation already familiar to you entirely explains the observations. (You should ask yourself why, for instance, it is an inadequate hypothesis to suppose that the ear length difference of the parental types depends on different members of a single allelic pair that shows incomplete dominance.)

The Multiple Gene Hypothesis.   The general type of result just summarized can be reasonably well explained in terms of the multiple gene hypothesis, originally called the "multiple factor hypothesis." This hypothesis, which represents one of the significant advances in genetic throught, we owe particularly to East and to a Swedish geneticist, Nilsson-Ehle. Since the time in which it was first proposed, around 1910, the multiple gene hypothesis has undergone many refinements and amplifications at the hands of a large number of workers in several fields. Its basic tenets, however, remain as cornerstones in our understanding of quantitative hereditary phenomena.

In its simplest form, the hypothesis proposes that many aspects of quantitative inheritance may be accounted for on the basis of the action and the segregation of a number of allelic pairs having duplicate and cumulative effects without complete dominance. This situation may be visualized in terms of a specific example.

A Hypothetical Model for Quantitative Inheritance.   For the sake of demonstration and argument, assume the following kind of model experiment involving plant height, which, like ear length, is a quantitative character.

1. A cross is made between two true-breeding parent plants, one relatively tall and the other relatively short.
2. Under the conditions of the experiment, environment is assumed to be so uniform that it is not responsible for variation in plant height.
3. Genetic differences for height of the parents are assumed to reside at three independent loci, with the tall parent being homozygous for allelic forms to be designated by capital letters ($XX\ YY\ ZZ$), and the short plant being homozygous $xx\ yy\ zz$.

4. The alleles designated by small letters are inert with reference to plant height.
5. Each allelic form designated by a capital letter acts in such fashion as to contribute 3 inches of height in any plant in which it is present.
6. Each of the parents, apart from loci represented by X, Y, and Z, has the same genotype for plant height, and this is expressed by 60 inches of growth.

Under the assumptions we have just made the short parent ($xx\ yy\ zz$) is 60 inches tall. The tall parent is 78 inches. An F_1 hybrid ($Xx\ Yy\ Zz$) would be 69 inches high, which is exactly intermediate between the parents. And, as shown in Table 15-6, the mean height of F_2 plants would equal the height typical of the F_1; however, the F_2 population would show the effects of segregation by considerable variability in plant height.

Several of the results predicted for our hypothetical experiment conform

TABLE 15-6. *A Hypothetical Model Experiment for Illustrating a Simple Multiple Gene Interpretation of Size Inheritance.*

Individual contributions of genes are assumed to be:

$X = Y = Z = 3$ inches $x = y = z = 0$ inches

The residual genotype gives a plant 60 inches tall

Tall Parent (78 inches) $\times$ Short Parent (60 inches)
XX YY ZZ   xx yy zz

F_1: Xx Yy Zz (69 inches)

		GENOTYPE	HEIGHT		GENOTYPE	HEIGHT
F_2:	1	XX YY ZZ	78	2	Xx yy ZZ	69
	2	XX YY Zz	75	4	Xx yy Zz	66
	2	XX Yy ZZ	75	1	xx YY ZZ	72
	2	Xx YY ZZ	75	2	xx YY Zz	69
	4	XX Yy Zz	72	2	xx Yy ZZ	69
	4	Xx YY Zz	72	4	xx Yy Zz	66
	4	Xx Yy ZZ	72	1	XX yy zz	66
	8	Xx Yy Zz	69	2	Xx yy zz	63
	1	XX YY zz	72	1	xx yy ZZ	66
	2	XX Yy zz	69	2	xx yy Zz	63
	2	Xx YY zz	69	1	xx YY zz	66
	4	Xx Yy zz	66	2	xx Yy zz	63
	1	XX yy ZZ	72	1	xx yy zz	60
	2	XX yy Zz	69			

Number of active alleles	0	1	2	3	4	5	6
Height value (inches)	60	63	66	69	72	75	78
Frequency	1	6	15	20	15	6	1

with the actual findings of Emerson and East with reference to the inheritance of ear length in corn. These include the intermediacy of the F_1 as compared to the parents, the greater variability in F_2 than in F_1, and the fact that the F_2 and F_1 mean values are approximately equal.

However, we must recognize at the same time that several of the assumptions on which our model experiment is based are more or less unreal. Certainly, in practice, the influence of environment on phenotypic expression could not be eliminated. Our assumption that the several genes work to identical effect by adding equal amounts to plant height is likewise a vast oversimplification. And, finally, the assumption of a mere three allelic pairs acting to produce height differences is perhaps far removed from the complexity of most real instances of quantitative inheritance. Actually, of course, our model might be made more rather than less meaningful if we assumed a larger number of genes involved, each having a smaller individual influence on plant height. If this assumption were made, the F_2 population of the model would be modified in the direction of more nearly *continuous* variation, and would thus be more typical of quantitative inheritance. As the model stands, F_2 individuals fall into discrete classes, represented by 60, 63, 66.. .. .. 78 inches.

On the whole, then, our model would seem to explain a good deal, but its limitations must be understood. Models are conscious oversimplifications, devised to increase one's understanding of situations too complicated to be analyzed directly. Our hypothetical experiment is not meant to duplicate reality, but to provide insight into reality.

A Naturally Occurring Model for Quantitative Inheritance. Artificial models for quantitative inheritance of the kind we have examined are not based on ideas suddenly snatched from thin air. A good deal of their strength depends upon the fact that they are strongly suggested by the analysis of certain real genetic situations. A classical example of the latter is provided by the genetics of kernel color in wheat, studied extensively by Nilsson-Ehle.

Starting with true-breeding white kernel and red kernel parents, Nilsson-Ehle found that in different strains of wheat different F_2 ratios could prevail. In some strains, segregations of 3 reds to 1 white were observed; these are clearly instances of a single gene difference. In other strains, however, among the F_2 individuals the numbers of reds greatly exceeded those expected on the basis of a 3:1 relationship. Certain F_2 populations showed close approximations to a ratio of 15 red to 1 white; others seemed to be best described by a ratio of 63:1. The 15:1 can be explained as a modification of a 9:3:3:1 ratio, the assumption being that only the double recessive individuals among the segregants are white. Likewise, the 63:1 ratio can be ascribed to the segregation of three independent pairs of alleles in the F_2, where only the triple recessives are white. Nilsson-Ehle was able to confirm these explanations through the analysis of the results of crosses designed to test the genotypes of F_1 and F_2 individuals.

TABLE 15-7. The Relationship of Genotype to Color Intensity of Wheat Kernels Seen in Crosses Carried to an F_2.

Parents: $R_1R_1R_2R_2$ (Dark Red)	×	$r_1r_1r_2r_2$ (White)

F_1: $R_1r_1R_2r_2$ (Medium Red)

F_2:	GENOTYPE	PHENOTYPE	
1	$R_1R_1R_2R_2$	Dark red	
2	$R_1R_1R_2r_2$	Medium dark red	
2	$R_1r_1R_2R_2$	Medium dark red	
4	$R_1r_1R_2r_2$	Medium red	15 Red
1	$R_1R_1r_2r_2$	Medium red	to
2	$R_1r_1r_2r_2$	Light red	1 White
1	$r_1r_1R_2R_2$	Medium red	
2	$r_1r_1R_2r_2$	Light red	
1	$r_1r_1r_2r_2$	White	

Summary of Phenotypes:

Dark red	Medium dark red	Medium red	Light red	White
1	4	6	4	1

These experiments, and others like them, are important because they show us clearly that multiple genes in the same organism may affect the same character. But Nilsson-Ehle's determination of the genetics of kernel color in wheat goes even farther in promoting our understanding of quantitative inheritance. The F_2 ratio of 15 red to 1 white, for example, becomes highly instructive when you realize that not all the red kernels are of the same intensity of color, and that this variation can be related directly to genotype. Table 15-7 describes how color intensity in wheat kernels depends upon the number of genes present that are active in promoting color. Thus kernel color, which on superficial analysis would seem to be a perfectly discontinuous character, on close study assumes many of the aspects of quantitative inheritance. Of course, the color variation is not quite continuous, since the different classes of reds can be told apart, but it is this very fact which permits direct analysis of the situation in terms of particular genes!

In populations where three gene pairs for kernel color are segregating, the different color classes are much more difficult to distinguish. As a consequence, a much closer approximation to continuous variation exists. You can well imagine that if even more such gene pairs were found segregating in a population, and especially if there were an appreciable environmental effect on kernel color, class differences would become imperceptible, and a typical state of continuous variation would prevail.

The Nature of the Genes Affecting Quantitative Characters. We have already said enough about the multiple gene explanation of quantitative inheritance to indicate that it is at least a good working hypothesis. As such, it can be used as the basis for further exploration of the phenomena it begins to explain. A fundamental idea in the hypothesis is that back of quantitative characters are genes. Presumably these are genes in chromosomes, much like genes we have studied before except that their individual contributions to phenotypic differences are very much smaller. Indeed these individual contributions are usually completely obscured by the effects of the genotype as a whole and by the influences of environment. K. Mather, of the University of Birmingham, England, has called such genes *polygenes*. He thus distinguishes them from *major* genes, which are readily identifiable because of the pronounced effects of their individual functions.

The fact that we make terminological distinctions between "multiple" genes and "major" genes does not mean that there is no overlap of the two categories or no area in between them. We have discussed how the genes for kernel color in wheat provide one kind of intermediate instance.

Duplicating Effects Produced by Major Genes and Multiple Gene Systems. The phenotypic effect usually ascribed to the operation of a particular multiple gene complex may be more or less duplicated by the consequences of the action of a single major gene. The normal, continuous range of stature in man, for instance, seems almost certainly to depend upon multiple genic effects. The stature of a very short person may usually be accounted for by the combined influences of a good many different genes. However, a single gene for dwarf stature may give rise to the same end result, at least insofar as height in inches is concerned.

The Possible Role of Major Genes in Multiple Gene Systems. There seems to be no good reason why certain genes should not serve a dual capacity by simultaneously affecting both quantitative and qualitative characters. Some evidence does exist that this kind of situation occurs. In white clover, for example, two independent dominant genes interact to cause mottling and lesions of the leaf blades, a "qualitative" difference from the normal smooth green. In addition, however, the dosage of the dominant genes which interact to give mottling has a pronounced effect on leaf number, which is generally considered a quantitative characteristic of the plant.

Linkage Shown by Multiple Gene Complexes. Finding the linkage relations of members of a multiple gene complex is no simple matter. The primary difficulty, of course, is that members of such systems seldom produce individually identifiable phenotypic effects. There are, however, several more or less well-established instances of linkage between major genes and multiple genes.

In 1923, Karl Sax, now Director of the Arnold Arboretum at Harvard, found that color in beans, which is under the immediate control of a single gene, shows linkage with bean weight, a quantitative character. Similarly, Lindstrom has shown that size of tomatoes, as determined in weight, is linked with skin color. In Drosophila, major genes in all four chromosomes appear to be linked to different genes for egg size, which is quantitative in expression. And in the mouse, the gene for brown coat color is apparently in the same chromosome as genes for a number of size characters, including adult weight and length of bone in the hind limb.

Estimating the Number of Members in a Multiple Gene System. Knowledge of the number of genes involved in the expression of quantitative characters would facilitate the development of new and better methods for investigating phenomena of quantitative inheritance. Such knowledge could also be put directly to use by plant and animal breeders, who must often deal with the practical problem of predicting probabilities for recovering, from a segregating population, individuals showing the extreme forms of a quantitative character. For example, how often in a population of dairy cattle showing segregation for butterfat production can one expect appearance of the best kind of producer? What is the probability that in the progeny of hybrid tobacco plants the breeder will be able to find at least one individual as tall as the tallest of the original parents? Obviously the solution of such problems depends in large part on the number of genes involved.

A bit of simple reasoning provides a way for estimating the number of genes operating in a given multiple gene system, when the system approaches the simplicity of the models we discussed earlier. Go back to Table 15-7, which summarizes one of Nilsson-Ehle's naturally occurring models of quantitative inheritance. You see that under conditions of two independently segregating allelic pairs which show no dominance and have duplicating, cumulative effects, one-sixteenth of the segregating population in F_2 should be dark red, or, in other words, can be expected to show an extreme expression of the character. The generalized prediction under similar circumstances is that $(\frac{1}{2})^n$ describes the expectation for an extreme phenotype when $n =$ the number of segregating alleles. Table 15-8 shows the essential relationships for one, two, three, or four allelic pairs.

With this table, it is simple to apply the kind of reasoning which can lead to an estimate of the effective number of gene pairs in a multiple gene

TABLE 15-8. Probability of Occurrence of Individuals Manifesting an Extreme Expression of a Quantitative Character, Under Conditions Where Independently Segregating Allelic Pairs Have Duplicate, Cumulative Effects.

NO. OF ALLELIC PAIRS	NO. OF SEGREGATING ALLELES	FRACTION OF POPULATION SHOWING AN EXTREME EXPRESSION OF THE CHARACTER
1	2	$(1/2)^2 = 1/4$
2	4	$(1/2)^4 = 1/16$
3	6	$(1/2)^6 = 1/64$
4	8	$(1/2)^8 = 1/256$

system. In brief, if an F_2 population shows approximately ¼₄ individuals of each of the extreme phenotypes, it can be supposed that three segregating allelic pairs are involved. If approximately ½₅₆ of such a population were the frequency of one of the extreme types, we might conclude that four pairs of alleles affecting the character had segregated. Unfortunately, the method we have described is of little use when five or more allelic pairs are involved. From a variety of lines of evidence, geneticists have been led to believe that many quantitative characters represent the composite influence of genes at more than 10—perhaps occasionally more than 200—loci.

Other, more complicated ways of estimating gene number for quantitative characters have been formulated and are available in the genetic literature. But no methods so far devised are able to take sufficiently into account the complications of overlapping effects of the environment, linkage among members of a multiple gene system, differences in dominance relationships among such members, and individual variations in expression of the effects of gene action. Most attempts to determine number of multiple genes, then, must be characterized as brave efforts rather than as successfully completed missions. However, the picture is not entirely discouraging. Probably for some characters, reasonable approximations of the numbers of multiple genes in operation have already been attained. And if geneticists are never able to do better than give orders of magnitude for these numbers, still the information will be helpful in the solution of some of our most important genetic problems.

Gene Action in Multiple Gene Systems. We have already indicated that a weakness in our hypothetical model for quantitative inheritance is the assumption of simple additive effects of the action of all the operative genes involved. The assumption at first sight is attractive, largely, perhaps, because it is simple. It also appears to have some force, because it is suggested by the experiments of Nilsson-Ehle with kernel color in wheat, which have long served as models and as standard points of departure for the investigation and interpretation of quantitative inheritance. Neither of these reasons is sufficient for generalizing the assumption, however, in face of the fact that many of the data of quantitative inheritance cannot be easily reconciled with a theory of additive action. Moreover, duplicate genes of the kind involved in kernel color of wheat may be somewhat atypical, and perhaps relatively rare. You will remember that among wheats hexaploid and tetraploid species as well as diploids are found. It seems reasonable to suppose that the presence of two and three allelic pairs for red kernel color in wheat may be accounted for by reduplications of genomes. If this is the case, relationships among these duplicate genes are probably not typical of multiple gene associations in general.

The data of a good many studies of quantitative inheritance indicate that gene substitutions may have geometric rather than arithmetic effects. In other words, the genes seem to contribute their effects not so much by add-

TABLE 15-9. *Mean Fruit Weight in Grams of Different Tomato Crosses.* (*After MacArthur and Butler,* Genetics, 23:254, 1938.)

LARGER PARENT		SMALLER PARENT	LARGE P	SMALL P	F_1	GEOMETRIC MEAN	ARITHMETIC MEAN
Parents Differing Greatly in Size							
Large Pear	×	Red Currant	54.1	1.1	7.4	7.4	27.6
Putman's Forked	×	Red Currant	57.0	1.1	7.1	7.7	29.0
Tangerine	×	Red Currant	173.6	1.1	8.3	13.2	87.3
Devon Surprise	×	Burbank Pres.	58.0	5.1	23.0	17.2	32.5
Honor Bright	×	Yellow Pear	150.0	12.4	47.5	43.3	81.2
Parents of More Nearly the Same Size							
Peach	×	Yellow Pear	42.6	12.4	23.1	23.0	27.5
Dwarf Aristocrat	×	Peach	112.4	42.6	67.1	69.5	77.5
Albino	×	Honor Bright	312.0	150.0	160.0	217.0	231.0

ing or subtracting constant amounts but rather by multiplying or dividing the effect of the residual genotype by some constant amount. The average value of a quantitative character in F_1 in such a system more nearly approximates the geometric than the arithmetic mean between the parents.

In Table 15-9, which summarizes some genetic studies of size in tomato fruits, you will find that wherever the parents differ greatly in size the geometric mean of the parent values provides much the better fit to the F_1 average values. For example, in the first combination summarized in the table, let *LP* symbolize one Large Pear genome, and *RC* stand for a Red Currant genome. Then, compare the mean values, $RC/RC = 1.1$ grams, $LP/RC = 7.4$ grams, and $LP/LP = 54.1$ grams. These values provide a geometric series in which the effect of substituting each *LP* genome is to multiply by approximately 7. If you do this multiplication, you will obtain a series 1.1 : 7.7 : 53.9, which closely resembles the values found experimentally.

Another kind of approach to the problem of multiple genic action is being made by H. H. Smith, geneticist at Cornell. His method is to study the effects on quantitative characters of adding single extra chromosomes into hybrids between different species of Nicotiana and also into the parental species themselves. The character being studied most extensively is length of the corolla of the flower, which is admirably adapted to quantitative genetic analysis because of the ease of taking accurate measurements and because corolla length is relatively insensitive to environmental influence.

Different blocks of multiple genes, as identified by the particular chromosome added to a diploid complement, have different effects on the expression of quantitative characters. However, for the genes in a particular chromosome the effects are characteristic and usually conform to the concept of geometric action. For example, chromosome 1 of *Nicotiana langsdorffii* when added to the F_1 interspecific hybrid *N. langsdorffii* × *N. sanderae* has the effect of reducing corolla length to 0.8 of that found in normal hybrids (i.e., those not trisomic). Almost the identical result is obtained when this same chromosome 1 is added either to *N. sanderae*, which has relatively large flowers, or to *N. langsdorffii*, which has relatively small flowers. In both instances, the extra chromosome acts to multiply the normal mean by the constant 0.8; it cannot be acting in arithmetic fashion to subtract a constant quantity.

The Status of the Multiple Gene Hypothesis. Your own reaction as a student must be that the over-all picture of multiple genic action is exceedingly complicated. Professional geneticists would certainly concur in this judgment. At the present time, the physiological significance of results like those we have just discussed is entirely unknown. There are other serious gaps in our information that are only bridged temporarily by the expedient of drawing analogies from the behavior and action of major genes. What one can say with fair confidence is that different groups of multiple genes present different problems. Multiple genes can act either in plus or minus directions with reference to quantitative inheritance. In some instances they appear to act arithmetically, in others geometrically.

Keys to the Significance of This Chapter

Variation in some of the most important characteristics of organisms, such as size and shape, is not expressed in discrete steps. Individuals therefore do not fall into distinct classes with respect to such characteristics, and can only be reasonably described by quantitative measurements.

Effective summarization and manipulation of the data of quantitative inheritance require the use of appropriate statistical techniques. Beyond this, it is desirable to employ special mathematical methods for establishing the reliability of the techniques used in studying quantitative inheritance.

Typical instances of quantitative inheritance apparently depend upon the composite activity of multiple genes, which are individually unidentifiable because their separate effects are relatively insignificant to the phenotype. These genes appear not to differ in principle from genes with major effects. In fact, a gene may exert a major effect on one character and at the same time act as a member of a multiple gene complex affecting another trait of the organism. Different multiple gene complexes appear to vary considerably in the number of individual components. As few as three loci may be involved in the ordinary range of expression of some quantitative characters, but hundreds of loci may be involved in the expression of others.

The nature of gene action in multiple gene systems remains rather obscure at the present time. But it is clear that multiple genes do not operate entirely through simple additive effects. In fact, many cases of quantitative inheritance seem to show evidence for geometric rather than arithmetic action.

Doubtless, different multiple genes act in different ways and in different directions. And very likely, similar phenotypic effects may be obtained by a variety of multiple gene combinations acting under a variety of environmental circumstances.

References

Burton, G. W., "Quantitative Inheritance in Pearl Millet." *Agr. J.*, **43**:409–417, 1951. (Presents a wealth of data on quantitative inheritance which have been utilized for Questions and Problems for this chapter.)

Charles, D. R., and Smith, H. H., "Distinguishing between Two Types of Gene Action in Quantitative Inheritance." *Genetics*, **24**:34–48, 1939. (An amplification of the characteristics of arithmetic as against geometric gene action in multiple gene systems.)

Davenport, C. B., "Heredity of Skin Color in Negro-White Crosses." *Carnegie Inst. Wash. Pub.* 188, 1913. (The details of a study of the only quantitative character in man "for which a reasonably well-founded specific hypothesis of multifactor inheritance has been proposed" [see reference to Stern, below].)

Mather, K., "Polygenic Inheritance and Natural Selection." *Biol. Rev.*, **18**:32–64, 1943. (A meaningful treatment of many of the fundamental concepts of quantitative inheritance. Applicable both to this chapter and the next.)

———, "The Genetical Theory of Continuous Variation." *Proc. Eighth Intern. Congr. Genetics*, 376–401, 1948. (An important article for students who have had some experience with methods of statistical analysis.)

———, *Biometrical Genetics*. New York: Dover Publications, 1949. (Concise treatment of mathematical analysis of continuous variation.)

Panse, V. G., "Application of Genetics to Plant Breeding. II. The Inheritance of Quantitative Characters and Plant Breeding." *J. Genetics*, **40**:283–302, 1940. (For students who have had a course in statistics.)

Smith, H. H., "Recent Studies on Inheritance of Quantitative Characters in Plants." *Botan. Rev.*, **10**:349–382, 1944. (A complete and concise review, accompanied by an extensive reference list.)

Snedecor, G. W., *Statistical Methods*. Ames: Iowa State College Press, 1946. (Readable, understandable, and particularly suited to students in the biological field.)

Stern, C., *Principles of Human Genetics*. San Francisco: W. H. Freeman and Co., 1949. (Pages 325–332 are devoted to a summary and discussion of the material in the reference to Davenport, above.)

Sumner, F. B., "Genetic and Distributional Studies of Three Sub-Species of Peromyscus." *J. Genetics*, **23**:275–376, 1930. (Massive data on quantitative differences among various geographic races of deer mice.)

Wexelsen, H., "Quantitative Inheritance and Linkage in Barley." *Hereditas*, **18**:307–348, 1934. (Analysis of the inheritance of length of spike internodes in barley.)

Questions and Problems

15- 1.   What do the following terms signify?

arithmetic mean
continuous variation
discontinuous variation
expressivity
frequency distribution
geometric mean
median
midclass value
mode

modifying genes
multiple gene hypothesis
normal distribution
penetrance
polygenes
qualitative character
quantitative character
standard deviation
standard error

15- 2.   An extensive pedigree, studied by Mohr and Wriedt, shows the distribution of *minor brachydactyly* (short index finger) in a human family. If individuals are classified either as being normal or brachydactylous, without designating differences in degree of finger shortening, brachydactyly follows the inheritance pattern of a single dominant gene. However, the situation is complicated by the fact that some brachydactylous individuals have an extremely short index finger, while others have this finger only slightly shortened. What might explain the variable expressivity of brachydactyly in this pedigree?

15- 3.   In general, variability in penetrance and expressivity has made the analysis of genetic traits in man more difficult than in Drosophila. Why?

The results of certain crosses between Negroes and whites indicate that skin color differences may depend upon allelic substitutions at two independent loci. Whites can be designated by the genotype *aabb;* Negroes by the genotype *AABB.* The active alleles for pigmentation, *A* or *B*, are supposed to have independent cumulative effects upon the intensity of coloration. Thus an individual with any two active alleles (*e.g., AAbb* or *AaBb*) is darker than an individual with only one active allele but lighter than an individual carrying three active alleles. Under this scheme, individuals may fall into one of five classes: white, light brown, medium brown, dark brown, or black. Use this interpretation, which incidentally does not hold satisfactorily for all color differences emerging from white-Negro crosses, in answering the next four questions.

15- 4.   How does the preceding interpretation of skin color inheritance compare with Nilsson-Ehle's analysis of the genetic basis of kernel color in wheat?

15- 5.   Is it proper to refer to skin color in man as a quantitative character? Elaborate.

15- 6.   Can the first-generation progeny of white-black matings produce black offspring? White offspring?

15- 7.   Does every marriage between two medium-brown individuals offer the possibility of progeny showing either lighter or darker skin colors?

15- 8.   In experiments conducted by Wexelsen, in Norway, the mean internode length in spikes of the barley variety Asplund was found to be 2.12 mm, and of the variety Abed Binder, 3.17 mm. The mean of the F_1 derived from a cross between these varieties was approximately 2.7. The F_2 gave a continuous range of variation from one parental extreme to the other. Analysis of the F_3 population indicated that in F_2, 8 out of the total of 125 individuals were of the Asplund type, giving a mean of 2.19 mm. Eight other individuals were similar to the parent Abed Binder, giving a mean internode length of 3.24. Which does internode length in spikes of barley seem to be—a qualitative or a quantitative character? Why?

15- 9. From the information given in the previous question, how many gene pairs involved in the determination of internode length appear to have been segregating in F_2?

Burton has made extensive studies of quantitative inheritance in pearl millet, an important pasture crop in the southeastern United States. Following is a frequency distribution for number of leaves per stem in a pearl millet cross. Utilize these data in answering the next five questions.

Number of Leaves per Stem

	9	10	11	12	13	14	15	16	17	18	19	20	21	22	23	N
P 16		1	17	55	66	34	5									178
P 782				3	6	6	16	17	23	50	29	20	12	4	1	187
F_1			5	5	28	51	58	27	5							179
F_2	1	8	37	144	303	454	452	322	153	31	8					1913

15-10. For each of the populations shown in the preceding frequency distribution calculate $\bar{x}$, σ, and S. E.

15-11. Compare the different σ values you obtain. What might explain the differences?

15-12. Calculate the arithmetic mean between the two parental means, and also the geometric mean. Which of these values is closer to the observed F_1 mean value?

15-13. From the fact that one of the parental extremes (P 782) was not recovered in an F_2 population of almost 2000 individuals, what general conclusion may you draw about the number of genes determining leaf number?

15-14. Why must your answer to the preceding question remain tentative?

Burton has also studied the inheritance of head length in pearl millet crosses. Utilize the following frequency distributions for answering the next four questions.

Midclass Values in Inches for Head Length

	2	3	4	5	6	7	8	9	10	11	12	13	14	15	16	N
P 16					3	38	72	12	1							126
P 18	1		7	40	50	15	2									115
F_1								1	88	66	1					156
F_2		5	5	11	20	54	120	358	576	524	245	90	15	1		2024

15-15. For each of the populations shown in the preceding frequency table calculate $\bar{x}$, σ, and S. E.

15-16. Is the relatively large σ value for F_2 expected? Justify your answer.

15-17. Compare the $\bar{x}$ values of the F_1 and F_2 populations with the parental means. Is the picture you obtain typical of cases of quantitative inheritance you have studied so far? If not, in what respects does it differ?

15-18. Is the type of gene action assumed in the hypothetical model for quantitative inheritance discussed in this chapter adequate to explain the results detailed above? Discuss.

Utilize the following information in answering the next six questions. Assume a situation where genes *A*, *B*, *C*, and *D* have duplicate, cumulative effects and are independently inherited. Each of these genes contributes 3 cm height to the organism when present. In addition, a gene *L*, always present in the homozygous state, contributes a constant 40 cm of height. Neglecting variation due to environment, an organism *AABBCCDDLL*, then, would be 64 cm high, and one *aabbccddLL* would be 40 cm.

A cross is made *AAbbCCDDLL* × *aaBBccDDLL* and carried into F_2.

15-19. How would F_1 individuals compare in size to each of the parents?

15-20. Compare the mean of the F_1 with the mean of the F_2.

15-21. What proportion of the F_2 population would show the same height as the *AAbbCCDDLL* parent?

15-22. What proportion of the F_2 population would show the same height as the *aaBBccDDLL* parent?

15-23. What proportion of the F_2 population would breed true for the height shown by the *aaBBccDDLL* parent?

15-24. What proportion of the F_2 population would breed true for the height characteristic of F_1 individuals?

CHAPTER 16

Inbreeding and Selection

INTEREST IN phenomena of quantitative inheritance originated long before Mendel's time. Plant and animal breeders have been working with quantitative characters on a practical basis for hundreds or perhaps even thousands of years. Beyond this, not a little of our interest in, and our information about, quantitative inheritance stems from age-old observations of people about people. Much of this knowledge and interest relates to the genetic effects of inbreeding and selection.

Mating Systems. For our present discussion, we will make a simple distinction between two systems of mating, *inbreeding* and *outbreeding*. These terms are used to describe whether within a line of descent there are few or many common ancestors. Inbreeding refers to the situation where progeny are produced by closely related parents. Outbreeding describes matings between individuals not closely related. We will treat these terms more quantitatively in Chapter 23.

Inbreeding and outbreeding, as words and as concepts, must be understood in a relative, rather than an absolute, sense. For instance, in man the progeny of first-cousin marriages are more *inbred* than are the offspring of marriages between second or third cousins. Brother-sister marriages, if they were not forbidden in modern societies, would offer the possibility of still closer inbreeding than is found in first-cousin marriages. And although brother-sister matings are the closest form of inbreeding possible in higher animals, certain higher plants, and many lower forms in both the plant and animal kingdoms, are able to carry out self-fertilization, which is the most drastic of all kinds of inbreeding. But even self-fertilization encompasses significant variation. Compare self-fertilization in corn, for example, with autogamy in Paramecium, where self-fertilization involves genetically identical gamete nuclei. You can make this comparison on the basis of material presented in Chapter 8.

Inbreeding

Deleterious Effects Associated with Inbreeding. Generally speaking, people tend to associate inbreeding with unfavorable effects. There are many expressions of this attitude. Some belong in the nebulous realm of old wives' wisdom, but others are spoken with more authority. Most of us are aware, for example, of church or governmental regulations whose purpose is to prevent marriages between relatives of a certain closeness of kinship. All of the states in this country forbid marriages of nearer relatives than first cousins, while some forbid first-cousin marriages as well.

Reinforcing the attitude that inbreeding, on the whole, is something to be avoided are the observations and judgments of the early plant and animal breeders. And in the field of pure biological science, we can find such statements as the one by Charles Darwin, in 1862, that nature "abhors perpetual self-fertilization."

What has led to the idea that inbreeding is to be avoided? For one thing, inbreeding seems to suffer in contrast with its antithesis, outbreeding, which in present popular stereotype is usually represented by such mighty examples as hybrid corn and the mule. Darwin, thinking in terms of adaptation

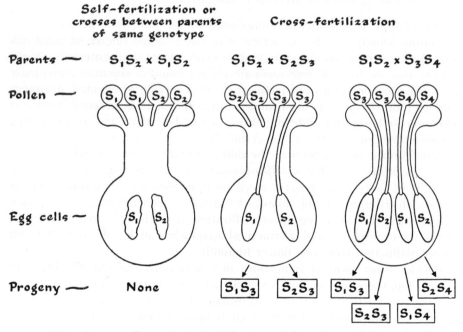

Figure 16-1. *In a number of groups of plants, including clovers, cherries, tobacco, and evening primroses, multiple allelic series determine compatibility in sexual reproduction. Pollen tubes carrying a given incompatibility allele fail to grow properly in stylar tissue carrying the same allele for incompatibility. Cross-compatibility depends upon genotype, and, as shown in the figure, some, all, or none of the pollen of a given plant may function effectively in the stylar tissue of another. Incompatibility alleles are usually designated S_1, S_2, S_3, and so on. At least forty different alleles for incompatibility are known in red clover. (After Crane and Lawrence, J. Pomol. Hort. Sci., 7:290, 1929.)*

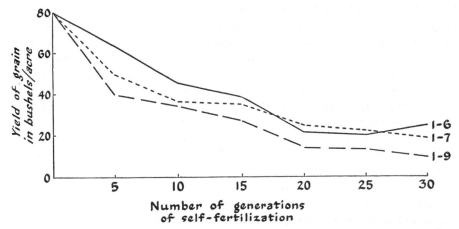

Figure 16-2. *Effect of thirty generations of continued inbreeding on the yield of three different lines of corn. (After Jones, Genetics, 24:463, 1939. Courtesy of Connecticut Agricultural Experiment Station.)*

and evolution, was particularly impressed by the numerous devices among organisms which tend to encourage or to ensure some degree of outbreeding. We have mentioned before that in many plants, and especially among higher animals, the different sexes are always found in separate individuals. This situation precludes self-fertilization, thus serving as effective insurance against inbreeding in its most intense form. Still more impressive is the fact that among hermaphroditic organisms, a number of means for promoting cross-fertilization are found. In certain hermaphrodites, self-fertilization is impossible because gametes of the different sexes mature at quite different times; in others, *hereditary self-incompatibility* favors outbreeding. Figure 16-1 shows a type of genetic mechanism for self-incompatability that is widely distributed among plants. Even where self-fertilization can take place, ways of forwarding cross-fertilization are strikingly frequent. In orchids, for example, complex structural adaptations of the floral parts foster insect pollination from one flower to another.

Besides these general indications of a superiority of outbreeding over inbreeding, there are numerous specific instances where inbreeding appears to give rise fairly directly to unfortunate biological consequences. For example, we can consider briefly what happens when corn plants are self-fertilized, and then their progeny are self-fertilized, and their progeny's progeny, and so on for a number of generations. Typically, after a few generations the material separates into distinct lines that become more uniform following each self-pollination. Plants with unexpected deleterious characters are likely to appear, such as white seedlings, virescents, yellow seedlings, and dwarfs. Many of the lines die out. Those that survive show a general decline in size and vigor that can be described in the kind of measurements that we have previously utilized for quantitative characters. This is illustrated in Figure 16-2, where you can see graphed the yield of three lines of corn over a period of thirty generations of self-fertilization. Notice the leveling of the yield after about twenty generations. In this same experiment, uniformity of height for each line was attained somewhat earlier. By the twentieth generation, each line had become constant for all visible characters, except for variation that could be ascribed to environment.

Somewhat similar results have been noted when certain other plants are inbred. And animal breeders, too, have observed that "weaknesses" may appear following intensive inbreeding. Turning to the area of human genetics for another of many possible examples, we can point to the fact that a disproportionate number of cousin marriages is found among the parents of albinos. We will return to a specific consideration of this phenomenon in Chapter 20.

We can appreciate, then, why inbreeding has been thought to be biologically undesirable. And we should pursue the matter by asking two questions. Is inbreeding as such directly accountable for the biological evils often associated with it? If not, what is the relationship between inbreeding and its apparently deleterious effects?

You might begin to answer the first question for yourself if you were to take a survey of the typical life histories of various organisms. You would find, perhaps to your surprise, that in many successful groups of plants, self-fertilization is the habitual means of reproduction. You would probably conclude that if oats, peas, beans, and tomatoes, for example, flourish under generation after generation of intensive inbreeding, the practice of inbreeding as such can scarcely be judged harmful.

Your conclusion might be reinforced in various ways. Examination of human family histories would reveal that by no means does inbreeding always lead to disaster. One of the nobler lines of kings and queens known in history, the Ptolemy line in Egypt, was maintained through brother-sister marriages. Much the same lesson can be taken from the experiences of breeders of animals. If you own a fine purebred dog, you need not be astonished to find a good deal of common ancestry in its pedigree. From planned experiments, too, there is abundant evidence that inbreeding does not always produce harmful effects. A clear demonstration of this fact is that vigorous lines of albino rats have been maintained after more than a hundred generations of brother-sister mating.

Inbreeding and Homozygosis. In summation, we can say that deleterious effects seem to follow more frequently on inbreeding than could be expected from mere chance; nevertheless, inbreeding is not in itself necessarily harmful. Further clarification of the situation calls for a closer and more precise analysis. We must turn from a description of end effects to a study of genetic mechanisms.

One outstanding genetic effect of inbreeding accounts for many of the other effects associated with it. Inbreeding results in *homozygosis*, or, if you will, the homozygous state at numerous genetic loci. Let us first consider this principle in its simplest form, by seeing what happens as the result of self-fertilization in organisms heterozygous for a single pair of alleles, *A-a*. You know that from *Aa* selfed we expect a progeny of ¼*AA*, ½*Aa*, and ¼*aa*. For that half of the progeny which is *Aa*, reproduction through self-fertilization will again give rise to ½ heterozygous offspring and ½ homozygous, with equal numbers of *AA* and *aa* individuals being expected. For that half of the progeny which is either *AA* or *aa*, however, self-fertilization can produce only offspring that are genotypically identical with their parents. Over a series of generations, then, assuming heterozygous parents to begin with, we might expect that the proportion of heterozygotes would be reduced by half in each succeeding generation. Correspondingly, there should be an increased frequency of homozygotes.

Perhaps you can see this principle more readily after examining Figure 16-3, which shows the results of self-fertilization over a period of four generations. Notice that for our simple model we have made the assumption that each genotype reproduces equally well, a situation not always found in actuality. And if you wonder why we chose 1600 individuals to start with, it should be explained that the number is an arbitrary one chosen to permit the expected progeny to come out in simple whole numbers. The results speak for themselves. Beginning with 1600 individuals, all *Aa*, four generations of self-fertilization will produce a population with 15 homozygous individuals for every heterozygote. A continuation of self-fertilization over succeeding generations would further reduce the frequency of heterozygotes.

For simplicity's sake we have begun our discussion of inbreeding and homozygosis in relation to single allelic pairs. Except where organisms are

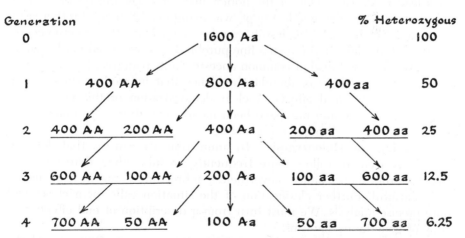

Figure 16-3. *Reduction in heterozygosity over four generations of self-fertilization.*

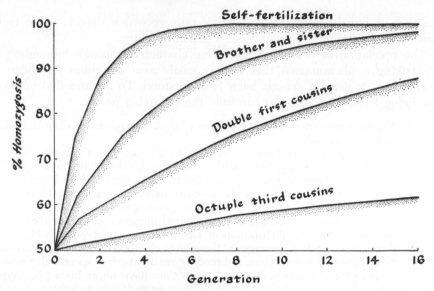

Figure 16-4. *The percentage of homozygosis in successive generations under various forms of inbreeding, as indicated by the closeness of relationship of the parents.* (*After Wright,* Genetics, 6:172, 1921.)

already highly inbred, however, most individuals are doubtless heterozygous for many allelic pairs. The effects of inbreeding operate on all the genetic loci, so that quantitative characters as well as characters determined by major genes are subject to its influence.

What we have said about self-fertilization and homozygosis applies directly but to somewhat lesser degrees to other forms of inbreeding. Brother-sister matings continued over a number of generations also result in increasing homozygosis, but somewhat more slowly. Less drastic forms of inbreeding are correspondingly less efficient in producing homozygosis. These differences are brought out in Figure 16-4.

Bringing Recessive Characters to Light Through Homozygosis. We now have at hand an essential clue to why inbreeding is associated with deleterious consequences. In a non-inbred population, deleterious recessive genes may often be concealed by their normal dominant alleles. Inbreeding, however, favors segregation into homozygotes, so that if deleterious recessive alleles are carried in a population they quickly come to light.

Natural populations in which inbreeding is not the rule do indeed carry deleterious recessive factors in fairly high frequencies. Dobzhansky and co-workers at Columbia have investigated wild populations of *D. pseudoobscura* and found that the majority of individuals carry deleterious recessive mutants. That much the same situation holds in corn was indicated in our earlier discussion of inbreeding in this organism. And the fact that a large fraction of human individuals showing rare, recessive defects come from cousin marriages helps to round out a general picture.

The revelation of deleterious recessive characters through inbreeding is so striking a phenomenon that it may easily assume undue significance, even when its general genetic basis is understood. To be sure that you are not being led astray, consider carefully the following points:

1. Not only *deleterious* recessives come to light through inbreeding but other recessives as well.

2. Inbreeding does not favor an increase in the number of recessive alleles; it merely gets them placed where they can be detected phenotypically. One way to assure yourselves in this matter is to turn back to Figure 16-3, where you will see that in the original parental generation 1600A and 1600a alleles were present. In the last generation shown in the diagram, the proportions, and in our case the actual numbers, of alleles are exactly the same. Only the distribution of alleles among genotypes has changed.

3. With reference to homozygosis, the effects of inbreeding are the same for dominants as for recessives. Inbreeding may have less spectacular consequences for dominants, however, since they have never been phenotypically submerged and thus cannot be brought suddenly to light.

Inbreeding and the Fixation of Genetic Characters. We have said that continued inbreeding results in homozygosis. Another way of putting the same idea, with a slight but important shift in emphasis, would be to say that inbreeding results in the fixation of genetic characters. To place the argument in more specific form, assume a group of organisms heterozygous for two gene pairs (*AaBb*). Inbreeding might result in the formation of four homozygous lines—*AAbb, aaBB, aabb,* and *AABB*. With reference to the characteristics determined by these genotypes, the lines would be true-breeding within themselves, barring the possibility of mutation. If a greater number of heterozygous loci were involved in the first place, the same principle would still hold. After sufficiently long and intense inbreeding, the population would become separated into genetically distinct groups, each uniform within itself. This effect of inbreeding has implications of prime importance in evolution, and in plant and animal breeding as directed by man.

Selection Within and Among Inbred Lines

The evolutionary process—unconsciously—and plant and animal breeders—consciously—have in common that they are both constantly testing for superior types. The criteria for "superior" are not necessarily the same in nature and on the farm, since the emphasis of evolution is on survival value, and the goals of plant and animal breeders are determined by a variety of human needs and desires. Both evolution and practical breeding, however, in large part rely on a process of *selection*, in which individuals with certain characteristics are favored for reproduction.

The Selection Experiments of W. Johannsen. Before we can begin to deal properly with some of the subtleties of selection and population change, we need to clarify certain basic attributes of selection and its consequences. Of these attributes, two are particularly fundamental to an understanding of evolution and of breeding principles:

1. Selection is effective only when based on differences that are heritable.
2. Selection does not create variation; it only acts on variation already present among organisms.

Any misconception of these two points is likely to lead the student or the practitioner of genetics into curious and unproductive byways. And it is fortunate that almost as soon as widespread investigations in Mendelian heredity began, brilliant experimentation provided a solid basis for an understanding of selection. In the early 1900's, a Danish plant scientist, W. Johannsen, began experiments to test some of the ideas about selection which were then current. Like Mendel, he turned to a common garden plant for his experimental material; also like Mendel, he had the happy faculty of being able to follow a trail of experimental facts to logical and significant conclusions.

In a notable sequence of experiments carried out with the Princess variety of garden bean, Johannsen investigated the possibilities of selecting for weight of seed. Starting with a mixture of seed obtained from many different plants, he found initially that progenies derived from heavier seed in general had greater average seed weight than progenies obtained from lighter seed. This result indicated that selection had been effective.

To explore the problem further, Johannsen refined his experimental approach. He chose 19 seeds, each derived from a different mother plant, and grew them into 19 progeny plants. These produced their own lots of seed, which were kept separate. Within each seed lot, weights varied from one

TABLE 16-1. The Effects of Six Years of Selection in Pure Line No. 19 of the Princess Bean. In each generation, the lightest and the heaviest seeds were selected for propagation. (Data from Johannsen, Elemente der Exacten Erblichkeitslehre. Jena: Gustav Fischer, 1926.)

HARVEST YEAR	AVERAGE WEIGHT OF SELECTED PARENT SEEDS		AVERAGE WEIGHT OF PROGENY SEED	
	Lighter Seeds	Heavier Seeds	Lighter Seeds	Heavier Seeds
1902	30 cg	40 cg	36 cg	35 cg
1903	25	42	40	41
1904	31	43	31	33
1905	27	39	38	39
1906	30	46	38	40
1907	24	47	37	37

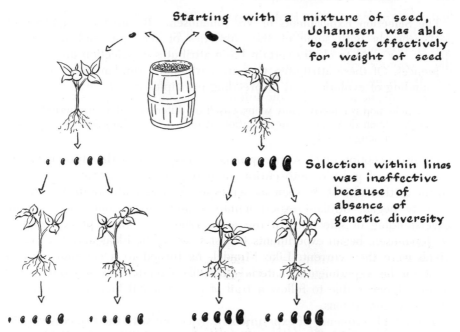

Starting with a mixture of seed, Johannsen was able to select effectively for weight of seed

Selection within lines was ineffective because of absence of genetic diversity

Figure 16-5. *Johannsen distinguished between genetic and environmental sources of variation, and showed that only genetic variation is subject to effective selection.*

individual to another, falling into arrays roughly approximating normal distributions. Johannsen propagated his 19 separate lines by selecting from each seed lot the heaviest and the lightest seeds. This procedure was followed for several generations, with the kind of result shown in Table 16-1. In short, *there was a remarkable tenacity of weight averages within each line, generation after generation, no matter whether the line was reproduced by its heaviest or by its lightest seed.* After six generations of selection in Line 19 the smallest parent seed produced a progeny with an average weight of 37 centigrams, while the largest parent seed also produced a progeny averaging 37.

Johannsen's results are perfectly understandable if we remember that beans are normally self-fertilizing and if we recall that inbreeding leads to homozygosis. The parent beans with which Johannsen started his second series of experiments were, therefore, each homozygous. Progeny of any individual bean could not show genetic segregation; they constituted what Johannsen named a *pure line*. Differences among members of a single progeny could be due only to environment. *Selection within pure lines, then, is ineffective because it is biologically meaningless.* Each generation is built on exactly the same genetic base and has precisely the same capacities for variation in response to environmental influence as had its parents.

The reason that Johannsen had some success in selecting for size in his first series of experiments is also apparent. The population out of which he made his original selections was not a pure line but a mixture of pure lines, and so presented genotypic as well as phenotypic variation. By separating the genotypes with relatively greater inherent capacities for expression of size, it was possible to raise the mean size of a group of progeny to a level higher than the average for the initial population. Johannsen's experiments are schematically summarized in Figure 16-5.

The great contributions of these experiments were: first, to distinguish effectively between heritable and nonheritable variation; second, to emphasize that inbreeding does indeed lead to genetic homogeneity; third, to demonstrate that selection does not create variation; and fourth, to reaffirm, on the other hand, that selection within a group that is genetically diverse may change the character of subsequent populations. In addition, Johannsen's studies demonstrate in a striking way the sensitivity of quantitative characters to environmental influence, and point to the hopelessness of trying to deal with quantitative variation in living things unless heredity and environment are adequately distinguished and placed under some sort of control.

Hybridization of Inbred Lines

Hybrid Vigor in Corn. Reference to Figure 16-2 will recall to you that inbreeding corn over a period of generations leads to successive reductions in vigor. Sometimes, inbred lines die out entirely. Where they do not, a time comes when continued self-fertilization is accompanied by no increase in deleterious effects. Presumably this stabilization occurs when homozygosity is reached. You will not suppose, of course, that such a characteristic as yield will ever be entirely constant, even in a homozygous line. Yield, like most quantitative characters, is sensitive to fluctuations of environment, and planting seasons differ sufficiently from one year to the next to provide a basis for appreciable variation in phenotypic expression.

If two different inbred lines of corn are crossed, the hybrid progeny display *heterosis*. They are almost always strikingly more vigorous than their parents. Usually such hybrids are vigorous by any standards. But to clear up a fairly common misconception, it should be said that hybrid corn plants are not unique in vigor or even markedly superior to the best plants of open-pollinated origin. In fact, certain open-pollinated plants are superior to many hybrids. The basic reason for the success of hybrid corn in our agricultural economy is that members of an F_1 hybrid group show a uniformity of high-level performance not found in open-pollinated varieties. After the F_1 generation, however, characters like height and yield are not maintained at so high and uniform a level. In a study by N. P. Neal, of the University of Wisconsin, the yield of ten different corn hybrids was compared in the F_1 and F_2 generations. The first-generation hybrids gave an average yield in bushels per acre of 62.8; the average yield for the same hybrids in F_2 was only 44.2. These results are typical. They should remind you of facts that emerged in the preceding chapter, where we discussed quantitative inheritance uncomplicated by heterosis. You will remember that for quantitative characters in general, the F_2 is much more variable than the F_1, and encompasses a whole spectrum of variation. Increased variability after the F_1 results from genetic segregation and recombination.

Explanations of Hybrid Vigor. Heterosis is a phenomenon that is at once intriguing and practically important. It is manifested in different groups of organisms, being by no means confined to corn, or even to plants. No doubt what is called hybrid vigor in various groups of organisms is not everywhere the same phenomenon. But these various manifestations doubtless have much in common, and a satisfactory explanation of one will aid considerably in understanding others.

All attempts to explain hybrid vigor stem from one basic fact. This is that the vigor is found associated with the heterozygous state. A synonym for hybrid vigor, already utilized, serves to emphasize this point. In 1914, G. H. Shull, an American geneticist who was one of the pioneer students of hybrid vigor in corn, proposed the term *heterosis,* a kind of contraction of *heterozygosis,* as a word likely to be useful in connoting the increase of size and vigor following crossing. We will use *heterosis* and *hybrid vigor* interchangeably, as is common practice in the literature of genetics.

Most genetical theories designed to explain heterosis fall into one of two categories:

Explanations Based on Interaction of Alleles. A number of geneticists have proposed, in one way or another, that heterozygosity *per se* is essential for heterosis. Reduced to simple terms, theories of this kind say that if there are the alleles a_1 and a_2 for a single locus, the heterozygous combination a_1a_2 is superior to either of the possible homozygotes, a_1a_1 or a_2a_2. Obviously this is a kind of dominance interaction new to us in this book. To express it, the term *overdominance* has been suggested. The implication is usually that alleles a_1 and a_2 do separate things, and the sum of their different products, or some reaction product between them, is superior for vigor to the single products produced by either allele in the homozygous state.

There is considerable evidence that different alleles at a single locus are indeed able to do different things. For example, in several organisms members of multiple allelic series have been found to produce different blood antigens. In heterozygous combination, each different allele can be shown to give rise to its own peculiar product. Also pertinent to the general argument is the fact that a number of instances have been described where a heterozygote gives more extreme phenotypic effects than either homozygote. One instance, reported for Drosophila by Curt Stern, involves the mutant gene *cubitus interruptus* and a special wild-type allele which Stern calls a "position allele" because its normal dominance relations have been disturbed by a chromosome rearrangement near its locus. The allele for *cubitus interruptus* gives rise to deficient venation in the wings, and is designated *ci*. The "position allele" is written $R(+)$. A comparison of homozygotes and heterozygotes is given below:

Homozygotes $R(+)/R(+)$ = Normal
Homozygotes *ci/ci*   = Moderate degree of deficient venation
Heterozygotes $R(+)/ci$ = Extreme degree of deficient venation
(From Stern, *Genetics*, 33:215, 1948.)

Here, if deficient venation is considered as the antithesis of vigor, we have a kind of "negative heterosis." The main point is that the experiment gives us a clear example where heterozygosity *per se* results in a deviation more extreme than is produced by either homozygote.

Results bearing directly on the relationships of heterozygosity to vigor have come from the work of Ake Gustaffson of the Institute of Genetics, Svälof, Sweden. He has utilized spontaneous mutations within pure lines; these permit the comparison of homozygotes and heterozygotes under conditions where the entire residual genotype is closely controlled. In the pure-line variety of barley called *Golden*, he reports that *heterozygotes for the chlorophyll mutants albina 7 and xantha 3 show consistent advantages over the homozygous normals* in spike and kernel number and in kernel weight. The homozygous mutant types are lethal. A few other observations similar to Gustaffson's have been described, but it is not yet known whether they are exceptional or whether they represent a situation of wide occurrence.

Explanations Based on the Interaction of Different Dominant Genes. Many geneticists have felt that heterosis does not require overdominance, but that it can be rather simply explained in terms of ordinary dominance of genes relatively favorable for vigor and the corresponding recessiveness of genes unfavorable for vigor. The reasoning behind this second kind of explanation can be most readily seen if we return to the effects of inbreeding.

We have already discussed how, in groups of organisms that are normally not inbred, deleterious recessive mutant genes may accumulate because they are masked by dominant normal alleles. Deleterious dominant mutations tend to be eliminated from populations rather rapidly because they are immediately and continuingly subjected to adverse natural selection. Among normally inbred groups, even deleterious recessives do not accumulate to any great degree. Inbreeding leads to homozygosity, and thus in these groups unfavorable recessives are subject to much the same sort of pruning through natural selection as occurs for deleterious dominants everywhere. This continual process of pruning away undesirable recessive genes in naturally self-fertilized organisms accounts for the fact that such plants as oats can maintain a level of vigor apparently as high as is found among naturally cross-fertilized plants.

If one makes a cross between unrelated inbred lines of corn, it is likely, indeed almost inevitable, that at particular loci the parent lines will differ depending on whether dominant or recessive alleles have become homozygous through the inbreeding process. Thus if we were to designate five loci in a hypothetical cross between inbreds, a representative situation might be as follows:

Inbred I   *aaBBCCddEE* × Inbred II   *AAbbCCDDee*
            F₁   *AaBbCCDdEe*

If the different recessive alleles are even mildly unfavorable to vigor, the hybrid, having the relatively favorable dominant alleles at more different loci than is true for either inbred, should be more vigorous than either parental line. A look at the hypothetical cross will also help to make it clear how it is that uniformity is a characteristic of hybrid corn. Since the parental inbred lines typically are homozygous, their progeny must be *genetically uniform*. You realize, of course, that this is not the same as saying the progeny are *homozygous*.

The above general explanation of heterosis is different in a fundamental way from the first kind of theory we discussed. Since in the second case it is assumed that heterozygosity is largely incidental to the phenomenon of hybrid vigor, it should be possible to obtain lines of corn that breed true for the vigor found in particular hybrids. For instance, the hypothetical F₁ individuals *AaBbCCDdEe*, if intercrossed or self-fertilized, should give some progeny of the genotype *AABBCCDDEE*. Continued failure, in actual experiments, to find true-breeding lines as vigorous as F₁ hybrids might be taken as evidence in favor of theories based on allelic interaction. For if the heterozygous condition as such accounts for hybrid vigor, then this kind of vigor could not be expected to be stabilized in homozygous lines.

In corn, fixing the vigor of F₁ hybrids into true-breeding lines has not so far been possible. It has been pointed out, however, that the recovery of lines homozygous for all the favorable alleles for a multiple gene character may pose a Herculean task for the plant breeder. If expression of vigor is influenced by genes at, say, thirty different loci in a hybrid, the probability of recovering one particular homozygous combination among the progeny of this hybrid is small. Singleton has calculated that it would require a land area more than 2000 times the total land area of the earth to grow enough corn plants to have an even chance of obtaining one such homozygous combination, even if there were independent recombinations among the thirty loci. Moreover, since quantitative characters are susceptible to environmental influence, the detection and preservation of a particular genotype might be immensely difficult. Finally, linkages among favorable dominant genes and unfavorable recessives would reduce still more the probability of recovery of multiple dominants. Since many loci are likely to be involved in expressions of vigor, such linkages are to be expected. At present we cannot tell whether fixing heterotic vigor into homozygous lines of corn is impossible or whether it is only an infinitely arduous task.

Our present judgment of the different explanations for hybrid vigor must be in the nature of a compromise. There are rather good indications that either allelic interaction or a complex of dominant linked genes may feasibly account for heterosis as we see it, for example, in corn. In fact, there appear to be no obvious reasons why in given instances both systems should not operate simultaneously in producing heterotic effects. However, true understanding of the causes of heterosis must wait for a better understanding of gene action, of dominance, and of other fundamental genetic phenomena, particularly as they relate to quantitative inheritance.

Various Manifestations of Heterosis. Under any of the hypotheses for heterosis considered here, specific phenotypic consequences would depend upon which genetic loci were represented by different alleles in the parents. Genic balance and environmental and other considerations would also affect phenotypic expression. Consequently, we need not be surprised that hetero sis is manifested in a variety of ways in different organisms and under dif ferent conditions.

First, in many hybrids nothing that might reasonably be called "hybrid vigor" has been observed. As we saw in Chapter 15, very often F_1 hybrids are intermediate between their parents in quantitative characters. We also saw cases of *geometric* inheritance, where the mean of the F_1 is smaller than the arithmetic average of the parents. Sometimes the hybrid value is less than that of either parent. An instance of this kind has been reported for hybrids between closely related species of vetches, where the hybrids are dwarfs, considerably smaller than their parents.

When heterosis is manifested, it may be expressed otherwise than as increase in height or bulk. In certain soybean hybrids, increases in the numbers of nodes, pods, and seeds have been observed, but plant size seems little affected. Quite frequently, interbreed hybrids in the domestic fowl show faster growth than do their purebred parents, although at maturity the hybrid birds are usually intermediate between the parents in size. Crosses between White Leghorn and Barred Plymouth Rock chickens have had the effect of increasing the hatchability of eggs. Increased fecundity has been found to follow on crossing inbred strains of Drosophila. Other reported heterotic effects in various hybrid organisms include increased disease resistance and greater tolerance to extremes of environment such as heat and cold.

The Fixation of Heterosis. Our discussion of hybrid vigor in corn dealt with the experimental difficulty of fixing heterosis, especially if it is due to the heterozygous condition as such. However, among various organisms, genetic mechanisms exist which tend to preserve favorable genic and allelic combinations from disintegration through recombination. Three of these mechanisms will be discussed briefly.

Asexual Reproduction. Even if a parent organism is highly heterozygous, its genotype is faithfully perpetuated when reproduction is by asexual means. Plant breeders have often taken advantage of such a situation. For example, Coastal Bermuda grass, which is planted for forage in the southeastern states, was obtained at a Georgia experiment station as a hybrid between two strains of Bermuda from South Africa. The superior qualities of the original hybrid plant were recognized, and it has been widely propagated by means of stolons or rhizomes. There is no difficulty about getting Coastal Bermuda to "breed true," because asexual reproduction circumvents segregation and recombination.

Balanced Lethals. We mentioned in Chapter 10 that multiple reciprocal translocations in *Oenothera lamarckiana,* the evening primrose, result in the formation of a large circle of chromosomes at meiosis. Chromosomes derived from one parent alternate with those derived from the other in this chromosomal ring. At metaphase, the orientation of chromosomes is such that all the chromosomes of maternal origin go to one pole, and all those of paternal origin to the other. The two chromosome complexes which are kept separate by this unusual behavior at meiosis are called *gaudens* and *velans.*

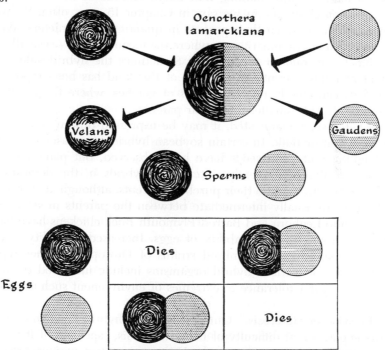

Figure 16-6. Oenothera lamarckiana *is a complex hybrid made up of the two chromosome complexes "gaudens" and "velans." Homozygous types never appear, since each complex carries a zygotic lethal. (After Cleland,* Botan. Rev., *2:320, 1936.)*

Although the evening primrose produces male and female gametes of both the gaudens and the velans type, individuals that are *gaudens/gaudens* or *velans/velans* never appear. This is because the two complexes carry different lethals which prevent the development of fertilized eggs when either kind of lethal is homozygous. Figure 16-6 diagrams the situation in *Oenothera lamarckiana,* and serves to illustrate *balanced lethal* systems in general.

Balanced lethals represent a second kind of genetic mechanism which permits heterozygotes to breed true.

Amphidiploidy. You will remember from Chapter 11 that in amphidiploids different genomes are brought together in the same nucleus, and are doubled so that they can be reproduced in regular fashion at meiosis. If such a combination of different genomes in an interspecific or intergeneric hybrid acts to produce a heterotic effect, this effect may be maintained over an indefinite number of generations.

The Biochemical Basis for Hybrid Vigor. If it were possible at this time to describe the biochemistry of heterotic effects, no doubt a dynamic situation of great interest would be revealed. So far, there is little precise information on the subject. However, strong impetus toward what appears to be a promising line of approach has been given by an investigation which compared hybrids and their parental types with reference to responses to chemical growth factors. In this study, conducted in 1941 by W. J. Robbins at the New York Botanical Garden, excised root tips from inbred lines of tomatoes and from the hybrid between them were grown in liquid culture medium to which various vitamin supplements were added. It was found that one of the parental varieties, Johannesfeuer, showed a greater response to pyridoxin than did the other, Red Currant. However, Red Currant responded to a greater degree to supplements of nicotinamide. A reasonable interpretation is that Red Currant is relatively deficient in its capacity to make its own nicotinamide, while Johannesfeuer is relatively deficient in its capacity to synthesize pyridoxin. Presumably these differences between the two parental varieties, which are genetically quite stable, are hereditary. When growth of hybrid roots was studied, the results were consistent with the interpretation that the hybrid was deficient in neither pyridoxin nor nicotinamide, and that it therefore enjoyed an advantage over both parents. There was even some evidence that the hybrid had a relatively greater ability to synthesize pyridoxin and nicotinamide than did either parent. These results indicate that heterosis is an expression of the activity of favorable concentrations and combinations of chemical factors for growth, produced as the result of complementary gene action in hybrids.

Heterocaryotic Vigor in Fungi. Strictly speaking, vigor associated with the heterozygous condition cannot occur in monoploid organisms like Neurospora. But Neurospora and other fungi sometimes give a monoploid's version of the heterozygous condition, and under this condition heterotic effects have been observed. The analysis of this phenomenon, closely related to hybrid vigor and called *heterocaryotic vigor*, has been tremendously fruitful.

The cells of a Neurospora mycelium are typically multinucleate. If the mycelium has arisen from a single isolated ascospore, the nuclei are genotypically identical (assuming that no mutations have occurred). When mycelia of different genetic origin are in proximity, however, vegetative fusions of the hyphae may take place, and nuclei may be interchanged. A mycelium containing nuclei of diverse genotype within the common cytoplasm of a single cell is called a *heterocaryon*. Such a condition of heterocaryosis has obvious analogies with the heterozygous state. You will see at once what is perhaps the chief difference between the two. This is that in heterocaryosis the different allelic representatives of a particular locus are separated by nuclear membranes (Fig. 16-7). With reference to gene dosage, heterocaryosis is more versatile, since the ratios of different kinds of nuclei within a heterocaryon are not mechanically fixed.

When the growth of a heterocaryon is compared with that of its individual component strains, the heterocaryon sometimes shows remarkable advantages in vigor and rate of growth, which by most criteria resemble heterosis. The biochemical basis of heterocaryotic vigor is well understood, largely because the study of biochemical genetic phenomena in Neurospora has been carried to a relatively advanced state. You can see this basis clearly by following some experiments carried out by G. W. Beadle and V. Coonradt.

In their investigations, these workers utilized mutant strains of Neurospora characterized by deficiencies in the capacity to synthesize certain vitamins which the wild-type mold can make for itself from simpler compounds. Two such strains are the *nicotinicless* and the *pantothenicless*. In

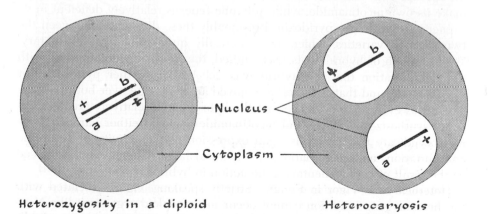

Heterozygosity in a diploid   Heterocaryosis

Figure 16-7. *In heterozygosity, the different alleles are in the same nucleus; in heterocaryosis, the alleles are in separate nuclei.*

the former, mutation at a particular locus has resulted in an inability to synthesize nicotinic acid; in the latter, mutation at a different locus blocks the synthesis of pantothenic acid. Both compounds are vitamins, and essential for growth. The effect of the mutations we have described is to limit growth of each mutant strain to environments which provide the vitamin that the mutant itself can no longer make. Thus, on a medium containing neither nicotinic nor pantothenic acid, attempts to culture the mutant strains individually are unsuccessful, and no growth can be obtained. However, if the two strains are inoculated together onto this same type of medium, a luxuriant mycelium arises, which grows as well as the original wild type from which the mutant strains were derived.

The explanation is simple and convincing. Inoculation of the two mutant strains side by side results in heterocaryon formation. The pantothenicless nuclei can synthesize nicotinic acid, since they have the appropriate wild-type allele. Similarly, the nicotinicless nuclei can produce pantothenic acid. Working in concert in a kind of intracellular, internuclear symbiosis, the two genotypes of nuclei within a heterocaryon are together able to do everything required for vigorous growth. The situation is summarized in Figure 16-8. You should compare it with the suggested basis for heterosis in hybrid tomatoes that was presented in the preceding section.

"One-Gene Heterosis" in Neurospora. A mutant strain of Neurospora, analogous to *nicotinicless* and *pantothenicless*, is deficient in the synthesis

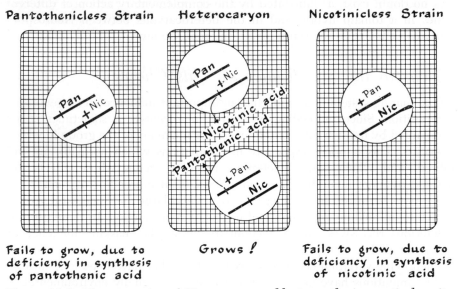

Figure 16-8. *Mutant strains of Neurospora unable to synthesize particular vitamins cannot grow on media lacking these vitamins. However, strains deficient for different vitamins may form heterocaryons and produce vigorous growth when inoculated together on these same media. This is because in the heterocaryon the different nuclei supplement each other's activities.*

of p-aminobenzoic acid, and will not grow unless this vitamin is present in its medium. A different mutant is in the peculiar condition of being sensitive to the p-aminobenzoic acid it produces; ordinarily, it fails to grow unless its medium is supplemented with sulfanilamide or some other sulfa drug which counteracts the effect of the p-aminobenzoic acid. By crossing the two strains, Sterling Emerson, of the California Institute of Technology, has obtained a double mutant carrying both the gene (*pab*) which blocks p-aminobenzoic acid synthesis, and the gene (*sfo*) whose action leads to a sulfa requirement. If the double mutant is allowed to form a heterocaryon with a strain which also carries the *sfo* gene but has the wild-type allele of *pab*, growth occurs on media containing neither sulfonamide nor p-aminobenzoic acid. Emerson's interpretation is that "growth results from a balance between the production of p-aminobenzoic acid by one type of nucleus and the lack of production by the other to give an amount tolerated by strains carrying *sfo*, yet still sufficient for growth."

Here, in contrast to the instance of heterocaryosis we examined earlier, a heterotic effect is produced by allelic diversity at a single locus. You will find the situation comparable to that in Golden barley, where heterozygosity at the locus of a chlorophyll mutant gives increased vigor. Emerson's study is important because it provides us with a clearly defined physiological mechanism for one-gene heterosis, and serves as a model for interpretations of heterosis based on allelic interaction. Other mechanisms for heterosis no doubt exist, as illustrated by the complementary action of different genes in a tomato hybrid and in the heterocaryons between Neurospora mutants deficient in the synthesis of different vitamins.

Keys to the Significance of This Chapter

The mating system of a group has an important influence on its genotypic composition. Since inbreeding promotes *homozygosis*, it sometimes is accompanied by unfavorable consequences for members of the group in which it occurs. This happens especially in populations which normally are not inbred, and which carry deleterious recessive genes whose effects are masked by more favorable dominant alleles. That inbreeding as such is not deleterious is proved by the fact that for several large and successful groups of plants inbreeding is the habitual means of reproduction. In these groups, deleterious recessives cannot accumulate under the masking influence of dominant alleles.

Phenotypic variation occurs even within lines that have been long inbred. Unless mutations have occurred, this variation is usually environmental in source and cannot be utilized as the basis for effective *selection*. Only *genetic variations* are subject to selection.

Heterozygosity is often accompanied by vigor. Whether this hybrid vigor, or heterosis, is due to interactions between alleles or to interactions of different dominant genes is not yet certain. Probably both systems operate. Precise laboratory experiments have provided us with models for the physiological bases of such systems.

References

Beadle, G. W., and Coonradt, V. L., "Heterocaryosis in *Neurospora crassa.*" *Genetics*, 29:291–308, 1944. (Deals in a succinct way with various aspects of heterocaryosis. The experimental utilization of heterocaryons to establish the dominance relations of allelic pair members in a monoploid is of particular interest.)

Crow, J. F., "Alternative Hypotheses of Hybrid Vigor." *Genetics*, 33:477–487, 1948. (A treatment based on considerations of population genetics.)

Dobzhansky, Th., "Genetics of Natural Populations. XIX. Origin of Heterosis through Natural Selection in Populations of *Drosophila pseudoobscura.*" *Genetics*, 35:288–302, 1950. (Gives evidence for heterotic effects produced by co-adapted polygene complexes in inversion heterozygotes of *D. pseudoobscura.*)

East, E. M., "Heterosis." *Genetics*, 21:375–397, 1936. (A review article. Examines certain of the conflicting ideas on heterosis, and gives an idea of the development of thought in this field.)

————, and Jones, D. F., *Inbreeding and Outbreeding.* Philadelphia: Lippincott Co., 1919. (A classic in genetics, having much more than historic interest, although written some decades ago.)

Emerson, S., "A Physiological Basis for Some Suppressor Mutations and Possibly for One Gene Heterosis." *Proc. Nat. Acad. Sci.*, 34:72–74, 1948. (The ingenious experimental analysis of a situation that has important implications for our understanding of heterosis.)

Gowen, J. W., Stadler, J., and Johnson, L. E., "On the Mechanism of Heterosis— The Chromosomal or Cytoplasmic Basis for Heterosis in *Drosophila melanogaster.*" *Am. Naturalist,* 80:506–531, 1946. (The manifestation of heterosis in egg production in Drosophila.)

Johannsen, W., *Ueber Erblichkeit in Populationen und in reinen Linien.* Jena: Gustav Fischer, 1903. (Often ranked with Mendel's paper as one of the cornerstones of modern genetics.)

Lewis, D., "Structure of the Incompatibility Gene. II. Induced Mutation Rate." *Heredity*, 3:339–355, 1949. (One of a series of articles reporting investigations of the action of *S* genes. Reference to earlier significant papers by Lewis, and others, may be found in the bibliography.)

Lindegren, C. C., "The Genetics of Neurospora. V. Self-Sterile Bisexual Heterokaryons." *J. Genetics*, 28:425–435, 1934. (The discussion on pp. 432–434 deals with the significance of heterocaryosis in evolution.)

Müntzing, A., "On the Causes of Inbreeding Degeneration." *Arch. Julius Klaus-Stiftung Vererbungsforschung, Sozialanthropol. u. Rassenhyg.* Supplementary volume to vol. 20:153–163, 1945. (A brief and readable essay, in English, touching on major aspects of inbreeding and heterosis.)

Richey, F. D., "Hybrid Vigor and Corn Breeding." *J. Am. Soc. Agron.*, 38:833–841, 1946. (Phenomena and theories of heterosis briefly reviewed, with commentary.)

Robbins, W. J., "Growth of Excised Roots and Heterosis in Tomato." *Am. J. Botany*, 28:216–225, 1941. (Experiments bearing on the physiological basis of heterosis.)

Stebbins, G. L., "Reality and Efficacy of Selection in Plants." *Proc. Am. Phil. Soc.*, 93:501–513, 1949. (A readable essay on natural selection as it relates to evolution.)

Stout, A. B., "The Genetics of Incompatibilities in Homomorphic Flowering Plants." *Botan. Rev.*, 4:275–369, 1938. (A detailed review of genetically determined incompatibilities in flowering plants.)

Suneson, C. A., "Survival of Four Barley Varieties in a Mixture." *J. Am. Soc. Agron.*, 41:459–461, 1949. (Brief report on the survival of types within a mixture of barley varieties grown over a 16-year period. Significant with reference to ideas of natural selection and survival.)

Wright, S., "The Effects of Inbreeding and Crossbreeding on Guinea Pigs." *U. S. Dept. Agr. Bull.* No. 1090, Professional Paper, 1922. (Extensive data illustrating the decline in vigor and the fixation of characteristics resulting from inbreeding.)

Questions and Problems

16- 1.   What do the following terms signify?

balanced lethal	inbred line of corn
heterocaryosis	natural selection
heterocaryotic vigor	outbreeding
heterosis	overdominance
homozygosis	pure line
hybrid vigor	self-incompatibility
inbreeding	

16- 2.   Would a law banning marriages between individuals and their step-parents be well founded on genetic principles?

16- 3.   In some lines of corn, monoploids occur with a frequency of about one per thousand sporophytes. Occasionally these monoploids produce pollen and egg cells containing complete genomes. It is possible through self-pollination of a monoploid plant to obtain a diploid line derived from a monoploid, and to maintain the line through further selfing. Would selection within such a diploid line, for size, for example, be likely to be effective? Explain your answer.

16- 4.   What is a circumstance under which inbreeding does not have deleterious consequences?

16- 5.   Demonstrate that inbreeding *per se* does not favor an increase in the frequency of recessive alleles in a population, but affects only the distribution of the alleles among genotypes.

16- 6.   Which would be more likely to carry a fair number of deleterious recessive genes: (a) a natural population representing a line of organisms that has been reproducing vegetatively over a number of generations, or (b) a natural population representing a line in which self-fertilization has been habitual? Justify your answer.

Base your answers to the next five questions on the information summarized in Figure 16-1.

16- 7. Explain how the S series of alleles fosters hybridity in a population.

16- 8. With an S_1S_3 plant as the ♂ parent, what percentage of its pollen would be able to function in a cross with an S_3S_4 ♀?

16- 9. Does one of the parental genotypes appear in the progeny of parents that cross but have one S allele in common in their genotypes? If so, is it the genotype of the pollen parent or of the seed parent?

16-10. What can be specified about the genotypes of the parents when a progeny can be separated into four self-incompatible groups, each of which is compatible with all the others?

16-11. Would you or would you not be able to make successful crosses involving each of the four groups and each of the two parents referred to in the preceding question?

16-12. Refer back to Question 15-17 and see whether you can now deal with this question in a more satisfactory way.

16-13. Discuss the implications of the fact that it has not so far been possible to isolate lines of corn that breed true for the high degree of vigor and uniformity found in hybrid corn. Include a consideration of possible reasons for this failure.

The next six questions should be considered as a sequence.

16-14. One of the first mutants discovered in Drosophila by Morgan was *beaded,* a wing character. At first it was not possible to obtain a true-breeding stock of beaded. Instead, whenever two beaded flies were mated, a progeny of about ⅔ beaded and ⅓ normal was obtained. What might account for this unusual ratio, and for the fact that true-breeding stocks of beaded could not be established?

16-15. Do the results given in the preceding question indicate that the allele for beaded is dominant or recessive? Discuss.

16-16. After a time, a stock of Drosophila that bred true for the phenotype beaded was isolated. But when these beaded flies were bred with normals, a ratio of 1 normal : 1 beaded was observed in the progeny. Was the true-breeding stock for beaded homozygous for the *Bd* allele? Explain.

16-17. Experimental analysis showed that the true-breeding beaded stock was in reality a balanced lethal system involving the allelic pairs $Bd/+$ and $l/+$, with l being a recessive lethal gene closely linked to the locus of beaded, in the third chromosome. Diagram the combination of the alleles in the homologous chromosomes 3 that is necessary if a true-breeding stock for the beaded phenotype is to be maintained *via* balanced lethals.

16-18. What change in the phenotype of the progeny would be noted if crossing over occurred between the two loci involved in this balanced lethal system?

16-19. What kind of chromosomal aberration might have the effect of suppressing, in a very effective way, crossing over between the loci of *Bd* and *l*?

16-20. Suppose that *nicotinicless* and *pantothenicless* strains of Neurospora are inoculated together onto a medium containing neither nicotinic nor pantothenic acid, and that a luxuriant mycelial growth develops. How would it be possible to tell experimentally whether the situation represented true heterocaryosis or whether the two strains were merely "cross-feeding," i.e., exchanging growth factors by way of their common medium?

16-21. Mutant strains 27947 and 29997 of Neurospora are both characterized by a deficiency in the capacity to synthesize arginine. By all biochemical criteria that have been tried, these strains are indistinguishable. Separately inoculated onto media not containing appropriate amino acid supplements, both these strains fail to grow. Inoculated together onto similar media, a mycelium is formed which grows linearly at a rate of 3.5 mm/hr. Is it possible from this result to state whether strains 27947 and 29997 represent independent mutations at the same locus having to do with arginine metabolism or whether they represent mutations at two different loci, each of which is concerned in arginine metabolism? Amplify your answer.

16-22. Corn breeders have carried out extensive programs of *convergent improvement*. Under this practice, an F_1 hybrid is backcrossed to each parental inbred over a succession of generations. At the same time, selection is carried on within each backcross line for favorable characters of the nonrecurrent parent. Which would be more homozygous, an F_1 hybrid between the original inbreds or an F_1 hybrid between "recovered inbreds" resulting from the backcross program?

16-23. Results of convergent improvement programs, referred to in the previous question, indicate that hybrids between "recovered inbreds" are at least as vigorous as hybrids between "original inbreds." Does this result suggest that heterozygosity as such determines heterosis? Discuss.

CHAPTER 17

Genes and Cellular Biochemistry

ORDINARILY we detect the presence of a gene by some phenotypic characteristic of the organism far removed from the primary activity of the gene. For example, people differ as to whether they have hair on the mid-digital segments of their fingers (excluding thumbs). The evidence available indicates that presence of mid-digital hair may be due to a single dominant gene. It is obvious that the gene involved somehow accomplishes its effect in terms of the chemistry of the organism. It is almost equally apparent that numerous and complex events intervene between the original chemical change initiated by the gene and the eventual manifestation of the character. In fact, the trail of events leading from gene to mid-digital hair appears to be so tenuous that no one knows as yet how to back-track from phenotype to gene in order to find out just what is the primary chemical action of the gene.

Most heritable characteristics that have been studied by geneticists offer the same kind of difficulties that mid-digital hair does. The phenotypic attributes that geneticists are able to detect and to work with usually give few clues as to the nature of gene action. However, in a number of special instances the activities of genes have been traced to the molecular level. This number is growing rapidly.

The Molecular Basis of Phenotype

Sickle Cell Anemia. Under the right conditions for observation, red blood cells of certain people show sickle shapes, oat shapes, and other eccentric variations from the normal disc shape. This phenomenon, called *sickling*, is found in a fairly high proportion of American Negroes. In many instances, sickling seems not to have serious consequences for an affected individual. However, some persons whose blood cells sickle are afflicted with a severe hemolytic anemia that markedly reduces their life span. This condition is called *sickle cell anemia*. The milder condition of sickling without anemia is called *sickle cell trait*. These differences appear to depend on a single pair of alleles, such that:

$$Sk \; Sk \longrightarrow \text{sickle cell anemia}$$
$$Sk \; sk \longrightarrow \text{sickle cell trait}$$
$$sk \; sk \longrightarrow \text{normal}$$

Characteristic molecular differences among normals, persons with the sickle cell trait, and sickle cell anemics can be shown if solutions of their hemoglobins are separately examined on the basis of migration in an electrical field. Hemoglobin, the oxygen-carrying component of the blood, is a complex molecule consisting of a protein and an iron-containing compound. Under appropriate experimental conditions in an electrophoresis apparatus, the hemoglobin of normals migrates toward one pole, while that of sickle cell anemics carries an opposite electrical charge and migrates toward the other pole. The hemoglobin of persons who are heterozygous for the sickling gene separates into fractions, with one fraction moving toward each pole; it behaves much as a mechanical mixture of hemoglobins taken from the two homozygous types. These relationships are shown in Figure 17-1.

Continuing investigation of different hemoglobins is adding greater complexities to this picture. However, we already have at hand the basis for drawing a conclusion of general significance. Each allele at the *sickling* locus determines a different molecular specificity, which somehow is translated into more remote phenotypic manifestations, expressed in part in the shapes of red blood cells.

Genes, Anthocyanin Molecules, and Flower Coloring. Many of our best examples of relationships between genes and biochemistry apply to phenotypic variation in color. Even an investigator who is not chemically minded must recognize that the color phenotype is founded on chemistry. And the investigator who has biochemical techniques at his command can go immediately to analyzing the pigments concerned in order to get at the molecular basis of phenotype. This kind of approach has been successfully applied to the biochemical genetics of flower color in many different plants.

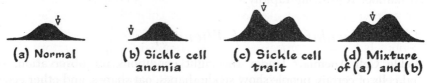

(a) Normal   (b) Sickle cell anemia   (c) Sickle cell trait   (d) Mixture of (a) and (b)

Carbonmonoxyhemoglobins in phosphate buffer pH 6.90

Figure 17-1. *The migration of hemoglobins in an electrical field. Using the arrows as points of reference, you can see that under certain conditions the hemoglobin (a) of normal persons migrates toward one pole and the hemoglobin (b) of sickle cell anemics migrates toward the other. The hemoglobin of persons with sickle cell trait behaves much the same as a mixture of a and b. (After Pauling, Itano, Singer, and Wells,* Science, *110:545, 1949.)*

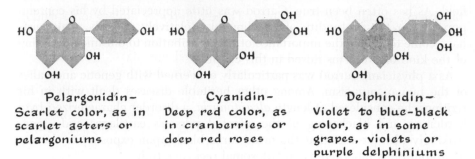

Pelargonidin—
Scarlet color, as in
scarlet asters or
pelargoniums

Cyanidin—
Deep red color, as
in cranberries or
deep red roses

Delphinidin—
Violet to blue-black
color, as in some
grapes, violets or
purple delphiniums

Figure 17-2. *The plant pigment molecules shown above differ only in the number of hydroxyl (—OH) groups on the lateral benzene ring. These simple chemical differences, important in their effect on phenotype, are determined by the activities of particular genes.*

The typical colors of flowers are largely due to a group of pigments called *anthocyanins* and to some of their chemical relatives. Anthocyanins are water soluble and may be found dissolved in the sap of certain cells of flowers, or of other plant parts. They include various red and blue pigments.

The chemical makeup of an anthocyanin consists of one or two molecules of a sugar in combination with an *anthocyanidin*, which is the portion of the anthocyanin molecule that gives color. Typical anthocyanidins are shown in Figure 17-2. The three examples, as viewed from left to right, are pigments that show increasing blueness. The molecular basis of this increasing blueness seen in the series pelargonidin, cyanidin, and delphinidin depends upon an increase in number of hydroxyl (—OH) groups on the lateral benzene ring. The substitution of —OH groups on this ring is accomplished through the activities of particular genes.

Genes affect anthocyanin pigmentation in other specific ways. Certain genes can accomplish methylation of particular hydroxyl groups on the lateral benzene ring, thus converting —OH into —OCH$_3$ groups. Other factors being constant, increased methylation of this kind results in increased redness of pigment color. The position of attachment of the sugar molecules which in nature are combined with the anthocyanidin molecules is also under genetic control and likewise influences color. A significant aspect of these examples is their indication that the basic activities of genes are not mysterious but involve processes perfectly familiar to the laboratory chemist. Genes would appear to act through simple, understandable chemical changes, for example through methylations, oxidations and reductions, and other reactions that follow the established laws of chemistry.

Alcaptonuria. In 1909, an English physician named Garrod wrote a book called *Inborn Errors of Metabolism*. The title might be paraphrased as "heritable defects in body chemistry." Garrod, at that early date in the history of genetics, was already interested in the control of specific chemical reactions by genes, a concept often thought to be among the most modern in its field. As has often been true, Garrod was little appreciated by his contemporaries for the profundity of his thought. Relatively recently, geneticists have come to realize the importance of his contribution to our understanding of the kind of problems raised in this chapter.

As a physician, Garrod was particularly concerned with genetic anomalies of the human organism. Among other heritable diseases dealt with in his writings, he considered at length *alcaptonuria,* a disorder characterized by a hardening and blackening of the affected person's cartilages and—more strikingly—by the fact that the urine turns black upon exposure to the air. Alcaptonuria is inherited as an autosomal recessive trait.

The molecular basis of alcaptonuria has been known for a long time, largely because in this disease, as in flower pigmentation, the presence of a colored substance offers a focal point for chemical analysis. In alcaptonurics, the blackness of the urine is due to the presence of an unusual component, *homogentisic acid.* The abnormality of the situation lies in the fact that homogentisic acid accumulates in the urine of alcaptonurics, whereas in normal people it is broken down into the simpler substance acetoacetic acid. This reaction is accomplished under the influence of an enzyme which is present in the blood serum of normal persons but seems to be absent from the sera of alcaptonurics. We may summarize the situation for normals and for alcaptonurics as follows:

$$\text{NORMALS:} \qquad \text{homogentisic acid} \xrightarrow[\text{(enzyme)}]{\text{gene } A} \text{acetoacetic acid}$$

$$\text{ALCAPTONURICS:} \qquad \text{homogentisic acid} \xrightarrow[\text{(no enzyme)}]{\text{gene } a} \text{(no reaction)}$$

Stepwise Metabolism Under Gene Control

So far we have been considering single genes in relation to single biochemical reactions. If our purpose is to obtain a meaningful picture of life processes, this is a great over-simplification. Neither genes nor chemical reactions occur in isolation in the cell. As a first step toward amplifying the picture, we need to ask questions such as the following: Where does homogentisic acid come from? What happens to the acetoacetic acid that is formed from homogentisic acid as the result of enzyme action?

The Sources of Homogentisic Acid. The answer to the first question is particularly enlightening. Homogentisic acid is derived from phenylalanine and tyrosine, two of the amino acids which serve as building blocks for proteins. When alcaptonurics are fed increased quantities of phenylalanine and tyrosine, there is a corresponding increase of homogentisic acid excreted in the urine. Increased consumption of phenylalanine and tyrosine by normal individuals is not followed by such an accumulation of homogentisic acid in the urine. These results are easily explained if we assume that homogentisic acid is only an intermediate stage in the normal metabolic break-down of phenylalanine and tyrosine. It represents a way station in a series of transformations leading to the final degradation of the original amino acids. In alcaptonurics, this way station becomes a final stopping place. In normal persons, acetoacetic acid, the normal conversion product of homo-gentisic acid, is another and later way station. Acetoacetic acid is ultimately transformed into the very simple substances carbon dioxide and water.

Phenylketonuria. Other way stations in the degradative metabolism of phenylalanine and tyrosine are known. Some of these have been recognized on the same basis as homogentisic acid; that is, gene mutation resulting in a block in metabolism has led to the accumulation of an intermediate sub-stance that normally would be subject to further transformation. This is clearly true in the disease *phenylketonuria,* which is inherited as a simple recessive. The major clinical condition of phenylketonuria is a type of ex-treme mental defect; affected individuals are called "phenylpyruvic idiots." This overt symptom is accompanied by the excretion of abnormally large amounts of phenylpyruvic acid in the urine. In phenylketonurics, phenyl-pyruvic acid excretion can be increased by enlarging the intake of phenyl-alanine or of phenylpyruvic acid itself. Persons with a normal gene at the locus for phenylketonuria are able to oxidize phenylpyruvic acid into the compound p-hydroxyphenylpyruvic acid. This latter substance is one of the precursors of homogentisic acid.

Over-All Picture of Phenylalanine-Tyrosine Metabolism in Man. Based on the type of information we have just presented, there has emerged a pic-ture of the degradative metabolism of phenylalanine and tyrosine in man, which is summarized in Figure 17-3. You will note that albinism, which is usually inherited as a simple recessive condition in man, finds a place in this scheme. The *melanin* compounds that are the basis of much of our pigmen-tation are derivatives of phenylalanine and tyrosine. Albinism represents a case of genetically determined inability to convert precursor substances into melanin pigments.

A fourth probable instance of genetic block in the sequence of transforma-tions pictured in the figure is represented by the disease *tyrosinosis.* Here the anomaly is inability to oxidize p-hydroxyphenylpyruvic acid. Ingestion of precursors of this compound, including tyrosine, leads to its accumulation in the urine, in the same manner as the accumulation of phenylpyruvic acid in phenylketonurics and of homogentisic acid in alcaptonurics. Since only a single individual with tyrosinosis has been studied, nothing is known about the heritability of this disease. A reasonable speculation is that tyrosinosis is the consequence of gene mutation leading to a particular block in metab-olism.

The scheme presented in Figure 17-3 is partly tentative. Its main features are almost certainly correct, but it could be made more precise and accurate

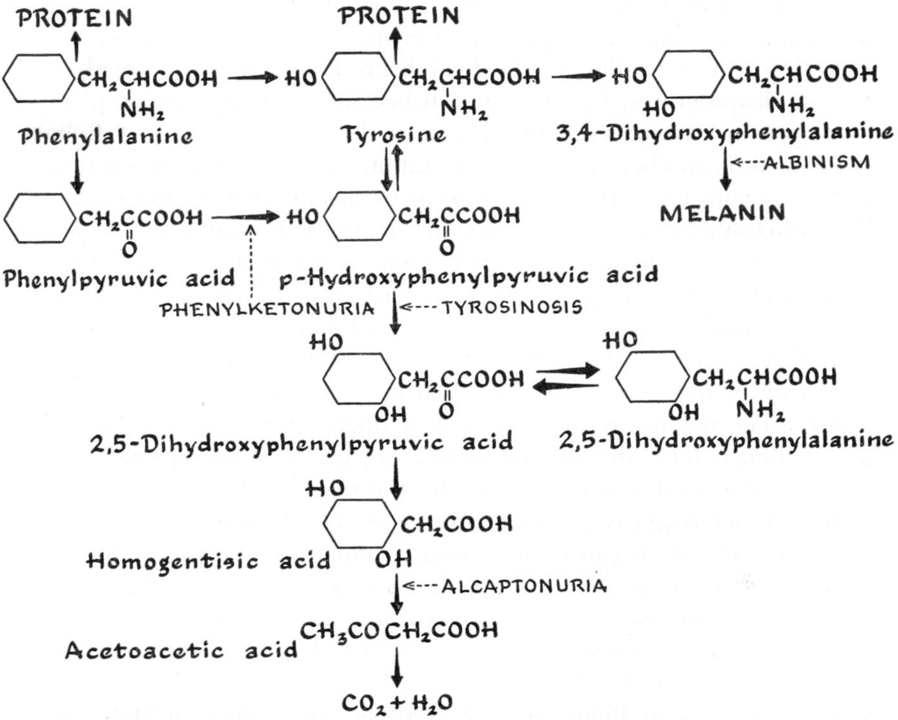

PROTEIN
↑
⬡CH₂CHCOOH → HO⬡CH₂CHCOOH → HO⬡CH₂CHCOOH
  |NH₂ |NH₂   HO |NH₂
Phenylalanine   Tyrosine   3,4-Dihydroxyphenylalanine
↓   ↕↑ |←---ALBINISM
⬡CH₂CCOOH → HO⬡CH₂CCOOH   MELANIN
    ||O ||O
Phenylpyruvic acid ┊ p-Hydroxyphenylpyruvic acid
        PHENYLKETONURIA |←--- TYROSINOSIS

        HO   HO
        ⬡CH₂CCOOH ⇌ ⬡CH₂CHCOOH
            OH ||O   OH |NH₂
2,5-Dihydroxyphenylpyruvic acid   2,5-Dihydroxyphenylalanine

            HO ↓
            ⬡CH₂COOH
Homogentisic acid   OH
                    |←---ALCAPTONURIA
                    CH₃CO CH₂COOH
Acetoacetic acid
                    ↓
                 $CO_2 + H_2O$

Figure 17-3. *Scheme for the metabolism of phenylalanine and tyrosine in man.* (After Beadle, Chem. Revs., 37:28, 1945.)

if the effects of mutation of other genes concerned in that area of metabolism could be studied. We will have to wait for such mutations to turn up in the natural course of events, since there are good reasons why persons should not be bombarded with X-rays in order to create mutations for the geneticist or biochemist to study. Amplification of the scheme may therefore come relatively slowly. Nevertheless, even as it stands, the scheme represents an important contribution to the biochemistry of man. More important than the reactions themselves are the concepts involved. Briefly, these are:

1. Metabolism occurs in stepwise fashion, with compounds being converted into other compounds in orderly sequences of transformation.
2. Specific unit processes in the chains of chemical events that make up metabolism are under the control of particular genes.
3. Mutation of genes governing such unit processes may lead to blocks at various points in the pathways of metabolism.
4. The primary consequences of such blocks may be (a) inability to produce certain compounds that are normal metabolites, and (b) accumulation of precursors normally subject to conversion into other compounds in a reaction sequence.

Nutrition and Genetic Capacity for Biosynthesis

The concepts just summarized have such far-reaching implications that it is important to affirm their validity and to discover how widely they apply. In general, the study of metabolism through genetic differences in natural populations has severe limitations. Most important of these limitations are the relatively low rate of spontaneous mutation and the fact that mutations of many genes which control vital functions are lethal. The first difficulty can be resolved by inducing mutations with agents such as X-rays, ultra-violet light, or mustard gas. The more difficult problem of identifying and preserving mutations which may ordinarily be lethal was met by G. W. Beadle and E. L. Tatum in a method of experimental approach developed at Stanford University in the early 1940's. This method is directly related to fundamental nutritional attributes of Neurospora. In principle, it applies to organisms in general.

Utilization of Minimal and Complete Media in Detecting and Preserving Biochemical Mutant Strains. Wild-type Neurospora has simple nutritional requirements. If these needs are reduced to the fewest and simplest on which the mold will grow normally, they are found to include the following: (1) certain inorganic salts; (2) some suitable carbohydrate, such as the sugar sucrose; and (3) one fairly complex organic compound, the vitamin biotin. These substances constitute the "minimal" medium of Neurospora. From this minimal medium, wild-type Neurospora can synthesize all the other components of its living substance, including amino acids, vitamins, purines, and pyrimidines. This is shown by the fact that the mold incubated on minimal medium under aseptic conditions contains all these kinds of substances in its mycelium.

Beadle and Tatum assumed that Neurospora transforms the components of minimal medium into vitamins, amino acids, and the like through orderly processes of stepwise metabolism under gene control. The basis of this assumption was the picture of phenylalanine-tyrosine metabolism in man, and other similar findings. It was thought that mutations of genes concerned in the biosynthesis of compounds essential for growth would result in new growth factor requirements for the strains in which the mutations had occurred.

Suppose, for example, that mutation should inactivate some gene that normally promotes a step in the biosynthesis of thiamine from appropriate substances in the minimal medium. Since thiamine is an essential growth substance, with many important functions in metabolism, a strain of Neurospora carrying the mutant gene would presumably be unable to grow on the minimal medium. In other words, on the minimal medium such a mutant gene would be a lethal. We have already learned, however, that "lethal" genes can sometimes be circumvented, as in the cases of albino corn fed on sugar solution or of diabetic people provided with insulin. In the same way, a mutant strain of Neurospora unable to synthesize thiamine might be preserved if thiamine were provided as a nutritional supplement to the minimal medium.

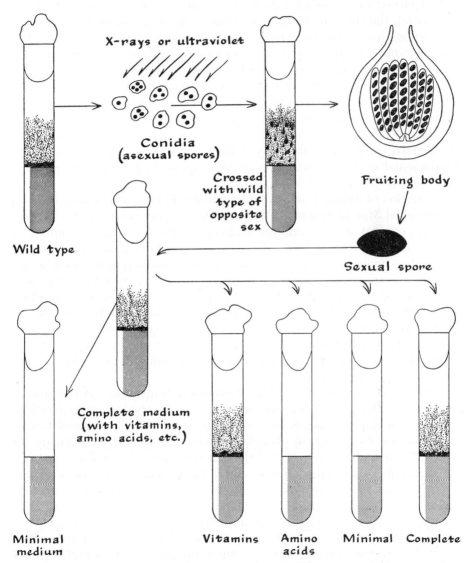

X-rays or ultraviolet

Conidia (asexual spores)

Wild type

Crossed with wild type of opposite sex

Fruiting body

Sexual spore

Complete medium (with vitamins, amino acids, etc.)

Minimal medium

Vitamins

Amino acids

Minimal

Complete

Figure 17-4. *Outline of procedure for producing, detecting, and classifying biochemical mutant strains in Neurospora. The illustration indicates production of a mutant deficient in the synthesis of some vitamin. The particular vitamin involved could be determined by inoculating the mutant strain into culture tubes containing individual vitamins such as thiamine. (After Beadle; Baitsell,* Science in Progress, *Fifth Series,* Yale University Press, *1947, p. 176.)*

With these ideas in mind, Beadle and Tatum irradiated wild-type Neurospora with the expectancy of producing mutant strains with various newly acquired nutritional needs. Anticipating that mutations of this kind would be lethal for the mold cultured on minimal medium, the investigators grew their isolates from irradiated Neurospora on so-called "complete" media. The components of complete media included yeast and malt extract, hydrolyzed casein, and other materials rich in a variety of vitamins, amino acids, and all kinds of substances which might be expected to be essential metabolites and whose biosynthesis might be interfered with by mutation. From individual cultures of this kind, transfers of conidia were made to minimal medium. Failure of such transfers to grow on the minimal medium was taken as preliminary evidence that mutation had occurred.

Out of a series of thousands of isolates from irradiated wild type, many different strains were found to be unable to grow on minimal medium although they could grow on complete media. Crosses of these strains back to wild type proved that inability to grow on minimal medium was due to gene mutation, and in most instances the growth deficiency was referrable to the locus of some single gene. Systematic investigation of the nutritional attributes of a mutant strain almost always revealed that some single substance added to the minimal medium satisfied the growth requirement. As a working hypothesis, such substances can be thought of as representing metabolites in Neurospora whose biosynthesis has been blocked in the mutant strain. The general procedure for producing, detecting, and classifying biochemical mutant strains is summarized in Figure 17-4. Table 17-1 lists a number of the different kinds of biochemical mutant strains that have been produced in Neurospora. The existence of these diverse mutant strains is substantial confirmation of the validity of the basic assumptions of Beadle and Tatum and of the soundness of their reasoning.

Utilization of Biochemical Mutant Strains in Establishing Pathways of Biosynthesis. The procedure by which wild-type Neurospora synthesizes a metabolite from the constituents of minimal medium may often be expected to include a number, sometimes a large number, of steps. If each of

TABLE 17-1. Different Biochemical Mutants of Neurospora. (Information from Houlahan, Beadle, and Calhoun, Genetics, 34:493, 495, 1949.)

THE DIFFERENT MUTANTS ARE IDENTIFIED BY THE COMPOUNDS THEY REQUIRE FOR GROWTH.	
VITAMINS	Thiamine, pyridoxin, p-aminobenzoic acid, pantothenic acid, inositol, nicotinic acid, choline, riboflavin
AMINO ACIDS	Arginine, leucine, lysine, methionine, phenylalanine, proline, threonine, tryptophane, valine, serine, histidine
OTHER COMPOUNDS	Adenine, pyrimidine, succinic acid, sulfonamide

these steps is under the control of a different particular gene, then it is conceivable that mutation at any one of several different loci might give rise to the same growth factor requirement. Assume that essential metabolite A is normally synthesized via a series of precursor substances, B, C, D. Assume also that the transformations of precursors which eventually lead to A are each under gene control. As shown below, mutation of either gene H or gene F might block the production of A and give rise to a growth factor requirement for A.

$$\text{gene } E \xrightarrow{\hspace{2cm}} \text{substance } D \xrightarrow{\text{gene } F} C \xrightarrow{\text{gene } G} B \xrightarrow[\displaystyle h]{\text{gene } H} (A)$$

$$\text{gene } E \xrightarrow{\hspace{2cm}} \text{substance } D \xrightarrow[\displaystyle f]{\text{gene } F} (C) \xrightarrow{\text{gene } G} (B) \xrightarrow{\text{gene } H} (A)$$

Although the growth factor requirement after either mutation might be satisfied by substance A, mutation at the two different loci would produce quite different sorts of biochemical situations. In the first instance (mutation of gene H), the requirement for substance A might be specific. In the second instance (where genes G and H are left intact, and where C can be converted to B and then into A if only the organism can procure some C), either C or B should be able to replace A as a growth factor supplement for the mutant strain. Many actual situations corresponding in principle to this hypothetical case have been found.

Such situations lend themselves to the experimental investigation of pathways in biosynthesis. The basis of such investigations is a study of substitutions that can be made for a growth factor requirement common to a series of genetically different biochemical mutant strains. This can be illustrated from a study of mutant strains of Neurospora unable to synthesize the amino acid arginine.

Genetic Control of the Biosynthesis of Arginine in Neurospora. Treatment of wild-type Neurospora with mutagens has produced several genetically different mutant strains each of which is characterized by a requirement for arginine. Biochemically these strains may be classified on the basis of possible substitutions that may be made for arginine in satisfying the growth factor requirement. One strain has a specific requirement for arginine; other strains grow normally if either arginine or citrulline is added to the minimal medium; still different strains are able to grow on a supplement of arginine, citrulline, or ornithine. These relationships are summarized in Table 17-2.

A logical interpretation is that the mutant genes characteristic of the different strains represent blocks at points in a metabolic pathway where their normal alleles control a biosynthetic sequence that is $\longrightarrow$ ornithine $\longrightarrow$ citrulline $\longrightarrow$ arginine. This is illustrated in Figure 17-5. Notice how

TABLE 17-2. *Growth of Mutant Strains of Neurospora. (Data from Srb and Horowitz,* J. Biol. Chem., **154:**133, *1944.)*

The values represent the dry weight in mg after 5 days on liquid minimal medium supplemented with 0.005 mM of arginine, ornithine, or citrulline.

MUTANT STRAIN NO.	ARGININE	CITRULLINE	ORNITHINE	NO SUPPLEMENT TO MINIMAL MEDIUM
21502	37.2	37.6	29.2	0.9
27947	20.9	18.7	10.5	0.0
34105	33.2	30.0	25.5	1.1
30300	37.6	34.1	0.8	1.0
33442	35.0	42.7	2.5	2.3
36703	20.4	0.0	0.0	0.0

citrulline is converted into arginine by a substitution of nitrogen for oxygen, and how the addition of —CO and —NH₂ to ornithine produces citrulline. The wild-type genes control simple chemical additions to precursor molecules until arginine is finally built up. An interesting point is that these terminal stages of arginine synthesis in Neurospora correspond closely to a sequence that had earlier been proposed as occurring in the liver of mammals. It is also interesting that a search among different lactic acid fermenting bacteria has revealed the existence of types whose growth factor requirements are the same as in the different biochemical mutant types of Neurospora. This finding, shown in Table 17-3, emphasizes that the labora-

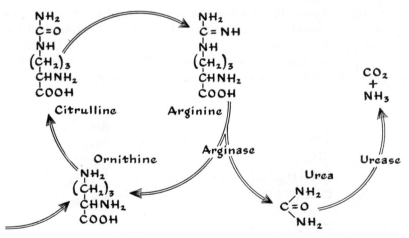

Figure 17-5. *The ornithine cycle in Neurospora. All steps in this sequence of reactions, except those involving urease and arginase, are known to be gene controlled. (After Srb and Horowitz,* J. Biol. Chem., **154:**137, *1944.)*

TABLE 17-3. Comparative Effects of Arginine and Related Compounds on Growth† of Lactobacilli in Arginine-Free Media. (After Volcani and Snell, J. Biol. Chem., 174:895, 1948.)

ORGANISM	ADDITIONS TO ARGININE-FREE MEDIA			
	None	Ornithine	Citrulline	Arginine
L. fermenti	0	+	+	+
L. casei	0	0	+	+
L. mesenteroides	0	0	0	+

† 0 = no growth; + = good growth, assuming an appropriate concentration of the supplement.

tory production of biochemical mutations in Neurospora is only an acceleration of processes that occur spontaneously in nature. In fact, loss in synthetic capacity due to gene mutation is doubtless one of the major causes of the diversity in nutritional requirements among the various kinds of organisms.

Accumulation of Precursors as the Result of Genetic Blocks in Biosynthetic Reactions. Where the reaction chains leading to the synthesis of growth factors in wild-type Neurospora are unbroken, precursor substances are seldom found in sufficient quantity to be easily detected. But when gene mutation breaks the reaction chain of a biosynthesis, precursors may accumulate behind the genetic block. This kind of situation provides remarkable opportunities for isolating and identifying intermediate substances in metabolism. A particularly good example is found in an investigation, made by N. H. Horowitz at the California Institute of Technology, of mutant strains of Neurospora unable to synthesize the amino acid methionine.

On the basis of substitutions that could be made for the methionine requirement of his several mutant strains, Horowitz first established the following genetically controlled stages in the synthesis of methionine: —→ cysteine —→ homocysteine —→ methionine. The conversion of cysteine to homocysteine provides an especially intriguing problem:

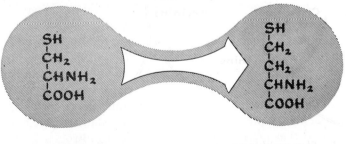

Cysteine   Homocysteine

How does cysteine become homocysteine?

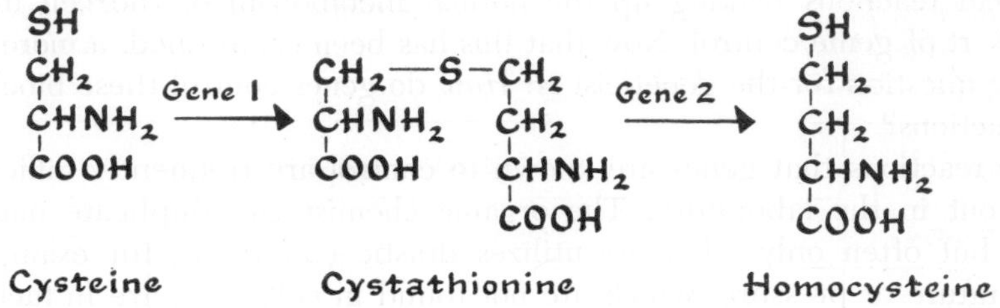

Figure 17-6. *In wild-type Neurospora, the conversion of cysteine to homocysteine is a stepwise process under genic control. A mutant strain in which gene 2 has mutated accumulates cystathionine in its culture medium. When this substance is added to minimal medium, it permits growth of a mutant strain in which gene 1 has mutated. (Based on work of Horowitz, J. Biol. Chem., 171:258, 1947.)*

Is an extra CH_2 just "slipped into" a cysteine molecule? Chemically, this would be difficult.

Two genetically different mutant strains were found to be unable to convert cysteine to homocysteine, suggesting that perhaps the transformation that normally occurs in wild type may take place as two steps, each under the control of a different gene. When it was found that one of the strains accumulates a substance on which the other can grow, this suggestion was confirmed. The substance that accumulates was isolated and identified as cystathionine. Reference to Figure 17-6 will show you the considerable ingenuity of the biochemical mechanism by which genes solve the problem of conversion of cysteine to homocysteine. The mechanism does not involve "slipping in" a CH_2 group; it involves simply condensing a 3-carbon-sulfur chain with a 4-carbon chain, then splitting the sulfur from the three carbon atoms with which it was originally associated.

Genes and Enzymes

You have just seen how the study of experimentally produced biochemical mutant strains of Neurospora provides evidence that genes control the fundamental reactions by which nutrients are converted into the various chemical constituents of the organism. Studies of this kind have now been carried out with many organisms, particularly among the bacteria, fungi, and algae, and variants similar to those produced in Neurospora have been found. Mostly these variants are characterized by requirements for particular vitamins, amino acids, or other essential growth substances. But mutants have also been found that are deficient, for example, in nitrogen fixation, in carbon dioxide fixation, in chlorophyll synthesis, or in various aspects of carbohydrate metabolism. There can be little question, then, that most of the chemical reactions making up the normal metabolism of the cell involve some sort of genic control. Now that this has been established, a more compelling question for the geneticist is: *How* do genes control these biochemical reactions?

The reactions that genes are known to control are frequently difficult to carry out in the laboratory. The organic chemist can duplicate many of them, but often only when he utilizes drastic conditions, for example of temperature or pressure, which are not found in cells, and are in fact generally incompatible with the maintenance of life. Yet these same reactions go on in cells under much less extreme circumstances. As is well known to students of biology, this is possible because the cellular reactions are promoted by efficient biological catalysts called *enzymes*.

Apparently direct associations between genes and enzymes have been demonstrated in a number of instances. For example, in rabbits a particular dominant gene determines the presence in the blood of an enzyme, atropine esterase, that promotes the molecular cleavage of atropine into tropine and tropic acid. Rabbits homozygous for the recessive allele of this gene lack demonstrable atropine esterase activity. You will remember similar situations in the comparisons of white- and yellow-fatted rabbits, of normal persons and alcaptonurics, and of cyanide-producing and noncyanide-producing clover. The general conclusion is almost inescapable that genes must control their appropriate biochemical reactions through the medium of the enzymes that catalyze these reactions.

The concept we have just expressed integrates two fundamental approaches to the nature of living things—the biochemical approach and the genetic approach. If a biochemist were asked to describe a given organism in the briefest fashion possible, he would probably reply by listing what he knew of its enzyme systems. A geneticist confronted by the same question would write out as much as he knew of the organism's genotype. Each would no doubt admit that a plant or animal is more than the sum of its enzymes, or of its genes. However, the biochemist would feel that if he knew all the enzyme systems of an organism he would not only know a good deal about its activities at the molecular level but could make successful predictions about many of its other characteristics as well. The geneticist would feel much the same way. He would say: "Tell me what its genes are, and I will tell you the potentialities of the organism." Since it is increasingly clear that genes do, and indeed must, act through the medium of enzymes, the biochemical approach and the genetic approach to the nature of living things have many objectives in common.

The One Gene-One Enzyme Hypothesis. Enzymes are generally characterized by a high degree of *specificity* of action; that is, for the most part, each enzyme is active in promoting but a single kind of biochemical transformation. Many individual genes have been shown to have this same sort of specificity for biochemical reactions. Some geneticists have even suggested that genes may act directly as enzymes. But since certain gene-controlled biochemical reactions are known to be catalyzed by extranuclear enzymes, it seems too simple to suppose that genes in general exercise their catalytic function in metabolism by direct action. Nevertheless, the close association between certain genes and certain biochemical reactions does suggest that these genes may be rather directly responsible for the specificities of the enzymes that catalyze such reactions. The large number of cases where a particular gene mutation in Neurospora has been found to give rise to a growth factor requirement by blocking a single reaction in a biosynthesis is especially suggestive. Chiefly on the basis of this kind of finding, Horowitz has phrased a *one gene-one enzyme hypothesis,* as follows: "A large class of genes exists in which each gene controls the synthesis of, or the activity of, but a single enzyme."

The one gene-one enzyme hypothesis should not be taken to imply that a single gene working by itself can produce an enzyme. Enzymes are complex substances, composed at least in part of protein. Presumably an enzyme molecule is built up through stepwise processes in which many genes take part, since we know that even the amino acids that make up protein are synthesized in this fashion. The one-to-one relationship is thought of as existing between an enzyme and the gene that imparts the final molecular configuration that determines the enzyme's specificity.

How a gene might impart specificity to an enzyme is speculative. One idea is that the specificities both of genes and of enzymes reside in their surface properties. Genes, then, might act as master molecules, or templates, for enzyme production. You may be able to visualize this idea a little more effectively by thinking in terms of a vastly oversimplified model. Think of genes as having surfaces something like waffle grids, with each gene having a different grid pattern. Then think of the stuff of which enzymes are made as having something of a doughlike plasticity. If anything like this situation were true, genes, by coming into contact with the stuff of which enzymes are made, could impart specificities by determining particular surface configurations. The model we have used is not quite so exotic as it sounds, since some biological systems seem to operate on something closely resembling the waffle iron principle. Antigens, for example, are believed to determine complementary surfaces on their corresponding antibodies, perhaps by impressing their own surface configurations onto the plastic globulin proteins of which antibodies are made, or onto enzymes responsible for globulin synthesis, or onto "models" involved in the production of such enzymes.

Complexities in the Relationships of Genes, Enzymes, and Metabolism. The one gene-one enzyme hypothesis is a useful way of visualizing certain relationships between heredity and metabolism. Whether the relationships implied by this hypothesis hold for genes in general cannot yet be decided with certainty. Some geneticists feel that the experimental basis on which the hypothesis rests is too specialized to justify generalizations at this time.

Most of the evidence for the one gene-one enzyme hypothesis comes from biochemical mutants, like those of Neurospora, where mutation of single genes has interfered with single metabolic functions. It can be questioned whether the usual methods for detecting and preserving biochemical mutants provide the geneticist with a cross section of the different kinds of mutant forms that might be obtained, or whether these methods act selectively in favor of mutants whose characteristics are compatible with the one gene-one enzyme hypothesis. Conceivably, a single gene might determine the specificities of more than one enzyme. Mutation of such a gene might then lead to multiple growth factor requirements. The difficulties of anticipating all of these in a complete medium, and supplying the appropriate substances in available form and suitable concentration, might well be so great that such mutations would seldom be preserved. If this were true, our present picture of relationships between genes, enzymes, and metabolism would be far from complete.

Some instances of single gene mutations giving rise to dual or multiple growth factor requirements have been found. One of these, in Neurospora,

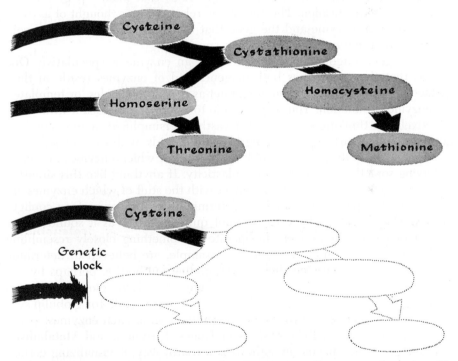

Figure 17-7. *Above, the normal course of threonine-methionine synthesis in wild-type Neurospora. Below, the effects of a genetic block prior to the synthesis of homoserine. Since homoserine serves as a precursor for both methionine and threonine, mutation at a single locus can give rise to an apparent dual growth factor requirement.* (*After Horowitz,* Advances in Genetics, *3:48, 1950.*)

involves a mutant strain having a nutritional requirement for both methionine and threonine, another amino acid. Close analysis of the situation has shown, however, that the biosynthesis of these amino acids has a common step, in which the compound homoserine serves as a precursor for methionine and for threonine also. When minimal medium is supplemented with homoserine alone, the nutritional requirements of the mutant strain are satisfied. By examining Figure 17-7 you will see how a genetic block that prevents the formation of a common precursor substance can give rise to apparently dual or multiple growth factor requirements.

There is another kind of situation where a genetic block that primarily affects a single biochemical reaction may lead to more than one growth factor requirement or to multiple derangements in metabolism. As you have seen several times before, genetic interference with a biochemical reaction may result in the piling up of substances that normally take part in the reaction. Sometimes such accumulated substances participate in unexpected side reactions and disturb normal metabolic processes in various ways. A puzzling case of this kind has been elucidated by the investigations of David Bonner. Among single gene mutant strains of Neurospora is one having a growth factor requirement for two amino acids, isoleucine and valine. Not only are both substances required but they must be supplied in a particular ratio of one to the other. At first glance, this might seem to indicate a deviation from the usual one gene-one biochemical reaction relationship. But Bonner has shown it to be highly probable that the primary effect of the gene mutation is to block only a single reaction—conversion of a precursor substance into isoleucine. Accumulation of this precursor behind the genetic block inhibits a second reaction, by which valine is normally made from one of its precursors (Fig. 17-8).

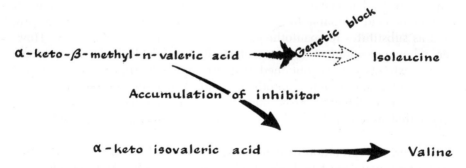

Figure 17-8. *A double growth factor requirement arising from a single gene mutation in Neurospora. Gene mutation results in an inability to transform a precursor compound into the amino acid isoleucine. The precursor accumulates and acts as an inhibitor of the biological synthesis of another amino acid, valine. Thus the mutant strain requires both isoleucine and valine in its culture medium.* (After Bonner, Cold Spring Harbor Symp. Quant. Biol., 11:19, 1946.)

The foregoing examples show you how dual growth factor requirements arising from single gene mutations are not necessarily incompatible with a primary relationship between one gene and one biochemical reaction. On the other hand, various findings suggest that a single gene may control the activity of more than one enzyme or that the activity of a single enzyme may be the concern of more than one gene. In the ascomycete Glomerella, several loci are involved in the genetic control of tyrosinase activity. Moreover, there is evidence from the same organism that a single gene mutation affects both tyrosinase activity and the activity of an enzyme concerned with the biosynthesis of tryptophane. Lactase production both in Neurospora and in the bacterium *Escherichia coli* seems to be under the control of several genes. In Neurospora, Yanofsky has shown that mutation of a single gene results in the loss of tryptophan desmolase activity but that a suppressor mutation at a different locus restores the enzyme. However, for the suppressor to restore the enzyme a particular allele must be present at the locus of the original block. Whether or not these different cases are truly irreconcilable with a one gene-one enzyme hypothesis will be resolved only when more is known about many things, including the nature of enzyme specificity.

An additional enigmatic complexity in the relationships of genes with enzymes should be mentioned. In at least two instances in Neurospora, gene mutation affects an enzyme system in such fashion that it does not operate in the living organism but can function when isolated from the organism and studied in test tube experiments. This curious kind of situation was first found by Wagner, of the University of Texas, in a mutant strain with a growth requirement for pantothenic acid, which is a member of the B vitamin complex. The facts in the case are as follows: (1) The immediate precursors of pantothenic acid are pantoyl lactone and β-alanine, which unite under specific enzyme catalysis in wild-type Neurospora to produce the pantothenic acid molecule. (2) The mutant strain with a requirement for pantothenic acid is unable to grow if pantoyl lactone and β-alanine are provided as substitutes for pantothenic acid in the culture medium. (3) However, when mycelium of the mutant strain has been killed with acetone, enzyme extracts can be obtained that are active in transforming pantoyl lactone and β-alanine into pantothenic acid. And under proper conditions, enzyme can be detected in the mutant mold *in vivo*. These findings might suggest that mutation has led to some minor modification of the wild-type enzyme.

However, interpretation of gene-enzyme relationships in the pantothenic acid mutant again must be hedged with uncertainty. It is not entirely clear whether the enzyme itself has been altered in the mutant strain, or whether an inhibitor acts on the enzyme, or whether some other possibility holds. It is clear that for the eventual clarification of gene-enzyme relationships, investigators will need to explore in several directions. These explorations promise to be fruitful in elaborating the nature of life processes.

Keys to the Significance of This Chapter

The various phenotypic differences of organisms must all be based on biochemical differences. Therefore, insofar as genes control phenotype, they must be acting to control the biochemistry of the organism.

Where gene action has been successfully analyzed in terms of biochemistry, genes appear to function by controlling particular biochemical reactions.

Metabolism occurs as interrelated chains of biochemical reactions, with genes controlling individual steps in these reaction chains.

When mutation inactivates a gene that normally governs some biochemical reaction, two primary consequences may occur: (a) deficiency of the normal reaction product; (b) accumulation of substances that normally participate in the reaction.

Genic control of biochemical reactions has been effectively studied with the use of mutant strains of microorganisms that have lost the power to synthesize essential metabolites.

The control of biochemical reactions by genes is probably achieved through the medium of enzymes.

Some evidence favors the hypothesis that the primary function of a single gene is to control the specificity of some particular enzyme.

The complexity of metabolism is so great that only a beginning has been made in studying the relationships of genes to cellular biochemistry.

References

Beadle, G. W., "Biochemical Genetics." *Chem. Rev.*, **37**:15–96, 1945. (Giving nearly complete coverage of the field of biochemical genetics to 1945, this is a valuable and authoritative review.)

————, "Genes and Biological Enigmas," Chapter 9 in *Science in Progress*, Sixth Series, pp. 184–249. New Haven: Yale University Press, 1949. (Sound treatment of the subject at a nonspecialized level.)

————, "Chemical Genetics," in *Genetics in the 20th Century*, pp. 221–239. New York: Macmillan Co., 1951. (A general discussion of major problems in the field.)

Bonner, D., "Biochemical Mutations in Neurospora." *Cold Spring Harbor Symposia Quant. Biol.*, **11**:14–24, 1946. (In the discussion with Delbrück, pp. 22–23, fundamental issues concerning genes and enzymes are raised.)

————, "Genes as Determiners of Cellular Biochemistry." *Science*, **108**:735–739, 1948. (An informal essay, in part bearing on relationships between genes and enzymes.)

Biochemical Aspects of Genetics. Biochem. Soc. Symp. No. 4. Cambridge: The University Press, 1950. (A series of brief reviews of various aspects of biochemical genetics, all pertinent to this chapter.)

Davis, B., "The Isolation of Biochemically Deficient Mutants of Bacteria by Means of Penicillin." *Proc. Nat. Acad. Sci.*, 35:1–10, 1949. (Describes an ingenious use for penicillin in screening biochemical mutants from nonmutants in populations of bacteria that have been exposed to a mutagen.)

Emerson, S., "Competitive Reactions and Antagonisms in the Biosynthesis of Amino Acids by Neurospora." *Cold Spring Harbor Symposia Quant. Biol.*, 14:40–48, 1950. (A healthful antidote to ideas that relationships between genes and metabolism are always straightforward and simple.)

Fries, N., "Experiments with Different Methods of Isolating Physiological Mutations of Filamentous Fungi." *Nature*, 159:199, 1947. (Brief description of a method for obtaining concentrations of biochemical mutants in relatively small populations of the mold Ophiostoma.)

Garrod, A. E., *Inborn Errors of Metabolism*. London: Oxford University Press, 1909. (This book and its second edition, 1923, represent the beginnings of biochemical genetics.)

Gray, G. W., "Sickle-Cell Anemia." *Sci. American*, 185: No. 2, 56–59, 1951. (A popular treatment, accompanied by good photomicrographs of sickle and normal blood cells.)

Haldane, J. B. S., "The Biochemistry of the Individual," in *Perspectives in Biochemistry*. Cambridge: The University Press, 1937. (A brief but brilliant and prophetic treatment of the scope and meaning of biochemical genetics.)

Horowitz, N. H., "Biochemical Genetics of Neurospora." *Advances in Genetics*, 3:33–71, 1950. (Summarizes briefly but meaningfully all of the major studies in this field to 1950.)

Lawrence, W. J. C., and Price, J. R., "The Genetics and Chemistry of Flower Colour Variation." *Biol. Rev.*, 15:35–58, 1940. (Gives a balanced picture of progress in one of the first areas of biochemical genetics to be explored.)

Sawin, P. B., and Glick, D., "Atropinesterase, a Genetically Determined Enzyme in the Rabbit." *Proc. Nat. Acad. Sci.*, 29:55–59, 1943. (A brief research report.)

Schopfer, W. H., *Plants and Vitamins*. Waltham: Chronica Botanica, 1943. (Chap. 19 deals with the genetic capacity for synthesis and the effect of its loss in relation to the evolution of microorganisms.)

Scott-Moncrieff, R., "A Biochemical Survey of Some Mendelian Factors for Flower Colour." *J. Genetics*, 32:117–170, 1936. (Detailed coverage of the field.)

Wagner, R. P., and Haddox, C. H., "A Further Analysis of Pantothenicless Mutants of Neurospora." *Am. Naturalist*, 85:319–330, 1951. (Details and discussion of an important investigation of gene-enzyme relationships in Neurospora.)

Wright, S., "The Physiology of the Gene." *Physiol. Revs.*, 21:487–527, 1941. (Cogent and penetrating. The original treatment of "Theories of Dominance and Factor Interaction," pp. 514–520, is particularly important.)

Questions and Problems

17- 1. Define or specifically identify the following: (*continued on p. 370*)

anthocyanin	enzyme
complete medium	enzyme specificity

A. E. Garrod   minimal medium
inborn errors of metabolism   one gene-one enzyme hypothesis
genetic block in metabolism   one gene-one reaction relationship
growth factor requirement   precursor substance

17- 2. In many areas of genetics, studies of man have been rather unproductive as compared with studies of certain other organisms. What may account for the fact that human genetics has been relatively productive of information bearing on our understanding of relationships of genes and biochemistry?

17- 3. Would you expect that alcaptonurics given large amounts of phenylpyruvic acid in their food would excrete increased amounts of homogentisic acid in their urine? Given *p*-hydroxyphenylpyruvic acid? Acetoacetic acid? Explain your answers.

17- 4. Penicillium does not require biotin in its culture medium as Neurospora does. Is this a reason for thinking that biotin plays no role in the cellular biochemistry of Penicillium? Amplify your answer.

17- 5. Why is Neurospora not suitable for studying the biosynthesis of biotin by means of mutant strains?

17- 6. Among mutants of Neurospora, two are known that require choline supplements to their media. In each strain, the growth factor requirement is the effect of a single gene mutation. Strain 1 can grow if either monomethylaminoethanol or dimethylaminoethanol is substituted for choline. Strain 2 can grow on the dimethyl compound but not the monomethyl; however, it does accumulate this latter compound in media in which it grows. Suggest an outline scheme for the biosynthesis of choline in Neurospora.

17- 7. Assume that among microorganisms in general the pattern of biosynthesis of thiamine is as follows:

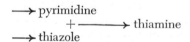

All microorganisms utilize thiamine in their metabolism. Some can make it according to the scheme outlined above; others must have it provided among their nutrients. Among the latter, certain ones are able to grow if provided with a particular fraction of the thiamine molecule. Thus Mucor is able to grow either on thiamine or on its thiazole fraction; Rhodotorula either on thiamine or on its pyrimidine fraction; Phycomyces either on thiamine or on a combined supplement of pyrimidine plus thiazole; while Glaucoma has a specific requirement for the intact thiamine molecule. Show how gene mutation might readily explain each of the different growth factor requirements noted above.

17- 8. Suppose that you have been conducting a search for biochemical mutant strains of Neurospora. After treating wild type with nitrogen mustard, you isolate a strain unable to grow on minimal medium. You can find no single substance which permits growth when added to minimal medium, but the addition of two separate compounds does satisfy the growth requirement of this strain. What different biochemical genetic situations might account for your finding?

17- 9. It has been only rather recently discovered that certain strains of bacteria can be crossed. Before this discovery, however, investigators found that treatment of bacteria with X-rays, mustard gas, and ultraviolet light produced strains with growth factor deficiencies, e.g., for phenylalanine, biotin, and methionine. How would this finding bear on the question: Do bacteria have genes?

17-10. To give us a more vivid conception of gene action, geneticists have sometimes drawn analogies between genes and factory workers along assembly lines. Detail such an analogy on the basis of what you have learned in this chapter about gene action. Are there points at which your analogy breaks down?

17-11. Can you suggest a better analogy for gene action than the one suggested in the preceding question?

17-12. Might the many known albino and virescent mutants of corn be useful in studying the biosynthesis of chlorophyll? Discuss.

17-13. Thus far no sexual stage has been found in the life cycle of Penicillium. As compared with a mold like Neurospora, which can reproduce sexually, would Penicillium be well suited for each of the following types of study? Tell why, in as specific terms as possible.

    a. The production of biochemical mutant strains.
    b. Study of the rate of production of induced biochemical mutants.
    c. Studies bearing on the one gene-one enzyme hypothesis.
    d. The establishment of biosynthetic pathways through the investigation of biochemical mutant strains.
    e. The establishment of linkage groups.
    f. Analysis of induced chromosomal aberrations.

17-14. A Neurospora mutant was found initially to require a supplement of leucine to the minimal medium. However, after long laboratory culture it was found sometimes to grow on media lacking leucine. Among possible explanations of this phenomenon are: (a) back-mutation of the mutant gene to wild type; (b) mutation at another locus which "suppresses" the effect of the original mutant gene; (c) physiological "adaptation" involving no genetic change; (d) contamination of the mutant cultures with wild-type Neurospora. Outline a series of systematic experiments you might perform to determine which of these possibilities is the correct explanation.

17-15. Substances sometimes accumulate behind metabolic blocks that result from gene mutation. How might this provide insight into the fact that a single gene may have multiple phenotypic effects?

17-16. Suggest two other types of biochemical genetic situations that would provide possibilities for multiple phenotypic effects resulting from a single gene mutation.

17-17. In Chapter 4 you were introduced to certain modifications of the 9:3:3:1 phenotypic ratio that result from interactions between nonallelic genes. Outline a generalized gene-controlled reaction system that would account for a 9:7 ratio.

17-18. Outline a generalized gene-controlled reaction system that would account for a 9:3:4 ratio.

CHAPTER 18

Genes and Development

In THE PRECEDING chapter we considered some of the ways in which genes appear to be related to the biochemical processes that occur in cells. Gene differences are reflected at the cellular level in different capacities for biochemical synthesis and degradation. Much remains to be learned, through current and future research, about the precise mechanisms by which genes affect these cellular potentialities.

In this chapter we shall turn to an even more complex, and perhaps correspondingly more challenging, level of genic effects. In multicellular individuals, how do genes affect the processes of growth and differentiation, and the functions of the individual as an organism?

An answer to this question, in terms of what we have already learned, may at first appear obvious. If it is true that genes in some way control the biochemical reactions that occur in cells, they must also control the growth, differentiation, and continuing function of the individual which depend ultimately on these same biochemical processes. The genes, therefore, must affect the development and physiology of the organism through their effects on the specific biochemistry of the cells of which the organism is built.

But new complexities arise when we turn to the level of the organism. These are apparent in two sets of facts, which when placed side by side seem incompatible:

The multicellular individual is typically an integrated collection of very diverse cells. These cells differ visibly, chemically, structurally, and functionally. They all originate from a single cell, the zygote.

We presume that successive mitotic divisions generally provide all the somatic cellular progeny of a fertilized egg with the same chromosomal and genic constitution. If the genes in these cells are to be considered identical, how can they be responsible for the cellular differences?

There can be little doubt that variations *among individuals* are often based on gene differences, responsible for the characteristics of individual biochemistry. But how are we to explain the variations from cell to cell that exist *within an individual?*

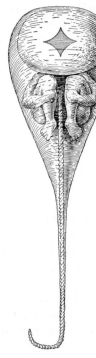

Figure 18-1. *Some early biologists thought they could see a miniature man within each sperm head. (After* A History of Biology, Re- *vised Edition,* A General Introduc- tion to the Study of Living Things, *by Charles Singer, Henry Schuman, Inc., Publishers, p. 499; from Hart- soeker, 1694.)*

Development Is Epigenetic, and Genes Act in Epigenetic Systems. One of the historic advances in biological thought came with the recognition that development is not a matter of simple enlargement of a preformed germ, complete in all its parts (Fig. 18-1). Rather, development is *epigenetic.* The individual is built and continuously rebuilt anew, beginning with the materials provided him by the fertilized egg and by his environ- ment. Through a steady and subtle succession of changes, the organism at any given time is a system in flux. It is modified from a state prevailing in its past, and upon which the present system has been built, toward a state that will transiently characterize its future, and that will in turn be built upon the present system.

The details of this building and rebuilding process are determined by the materials present at each stage of development and by the time and manner in which these materials become available. Development, from this point of view, does not stop at some arbitrary stage in the life of the individual; it is coincident with life, and an individual that has stopped developing is dead.

A complex network of interrelated processes generally interposes between the *gene,* on the one hand, and the *final phenotype,* on the other. What reactions and interactions are possible for the product of any gene, in any cell or group of cells, must depend in large part on the substrates and interactants that the previous history and present circumstances of the cell have introduced into its composition. Thus, the effective action of any gene at any particular time in development and at any particular place in the individual may often depend on the pattern already established at that time and place.

Given some material difference between two cells in a developing individual, the identical nuclei of these cells may have quite different effects on the forms and functions the cells assume. For example, consider a gene A, governing the specificity of an enzyme E_A, which acts on substrate S_A, converting it to product P_A:

$$\text{gene } A$$
$$\downarrow$$
$$\longrightarrow \text{ substrate } S_A \xrightarrow{\text{enzyme } E_A} \text{ product } P_A \longrightarrow$$

The formation of P_A in any cell having E_A will depend on the availability of S_A in that cell and on the prevalence of local conditions permitting E_A to act as shown. If the difference between the two cells we are considering includes a difference in the amount of S_A present, or a difference in whatever conditions or materials may be necessary for gene A to affect the formation of E_A, or in conditions or materials influencing the action of E_A, then the amount of specific product formed will very probably be different in the two cells. The fact that the two cells both have the same gene, A, is only part of the story; the gene must act under similar circumstances and in similar cellular environments to have similar effects on the two cells. Differences in these circumstances or environments can be expected to have immediate effects on the nature and amount of the products of nuclear action.

Furthermore, very widespread and profound differences may eventually result from a relatively simple beginning of the sort we have just been considering. If, for example, the product P_A is involved in other cell reactions—as it is very likely to be—then these in turn will be affected by the amount of P_A produced. These dependent reactions may affect others, and these others, until the structure and metabolism of the two original cells, and of their cellular progeny, are very different. All this can occur in spite of the continued *genetic* identity of the two cell lines.

A primary goal in understanding the genetic basis of differentiation is to search out how initial differences, even minor ones, may become established among the cellular progeny of a fertilized egg.

The Egg as an Organized System. Because the egg is a single cell, we may be tempted to consider it a simple, rather homogeneous blob of protoplasm except for the nucleus it contains. In all probability, nothing could be further from the truth. We know from the study of unicellular plants and animals that a high degree of internal differentiation can be achieved by single cells. Protozoa, for example, typically have visible "organelles" that perform within the single cell the specialized functions of life delegated to whole organs and organ systems in multicellular animals. There is good reason to believe that eggs are also organized into precise patterns.

Granted an inhomogeneous egg, we can observe that a division of this egg need not give identical products. The mitotic mechanism, with its vir-

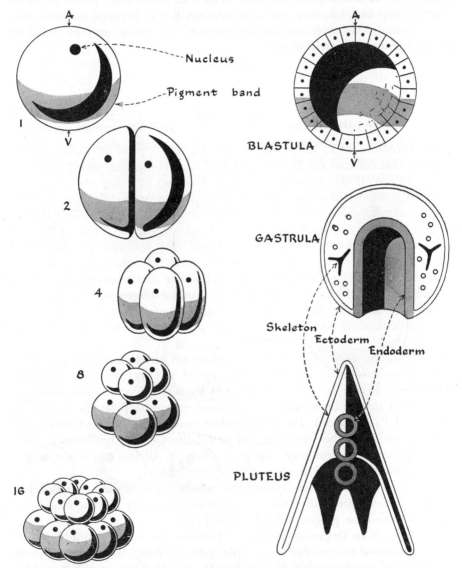

Figure 18-2. *The egg of a certain species of sea urchin has a subequatorial band of pigment. This can be traced through successive cleavage divisions, and even through the blastula and gastrula stages until the embryo becomes the type of larva called the* pluteus. (*After Barth,* Embryology, *Dryden, 1949, p. 26.*)

tual guarantee of *nuclear* identity in the daughter cells, offers no similar guarantee of identity in *cytoplasmic* materials. On the contrary, it is a matter of simple observational fact that certain materials are regularly distributed unequally to the daughter cells at particular points in development.

The egg of a certain species of sea urchin, for example, has a subequatorial band of red pigment granules (Fig. 18-2). These granules stay in place during early development, and they can be observed and followed as indicators of the way in which the original egg cytoplasm is divided up among the daughter cells when the egg cleaves. You will note that the first cleavage plane is so oriented as to produce two similar daughter cells, and the second divisions also occur along the symmetrical axis. The next divisions, however, are at right angles to the first two, and the pigment bands record the inclusion of the part of the original egg cytoplasm marked by the pigment into the *lower* cells of the figure, while the *upper* cells are essentially free of this material. As development proceeds, these different cell types diverge further, the derivatives of each part of the original egg cytoplasm regularly making unique contributions to the developing individual.

It is possible, simply by shaking the embryo at the four-cell stage in calcium-free sea water, to separate the cells without injuring them. When this is done (Fig. 18-3), each of the four isolated cells develops into a sea urchin larva that is normal except for being about a quarter of the usual size.

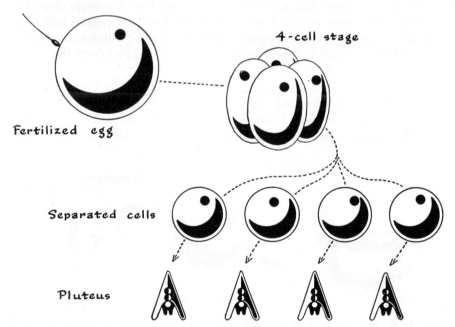

Figure 18-3. *Each of the four cells formed by the first two cleavage divisions in the sea urchin, when separated from the others, can form a complete embryo. (After Barth, Embryology, Dryden, 1949, p. 8.)*

Animal half

Dauerblastula

Figure 18-4. *If a sea urchin egg is cut in two at right angles to the symmetrical axis, the top (animal) half when fertilized develops into a hollow, ciliated ball of cells.* (*After Barth,* Embryology, *Dryden, 1949, p. 29.*)

In contrast to this experiment, eggs can be cut in two at right angles to the symmetrical axis, and the "top" (*animal*) or "bottom" (*vegetal*) halves fertilized separately. (The position of the nucleus varies in different eggs, so it can be included in either half when the egg is cut.) The embryo that results from fertilization of the animal half (Fig. 18-4) is unable to develop the internal tissues characteristic of the normal larva; it becomes a hollow ball of cells with long cilia, with which it swims about for many days, but then it dies. The embryo that develops from the fertilized vegetal half of an egg is also incomplete and abnormal. However, it differentiates much more than, and becomes very different from, an embryo deriving from the animal half (Fig. 18-5).

The observations illustrated in Figures 18-3, 18-4, and 18-5 appear to tell a consistent story. A sea urchin egg is organized in some material fashion, along a central axis running from the vegetal to the animal pole. This axis is at right angles to the pigment band. The first two cleavage planes run

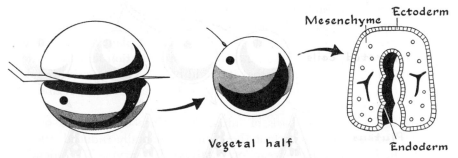

Mesenchyme Ectoderm

Vegetal half

Endoderm

Figure 18-5. *The vegetal half of a sea urchin egg, under the conditions of Figure 18-4, develops into a complex but incomplete embryo.* (*After Barth,* Embryology, *Dryden, 1949, p. 29.*)

along this axis, and the four cells formed are essentially alike with regard to their visible contents, and like the egg in their organization. It need not be surprising, therefore, that any one of these four cells can give rise to a qualitatively normal embryo. The next divisions in normal development, however, are at right angles to the first two, and the resulting daughter cells are visibly different in their cytoplasmic contents. Different materials are included in the cytoplasm of the two daughter cells of these divisions, and these materials appear to play a determining role in the direction that these cells and their cellular progeny will take in differentiation.

If you will refer back to the basis of initial divergence diagrammed on page 374, you can see how the dissimilarity of the cytoplasms of the cells formed by cleavage of the egg may affect differentiation. As the inhomogeneous egg is partitioned by successive divisions, various kinds and amounts of substrates are offered the gene products in different cells. In our model, S_A may be present in relatively unlimited amounts in some cells; it may be present but limited in others, and absent in others. Some of the eventual effects of such differences on the differentiation of the genetically identical cells will be obvious to you.

Inhomogeneity of Environment. As successive divisions increase the number of cells formed from the fertilized egg, the immediate environment of some of these cells will differ from that of others. For example, some will be on the surface, with relatively free access to oxygen, water, salts, and other materials reaching them through the egg membranes, and with similarly free access to a large external reservoir for the disposal of soluble wastes. Others will be covered by the surface cells and buried among their neighbors, dependent on them for whatever external materials may be passed on to them. The cells below the surface, on the other hand, will often have more generous supplies of the stored materials of the yolk. It is easy to conceive that the metabolic mechanisms established in these interior cells, under conditions of limited oxygen but virtually unlimited food supplies, are likely to be quite different from those established at the surface. Somewhat similarly, in the seed plants, physiological gradients are set up along lines radiating from the vascular supply to the developing seed.

So diverse are the environments in which different plant and animal eggs develop, and so varied are the kinds of egg organization and the patterns followed in early development, that it would be difficult to generalize about the nature of the environmental gradients that are established, or about the effects of these gradients.

Referring again to the basis of initial divergence diagrammed on page 374, you can see how important these environmentally induced gradients may be. If, for instance, the reaction catalyzed by enzyme E_A depends on the oxygen available to the cell, then the rate of formation of the product P_A, and the amount formed, may be quite different in surface and interior cells. This is then likely to have widespread effects on the later history of these cells and their descendants.

You will be able to postulate a great variety of similar effects on development that result from the environmental gradients that we have suggested and others that may occur to you.

Genes and the Organization of the Egg Cytoplasm. Our simplified discussion of the cytoplasmic organization of a sea urchin egg is a very small sample indeed of the work in descriptive and experimental embryology bearing on this subject. The eggs of different species differ greatly in the nature and degree of inhomogeneity so far detected in their cytoplasm. This minimum example, however, may be regarded as having achieved its primary purpose. It suggests that during cleavage various materials of the egg cytoplasm are separated into different presumptive parts of the developing embryo. At the same time, the immediate environments of cells in different parts of the embryo are becoming diverse. These facts offer a reasonable basis for understanding how the cells of the developing individual, assumed to be genetically identical, may nevertheless diverge in form and function.

If the organization of the egg cytoplasm has an important role in initial development, then the mechanisms through which this precise organization is achieved become important to us here. Such experimental criteria as exist suggest that the genetic constitution of the female producing the eggs may play a significant part in determining the pattern of this organization. One of the most pertinent examples is the "maternal effect" on the direction of coiling in snail shells described in Chapter 13. You will recall that a pattern appears to be imposed upon the egg by the maternal genotype, perhaps during the time when the primary öocyte, having the same nuclear constitution as the somatic cells, is developing under the control of its own nucleus. This inherent pattern is expressed in the planes of the first two cleavage divisions, which determine whether the developing shell will coil dextrally or sinistrally. It is not affected by the genotype of the sperm that functions in fertilization of the egg, or by the genotype of the zygote.

Examples of precise genic effects on the organization of egg cytoplasm as clear as that of snail shell coiling are rare. This is to be expected, because most mutations causing sharp changes in this fundamental characteristic would have profound early effects on the developmental patterns of the embryos, and would be likely to result in embryos so aberrant as to be inviable. Perhaps the patterns are affected by numerous genes with individually small effects, and therefore are not often subject to analysis as qualitative characteristics.

In Chapter 13, we indicated that true cytoplasmic inheritance, based on self-duplicating cytoplasmic particles, might be concerned with differentiation. This possibility is at present highly debatable. It has neither been established nor ruled out by experimental evidence. It should be clear from our preceding discussion, however, that a basis for understanding how differentiation might occur does not require the postulation of "plasmagenes."

Genic and Developmental Differences Among Individuals

The preceding part of this chapter has been devoted mainly to an attempt to understand how the cells of *any particular individual,* assumed to be genetically identical, may nevertheless become different in form and function. We now turn to development in *genetically different individuals.* It is from this kind of consideration that most of our information about the role of genes in development has been derived.

Refer once more to the basis of initial divergence suggested on page 374. We have seen how local environmental conditions and the cytoplasmic segregation of substrates and interactants can affect profoundly the course of gene-directed reactions in differentiating tissues of a single individual. In every connection, so far, we have assumed that gene A, which we have diagrammed as acting through enzyme E_A, remained the same in all these cells. We made this assumption because we have as yet no reason to believe that changes in genes or chromosomes in the developing tissues of an individual have any general or consistent causal relationship to normal differentiation.

Now, when we trace developmental pathways in different individuals, an additional, powerful tool is placed in our hands. We can compare the developmental effects of gene A with the effects of an alternative form of this gene, say a. We know that this allelic substitution has an effect on development in terms of some final phenotypic difference, because it is only through such phenotypic differences that we become aware of this particular gene in the first place.

The definition of a standard type for a species involves the recognition of a standard course of development. A mutant phenotype, then, results from a precise deviation from this standard developmental plan, and this deviation traces back to an ultimate basis in a genic difference from the standard type.

Initial and Derived Developmental Effects of Genes. Probably many of the genes affect processes common to all the living cells of an individual, all during his life. The primary detectable effects of genes most important to differentiation, however, seem generally to be limited to particular types of cells and tissues, or to particular times in development. It is easy to see why this should be, in terms of our previous discussion. Gene A may find a cellular environment, at a particular place and time in the developing individual, that permits its playing a determining role in the biochemistry of that tissue. This in turn may set up a new cytoplasmic environment in which the products of other particular genes are able to work. The local environments become progressively more diverse in different parts of the embryo through increasingly divergent interactions between nuclei and gene-affected cytoplasms. Different genes may, therefore, encounter the conditions necessary for their action at different times and places in the individual.

Given an initial genic effect in a particular tissue at a particular time, widespread consequences for the developing individual as an organism may derive from the secondary effects of this tissue upon the functions of other tissues. Here, we are dealing with a level of gene action characteristic of the organism. The basis for initial gene action in development is probably specific genetic direction of particular biochemical reactions that occur in some differentiating tissues and not in others. The initial observed developmental deviations therefore probably rest on preceding biochemical deviations. From this point of view, initial gene action in development is a matter of "genes and cellular biochemistry" on a local basis in the developing organism. This subject was considered in Chapter 17, and in its application to differentiation it was the main concern of the earlier part of this chapter.

The *derived* gene effects, which are mediated through the functional interactions of different tissues, are critically involved in the integration of development, so that the individual develops as an organized whole. We should evaluate briefly the broad developmental significance of this kind of integration.

Developmental Interactions of Cells and Tissues. Materials elaborated by one group of cells may diffuse to adjacent cells, or be transported by the circulation to distant tissues. Such materials play an important part in regulating the development of different tissues and organs with respect to each other, and thus in integrating the normal development of the individual as a whole.

Consider the example of Figure 18-6. Here a region of an amphibian embryo in the early *gastrula* stage is transplanted to abnormal positions in older embryos. You should note, first, that the region involved would normally form the eye as the embryo developed (as shown in *A*). If this tissue is simply removed from the embryo and permitted to develop by itself (*B*), it forms only a ball of undifferentiated tissue. Transplanted to various strange positions in older embryos (*C, D, E*), it forms a variety of complex, organized tissues. *What it forms is characteristic of the region to which it was transplanted.* Evidently, the "presumptive eye" region of the very early embryo is not fixed in terms of its potentialities; it is capable of responding in various ways to the influences surrounding and permeating it.

This broad plasticity is lost as development proceeds; pieces of later embryos transplanted to foreign positions may develop only according to their determined patterns. For example, in Figure 18-7, the eye region of an embryo in the *neurula* stage, when transplanted to position *E* on an older embryo, develops only into an eye. This is in contrast to the result in *E* of

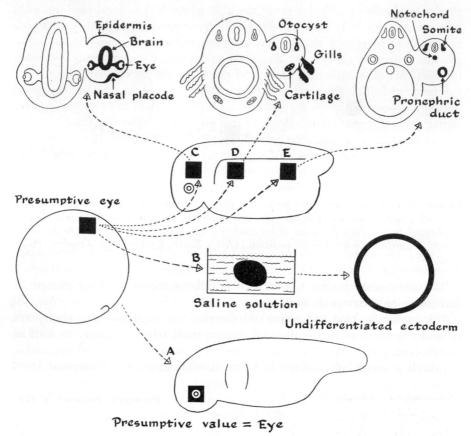

Figure 18-6. *A region of an amphibian embryo in the early gastrula stage will later normally develop into the eye* (A). *If this region is removed, and allowed to develop by itself, it does not differentiate* (B). *If it is transplanted to strange positions on older embryos* (C,D,E), *it can produce various organs and tissues, depending on where it is put.* (After Barth, Embryology, Dryden, 1949, p. 74.)

the preceding figure, where the transplant came from the much younger gastrula stage.

Not only is a transplant often influenced in its differentiation by its position in the new host, but the transplant sometimes influences profoundly what happens in the surrounding host tissues. This is illustrated in Figure 18-8, where a piece of one very early embryo, transplanted into a strange region in another embryo of the same age, induces the formation of a "secondary embryo" in its new host. Most of this secondary embryo is composed of host tissues, which, under the influence of the transplant, are caused to differentiate in complex, organized directions not normal for their positions. This kind of interaction among embryonic tissues, whereby one group of

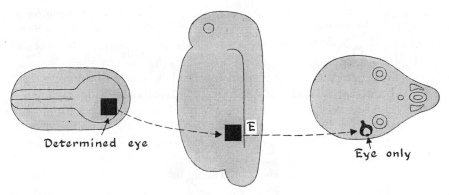

Figure 18-7. *By the time the embryo reaches the* neurula *stage (much later in development than the* gastrula *of Figure 18-6), the eye is determined. Transplanted to position E on an older embryo, the eye region goes on to form an eye, regardless of its strange position. (After Barth,* Embryology, *Dryden, 1949, p. 77.)*

cells evokes and appears to control the differentiation of other groups of cells, is called *embryonic induction.*

The particular kind and extent of induction accomplished by a transplant typically depend on the embryonic region from which it came, as well as on the region to which it is transplanted. The striking result just discussed, in which a secondary embryo is induced, characterizes a transplant from

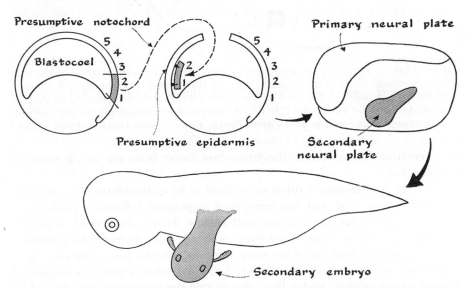

Figure 18-8. *A particular piece of one early embryo, transplanted to another, induces its host to form a secondary head in that region. (After Barth,* Embryology, *Dryden, 1949, p. 78.)*

a special region of the early embryo called *the organizer*. This region can be subdivided, so that one can distinguish within it a "head organizer," which induces a head, and a "trunk organizer," for example. Other embryonic regions are capable of inducing host differentiation in other directions.

You will recognize that the type of interaction among developing tissues we have been discussing is most important to the normal development of the individual as an integrated whole. We learn about these interactions, for the most part, by experiments that interfere with their usual course —for example, by putting tissues in embryonic environments ordinarily strange to them. This helps us to understand normal epigenetic development, in which the progressive narrowing of potentialities and the adjustment through mutual interaction proceed with regularity toward the construction of an organized individual.

Our perception of this basis for differentiation also helps us to understand other aspects of embryology and evolution. For example, human embryos, like those of other mammals, birds, and reptiles, go about the development of the adult kidney in a curious fashion. They begin by forming a fleeting vestige of an excretory organ called the *pronephros,* which probably does not function for excretion in the human embryo, but which is clearly comparable to the primitive excretory organ of the lowliest vertebrates. In the roundmouth eels and hagfishes, the pronephros is the functional excretory organ of the young, and it is partially retained by the adult. It is also found in fishes that pass through a larval period, and in the tadpoles of amphibia.

In the embryos of higher vertebrates, the pronephros is succeeded by the *mesonephros,* the functional kidney of adult fish and amphibia. In reptiles, birds, and mammals this structure is largely replaced, in turn, by the kidney (*metanephros*). Some of the parts of the mesonephros persist to become parts of the adult urogenital system.

Why is our species compelled to build, during embryonic development, two successive excretory systems that do not function in excretion, before it constructs the functional kidney? Why do we retain this record of our evolutionary history in our current development? Evidence is accumulating that the pronephros and the mesonephros successively act as essential organizers for later developmental processes in their regions. Our species has not "learned" to build a kidney or other associated structures in this region *de novo,* but only to superimpose them on an ancestral course of development. We have shortened the development of the pronephros, for example, to its minimum essentials, but the development of some kind of pronephros remains an important prerequisite to our later normal development.

We will consider this subject from a more strictly genetic standpoint in the following section. Meanwhile, we should mention one other important category of integration already familiar to you. Our discussion up to this point has implied that the inductive and organizing interactions among groups of cells depend on the diffusion of regulating materials from *adjacent* tissues. In the *endocrine system,* however, proximity of interacting tissues is unnecessary. "Glands of internal secretion" elaborate materials that are transported to distant parts of the individual *via* the circulation, and these hormones evoke specific responses in particular, distant "target tissues." A similar system is important in the integration of plant growth and differentiation.

We are now in a position to examine some of the ways in which initial genic effects on particular tissues may have widespread consequences for other components of the developmental pattern. We shall survey this subject by selecting four categories of such effects.

Genic Effects on Systems of Embryonic Induction. There are two main ways in which genes may affect the integration of the developmental pattern accomplished through organizers or similar inductive mechanisms. These depend on the fact that there are two partners in any such system— the tissue that is doing the inducing and the tissue that is being induced. Thus, on the one hand, gene-controlled deviations from the normal biochemical pattern in a developing organizer may have marked effects on the ability of this tissue to organize normally the regions around itself. On the other hand, genes may affect the *competence* of tissues to respond normally to the organizing stimuli. We will describe an example only of the first of these alternatives here. Genetic effects of the second kind are most clearly illustrated through the closely similar changes in the competence of tissues to respond normally to hormones, and will be considered later.

For an example of an apparent organizer effect, we may consider one aspect of the action of a semidominant lethal in the mouse. Mice homozygous for "Danforth's short-tail" (*Sd*) have no tails at all; neither do they have a rectum or an anus, or urethra, or genital papilla; they usually lack kidneys, too, and several vertebrae of the lower part of the spinal column; and they may show a variety of additional abnormalities. When they are born alive, they die on their birthday.

The allele gets its name from Danforth's discovery of it in heterozygous mice, where its most regular and conspicuous effect is a shortening or absence of the tail. We will confine our immediate attention to a less conspicuous, but physiologically more important, aspect of the heterozygotes, their kidney and ureter anomalies. Figure 18-9 shows sketches of fourteen arbitrary classes of such anomalies, together with the frequencies of these classes among 109 individuals of genotype *Sd/+*. You will note that 7 per cent of these heterozygotes, in the population studied, appeared normal with respect to their kidneys and ureters, while the remainder showed varying degrees of reduction in size or even complete absence of one or both kidneys or ureters.

If you examine this figure carefully you will observe that several possible classes of abnormality are conspicuous by their absence. You do not find a kidney hanging in the figure by itself, as the adrenals may; wherever there

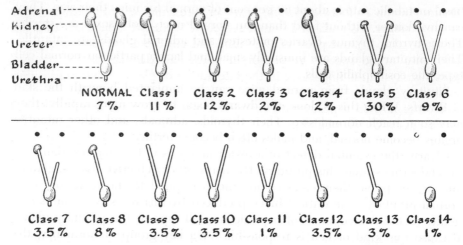

Figure 18-9. *Mice heterozygous for "Danforth's short-tail" show a variety of anomalies of kidney and ureter structure. (After S. Gluecksohn-Schoenheimer, in* Genetics of the Mouse *by H. Grüneberg, Cambridge University Press, 1943, p. 202).*

is a kidney, even a small one, a complete ureter extends to it. Whenever a ureter fails to reach the kidney region, the corresponding kidney fails to develop.

In brief, developmental studies on Sd heterozygotes strongly suggest that the ureter, which arises as a bud from the mesonephros, acts as a kind of organizer in inducing the formation of the metanephric part of the mammalian kidney. An early effect of the Sd allele in heterozygotes is interference with the normal elongation and branching of this mesonephric bud. The frequent reduction or absence of the kidney results from the failure of this organizing tissue to make adequate contact with the tissue it normally induces to form the capsules and secretory tubules of the kidney.

The other effects of the Sd allele, particularly in homozygotes, suggest that it may interfere much earlier in development with a chain of inductive relationships necessary to the eventual normal development of the whole posterior part of the embryo. Grüneberg has emphasized the importance of such observations in understanding similar human anomalies of medical significance.

Genic Effects on Endocrine Systems. Dwarf mice homozygous for a simple recessive appear to grow normally for a short while after birth, but their growth rate soon decreases, and by about the twelfth day they have stopped growing. They begin to lose weight, and some of them die. A little later, the survivors seem to reach some kind of equilibrium and begin to grow again slowly. They eventually reach about a quarter of the normal adult weight. Their bodily proportions differ somewhat from normal—for example, their tails and ears are shorter. They are slow and inactive; their basal metabolic rate is about 60 per cent of normal for mice their size. They can live longer without food than can normal mice. Both sexes are sterile. Their thyroid, thymus, ovaries or testes, and adrenal glands are infantile. Their pituitary glands are unusually small and lack a particular normal cell type, the eosinophilic cells.

Pituitary glands from normal mice can be implanted beneath the skin of dwarfs. When this is done, the dwarfs begin to grow more rapidly; they may soon reach normal size. Their thyroids, adrenals, and other infantile organs become normal, and males often become fertile.

Clearly, the essential defect of a dwarf mouse is in the "master gland" of his endocrine system, his pituitary. His many other defective tissues, glands, and organs prove themselves competent to respond to the secretions of a normal pituitary. The critical block produced by this recessive gene is evidently in the development of a particular cell type of the pituitary gland. Because this kind of cell is responsible for a key group of hormones, the consequences of this block are extensive and profound.

Numerous essentially similar examples of gene action on endocrine glands and on the production of diffusible or circulating substances might be cited. In human beings, for instance, certain extreme, inherited deviations from the normal range of stature seem to be endocrine in origin. A common type of sugar diabetes results from a primary failure in the hormonal function of the pancreas. *Cretins*, typically stunted both physically and mentally, result from thyroid malfunction.

Another important aspect of genic effects on endocrine systems remains to be sampled. Genetic differences may not only modify the kind or amount of hormones produced by the endocrine glands; they may also affect the sensitivity and the nature of the response of target tissues to particular hormones.

As an example, we may consider a common difference between male and female fowls. Cocks often show their sex in the structure of many of their feathers—the long, narrow, pointed feathers of hackles and saddle; the pointed feathers of cape, back, and wing bow; the long curving pointed "sickle feathers" of the tail; and so on. Hens usually show the contrasting feather characteristics; their feathers are short, broad, blunt and straight.

A great deal of work has been done in studying the control of these sexual feather characteristics. It is evident that the endocrine system is involved; for example, the administration of female sex hormones, or of thyroid or pituitary extracts, can evoke the development of "hen feathering" in a male. Patches of potentially cock-feathered skin transplanted to a hen ordinarily develop "hen feathering"—clear evidence that here it is the internal, endocrine environment that distinguishes the sexes. Similarly, patches of hen skin transplanted to a cock ordinarily become cock feathered, and the removal of the functional ovary of a hen results in modification of her feathering in the direction characteristic of the cock.

Now there are some breeds of fowl in which there is no normal sexual difference in feather character of the sort we have been discussing. The males as well as the females are "hen-feathered." In other breeds, there are some strains with cock-feathered males and others with hen-feathered males. This difference in the roosters is inherited, and can most simply be explained on the basis of a single pair of alleles, such that males of genotype *HH* or *Hh* are hen-feathered, while *hh* males are cock-feathered. Females of any genotype are normally hen-feathered.

How does the *H* allele act to control hen-feathering in cocks? T. H. Morgan, who pioneered in this work, as in Drosophila genetics, believed that the hen-feathered cocks were "endocrine hermaphrodites"; that their testes secreted female hormones responsible for their hen-feathering. This concept was based on Morgan's observation that hen-feathered Sebright bantam males, when castrated, became cock-feathered; it seemed clear, therefore, that their testes had been responsible for their hen-feathering.

Later work has suggested a different conclusion. It was found that a caponized Sebright cock that had become cock-feathered again became hen-feathered after implantation of a Leghorn testis. Evidently there was no significant difference between the testis of a normally cock-feathered male and that of a hen-feathered male with respect to its action on the Sebright feather development. Similarly, a castrate Leghorn male continued to be cock-feathered even after the establishment of a Sebright testis transplant.

Skin grafts studied by Danforth, at Stanford University, completed the story. He found that transplants of skin from a hen-feathered breed to cock-feathered hosts continue to develop hen feathers. This is in contrast to the results previously cited, where transplants between cock-feathered males and hen-feathered females acquire the sexual feather characteristics of their hosts.

We can summarize the situation briefly, simplifying it somewhat. Breeds that are homozygous *hh* show sexual differences in feathering that depend on the endocrine differences between males and females. Here, the genetic differences in feathering between the sexes involve mainly the effects of the sex chromosome-autosomal balance on the kinds and relative amounts of hormones developed, and the sexual differences in feather structure result from these initial genetic effects on endocrines. Differences between *hh* and *HH* or *Hh* roosters, on the other hand, in which those having the *H* allele are hen-feathered while *hh* males are cock-feathered, result from a genetic effect on the way the feather-producing tissues respond to hormones. The initial genetic effect here is in the skin itself, as a target organ, and not in the endocrine glands.

Genic Effects on Migrating Cells. Our discussion has dealt with genetic effects on substances that are elaborated in one part of the developing individual and subsequently affect other parts. Another rather common event in development is the differentiation, in particular regions, of whole cells that later migrate to other regions to become part of, and to affect the character of, other tissues. Examples are the *melanophores*, which may migrate from a region near the embryonic nerve cord to developing skin, hair, or feathers all over the embryo, and which produce the pigmentation of these tissues. Similarly, in many forms, the cells that are to become the ancestors of the germ cells migrate into the prospective genital regions from tissues far outside this region; and the red blood cells of adult cattle evidently descend from circulating embryonic cells that later "settle down" in the various blood-forming tissues of the individual.

Genes that affect such wandering cells or the patterns of their migration may, of course, have consequences far outside the original time and place at which the initial genetic divergence occurs. We need not discuss examples here; the many genes affecting the quality, quantity, and distribution of pigment in the coats of mammals and the feathers of birds are sufficiently obvious as illustrations.

Genic Effects on the Regulation of Growth and Metabolism. We will consider two additional ways in which a gene may affect the regulation of

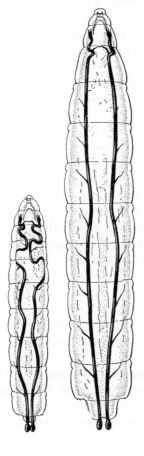

Figure 18-10. *A Drosophila larva homozygous for the "meander" lethal (left) is small in contrast with a normal larva its age, and its tracheae meander. (After Schmid, Z. Indukt. Abst. Vererb., 83:224, 1949.)*

growth and metabolism in the developing individual. One is to modify a metabolic process of direct importance to the whole organism. The second is to affect a metabolic process to some degree characteristic of a particular region at a particular time, and thus to change selectively the growth of this region relative to other parts of the individual.

As an instance in the first category, consider Figure 18-10, which contrasts a normal Drosophila larva with one showing the "meander" lethal characteristic discovered in 1943 by the Swiss embryologist Hadorn. This third-chromosome lethal gets its name from the wandering, curving course taken by the tracheae in the affected larvae. Larvae homozygous for the lethal cannot become pupae; they start to grow normally, but stop by the third day, when they have reached about half the normal size of larvae at pupation time, and they die as dwarf, misshapen larvae.

Schmid, at the University of Zürich, has subjected the development of the meander lethal to detailed study. The effects of this gene appear to be quantitatively comparable to the effects of starvation on normal larvae. Furthermore, transplantation studies have indicated that a block in the assimilation of protein is responsible for the lethal characteristic. This would appear to be a general block indeed, but it is evident that its effects are not the same on all organs of the larva. A very few tissues, like the tracheal trunks, continue to grow after the third day; others achieve only a fraction of their normal size. This fraction is characteristic for each organ; for example the salivary glands reach about one-third the normal size, while the testes and ovaries are about two-thirds as big as those of normal controls when the larvae are 96 hours old.

The kinds of internal compensation that make it possible for certain organs to continue growing for some time after a general block has stopped the growth of others are not well understood at present. Among the most fertile fields for the future cultivation of knowledge about the complex and important problems of growth are those that utilize genetic blocks of the sort illustrated by the meander lethal.

A somewhat similar genetic effect involves a modification of a general *regulatory mechanism,* like the control of body temperature. The frizzle fowl discussed earlier is an example.

Most of us have observed, in a general way, that the various parts of the human body grow at different rates. The sketches of Figure 18-11 illustrate this familiar fact. Growth of the head is extremely rapid in early development, while the trunk and appendages are later in starting, and relatively slow. If these relative rates persisted, adults would be monsters indeed by our present standards, with gigantic heads and dwarf limbs and trunks. As it is, however, the rapid relative growth rate of the head slows down toward the end of fetal life, and increasing proportions of the total growth are channeled into trunk and appendages.

Many of the details of how a person looks are governed by relative rates

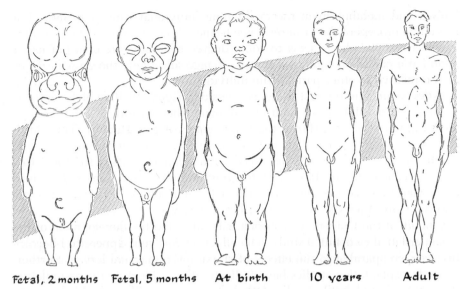

Fetal, 2 months   Fetal, 5 months   At birth   10 years   Adult

Figure 18-11. *Different parts of the human body grow at different rates.*

of growth. Consider noses as conspicuous examples. Most infants seem to be more or less "pug-nosed." By adolescence, however, the nose has usually become a rather large and dominant feature. During the interval between infancy and adolescence, the nose typically enjoys a high growth rate, relative to the growth rates of other facial components.

In line with the two general categories of genetic effects on the regulation of growth phrased at the beginning of this section, we can discern two kinds of effects on nose growth. The first involves the over-all growth of the individual. If his general growth slows down or stops unusually early, the proportions characteristic of earlier developmental stages may prevail. Thus, midgets usually have noses that are small, relative to the rest of their features, when compared with ordinary adult proportions in this regard. In the other direction, unusually prolonged growth, extending the period during which a relatively large fraction of total facial growth is diverted to the nose, typically results in disproportionately large noses. Thus "gigantism" in man is frequently associated with "coarse features," in which a relatively big nose plays an important part.

It is therefore apparent that genes affecting the final size that the individual reaches also secondarily affect the relative proportions of his parts. The initial genetic action may be an effect on total growth, and the differences in proportions may derive from the fact that various relative growth rates prevail for different parts of the individual.

On the other hand, particular genes sometimes single out for their individual effects particular components of the network of relative growth rates.

This would explain why some small people have relatively big noses, while some large people have relatively small ones.

Numerous studies, much more quantitative than our discussion of noses, have indicated that both types of genetic regulation of growth and metabolism described in this section are important to the patterns of development and evolution.

Keys to the Significance of This Chapter

Fertilization of the egg is followed by a succession of mitotic divisions through which the material of the egg cytoplasm is partitioned among many small cells. We assume these cells to be of identical genotypes. But cytoplasmic materials may be distributed unequally to the cleavage products, and dissimilar immediate environments impinge upon different parts of the embryo. The genetically identical nuclei of the individual therefore become involved in increasingly different reaction systems in various embryonic regions.

Once an initial basis for divergence has been established, regular genic effects on these differentiating reaction systems increase and regulate the divergence. The initial genic effects in this epigenetic sequence are presumably matters of "genes and cellular biochemistry" of the sorts described in Chapter 17. They involve the genetic control of specific biochemical reactions that can occur in some of the reaction systems that are becoming established, but not in others. Many genic effects, therefore, seem to be limited to particular times and places in development—to times and places in which the conditions necessary for the determinant action of these particular genes are encountered.

Many genes also have profound and widespread derived effects at some distance from the time and place of their initial action. Thus, genes may affect the integrating systems of embryonic induction, and of endocrines; and they may act in various other ways to influence broadly the processes of development.

While the problems of differentiation still constitute in large part an unsolved riddle that can be dealt with only speculatively in terms of our present very limited knowledge, approaches now seem to be at hand toward the solution of important aspects of this riddle. Present indications point to the genes as the essential catalysts of epigenetic development, whose regular transmission from generation to generation is of prime significance in the control of developmental patterns.

References

Allen, E., ed., *Sex and Internal Secretions.* Baltimore: Williams & Wilkins, 1939. (A compendium of endocrinological information. See especially the discussion of hen-feathering in the chapter by L. V. Domm.)

Barth, L. G., *Embryology.* New York: Dryden Press, 1949. (A clear and interesting elementary textbook on which part of our discussion of experimental embryology was based. See especially Chap. 1, "Embryology: Problems and Scope.")

Carroll, F. D., Gregory, P. W., and Rollins, W. C., "Thyrotropic-Hormone Deficiency in Homozygous Dwarf Beef Cattle." *J. Animal Sci.,* **10**:916–921, 1951. (Basis for Problems 18-2 and 18-3.)

Elrick, H., Albright, F., Bartter, F. C., Forbes, A. P., and Reeves, J. D., "Further Studies on Pseudo-Hypoparathyroidism: Report of Four New Cases." *Acta Endocrinol.,* **5**:199–225, 1950. (Recent work on the subject of Problems 18-4 and 18-5.)

Ephrussi, B., "Chemistry of 'Eye Color Hormones' of Drosophila." *Quart. Rev. Biol.,* **17**:327–338, 1942. (A review, with references.)

Gluecksohn-Waelsch, Salome, "Physiological Genetics of the Mouse." *Advances in Genetics,* **4**:1–51, 1951. (An excellent and up-to-date review, discussing genic effects on the development and function of practically all organ systems.)

Grüneberg, H., *Animal Genetics and Medicine.* London: Hamish Hamilton, 1947. (See especially Chap. 3, "Some Principles of Developmental Genetics. . . . ," and Chap. 21, "The Urogenital System.")

Hadorn, E., "Developmental Action of Lethal Factors in Drosophila." *Advances in Genetics,* **4**:53–85, 1951. (A thoughtful, detailed, and stimulating review.)

Haldane, J. B. S., *New Paths in Genetics.* New York: Harper & Bros., 1942. (See especially Chap. 3, "Genetics and Development.")

Hämmerling, J., "Ein- und zweikernige Transplante zwischen *Acetabularia mediterranea* und *A. crenulata.*" *Z. Abstgs. Vererbungsl.,* **81**:114–180, 1943. (Stimulating transplantation studies on a unicellular alga, the source of Problems 18-6 to 18-8.)

Huxley, J., *Evolution, The Modern Synthesis.* New York: Harper & Bros., 1942. (See especially pp. 525–555, "Consequential Evolution: The Consequences of Differential Development," for consideration of relative growth and related phenomena.)

Schmid, W., "Analyse der Letalen Wirkung des Faktors *lme* (Letal-Meander) von *Drosophila Melanogaster.*" *Z. Abstgs. Vererbungsl.,* **83**:220–253, 1949. (Analysis of the meander lethal.)

Sturtevant, A. H., "The Vermilion Gene and Gynandromorphism." *Proc. Soc. Exp. Biol. Med.,* **17**:70–71, 1920. (Classic observation of genic effect on hormone-like materials, the source of Problems 18-15 to 18-17.)

Weiss, P., "Perspectives in the Field of Morphogenesis." *Quart. Rev. Biol.,* **25**:177–198, 1950. (A review, with many references, of current problems of development and differentiation.)

Weisz, P. B., "A General Mechanism of Differentiation Based on Morphogenetic Studies in Ciliates." *Am. Naturalist*, **85**:293–311, 1951. (A review of the processes of differentiation in ciliate protozoa leads to a general concept of development. Includes a bibliography of classic and current thought on this subject.)

Wilson, E. B., *The Cell in Development and Heredity*. New York: Macmillan Co., 1928. (This is the third edition of a true classic, old in years but modern in its approach and analysis. See especially the Introduction and Chaps. 13 and 14, "Growth, Cell-Division and Development" and "Development and Heredity.")

Wright, S., "The Physiology of the Gene." *Physiol. Revs.*, **21**:487–527, 1941. (A thoughtful integration in the field of gene action.)

Questions and Problems

18- 1. What do the following terms signify?

cleavage   internal environment
competence   migrating cells
differentiation   organizer
embryonic induction   relative growth rates
epigenetic   target tissue
hormone

The thyroid gland, which produces the hormone *thyroxin*, important in regulating general body growth and metabolism, is in turn regulated by a pituitary hormone, the *thyrotropic* hormone. The relationship can be diagrammed in general terms:

pituitary ⟶ thyrotropic ⟶ thyroid ⟶ thyroxin ⟶ body ⟶ metabolic
cells   hormone   cells   cells   regulation

18- 2. Certain dwarf cattle give gross evidence of aberrant thyroid function (Carroll, Gregory, and Rollins, 1951). At what points in the above sequence is it possible that the recessive allele responsible for this type of dwarfism might be acting?

18- 3. How might you get evidence indicating which of the possible blocks suggested by your answer to Question 18-2 is in fact the operating one?

In man, a rather rare disorder involves metabolic components normally regulated by the parathyroid glands. The disorder is somewhat variable, but the basic deviations from normal metabolism of calcium and phosphorous are typically expressed in aberrant bone growth; deposition of calcium in abnormal places, particularly in certain parts of the brain and under the skin; a round head and small stature; and, frequently, jerky involuntary movements and mental deficiency.

18- 4. The disorder described above is grossly similar to that caused by failure of the parathyroids to produce a normal supply of their hormones (*hypoparathyroidism*). However, patients with the disorder under discussion prove to have very active parathyroids, and they do not respond to the administration of additional parathyroid hormones. The disorder is therefore called *pseudo-hypoparathyroidism*. Albright *et al.*, describing the condition in 1942, referred to it as a "Sebright bantam syndrome." Can you discern the rationale of this reference in terms of our discussion of hen-feathering in Sebright bantams?

18- 5. Recent studies of a large family including several individuals affected with pseudo-hypoparathyroidism suggest that a single dominant allele, varying considerably in its final expression, is responsible for the characteristic segregating in this family. Discuss briefly the possible action of this allele.

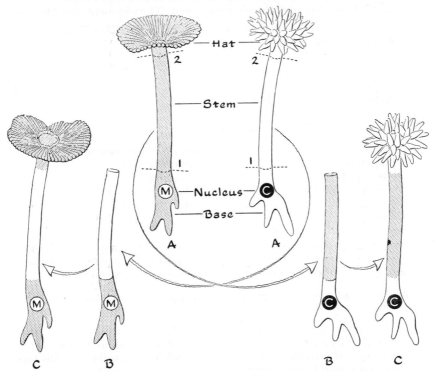

Figure 18-12. *Grafting experiments in Acetabularia have given important information about the control of patterns of regeneration. Left, grafting A. crenulata stem to the nucleated base of* A. mediterranea *results in the regeneration of a hat like that of* A. mediterranea. *Right, the reciprocal experiment. See Problems 18-6 to 18-8 (Diagrammatic; based on Hämmerling, Z. Abstg. Vererb. 81:114–180, 1943.)*

Figure 18-12 illustrates an experiment performed by Hämmerling on two species of the unicellular alga Acetabularia. *A. mediterranea* has an intact, umbrellalike "hat," while the hat of *A. crenulata* is deeply indented. The nucleus is imbedded in the base of each of these single cells, and the hat is borne on a long cytoplasmic stem.

18- 6. When the stem of *A. mediterranea* is cut off just at the base, and after removal of the hat the cut stem is grafted to a base of *A. crenulata* (Fig. 18-12B), a new hat is regenerated. Similarly, the reciprocal transplant of *A. crenulata* stem to *A. mediterranea* base regenerates a new hat. In each case, the hat regenerated has an eventual character consistent with the base from which it grows and different from the character of the intervening cytoplasmic stem (Fig. 18-12C). What do these results suggest relative to the cytoplasmic *vs.* the nuclear control of regeneration in Acetabularia?

18- 7.　In Acetabularia, if the nucleus of a cell is removed, and the hat alone is then cut off, a new hat will be regenerated at once. But if the adjacent part of the stem is removed when the old hat is cut off, the enucleate cell is unable to regenerate a new hat. Assuming a "hat-forming substance" responsible for regeneration, what can you say of the origin, qualitative control, and distribution of this substance in the intact cell?

18- 8.　If a stem with intact hat is transplanted from one species of Acetabularia to a base of the other, the hat retains its original character. What does this fact add to your discussion in answering Question 18-7?

18- 9.　We have seen that any one of the first four cells normally formed by cleavage of the sea urchin egg can give rise to a qualitatively normal individual. In snails, on the other hand, the two cells formed by the first cleavage, when isolated, develop differently. Assuming that initial segregation of cytoplasmic components is basic to differentiation, compare the probable relation of cytoplasmic organization to cleavage in snails and sea urchins.

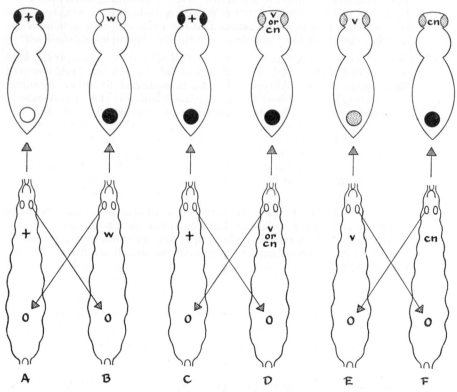

Figure 18-13. *Transplants of larval tissue have elucidated some aspects of gene action in Drosophila. See Problems 18-12 to 18-14. (After Ephrussi, Quart. Rev. Biol., 17:329, 1942.)*

18-10. Identical twins in man are derived from a single fertilized egg. Is the human egg probably more like the snail egg or the sea urchin egg (Question 18-9) with regard to its developmental organization?

18-11. The Dionne quintuplets are believed to have originated from a single egg. If cleavage results in the partitioning of cytoplasmic materials essential to the formation of a complete and integrated individual, what is the earliest cleavage division in which this critical partitioning may occur in man?

A technique for the study of genic effects on hormone-like materials in Drosophila has been developed and applied to good advantage by Ephrussi and Beadle. Figure 18-13 diagrams this technique and some of the results of its application. A piece of the larval tissue that would later give rise to the eye of the adult fly is transplanted to a genetically different larva. The developmental interactions between host and transplant are then observed, particularly in terms of the color developed by the transplanted eye disc as the host larva matures.

18-12. The reciprocal transplants shown in Figure 18-13A and B are typical of a large majority of Drosophila transplantation experiments. The larval disc from a wild-type fly develops the color characteristic of its own genotype, even when its differentiation and color development occur in a white-eye host. Similarly, a white-eye larval disc develops according to its own genotype, and is not influenced in any noticeable fashion by a wild-type host environment. Would you conclude that the white-eye gene acts on a circulating (hormone-like) material, or in the developing eye tissue itself?

18-13. The experiment diagrammed in Figure 18-13C and D represents the kind of exception from which a good deal of information has been derived. Here again, when wild-type discs are transplanted to either vermilion (v) or cinnabar (cn) host larvae, the transplants develop autonomously into wild-type eyes. But when vermilion or cinnabar discs are put into wild-type larvae, these discs do not develop according to their own constitution; instead, *they become wild type*. Assuming that the body of the wild-type host is capable of providing the developing eye tissue with circulating or diffusing materials that compensate for the genetic blocks in vermilion and cinnabar flies, derive a detailed explanation of these experimental results.

18-14. Figure 18-13E and F show the results of reciprocal transplants between vermilion and cinnabar larvae. Cinnabar discs developing in vermilion hosts maintain their cinnabar phenotype, but vermilion discs develop as wild type in cinnabar hosts. It is now known that these genes are concerned with sequential steps in a biochemical synthesis of hormone-like materials directly involved in eye pigment production:

$$\text{tryptophane} \xrightarrow{v^+} \underset{\text{("}v^+\text{ substance")}}{\text{kynurenine}} \xrightarrow{cn^+} \underset{\text{("}cn^+\text{ substance")}}{\text{hydroxykynurenine}} \rightarrow \rightarrow \text{pigment}$$

Using these facts, give a detailed explanation of the transplantation results.

In 1920, Sturtevant found a gynandromorph Drosophila that had developed from an egg with the following sex-chromosomal genotype:

$$\frac{sc \quad w^+ \quad ec \quad rb^+ \quad ct \quad v \quad g \quad f}{sc^+ \quad w^e \quad ec^+ \quad rb \quad ct^+ \quad v^+ \quad g^+ \quad f}$$

The mutant alleles involved, all sex-linked recessives, were: scute (*sc*), a bristle character; eosin (*w*°), an eye-color allele at the white-eye locus; echinus (*ec*), an eye characteristic; ruby (*rb*), an eye color; cut (*ct*), a wing-shape effect; vermilion (*v*) and garnet (*g*), eye-color mutations; and forked (*f*), a bristle character.

18-15. The male parts of Sturtevant's gynandromorph showed the recessive characteristics *sc, ec, ct, g,* and *f,* while the female parts showed *f* only. What was the chromosomal basis for this gynandromorph?

18-16. How might the failure of the male parts of Sturtevant's gynandromorph to display the characteristic *vermilion* be explained? (There is no question that vermilion would have been recognized if it had been present.)

18-17. How do Sturtevant's early observations compare with the later transplantation experiments involving vermilion (Problems 18-13 and 18-14)?

18-18. In view of the explanation of hen-feathering in cocks developed in the text of this chapter, how would you explain Morgan's observation that castrated Sebright bantam males become cock-feathered?

CHAPTER 19

The Gene

SINCE OUR recognition of the particulate basis of inheritance in Chapter 2, we have considered numerous aspects of the particles of heredity. We know where they are located in cells, the orders in which they are arranged in chromosomes, the frequencies with which they mutate, and ways to make them mutate more often. We are familiar with the processes of their transmission from generation to generation and the mechanisms through which they are parcelled out to the germ cells to recombine again in pairs at fertilization. Most of these things have been learned by combining the observation of cells and chromosomes under microscopes with the determination of genetic ratios in breeding experiments.

We have also approached a knowledge of genes from another, quite different direction. By characterizing the *consequences of genic differences* among individuals, we have drawn some tentative conclusions about how genes may act to affect development and differentiation. We have "worked backwards" from the final phenotypic alternatives affected by allelic pairs, through the developmental processes and the biochemical mechanisms by means of which these differences come about, toward some kind of definition of gene action in development and cellular biochemistry. If you will recall the way we phrased, in Chapter 1, the primary questions to be considered in this book (particularly as illustrated in the black fox, pp. 8 to 10), it must appear that we have gone some distance toward answering these questions, even though we have not by any means arrived at the goal of complete and definitive answers.

After this chapter, we will turn mainly to the consideration of genes at quite another level—the distributions of alleles in groups of individuals, and the applications of these distributions to problems of heredity in plant, animal, and human populations. Now, briefly, we will pause to evaluate what we have learned about the particles of heredity themselves, and what more we may learn from a sample of the additional information that may be brought to bear on this problem.

We will need to keep in mind two primary properties of genes that together constitute their biological significance.

1. At least once in each nuclear generation, each gene is specifically copied. We have spoken of this vital property of genes as "specific self-duplication"; at present this faculty seems likely to reside in the ability of each gene to organize cellular materials around it in such a way as to produce an exact copy of itself.

We have noted the ability of changed genes (mutations) to copy their new structures with similar precision. We know practically nothing about the details of this remarkable process of specific self-duplication, and we find no exact parallel for it in the inanimate world. Even the growth of crystals must represent an entirely inadequate model of gene duplication. This is not to be taken to mean that gene duplication represents a mysterious vital principle that must remain forever intangible, but only to recognize that we have much still to learn on this subject.

2. Genes produce specific effects on the biochemical patterns of cells. We assume that, besides duplicating themselves in each cell generation, genes liberate into the cell particular key substances, and that these are developed with the same order of precision and specificity as are the duplicated genes themselves. We do not know how the processes of gene duplication and of primary gene action are related. An economical hypothesis is that they are both part of the same essential property of the particle, that of organizing materials around it into a highly specific molecular pattern.

Physical and Chemical Attributes of Genes

The chromosome shows a precise differentiation along its length into regions that maintain their separate identities and peculiar specificities in their own duplication and in the elaboration of products important to the cell. We call each such region a gene. What can we say about the physical and chemical nature of these units of heredity?

Sizes of Genes. First of all, how big are genes? Since no one has yet seen a gene, or at least known that he was looking at one, gene dimensions have not been measured directly, as, for example, with an ocular micrometer in a light microscope. Although there are good reasons to believe that gene sizes are well below the limits of resolution of ordinary microscopes, certain indirect measures suggest that genes are big enough so that their pictures may possibly be taken with the electron microscope. In fact, one team of observers has suggested that certain large molecular units seen in electron microscope pictures of the salivary chromosomes of Drosophila may be genes. This conclusion is necessarily uncertain, since we do not know how much of, or what parts of, the chromosomes are truly genic. Moreover, the treatments that chromosomes must undergo to be observable in the electron microscope are drastic, and probably the components of chromosomes are modified to some degree by these treatments.

There are means other than direct observation and measurement for estimating gene sizes. For example, we might assume that a gene must be "hit" by an ionizing particle in order to be caused to mutate by an ionizing radiation (e.g., X-ray). Then, by relating the frequency of induced mutation to the density of ionizations in a treated tissue, the size of the target offered by a gene to the ionizing particles might be estimated. Several uncertainties would be involved in these assumptions and calculations; nevertheless, the sizes of virus and enzyme particles calculated by similar methods generally agree rather well with their direct measurements in electron microscope photographs. The diameter of one gene, assuming it to be a spherical particle, has been calculated by "target-size estimation" to be something like 6 millimicrons (0.000006 millimeters), and its "molecular weight" to be perhaps around 100,000. These are probably underestimates, because they are

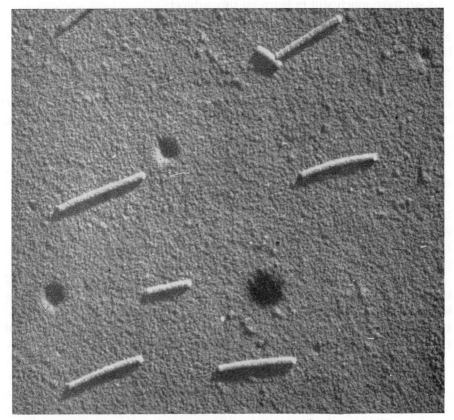

Figure 19-1. *An electron micrograph of tobacco mosaic virus, shadowed with uranium and magnified 67,000 times, shows the long virus rods of uniform length (two shown in the picture are fragments.) The black spot near the center of the picture is an unavoidable pinhole image of the microscope filament; there is also some nonvirus material, since this is not a highly purified preparation. (Courtesy of Robley C. Williams, Virus Laboratory, University of California.)*

based on detectable, nonlethal mutations induced at a particular locus. Such mutations presumably represent only a fraction of the total changes induced by ionizations.

A calculation that gives an upper limit for gene sizes can be made by estimating the number of genes per chromosome, measuring the chromosome, and then calculating the average volume of each gene that would be necessary to make up the total chromosome. Gene sizes so calculated are maximum sizes, because of the improbable assumption that all of the material of the chromosome is genic. Another uncertainty involves the number of genes in any given chromosome. In Drosophila, there is some reason to believe that in general each band in the salivary chromosomes may represent a locus. If we assume something of the order of 1000 genes in the X-chromosome (there are about 647 bands) and if we make some further assumptions about the length and diameter of the coiled gene thread in the metaphase X-chromosome, the volume of which can be measured, we come out with the estimate that the upper limit for the size of an average gene is that of a cylinder about 20 mμ. in diameter and 100 mμ. long. This would give a "molecular weight" of about 25 million. For comparison, the virus causing tobacco mosaic disease is a cylinder about 15×300 mμ., with a particle weight of about 40 million (Fig. 19-1). The virus causing poliomyelitis, one of the smallest of human pathogens, is thought to be no larger than 10 mμ. in any dimension.

Genes appear, therefore, to be somewhere between the size of a sphere 6 mμ. in diameter, and a cylinder 20 mμ. in diameter and 100 mμ. long. If they are on the average somewhere near the middle of this range, about 350 million of these particles in a single layer would be required to cover the cut end of an average human hair.

The Chemistry of Chromosomes. Chemistry has not yet advanced to the point of providing us with precise and detailed knowledge of the structure and composition of giant molecules like those making up genes and viruses. Doubtless many of the most exciting and important discoveries remaining for the not-too-distant future are those in the field of "molecular biology." We can hope that in time the biologically important macromolecules will be as well understood as much smaller and less complex organic and inorganic compounds are today.

Not only is the chemistry of large molecules difficult in itself, but the genes as objects of chemical study offer great additional obstacles. When we disrupt cells and fractionate their contents, we have no way of knowing when we are making progress toward the preparation of "pure suspensions" of genes, free from nongenic material. Even more difficult would be the problem of getting pure suspensions of particular alleles for chemical characterization, free of other genes. No doubt the analysis of other, more easily purified entities that are duplicated in living systems—viruses or the killer particles of Paramecium, for example—will contribute information of direct interest to genetics in this connection. In fact, analyses of different strains of some viruses have already shown that these strains differ in their amino acid composition. A way is perhaps at hand for attacking the chemical nature of mutation from this direction.

Since genes themselves cannot be isolated and analyzed, we must at present draw what conclusions we can from the isolation and analysis of chromosomes. This has been the subject of careful and extensive study.

The characteristic components of chromosomes belong to a class of compounds called *nucleoproteins*. These are made up of two, often rather easily separable, entities: *nucleic acids* and *proteins*.

The nucleic acid component of a nucleoprotein is in turn built up of *nucleotides,* which are believed to be put together something like the illustration in Figure 19-2. Each nucleotide seems to be like a plate, composed of a *nitrogenous base,* a *sugar,* and *phosphate*. The phosphate binds adjacent nucleotides together, and the plates appear to be piled in tall

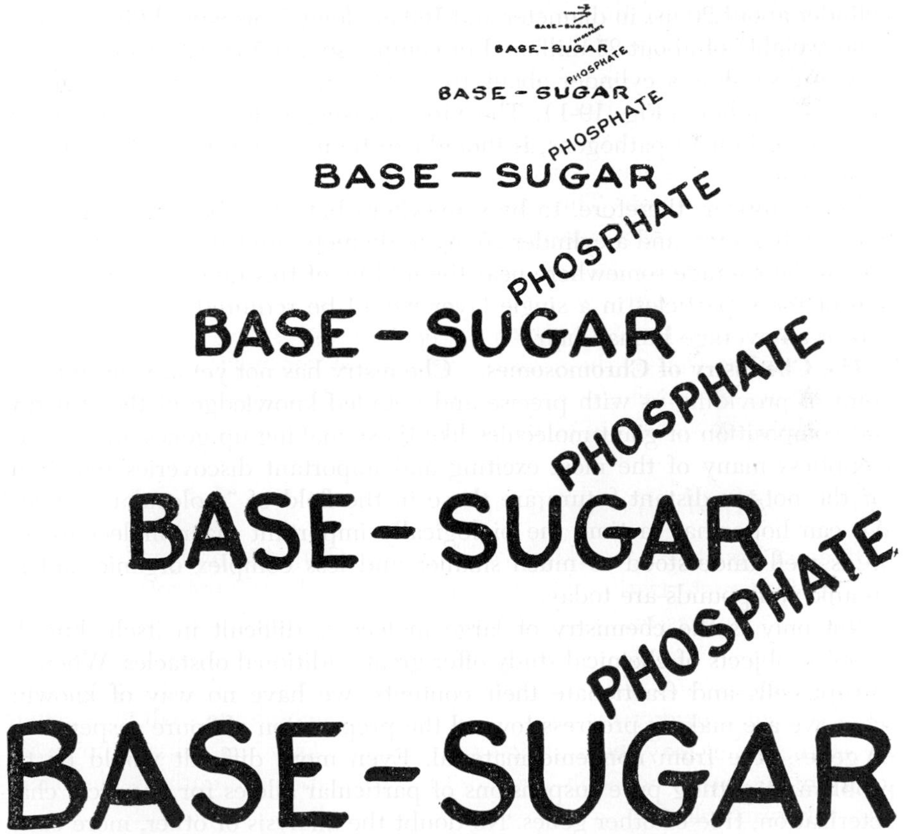

BASE-SUGAR

PHOSPHATE

BASE-SUGAR

PHOSPHATE

BASE – SUGAR

PHOSPHATE

BASE – SUGAR

PHOSPHATE

BASE - SUGAR

PHOSPHATE

BASE - SUGAR

PHOSPHATE

BASE-SUGAR

Figure 19-2. *Nucleic acids are probably stacks of nucleotides (base-sugar-phosphate), in which the phosphate groups connect adjacent sugars.*

stacks. These stacks are then in turn tied to the protein thread of the nucleoprotein.

Two primary classes of nucleic acids are currently recognized: *desoxyribose nucleic acid* (DNA) and *ribonucleic acid* (RNA). Chemically, these classes take their names from the *sugar* component—desoxyribose in one, ribose in the other. There are other chemical differences as well, in the bases they contain and in the way in which the phosphate binds the nucleotides together. The main biological distinction between DNA and RNA is that DNA appears to exist normally only in chromosomes, whereas RNA is found in the cytoplasm as well as in the nucleus. There is reason to believe that RNA-containing proteins are generally produced in the nucleus, where they occur especially in the nucleolus, and that at particular stages in the mitotic cycle they are liberated into the cytoplasm.

A way of studying the distribution of the nucleic acids in cells is to observe them by means of ultraviolet light near the wave length naturally absorbed by these compounds—about 2600Å. The two main types of nucleic acids can be distinguished by means of appropriate staining techniques; for example, a stain has been developed (*Azure-phthalate*) that stains RNA red and DNA blue.

It seems likely that certain characteristics of the nucleic acids, as yet not understood, confer upon genes and viruses their essential faculty for specific self-duplication. All known self-duplicating particles have a conspicuous content of nucleoprotein. The protein components of the nucleoproteins may vary widely, even from one cell type to another in the same individual. Furthermore, it would appear that it is DNA, rather than RNA, that is in general correlated with the faculty of self-duplication. Thus, the nucleic acids of the "transforming principle" in pneumococcus, and of kappa in Paramecium, as well as those distinguishing chromosomes from normal cytoplasmic nucleoproteins, are of the DNA class. The nucleic acids of certain plant viruses, however, are of the ribose type.

Other Attributes of Genes

Different geneticists, working with various organisms and with different criteria of characterization, have arrived at somewhat divergent concepts of the nature of genes and their action. We will list three of these concepts briefly.

1. *A gene is a unit of chromosomal structure not subdivisible by chromosomal breakage or crossing over.* This concept, which we shall take as our key to the gene, may seem at first self-evident. As you shall see, however, not all of the other concepts of or criteria for genes are entirely consistent with this principle.

2. *A gene is a unit in mutation.* *Mutation,* here, is used in a limited sense, as representing a change in a gene. Obviously, if you regard a mutation as a change in *a gene,* then *a gene* is the unit that mutates.

Suppose that you recognize two different mutations, a_1 and a_2, each recessive to the standard type. If a cross

$$a_1a_1 \times a_2a_2$$

gives standard-type offspring, it seems that a_1 and a_2 represent changes in different genes, and that the cross should properly be written

$$a_1a_1 \ a_2{}^+a_2{}^+ \times a_1{}^+a_1{}^+ \ a_2a_2 \longrightarrow a_1a_1{}^+ \ a_2a_2{}^+$$

Each parent has contributed the normal allele of a recessive mutant allele in the other.

If, however, the cross $a_1a_1 \times a_2a_2$ does not revert to type, but shows a variant phenotype like either parent or some similar kind or order of deviation from type, this is taken as evidence that the mutations a_1 and a_2 were changes in a single gene. We shall see that situations exist in which such a conclusion would be inconsistent with concept 1 above.

The test for allelism, indicated above, is a classic means of distinguishing two different mutations in a single unit in the germ plasm from a mutation in each of two different (nonallelic) units.

3. *A gene is a unit of biochemical action.* We observed in Chapter 17 that extensive studies have led to the hypothesis that each gene controls a specific biochemical reaction, and that each specific biochemical reaction is under the ultimate control of a particular gene. This relationship has been so regular that it has been possible to predict that blocks in a particular biosynthetic sequence at two different points will turn out to involve mutations in two different genes. Similarly, one can predict in general that if mutations at two different loci block the same sequence, then two different steps in the sequence are involved. Predictions of this sort have been subsequently verified by appropriate tests.

Since the biochemical reactions in living systems are commonly under the control of enzymes, the relationship suggested above has led to an extension in the form of the "one gene-one enzyme hypothesis" discussed in Chapter 17. It is but a step further to describe the gene as "the self-duplicating producer of an enzyme." It is proper to view such extensions of hypotheses with caution. The chemical nature of the immediate products of genes, like that of the genes themselves, remains speculative.

Contradictions, real or perhaps only apparent, among the three concepts of the gene listed above become evident when we consider *multiple allelic series.* We will therefore pause to consider a few such series, approaching them by way of the genetic control of blood types. You will recall that in Chapter 12 we discussed multiple alleles briefly, mainly from the standpoint of the numerous possibilities apparently open to a gene when it mutates.

The Human Blood Groups. It has been known for half a century that human beings differ in certain blood characteristics. The most striking demonstration of these differences can be observed when small samples of blood from two individuals, treated to prevent ordinary clotting of the samples, are mixed in a test tube. A common result in such mixtures is the clumping together of individual blood cells into irregular clusters. This phenomenon is called *agglutination*. Tests of this kind are of considerable clinical importance in determining what bloods may safely be used in transfusion.

When a blood sample drawn from a person is placed in a dry tube, the blood normally clots, and a yellowish fluid is pressed out of the clot as it shrinks. This fluid is called *serum*. Blood cells are entangled in the clot; by treatment with proper concentration of salt in water they can be washed out of the clot.

The incompatibility between the bloods of two individuals, indicated by agglutination when the bloods are mixed in the test tube, can be shown to result from a property of the *serum* that causes the blood cells of other individuals to agglutinate, and a property of the *cells* that causes them to be agglutinated by the serum of other individuals. The elements in the *serum* that account for this specific activity are called *antibodies;* the specific properties of the *cells* result from their possession of *antigens*. Thus, when the serum and cells of two individuals, A and B, are mixed in the different possible combinations, the results diagrammed in Figure 19-3 may be observed. Symbolizing the antigens of the cells as A and B respectively, and the corresponding antibodies in serum as α and β, we can define the individual differences involved:

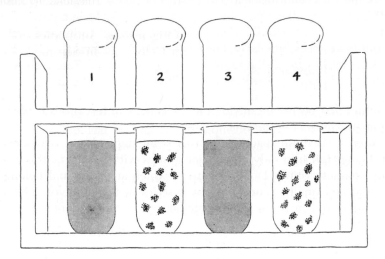

1. Serum of A, cells of A ⟶ no agglutination
2. Serum of A, cells of B ⟶ agglutination
3. Serum of B, cells of B ⟶ no agglutination
4. Serum of B, cells of A ⟶ agglutination

Figure 19-3. *When the blood serum of one individual is mixed with the blood cells of another, the cells may be agglutinated.*

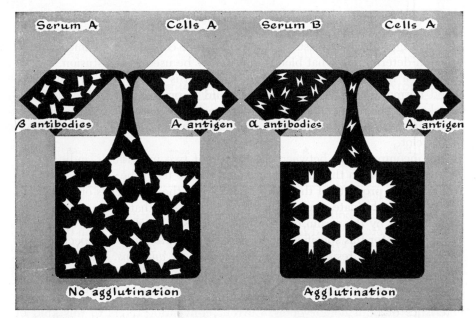

Figure 19-4. Right, *antibodies in serum unite specifically with their corresponding antigen, if it is present on the blood cells, to tie the cells together in clumps. Left, if the antibodies and antigens present do not correspond, no clumping occurs.*

	Antigen on Cells	Antibodies in Serum
Individual A	A	β
Individual B	B	α

The reaction that occurs on mixing these elements in test tubes is illustrated diagrammatically in Figure 19-4.

Our interest in these reactions at this point depends on two facts: (1) Human beings fall into only four major groups with regard to this antigen-antibody characteristic. (2) The group to which an individual belongs is a simply inherited quality, controlled by a series of three alleles. The alleles can be symbolized in terms of the cellular antigens they control:

Allele	Antigen
L^A	A
L^B	B
l	none†

(The letter L has been suggested by Strandskov (1948) as the basic symbol for alleles at this locus in recognition of Karl Landsteiner, who discovered the blood groups in 1900. This blood group system in humans is often called the Landsteiner Blood Groups.)

† To be qualified later.

The genotypes and corresponding cell and serum types of human beings are then as shown in Table 19-1.

TABLE 19-1. The Human Blood Groups.

GENOTYPES	CELLULAR ANTIGENS	SERUM ANTIBODIES	BLOOD GROUP
$L^A L^A$ or $L^A l$	A	β	A
$L^B L^B$ or $L^B l$	B	α	B
$L^A L^B$	A and B	none	AB
ll	none†	α and β	O

† To be qualified later.

You will note that both L^A and L^B appear as dominant to their allele l, since the heterozygotes $L^A l$ and $L^B l$ cannot easily be distinguished from the homozygotes $L^A L^A$ or $L^B L^B$, respectively. L^A and L^B, however, mutually lack dominance with respect to each other, since the heterozygote $L^A L^B$ is easily identifiable as blood group AB. But the heterozygote $L^A L^B$ is not really an intermediate between the two homozygotes $L^A L^A$ and $L^B L^B$; it shows characteristics of both homozygotes. Current convention refers to this kind of situation as *codominance,* to distinguish it from other types of interaction between alleles.

Genetic consequences of this situation should be clear to you. An individual of blood group O, for example, might come from a mating of two individuals of blood group A ($L^A l \times L^A l$), or from two individuals of blood groups A and B respectively ($L^A l \times L^B l$), or from certain other possible kinds of matings, but neither of his parents could be AB ($L^A L^B$). This kind of analysis is the basis of one sort of application of blood grouping to legal medicine—the solution of cases of possible baby mixups and of disputed paternity. The problems at the end of this chapter include several exercises in the use of genetic reasoning in this regard.

In transfusion, B or AB cells introduced into an individual of group A or O would react with the β antibodies present in the serum of such individuals. "Transfusion reactions" may be severe or even fatal. It is therefore important to "match" donor and recipient before a transfusion is made.

A thorough discussion of the human blood groups would include several extensions and qualifications of the information so far presented. We shall mention two:

1. Within the four major blood groups we have described, minor subdivisions have been recognized. The subtypes of A, for example, are called A_1, A_2, and so on. Insofar as the genetic determination of these types has been analyzed, it appears that a different allele controls each specific type. A complete list of the alleles at this locus would, therefore, begin L^{A_1}, L^{A_2}, L^{B_1}, and so on. Serologists now sometimes speak of a "pleiades" of genes at this locus; the extent of allelic diversity here must be great.

2. The allele l is listed as controlling the production of no antigen simply because humans do not normally have antibodies capable of reacting specifically with cells of ll individuals. Antibodies that react specifically with human O blood have, however, been found in some animal sera and even in rare human sera. The l allele therefore does govern the presence of a cellular antigen. The O antigen is of little medical concern, because of the absence of normal human antibodies against it.

Other Human Cellular Antigens. The Landsteiner blood groups are

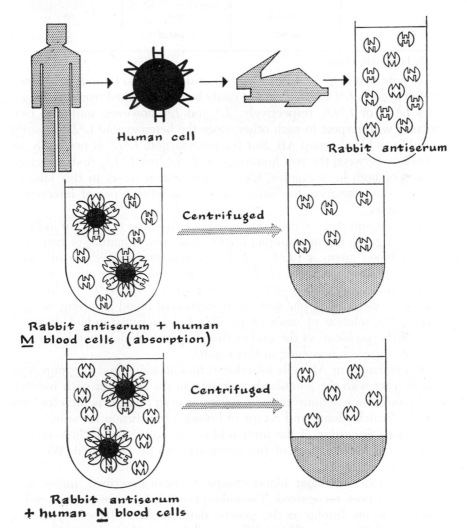

Figure 19-5. *A complex antiserum, produced by injecting human blood into a rabbit, can be fractionated by absorbing out part of the antibodies with blood cells from other persons. This often leaves antibody reagents that will react with blood from some but not all human beings.*

easily recognized because antibodies against the cellular antigens A and B occur normally, as an inherent quality of the blood of human beings lacking these antigens. A number of other red blood cell antigens, genetically unrelated to the L^A locus, can be identified by means of *immune* reactions resulting from blood transfusions or from injecting human blood into animals.

When human red blood cells are injected into rabbits, for example, the rabbits respond by producing very reactive antibodies against this foreign material. *Immune serum,* or *antiserum,* produced in this way will usually agglutinate human blood cells even when the serum is very greatly diluted. If you put three drops of a "good" antiserum of this sort into a quart of physiological salt solution, mix it up, take out two drops of the mixture and add them to a drop of a suspension of human red cells, you will find that the cells agglutinate nicely.

Such a serum is of little direct use in demonstrating individual differences in man. It reacts about equally well with the blood cells of all human beings, because the rabbit has elaborated antibodies against many materials shared by humans but foreign to rabbits. But by a technique known as *antibody absorption,* the serum can often be fractionated so that it will distinguish individual differences in human blood. This technique is illustrated diagrammatically in Figure 19-5.

Essentially, by mixing the serum with the blood cells of a person and then centrifuging down the cells, one can remove all antibodies reacting with the "absorbing" cells. This may leave behind in the supernatant antibodies that will react with the cells of other persons. In Figure 19-5, besides the general human antigens designated as "H" on the cell surface, two antigens (labelled M and N) were present on the cells used in injecting the rabbit. The rabbit elaborated three classes of antibodies, *anti-M, anti-N,* and *anti-H.* Mixing this antiserum with cells containing M (and of course H) but not N, and centrifuging down these cells leaves antibodies specific for N in the supernatant. Similarly, a "reagent" specific for M could be prepared by absorbing the antiserum with N human cells. These two reagents could then be used to identify four kinds of human blood (Table 19-2).

Regarding two human cellular antigens actually called M and N, and

TABLE 19-2. Possible Types of Human Blood, with Regard to Two Reagents.

TYPE	REACTION WITH REAGENT FOR M	REACTION WITH REAGENT FOR N
M	+	0
N	0	+
MN	+	+
None	0	0

identified in this manner, an interesting fact emerges from many tests. No human blood actually lacks both of these antigens. It turns out that M and N are controlled by alleles (just as A and B are), and there is no "O" group in this series. For a long time, the M-N alternative appeared to depend on a simple allelic pair; recent work, however, has shown that there may be greater allelic diversity at the *M-N* locus, somewhat like that previously suggested for the *L* locus.

In much the same way, a number of other characters of human red blood cells can be recognized. Some of these are identified by means of antibodies produced by human beings; other antibody reagents come from animal antisera. The cellular characters are often named from the families in which they were first identified, or sometimes after the responsible investigator. Thus the human cellular characteristics now identified include the Kell, Cellano, Lutheran, Levay, Lewis, Duffy, Jay, Miltenberger, Kidd, and Jobbins antigens in addition to A, B, O, E, G, H, M, N, S, P, X, Q, Gr, and Rh. Numerous genetic loci are "marked" by antigen-controlling genes, and since a good deal of allelic diversity is known at several of these loci, a very great variety of human blood types can be identified.

The Rh Locus. In Chapter 13, we introduced the subject of *erythroblastosis fetalis,* a result of placental transmission of antibodies elaborated by an Rh-negative mother carrying an Rh-positive embryo. The "Rh factor" was first named from tests of human blood with antisera produced by injecting other animals with *rhesus* monkey blood. Some human bloods reacted with certain of these antisera and others did not. The antigen responsible for the reaction was called the "rhesus factor," and reactive bloods were designated as Rh-positive, while those that failed to react were called Rh-negative.

The association between the rhesus factor and hemolytic anemia of the newborn (pp. 264 and 265) was quickly recognized, and this stimulated extensive studies under the direction of several investigators. More than a thousand references dealing with Rh have been published since the first work on this factor in 1939.

As is true for several of the other genes controlling cellular antigens, the Rh locus has turned out to be a very complex one. Spirited controversy has raged around the terminology and interpretation, both genetic and serological, of this complexity. The nomenclature that was accumulated as the complexity unfolded became unwieldy and difficult to follow, but efforts to change it have been debated because the suggested changes involved speculations as to the nature of the Rh-factors that not everyone was willing to grant. The differences of opinion involved in this controversy have not been resolved.

At the core of the difficulty is a factual observation about which there is little debate. A rather long series of Rh "alleles" has had to be named or symbolized in some way. These alleles need not be considered a continuous

ORIGINAL ANTI-Rh₀	CLASSIFIED FOR ANTI-Rh₀, THEN SUBDIVIDED WITH ANTI-Rh′
+ = 85%	+ = 70%
	0 = 15%
0 = 15%	+ = 2%
	0 = 13%

TABLE 19-3. Partial List of Rh Phenotypes.

series; they fall into groups on the basis of the antigens they control and the antibody reagents available. For example, the original anti-Rh reagent, identifying the original Rh-positive/Rh-negative alternative, reacted with the blood cells of about 85 per cent of North American whites. But a second anti-Rh reagent gave a different classification; some of the bloods that were positive to the original were negative to the new reagent, and some that were negative to the original were positive to the new. The classification of Rh reactions (phenotypes) on the basis of both these reagents looked like Table 19-3.

Now, how would you represent in genetic symbols the situation described in Table 19-3? One way is to assume, essentially as A. S. Wiener did, four alleles at the Rh locus, controlling the appearance, respectively, of four distinct antigens (Table 19-4).

This would give the genotypes and phenotypes shown in Table 19-5.

Extensive studies of the inheritance of these Rh types in human families have given results consistent with this kind of symbolism.

Another way of symbolizing the situation is to visualize, essentially as R. A. Fisher did, two different antigens, D and C, each of which may be present or absent. Actually, later discoveries also enter into Fisher's scheme, but in terms of our present discussion this method would lead to Table 19-6.

You will notice that although the two systems of nomenclature describe

TABLE 19-4. Partial List of Rh Alleles and Antigens.

ALLELE	ANTIGEN	REACTIONS OF ANTIGENS TO:	
		Anti-Rh₀	Anti-rh′
R^1	Rh₁	+	+
R^0	Rh₀	+	0
r'	rh′	0	+
r	rh	0	0

TABLE 19-5. *Partial List of Rh Genotypes and Phenotypes.*

GENOTYPES	PHENOTYPES Reactions of Cells to:	
	Anti-Rh$_0$	Anti-rh'
R^1R^1, R^1R^0, R^1r', R^1r or R^0r'	+	+
R^0R^0 or R^0r	+	0
$r'r'$ or $r'r$	0	+
rr	0	0

the same situation, they imply different bases for it. Distinctions between the two schemes are at two levels: that of the *antigens and their reactions with antibodies,* and that of the *gene and its control of the antigens.* In the first system, the gene is symbolized as a unit (e.g., R^1) controlling *an antigen* (e.g., Rh$_1$). This particular antigen is assumed to have the property of reacting with both of the antisera listed. In the second system, the corresponding "gene" is assigned a dual nature, that of controlling two antigens, each quite specific in its reactions with antisera.

The situation has been complicated (or perhaps in the long run clarified) by the discovery of:

1. An additional type of anti-Rh reagent (anti-rh″) that further subdivides the original Rh types (in the Fisher system, this reagent identifies another antigen, E).

2. Reagents (the so-called *"Hr" reagents*) that behave as the exact opposites of Rh reagents, and *react* with Rh-negative antigens while they *fail to react* with Rh-positive ones (in the Fisher system these recognize c, d, and e).

TABLE 19-6. *Partial List of C-D Types.*

ALLELE	ANTIGENS	GENOTYPES	PHENOTYPES Reactions of Cells to:	
			Anti-D (Anti-Rh$_0$)	Anti-C (Anti-rh')
DC	D and C	$\frac{DC}{DC}$, $\frac{DC}{Dc}$, $\frac{DC}{dC}$, $\frac{DC}{dc}$, $\frac{Dc}{dC}$	+	+
Dc	D	$\frac{Dc}{Dc}$, $\frac{Dc}{dc}$	+	0
dC	C	$\frac{dC}{dC}$, $\frac{dC}{dc}$	0	+
dc	—	$\frac{dc}{dc}$	0	0

3. Additional subdivisions within the major Rh types, so that the "C–c alternative" of Fisher, for example, is now represented by a series $C-C^u-C^w-c^v-c$, the "D–d alternative" by $D-D^u-d$, and the "E–e alternative" by $E-E^u-e$.

The debate over nomenclature may seem to be a tempest in a teapot, particularly since only the original Rh-positive *vs.* Rh-negative alternative is of any great clinical significance. About 92 per cent of all cases of erythroblastosis result from the incompatibility between mother and child recognized by this original kind of Rh reagent, the mother being Rh_0-negative and the baby positive. The remaining small percentage of incompatibilities between mother and fetus results only in part from finer differences at the Rh locus; the A–B–O blood groups, for example, are suspected of playing a part, occasionally. Other cellular antigens may also rarely be involved; for instance, the Cellano antigen was first recognized through antibodies found in the blood of the mother of a mildly erythroblastotic baby. To the clinician, therefore, only the Rh_0 (or D) typing of blood is of any great importance in the Rh series, and controversies over interpretation of the further complexities of Rh may seem largely academic. This clinical simplicity is fortunate from a practical point of view, but we must recognize that important fundamental problems are at stake in the "academic" controversy.

Our main problem concerns the nature of the "gene" at the Rh locus. Is it indeed a unit controlling the production of *an antigen?* Are the apparent multiplicities here largely at the level of antigen-antibody interaction? Or does the Rh locus actually comprise three or more closely linked genes, each with its specific antigenic product, as is implied when we label the locus *CDE?* Or is it to be considered a single gene which has been modified by mutation at three different points, each with its specific effect?

These questions relate in obvious ways to the three concepts of the nature of the gene listed earlier in this chapter. We cannot answer these questions at present, but we can perhaps amplify them somewhat by discussing some additional kinds of study.

Blood Cell Antigens in Animals. Only very rarely is there indication that different genes may interact in controlling the specificity of an antigen; almost always, an antigenic specificity is imposed by a single genetic locus. This consideration has led to the hypothesis that the *specificities of cellular antigens are virtually immediate products of the genes that control them.* If this is true, then the field of immunogenetics should be among the most fertile sources of information about the nature of genes and their products.

It is of some interest to note, therefore, that the existence of long multiple allelic series is a very common phenomenon in the field of immunogenetics. In dairy cattle blood cells, for example, at least 80 "alleles" have been described at a single locus, the *B* locus. As in the case of the Rh "alleles" in humans, a given "allele" at any of the several complex loci in cattle seems in general to confer numerous separately identifiable specificities on its product. But whether this appearance is real or results, at least in part, from the reactions of single related antigens with a multiplicity of antibodies is as debatable as it is in the simpler case of Rh in man. There is no evidence in cattle for the subdivision of any complex by crossing over. (Fisher has postulated, without the support of direct observations of recombination, that crossing over occurs within the Rh locus in humans.) Neither is there present indication in cattle of simple constituent "pairs of alternatives" (like the postulated C–c, D–d, and E–e "alternatives" in Rh, for instance) within the complexes.

Other species also display this same kind of immunogenetic complexity.

Position Pseudoallelism. In 1915, Bridges found a single male Drosophila carrying a spontaneous dominant mutation. The mutant had eyes somewhat smaller than wild type; the eyes were rough and showed a slight "gleam" from rumpled hairs on their surface. He called the mutation *star* (*S*). It was at locus 1.3 on the second chromosome.

In 1938, E. B. Lewis found a recessive mutation producing small, rough eyes when homozygous. It was also "mapped" at locus 1.3 on the second chromosome. Heterozygotes receiving star from one parent and the new recessive from the other had very small, rough eyes with many of their facets fused. It would seem that such flies did not receive the "normal allele" of star from one parent and the "normal allele" of the new recessive from the other; if so, they would have been expected to show only the dominant star phenotype.

This interaction in expression of star and the new recessive mutation, their similar map position, and their similar phenotypic effects by themselves, all indicated that star and the new mutation, "star-recessive," were alleles—mutations in the same gene. In conformity with this, when a reasonable number of flies heterozygous for star and "star-recessive" were tested, they were found to form only the two types of germ cells expected from simple segregation of alleles.

However, when Lewis checked a great many flies, he found that these two mutations were in fact separable by ordinary crossing over. Such crossovers were very infrequent; the recessive could be placed about 0.02 units to the right of S. This means only about one recombination in 5000. Even though they were rare, such exchanges clearly demonstrated that two loci, very close together, were involved. "Star-recessive" became *asteroid* (*ast*), and Lewis was able to produce both types of double heterozygotes:

$$\frac{S^+ \quad ast}{S \quad ast^+} \quad \text{and} \quad \frac{S \quad ast}{S^+ \quad ast^+}.$$

Now a point of broad interest became evident. The two types of double heterozygotes looked different (Fig. 19-6). The one on the left, of the sort that came from mating the original star and asteroid stocks together, had very small rough eyes and other abnormalities, *but the type on the right*

Figure 19-6. *The two kinds of doubly heterozygous star-asteroid Drosophila are phenotypically different. Left, in the* trans *arrangement,* $\dfrac{S^+ \; ast}{S \; ast^+}$, *the flies have smaller eyes and other abnormalities. Right, in the* cis *arrangement,* $\dfrac{S \; ast}{S^+ \; ast^+}$, *the flies are like heterozygotes for star alone. (From Lewis,* Cold Spring Harbor Symposia Quant. Biol., **16**:164, 1951.)

had eyes almost exactly like flies heterozygous for star alone. You will recognize this as an example of one kind of "position effect." The effect of *ast* is dependent on whether it has S or S^+ next it on the chromosome.

Several examples of this same kind of situation have been subjected to extensive analysis, not only in Drosophila but also in cotton and corn. Apparently similar observations have been made in Neurospora, mice, pigeons, Aspergillus, and doubtless in other organisms as well. When an apparent multiple allelic series can be shown to be fractionable by crossing over, and when the adjacent loci interact in position effects, suggesting a close relationship in developmental action for the adjacent genes, they are called "position pseudoalleles."

Position Pseudoalleles and the Origin of New Genes. It has long been suspected that new genes may arise in a two-step process. First, a small duplication may provide a chromosome with two representatives of an old gene. Second, one or the other of the duplicate genes may by mutation acquire a new function. We would then observe two genes where one had been before.

In such a situation, we might expect that the function of the new gene would be related to its old function, now being performed by its neighbor on the chromosome. The two might act on the same developmental process. Or they might control intimately related steps in a reaction sequence, such as the immediate product of one serving as the substrate for the other's action.

Many of the important attributes of this kind of speculation seem, in fact, to be represented in position pseudoalleles. In star-asteroid, for example, we can understand the position effect if we assume a reaction sequence,

$$\xrightarrow{\hspace{2cm}} A \xrightarrow{\quad ast^+ \quad} B \xrightarrow{\quad S^+ \quad} C \xrightarrow{\hspace{2cm}}$$

occurring on the chromosomal surface and necessary for normal eye development. Now, in

$$\frac{S \quad ast^+}{S^+ \quad ast}$$

this sequence is blocked in each chromosome, and we might expect an extreme effect. But, in

$$\frac{S \quad ast}{S^+ \quad ast^+},$$

while the sequence is blocked on one chromosome, it can proceed unchecked on the other. The result, in the second case, would be very much like that involved in heterozygosity for star alone. This checks with the experimental observation.

In other pseudoallelic series in Drosophila, cytological evidence indicates that the series are associated with adjacent chromosomal "repeats." And in cotton, Aspergillus, and Neurospora, biochemical study has suggested a close functional relationship in the actions of certain adjacent loci.

This consideration of position pseudoalleles suggests that a gene must be regarded as a unit of chromosomal structure, not subdivisible by crossing over. A unit so defined may also commonly act as a unit in mutation, and as a unit of biochemical action. But sometimes, two or more adjacent genes may be so related in their origin and function that they appear to act together as a unit in development and biochemistry.

Keys to the Significance of This Chapter

Genes are known from genetic studies to be particles with two vital abilities: that of specific self-duplication and that of elaborating highly specific primary products important in the physiology of cells. These attributes appear to be related in character and to depend on the remarkable faculty of genes to organize the cellular materials around themselves into precise molecular patterns.

Physical studies indicate that genes are probably no smaller than protein molecules having a molecular weight of about 100,000, and no larger than average-sized viruses. Chemically, genes are probably nucleoproteins—complexes of nucleic acids and proteins.

Attempts to define the nature of genes commonly involve the consideration of multiple allelic series. Such series, conceived as the result of various mutations in single genes, are particularly common in the field of immunogenetics. The specificities of antigens may be rather closely related to the genes that govern them. There are increasingly perplexing evidences that what appear to be genetic units may in fact control multiple specificities in their products. It is not, however, entirely clear at what level of gene action the immunologist works. Probably, at least part of the apparent complexity arises at the level of antigen-antibody interaction, rather than at the level of genic control of antigenic specificity.

Position pseudoalleles are adjacent loci, so closely associated in inheritance that they are rarely separated by crossing over, interacting in position effects and closely related in their developmental and biochemical action. They may represent a stage in the process through which new genes originate.

References

Caspersson, T., and Schultz, J., "Cytochemical Measurements in the Study of the Gene," in *Genetics in the 20th Century,* pp. 155–171. New York: Macmillan Co., 1951. (Techniques and results, primarily using ultraviolet absorption methods.)

Cole, L. J., and Shackelford, R. M., "White Spotting in the Fox." *Am. Naturalist,* 77:289–321, 1943. (Data and discussions on the subjects of Problems 19-15 and 19-16.)

Fisher, R. A., "The Rhesus Factor. A Study in Scientific Method." *Am. Scientist,* 35:95–102, 113, 1947. (An account of the "three-gene" interpretation of the Rh locus.)

Gluecksohn-Waelsch, Salome, "Physiological Genetics of the Mouse." *Advances in Genetics,* 4:1–51, 1951. (Note especially the complex developmental effects of numerous mutations in chromosome 9, pp. 38–46.)

Green, M. M., and Green, K. C., "Crossing-Over Between Alleles at the Lozenge Locus in *Drosophila melanogaster.*" *Proc. Nat. Acad. Sci.,* 35:586–591, 1949. (Competent, detailed analysis of a position-pseudoallelic series.)

Haldane, J. B. S., *New Paths in Genetics.* New York: Harper & Bros., 1942. (See especially pp. 58–60, in Chap. 2, "Genetics and Biochemistry," for a concise statement of a concept of genic control of various specificities.)

Irwin, M. R., "Genetics and Immunology," in *Genetics in the 20th Century,* pp. 173–219. New York: Macmillan Co., 1951. (A broad review of the hybrid field of immunogenetics.)

Lea, D. E., *Actions of Radiations on Living Cells.* New York: Macmillan Co., 1947. (See especially Chaps. 3, 4, and 5 for material pertinent to the target theory.)

Lewis, E. B., "Pseudoallelism and Gene Evolution." *Cold Spring Harbor Symposia Quant. Biol.*, **16**:159–174, 1951. (A thoughtful and well documented statement of the evolutionary aspects of position pseudoallelism.)

McClintock, B., "The Relation of Homozygous Deficiencies to Mutations and Allelic Series in Maize." *Genetics*, **29**:478–502, 1944. (Basis of Problems 19-11 to 19-14, and a classic report of a physical basis for pseudoallelism.)

Mirsky, A. E., "Some Chemical Aspects of the Cell Nucleus," in *Genetics in the 20th Century*, pp. 127–153. New York: Macmillan Co., 1951. (A summary of current information about the chemistry of chromosomes.)

Muller, H. J., "The Development of the Gene Theory," in *Genetics in the 20th Century*, pp. 77–99. New York: Macmillan Co., 1951. (Includes sections on changes in chromosomal structure, with interesting historical notes, and on gene reproduction.)

Pontecorvo, G., "New Fields in the Biochemical Genetics of Micro-Organisms." *Biochem. Soc. Symposia*, **4**:40–50, 1950. (A critical evaluation, with particular reference to the spacial relations of genes controlling sequential or otherwise related biochemical processes.)

Race, R. R., and Sanger, R., *Blood Groups in Man*. Springfield: C. C. Thomas, 1950. (An up-to-date and interesting discussion of the immunogenetics of human red blood cells.)

Roper, J. A., "Search for Linkage Between Genes Determining a Vitamin Requirement." *Nature*, **166**:956, 1950. (Reporting the pseudoallelic system concerned with biotin synthesis in Aspergillus, Problems 19-20 to 19-24.)

Stadler, L. J., "Spontaneous Mutation in Maize." *Cold Spring Harbor Symposia Quant. Biol.*, **16**:49–63, 1951.

Stephens, S. G., "A Biochemical Basis for the Pseudo-Allelic Anthocyanin Series in Gossypium." *Genetics*, **33**:191–214, 1948. (Source of Problems 19-17 to 19-19; an excellent statement and analysis.)

————, "Possible Significance of Duplication in Evolution." *Advances in Genetics*, **4**:247–265, 1951. (A critical summary, concluding that "the case for the divergence of duplicates is not proved.")

Wiener, A. S., *Blood Groups and Transfusion*, 3rd ed. Springfield: C. C. Thomas, 1943. (This book offers a thorough and clear discussion of various aspects of its subject, including genetic, medical, and anthropological considerations.)

————, "Heredity of the Rh Blood Types VII. Additional Family Studies, with Special Reference to the Genes R^z and r^y." *Proc. Eighth Intern. Congr. Genetics*, 500–519. (Issued as a supplement to *Hereditas*, 1948. A concise review with additional new data.)

Questions and Problems

19- 1. What do the following terms signify? (*List continued on p. 420.*)

agglutination	antiserum
antibody	codominance
antibody absorption	DNA
antigen	gene

immune serum
multiple allelic series
nucleic acid
nucleoprotein

nucleotide
position pseudoallelism
pseudoalleles
RNA

19- 2. What blood groups, and in what proportions, may be expected among the children of the following types of marriages?

a. $L^A L^B \times ll$
b. $L^A L^B \times L^A l$
c. $L^A L^B \times L^A L^A$
d. $L^A l \times L^B l$
e. $L^A L^B \times L^A L^B$

Example: In (a), offspring would be groups A ($L^A l$) and B ($L^B l$), in equal proportion.

19- 3. A woman of blood group A has a child of blood group O. A man accused of being the father of this child proves to be of blood group AB. What could you testify relative to the probable justice of the accusation? How would you phrase your testimony, if the man instead of being AB had been found to be A?

19- 4. Mr. and Mrs. Flam are perturbed to find a tape labelled *Boy Pham* on their week-old baby when they give him his first bath after bringing him home from the hospital. They are particularly disturbed when they discover that Mr. and Mrs. Sham also have a baby boy, born at the same hospital the same night as the Flam baby. Checking with the Shams, they find that the Sham baby was labelled *Boy Slam*, but that the Shams are sure that they have their own baby, because they have repeatedly been told that he looks just like Grandpa Sham. The Flams, however, don't believe that their baby looks like any human they've ever seen.

Blood tests on the individuals concerned give the following results:

	A—B—O	M—N	Rh_o
Mrs. Flam	A	M	Rh_o—positive
Mr. Flam	A	MN	Rh_o—negative
Mrs. Sham	A	N	Rh_o—positive
Mr. Sham	B	MN	Rh_o—positive
Boy Pham	O	MN	Rh_o—positive
Boy Slam	A	N	Rh_o—negative

Assuming that no other families or babies are involved in the possible mixup, which baby really belongs in the Flam family? (*Note:* The problem is of course fanciful; modern hospital identifications make such mixups virtually impossible, and in any case no resemblance to real people is implied in the names cited in this problem.)

In the discussion of color inheritance in mink (Chap. 4), we referred to, but did not discuss, an additional color. This attractive color pattern, called *royal silver,* is phenotypically similar to, but not identical with, the black cross pattern. The genetic relationship of these two characteristics is of some interest.

19- 5. When black cross mink heterozygous for wild type, with no royal silver in their ancestry, were crossed with royal silvers also heterozygous for wild type, with no black cross in their ancestry, the progeny were in the ratio of approximately 2 black cross : 1 royal silver : 1 wild type. Diagram the cross on the assumptions that:

    a. black cross and royal silver are controlled by the dominant alleles of independent genes with the mutant allele for black cross epistatic to that for royal silver;

    b. they are controlled by a multiple allelic series, with the allele for black cross dominant to that for royal silver and to the type allele, while the allele for royal silver is dominant to the type allele.

Do the results cited distinguish these alternative assumptions?

19- 6. Two of the black cross males among the progeny listed in Question 19-5, mated to wild-type females, gave only royal silver and black cross offspring: 12 royal silver and 8 black cross. Do these results support one of the assumptions in Problem 19-5, rendering the other unlikely?

19- 7. Now test a third assumption: that black cross and royal silver represent mutations in two different genes, but that these genes are linked, with 5 per cent recombination between them. Do the data in Problems 19-5 and 19-6 distinguish this assumption from that of multiple allelism? What sort of evidence would you require to accept the assertion that black cross and royal silver result from different mutations in a single gene?

At various times in this book, we have considered two different types of inherited human anemia: *sickle cell* anemia and *thalassemia*. In each instance, a dominant allele when homozygous produces a very severe anemia, but when heterozygous with its normal allele produces a very mild condition, distinguishable from normal only on the basis of careful laboratory examination of blood samples.

19- 8. At present, it is debatable whether sickle cell anemia and thalassemia are controlled by independent genes, or by linked genes, or by alleles. Can you suggest why the collection of critical data on this issue is very difficult in man? What kind of family combination would you need to resolve the issue?

19- 9. In Texas an individual called "Mike D." has a severe anemia, *with sickle cells and cells characteristic of thalassemia* (Powell *et al.*, 1950). One of Mike's parents shows the sickle cell trait (i.e., is heterozygous for sickling); the other shows thalassemia minor (i.e., is heterozygous for thalassemia). Diagram the genetic situation for Mike D. in terms of each of the three possibilities suggested in Question 19-8. What sorts of gene action or interaction might be assumed for each possibility, consistent with the fact that Mike is a severe anemic?

19-10. Mike D., married to a normal woman, has two children, one with sickle cell trait, the other with thalassemia minor. Do these children help to resolve the issues listed in Question 19-8? If this couple has more children, what types might you hope for to give information bearing critically on these issues?

McClintock, in 1944, described the genetic relationships among four chlorophyll characteristics of corn. These were: *green* (normal), *yellow-green, pale-yellow,* and *white.*

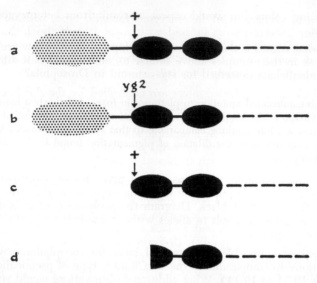

Phenotype appearing   Phenotype appearing
    when homozygous   following combinations

a+a   Green seedling   a+b, c or d _____ seedling
b+b   Yellow-green seedling b+c _____ seedling
c+c   Pale-yellow seedling   b+d _____ seedling
d+d   White seedling   c+d _____ seedling

Figure 19-7. *Genic and chromosomal deviations from standard type* (a) *in chromosome 9 of corn combine to produce a kind of pseudoallelic series.* (*After McClintock,* Genetics, 29:494, 1944.)

Green crossed to any of the three mutant types gave green F_1's, and 3 green: 1 mutant type in F_2. Similarly, both yellow-green and pale-yellow behaved as simple dominants to white.

19-11. On the basis of the information so far given you, diagram the results you would expect of the cross

homozygous yellow-green × a normal plant heterozygous for pale-yellow,

assigning appropriate symbols to alleles.

19-12. Actually, the cross postulated in Problem 19-11 gives only green seedlings. Diagram the cross on the basis of this additional information, listing in formal fashion the symbols utilized and the assumptions involved in your diagram, and recognizing that the combination yellow-green/pale-yellow is green.

19-13. McClintock found that white, in the examples above, was the result of a short terminal deletion in chromosome 9 (Fig. 19-7d). Pale-yellow resulted from an even shorter, similar deletion (Fig. 19-7c), while yellow-green was a recessive mutation at a specific locus very near the end of the same chromosome (Fig. 19-7b). The figure (lower left) lists the phenotypes of seedlings homozygous for these possibilities.
    Fill in the blanks in the list at the lower right in the figure, with the

seedling colors you would expect to result from heterozygous combinations.

19-14. In what regard is the genetic relationship between yellow-green and pale-yellow in the examples above similar to, and how does it differ from, the pseudoallelism described for star-asteroid in Drosophila?

The dominant autosomal mutation to platinum in foxes, lethal when homozygous, was described in Chapter 12. Another dominant mutation in foxes, also lethal when homozygous, produces a white marking comparable to that found in platinum. White-marked foxes, however, do not show the dilution of pigmentation found in the colored parts of the furs of platinums.

19-15. The cross platinum × white-marked gives litters with about ¾ of the normal number of pups. The surviving pups are in the ratio 1 platinum : 1 white-marked : 1 black. Diagram the probable genetic basis of this result, assigning symbols to alleles without committing yourself to chromosomal diagrams.

19-16. Construct a possible chromosomal basis for the platinum/white-marked relationship comparable to the McClintock type of pseudoallelism (Problems 19-11 to 19-14). What additional observations would you require to accept this basis as reasonably secure in fact (*cf.,* Cole and Shackelford, 1943)?

In cotton, normal flower petals are yellow with a basal spot of red (anthocyanin). Three mutant color types, in addition to the standard type, are of interest here:

Standard	Red spot, described above; entire petal "flushes" with red as the petal ages.
Ghost Spot	As in standard type, but basal spot is white, and petal does not flush on aging.
Spotless	No spot at all; clear yellow but petal flushes on aging.
Basic Spotless	No spot, and does not flush on aging.

Stephens has described a biochemical sequence in pigment synthesis, under the control of a pseudoallelic couplet of genes, in part as follows:

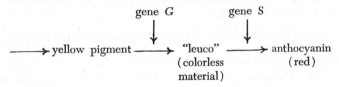

The genetic basis of the homozygous types listed above is then as follows:

Standard	= GS
Ghost Spot	= Gs
Spotless	= gS
Basic Spotless	= gs

G and S are assumed to be completely dominant to their respective alternatives. Crossovers between G and S occur very rarely.

19-17. What phenotypes would you expect in progeny and in F_2 of the following crosses, assuming the parents to be homozygous?

a. Standard × Ghost Spot
b. Standard × Spotless
c. Standard × Basic Spotless
d. Ghost Spot × Basic Spotless
e. Spotless × Basic Spotless
f. Ghost Spot × Spotless.

Example: In (a), F_1 would be GS/Gs (Standard), and F_2 would show 3 Standard : 1 Ghost Spot.

19-18. F_1 progeny of cross (c), are phenotypically indistinguishable from those of cross (f). In what regard is this example similar to the star-asteroid situation in Drosophila? In what important respect are the two instances of pseudoallelism different?

19-19. Discuss the possible significance of the pseudoallelic couplet in cotton in terms of the origin of new genes.

In 1950, Pontecorvo suggested that a class of characteristics in which to search for pseudoallelism would be that of gene-controlled biosynthetic deficiencies in which a critical material is normally produced and utilized in only very small quantities—a few molecules per cell. If such materials had to diffuse rather large distances from their points of origin in the cell to be utilized, then relatively large concentrations would need to be built up to insure that a sufficient number of molecules would reach their points of utilization. If, on the other hand, the points of origin and utilization were very near each other in the cell, a small number of molecules would suffice.

19-20. Taking a biosynthetic sequence for the vitamin biotin as an example, assume a three-step sequence:

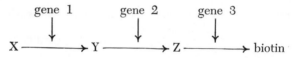

Illustrate or discuss Pontecorvo's hypothesis, contrasting a system in which genes 1, 2, and 3 are widely scattered in chromosomes with one in which they are part of a pseudoallelic series.

19-21. Testing Pontecorvo's hypothesis, Roper examined three different biotin-deficient mutants of the mold *Aspergillus nidulans*. He found that:

a. Each mutant strain differed from wild type in a single allele.
b. Crosses among the mutants, two by two, gave very small percentages of recombinants not requiring biotin.
c. These recombinants derived from crossing over, as shown by other markers on the chromosomes.
d. The loci of the three different mutations are all within a chromosomal segment about 0.2 crossover units long.

Diagram the chromosomal basis of these findings, and discuss their relationship to Pontecorvo's hypothesis.

19-22. Like Neurospora, Aspergillus is normally monoploid; meiosis occurs immediately after fertilization. Could you test for position effect associated with pseudoallelism in the biotin series under this condition? (Consider "heterokaryosis," p. 343.)

19-23. A technique has been developed for the production of diploid Aspergillus. How would you apply this technique to the detection of position pseudo-allelism in the biotin sequence?

19-24. What might you expect to observe in your answer to Problem 19-23, if:

a. The series is like Stephens' cotton, and does not show position effect?
b. The series is like Lewis' Drosophila, and does show position effect?

CHAPTER 20

Heredity in Populations

"**N**OT LONG AGO**,**" says paleontologist George Gaylord Simpson, "paleontologists felt that a geneticist was a person who shut himself in a room, pulled down the shades, watched small flies disporting themselves in milk bottles, and thought that he was studying nature." He adds that a similarly low opinion of paleontologists was generally held by geneticists, but that there is nowadays an increasing tolerance between these two branches of biological science.

You may not be much concerned about what geneticists and paleontologists think or have thought of each other. But since you are now studying genetics, you will doubtless be interested to know that the same relatively recent emphasis that has led to more common interests and greater mutual regard between genetics and paleontology has also broadened the values of genetics to many other branches of biology, including medicine and agriculture. This newer emphasis, as Simpson points out, is an increasing inclination and ability "to think in terms of populations." We will introduce some methods of thinking in terms of heredity in populations in this chapter.

Of the many differences between the usual "milk-bottle populations" of the laboratory on the one hand, and natural populations on the other, two are, from a genetic point of view, probably basic to almost all others. The first is that *the relative frequency of alleles at a locus under study in the laboratory is usually fixed by the design of the experiment at some convenient ratio.* Typically, two homozygous parents are crossed to begin an experiment; the alleles are therefore introduced in equal frequency. *In natural populations, on the other hand, the relative frequencies of alleles may vary greatly;* one allele at a locus may be homozygous in almost all the individuals of a population, and other alleles may be relatively rare. We need to know what effects these variations in the relative frequencies of alleles may have on the genotypes and phenotypes in the population.

The other essential difference between controlled and natural populations concerns the frequencies with which different genotypes and phenotypes mate and leave progeny. *In laboratory populations, a system of mating is usually sharply defined;* the experimenter typically first mates one homozygous class with another, then systematically self-fertilizes or intercrosses the F_1 heterozygotes or mates them back to homozygotes. In controlled plant and animal populations outside the laboratory, the breeder commonly entertains a wider variety of choices, but if he is eager to progress systematically toward the genetic improvement of his material, he adopts some regular system of mating and combines this with some form of selection. Thus, he may methodically outcross or inbreed, or adopt some other definite program based on genetic relationships among the animals or plants he selects as his breeding stock. Or he may select similar or dissimilar animals or plants and mate "likes" or "unlikes" together on the basis of phenotype only.

In natural populations, much more is generally left to chance. A good deal can be said, with respect to human reproduction, for example, in support of the adage that "marriage is a lottery." We will be mainly concerned in this chapter with *random* mating in natural populations—a "system of mating" that is characterized simply by the absence of any design imposed on the pattern of chance matings.

Gene Frequencies for M and N in Bedouins. We observed in the preceding chapter that human beings fall into three classes with respect to the red blood cell characteristics M and N:

		Reactions of Blood Cells to Reagents	
Type	Genotype	Anti-M	Anti-N
M	*MM*	+	0
MN	*MN*	+	+
N	*NN*	0	+

The characteristics M and N depend on alleles; strictly speaking, we should use some common basic symbol for the alleles and distinguish them by superscripts. Instead, we shall adopt the more convenient convention of referring to the alleles in terms of the antigens they control.

A population of 208 Bedouins of the Syrian desert, when tested for M and N, was distributed as follows:

M	MN	N	Total
119	76	13	208

(Data from Boyd, *Tabulae Biologicae*, **17**:234, 1939.)

A glance at these data may suggest that the Bedouins do not conform to Mendelian laws. We are now so accustomed to thinking in terms of 1:2:1

ratios for a simple allelic difference that a ratio like 119:76:13 seems unreasonable. But if you stop to consider this point for a minute, you will see that a 1:2:1 ratio is based on an equal frequency of the two alleles in the population being described; thus, $1MM : 2MN : 1NN$ includes four M and four N alleles in the total of eight representatives of this allelic pair in this ideal population. All that is really clear from a glance at the Bedouin distribution is that M was considerably more frequent than its allele among the Bedouins tested.

We can relabel the classes as genotypes:

MM	MN	NN	Total
119	76	13	208

and observe that there were $(119{\times}2) + 76 = 314M$, and $(13{\times}2) + 76 = 102N$ alleles in the total of $(208{\times}2) = 416$ representatives of this allelic pair in this population. Calculating this on a decimal basis, the *frequency* of M is $\dfrac{314}{416} = 0.75$, and N is $\dfrac{102}{416} = 0.25$. In other words, the M allele was about three times as frequent as the N allele among the Bedouins tested. About ¾ of the chromosomes of the pair bearing the M–N locus carried the M allele, and ¼ the N allele.

This calculation of the relative frequency of alleles in a population illustrates what is meant by *gene frequency*, the basic concept for understanding heredity in populations.

The Binomial Distribution of Genotype Frequencies. One of the primary advantages of computing gene frequencies on a decimal or fractional basis, as was done for M and N in the Bedouin population above, is that the frequencies so computed can be treated and manipulated as *probabilities*. For example, the probability that any given chromosome of the proper pair will carry the allele M, in the above population, is 0.75. The similar probability for N is 0.25. The probabilities of the different *genotypes* in the population, if these chromosomes are combined in pairs by chance, are therefore:

$$MM = 0.75 \times 0.75 = 0.56$$
$$\left.\begin{array}{l} MN = 0.75 \times 0.25 = 0.19 \\ NM = 0.25 \times 0.75 = 0.19 \end{array}\right\} = 0.38$$
$$NN = 0.25 \times 0.25 = 0.06$$

On the basis of random combinations we should therefore expect a distribution of genotypes, among the 208 Bedouins, of about:

$$0.56 \times 208 = 117 \ MM$$
$$0.38 \times 208 = 79 \ MN$$
$$0.06 \times 208 = 12 \ NN$$

This is very close to the actual distribution of 119:76:13.

These computations demonstrate a precision in the distribution of genotypes for *M* and *N* in Bedouins that was not evident in the unanalyzed frequencies. We can state the case in more general terms:

1. If p is the frequency of a particular allele *A*, and q is the frequency of its alternative *a*, then the chance distribution of genotypes in a population will be p²*AA* + 2pq*Aa* + q²*aa*.

By comparing this general statement with the specific example of *M* and *N* in Bedouins, you can easily see how the distribution is derived. If allele *A* occurs with frequency p, then when chromosomes carrying the *A* locus are combined in pairs at random, the probability that both members of a pair will carry *A* is p × p, or p². Similarly, the probability of the *aa* combination is q², and of *Aa* is pq + pq, or 2pq.

2. The distribution p² + 2pq + q² can be written in another way, $(p + q)^2$. This is the familiar *binomial*, about which we shall have a good deal more to say later.

3. In terms of the above symbolism, p + q = 1. For example, the *M* and *N* frequencies in Bedouins were p(*M*) = 0.75; q(*N*) = 0.25, and 0.75 + 0.25 = 1.00. We can eliminate the symbol p, when we wish to do so, by observing that p = 1 − q. Rewritten on this basis, the distribution of genotypes becomes (1 − q)²*AA* + 2q(1 − q)*Aa* + (q²)*aa*.

The fact that p + q = 1 simply means that our symbols *A* and *a* take account of all of the alleles at this locus in the population. If we are dealing with a multiple allelic series, we can either define the frequencies as p = frequency of *A*, and q = total frequency of all other alleles at this locus, and apply the same kind of analysis, or we can add other symbols. For the alleles controlling the human blood groups, for example, we can use:

$$p = \text{frequency of } L^A$$
$$q = \text{frequency of } L^B$$
$$r = \text{frequency of } l$$

TABLE 20-1. M and N Blood Types in Samples of Three Populations. (*From Boyd*, Tabulae Biologicae, **17**:230, 235, 1939.)

POPULATION	NUMBER TESTED	PHENOTYPES OBSERVED			GENE FREQUENCIES		PHENOTYPES EXPECTED		
		M	MN	N	p(M)	q(N)	p²(M)	2pq(MN)	q²(N)
American Indian (Pueblo)	140	83	46	11	0.76	0.24	81	51	8
Brooklyn, U.S.A.	1849	541	903	405	0.54	0.46	536	925	388
Australian Aborigines	102	3	44	55	0.25	0.75	6	38	58

Then $p + q + r = 1$. We will return to this kind of analysis later. The main point is that in calculating and applying gene frequencies for a locus the separate allelic frequencies must add up to unity.

Binomial Distribution of Genotypes in Other Populations. You may regard it as accidental that the 208 Bedouins tested for M and N showed so nice a "binomial distribution" of genotypes. In Table 20-1 several other populations are classified for M and N types.

You should check the *expected* column yourself, to be sure that you know how to calculate gene frequencies and expected genotypic frequencies from population data. Try some chi-square tests to see how closely the observed and expected agree.† You will find that in all three of these populations the observed distribution of phenotypes agrees satisfactorily with that expected from probability calculations based on the gene frequencies.

Another point is evident here. Different populations show markedly different frequencies of these alleles. The Pueblo Indians, like the Bedouins, have relatively more M alleles than N alleles, but this situation is almost exactly reversed in the Australian Aborigines; there N is three times as frequent as M. In fact, the comparison of gene frequencies in human populations is one way of describing these populations genetically.

The Binomial Distribution of Genotypes as an Equilibrium Distribution. The precision with which a variety of populations fits the chance distribution of genotypes for M and N suggests that this kind of distribution provides a general basis for the genetic structure of populations. If an allele A has a frequency p in a population, and allele a has a frequency q, and if $p + q = 1$, then chance combinations of gametes through random mating in this population will give in the next generation approximately the distribution shown in Table 20-2.

The binomial distribution of genotypes is therefore approximated in a single generation of random mating, and it is maintained in successive generations. A population enjoying this kind of genetic stability of structure is described as being in *equilibrium*.

The stability asserted above is of course not a matter of absolute and immovable fixation. Various factors act to move or to modify this particular

---

† In doing chi-square tests on these distributions, you should note that, although there are three classes, there is only one degree of freedom. This is because for any given total number of people typed for M and N, only one class can be filled in at random; once this class is filled the other two are automatically committed. For example, in a sample of 100 people having 50M alleles, any number up to 25 of these people may be of blood type M (MM). To fill this class in at random, suppose that 14 are MM. This means that the remaining 22M alleles are in heterozygotes, and the sample must be 14MM : 22MN : 64NN.

Incidentally, if you check this *hypothetical* population against the binomial expectation for the same gene frequencies, you will find that the two differ greatly. This should serve to convince you that the precision of the distribution in the *natural* populations we have been discussing reflects a significant aspect of population structure, and is not simply a result of the alegbraic manipulations in which we have indulged.

TABLE 20-2. Results of Random Combinations of Sperm and Eggs.

		Sperm		
		A(p)	a(q)	
Eggs	A(p)	AA(p²)	Aa(pq)	= p²AA + 2pqAa + q²aa
	a(q)	Aa(pq)	aa(q²)	

random equilibrium and to change the relative frequencies of genes and genotypes from generation to generation. The pressure of mutation from A to *a*, for example, serves to increase the value of q at the expense of p; and this is opposed by the pressure of reverse mutation, from *a* to A. If we were to consider only the values of p and q for many generations, we would find that under the counterbalancing pressures of mutation and reverse mutation an *equilibrium* for the value of p is achieved, and that the point at which this value stabilizes is determined by the relative rates of mutation in the two directions for the particular locus under study. Similarly, *selection,* in which one genotype or phenotype leaves (or is permitted to leave) fewer progeny than others, acts to modify the relative frequency of alleles from generation to generation. If individuals of blood type M were sterile or partly sterile, for instance, or were barred from marrying in Brooklyn, the relative frequency of N would increase in later generations, until this population reached and even surpassed the level of the Australian Aborigines in this regard. Similarly, migration, for instance of Bedouins into Brooklyn, would change the character of the Brooklyn population. And beneath all this, the sampling nature of Mendelian inheritance itself subjects the relative frequencies of alleles to chance variations.

These are all parts of the dynamics of population behavior basic to evolutionary change and to the improvement or deterioration of both natural and controlled populations. We will discuss them in more concrete fashion in the next chapter.

On the level of genotype and phenotype frequencies, still other variables enter to modify the chance binomial distributions. We have based the binomial equilibrium on random mating, in which each genotype mated with each other genotype with a frequency strictly proportional to the relative numbers of these genotypes in the population, that is, on a purely chance basis. But sometimes in nature, and often in controlled populations, there may be systematic deviations from this pattern of chance matings, so that one genotype, for example, may be more likely to mate with a similar genotype than with a different one. We have already seen, in the chapter on inbreeding, how over a period of time one such system may result in the relative increase in the proportion of homozygous genotypes at the expense of heterozygous ones. The effect of different systems of mating, departing from the random scheme, is often to establish stable equilibrium distributions of genotypes and phenotypes different from the equilibrium achieved under random mating.

Our choice of the M–N alternative for our introductory illustration was a considered one, based among other things on the following attributes of this particular characteristic:

1. Most people grow up, marry, have children, and die without ever knowing their M–N type. Even when the type is known, it does not influence decisions to marry or to have children. The frequencies of the different kinds of matings, with regard to M and N, are determined by the frequencies of the genotypes themselves within any freely intermarrying population.

2. The M–N alternative has no established effect on the survival or fecundity of humans. In other words, selection is not known to modify the relative frequencies of the M and N alleles in any population.

3. Since the heterozygote MN is phenotypically distinguishable from either homozygote, the frequency of each allele can be directly computed from the phenotype frequencies in the population. In the more common situation in which one allele is dominant, some aspects of the computations must be less direct. We will turn to this complication now.

Dominance and Gene Frequency. A lecturer recently explained an historical change in the skull shape of an Indian population as being in large part the result of the genetic dominance of alleles for the increasingly frequent broad, short skull. In the opinion of this speaker, the genetic dominance of an allele was supposed to be reflected in the numerical predominance in a population of the phenotypic characteristic this allele controlled.

The fallacy of this opinion will be evident to you. The frequency of a phenotype in a population depends on the frequency of the allele controlling it, and this in turn has no necessary relation to the dominance or recessiveness of the allele. For example, the allele for *fragile bones with blue sclera* (p. 303) is dominant to its normal alternative in man, but this condition is only rarely encountered in human populations. This is because this dominant allele is very infrequent, while its normal alternative is common. Many similar human examples might be cited.

As an example of genotype and phenotype frequencies for a dominant-recessive alternative in a population, we can consider the simply inherited difference in human ability to taste the compound called PTC (phenylthiocarbamide or phenylthiourea). Some people find this compound very bitter; they are called *tasters* for PTC. Others (*nontasters*) find it tasteless or virtually so. The difference depends on a simple Mendelian alternative, in which the allele for taster (T) is dominant to that for nontaster (t).

If the members of your class are tested, you will probably find that about 70 per cent are tasters, and 30 per cent nontasters. We can therefore write:

Phenotypes:	Tasters	Nontasters
Genotypes:	$TT+Tt$	tt
Frequencies:	0.7	0.3

Now we can assume that the population is at equilibrium under random mating for these alleles. If so, the genotypes should be distributed as follows:

If p = frequency of T
q = frequency of t
$p + q = 1$

Then the genotypes occur in the following ratio:

$$p^2TT : 2pqTt : q^2tt$$

We know that q^2 (the frequency of nontasters) = 0.3.
Therefore,

$$q = \sqrt{0.3}, \text{ and } q = 0.55$$
$$\text{since } p + q = 1,$$
$$p = 1 - q; \ p = 0.45$$

The probable distribution of genotypes in the population can now be computed:

p^2TT	:	$2pqTt$	:	q^2tt
$(0.45)^2$	:	$2(0.45)(0.55)$	:	$(0.55)^2$
0.2	:	0.5	:	0.3

The Utility of Gene-Frequency Analysis. The preceding section involves an important extension of our consideration of gene frequencies. Up to this point, we had been using rather obvious characteristics of a population to derive some information about gene frequencies. But we are now able to extrapolate from our knowledge of gene frequencies and their consequences to some characteristics of other populations that are not obvious, because the recessive allele is obscured by its dominant alternative in heterozygotes in the population. The calculation of the frequencies of homozygotes and heterozygotes among tasters is a case in point.

Suppose, for example, we should ask what kinds of children (with respect to the taster-nontaster alternative), and in what proportions, marriages between tasters would be likely to produce. Without the gene-frequency analysis, we could have observed that some of the taster parents would be likely to be heterozygous, and that whenever two such heterozygotes married, a quarter of their children on the average would be expected to be nontasters. But we could not often tell which of the taster parents actually were heterozygous, and except in rather special cases we could not make a statistical prediction for the children of tasters at all.

Knowing, however, that homozygotes (TT) and heterozygotes (Tt) should occur in the population in a ratio of 2:5, it is easy to predict the consequences of marriages between tasters with regard to this characteristic:

Probability of father's being heterozygous = $5/7$
Probability of mother's being heterozygous = $5/7$
Probability of both parents' being heterozygous = $5/7 \times 5/7 = 25/49$

Approximately half of the matings between tasters, therefore, will be between heterozygotes.

The other matings between tasters, $TT \times TT$ and $TT \times Tt$, will have no nontaster children.

The matings between heterozygous tasters will be expected to have children in the ratio: ¾ tasters : ¼ nontasters.

The probability of a nontaster child from a taster × taster marriage is therefore:

> Probability that a given mating is between two heterozygotes = ½
> Probability of nontaster child from this mating = ¼
> Probability of nontaster child from taster × taster mating = ½ × ¼ = ⅛.

Taster × taster matings in our population should therefore produce children in the ratio of approximately ⅞ taster : ⅛ nontaster. *One study reports an observed ratio of 464 taster : 65 nontaster children from such matings.†* *Is this in agreement with expectation?*

> Confirm by the same sort of calculation that marriages of taster × nontaster should produce children in the ratio of about $\frac{9}{14}$ *taster* : $\frac{5}{14}$ *nontaster*.
>
> We can work the above problem in several somewhat different ways. Two of these are shown below:

1. Probability that taster parent is heterozygous = 5/7
   Probability of nontaster children from heterozygous taster × nontaster = ½
   Probability of nontaster child from taster × nontaster mating = 5/7 × ½ = 5/14
   Probability of taster child from above mating type = $1 - \frac{5}{14} = \frac{9}{14}$.

2.

	Taster × Nontaster Matings		
	Frequency	Children	
		Taster	Nontaster
$TT \times tt$	2/7	2/7	
$Tt \times tt$	5/7	5/14	5/14
Total		9/14	5/14

One study reports an observed ratio of 242 taster : 139 nontaster children from such matings.† Is this in agreement with expectation?

The taster characteristic is interesting, but in itself it is of relatively little practical concern. For example, one can be a nontaster for PTC and still enjoy roast beef with mashed potatoes and brown gravy perfectly well. You will be able to see, however, how the kind of predictions made possible through gene-frequency analyses, introduced here by means of the taster-nontaster example, can sometimes be of great value in connection with simply inherited characteristics of greater human and medical concern.

† These data are from *The Principles of Heredity*, by L. H. Snyder, D. C. Heath & Co., 1951, p. 499.

Furthermore, the gene-frequency analysis provides a tool for genetic research in populations beyond laboratory control. The frequencies of phenotypes and the results of different types of matings in human populations,
for example, should be consistent with gene-frequency considerations. If a
given trait does not conform to expectation in this regard, and if there is
no good reason to suspect that nonrandom mating or selection, or some
other specified factor, is responsible for the deviations, then the investigator is likely to conclude that the basis of inheritance of the trait is more
complex than had at first been suspected. In fact, the only human genes
that may be considered as adequately studied are those that have been
subjected to detailed gene-frequency analyses and have met all the tests
that human population geneticists have devised on this basis. There are
several such tests.

This field is a rather complex mathematical and statistical one, and it
need not be explored further in this general text. Those who are interested
in the research aspects of human heredity will find, in the references cited
at the end of this chapter, techniques available for the distinction of different types of simply inherited characteristics, for the calculation of linkage intensities, for the measurement of penetrance, and for many related
and similar problems.

Special Aspects of Gene Frequency. Before turning to other subjects,
we will consider three rather special aspects of gene frequency. These involve, respectively, *sex linkage, multiple alleles,* and *cousin marriages.*

Sex Linkage. Since one sex is haploid for genes on the sex chromosome,
this sex cannot show the binomial distribution for chance combinations of
chromosomes in pairs.

If p = frequency of A
q = frequency of a
$p + q = 1$

Then the equilibrium distribution of genotypes will be:

In "XY" sex: $pA + qa$
In "XX" sex: $p^2AA + 2pqAa + q^2aa$

You will note that the gene frequency of a sex-linked characteristic can be
obtained directly from its frequency in the sex having a single X-chromosome.
This should check in specific ways with the frequency of the characteristic in
the XX sex. For example, the frequency of a sex-linked recessive characteristic among men should be the same as the square root of its frequency among
women, since the frequency of the recessive phenotype is q in men, q^2 in
women.

One consequence of this relationship is that sex-linked recessive characteristics are more common in men than in women. Among men, the recessive
phenotype occurs with the same frequency as the responsible allele does,
while among women the frequency of the phenotype is the square of the
gene frequency. Thus, if one man in ten were color blind due to the common
sex-linked gene for this characteristic, only one woman in one hundred

would show the same type of color blindness. The actual figures in our population are not far from these values, although the occurrence of types of color blindness other than the common kind we have been considering complicates the analysis somewhat.

Another interesting characteristic of sex-linkage is that equilibrium under random mating is not approximated in a single generation, as it is for autosomal alleles. This is because X-chromosomes are not combined randomly in pairs by random mating; a male receives his X-chromosome only from his mother and transmits it only to his daughters. The approach to equilibrium is, however, sufficiently rapid and close so that equilibrium for a sex-linked allelic pair can generally be assumed, for all practical purposes, after four or five generations of random matings.

If the generations overlap in time, so that they are not wholly distinct, the approach to equilibrium is more rapid.

Multiple Alleles. We deferred, earlier in the chapter, the gene-frequency analysis of multiple allelic series, and we should consider it briefly here. Taking the A, B, and O blood groups as an example,

$$\text{Let } p = \text{frequency of } L^A$$
$$q = \text{frequency of } L^B$$
$$r = \text{frequency of } l$$
$$p + q + r = 1.$$

Then the equilibrium distribution of genotypes under random mating is $(p + q + r)^2$. These are tabulated by phenotypes in Table 20-3.

The value of r is immediately obvious as the square root of the frequency of the O class. The values of p and q can be determined somewhat less directly. (In this determination, when we use a symbol $\bar{A}$, $\bar{B}$, $\overline{AB}$, or $\bar{O}$, we mean *the frequency of A, B, AB, and O phenotypes*.)

$$\bar{A} + \bar{O} = p^2 + 2pr + r^2$$
$$= (p + r)^2$$
$$\sqrt{\bar{A} + \bar{O}} = p + r$$

But, since $p + q + r = 1$, $\quad p + r = 1 - q$

therefore $1 - q = \sqrt{\bar{A} + \bar{O}}$

$$q = 1 - \sqrt{\bar{A} + \bar{O}}$$

Similarly, $p = 1 - \sqrt{\bar{B} + \bar{O}}$

PHENOTYPE	GENOTYPE	FREQUENCY
A	$L^A L^A$	p^2
	$L^A l$	$2pr$
B	$L^B L^B$	q^2
	$L^B l$	$2qr$
AB	$L^A L^B$	$2pq$
O	ll	r^2

TABLE 20-3. *Equilibrium Frequencies of Human Blood Groups.*

As an example of a population apparently in equilibrium for the human blood groups, we can turn again to Brooklyn (Table 20-4).

TABLE 20-4. Gene Frequencies for Human Blood Groups in Brooklyn. (From Boyd, Tabulae Biologicae, 17:166, 1939.)

NUMBER OF INDIVIDUALS TESTED	NUMBER OF BLOOD GROUPS				GENE FREQUENCIES		
	O	A	B	AB	$p(L^A)$	$q(L^B)$	$r(l)$
1849	808 (43.7%)	699 (37.8%)	259 (14.0%)	83 (4.5%)	0.24	0.10	0.66

The calculation of p, the frequency of L^A, is as follows:

$$p = 1 - \sqrt{B + O}$$
$$= 1 - \sqrt{0.14 + 0.437}$$
$$p = 0.24$$

You can check the values of q and r for yourself. You will note that the allele L^B is relatively infrequent in Brooklyn. It is even rarer in American Indians, with a frequency of only 0.007 in Pueblo Indians, for example. But it is more common in Orientals; in Canton, for example, it is more frequent than is allele L^A. The human blood groups provide a good anthropological tool in the genetic description of human populations.

In such a city as Brooklyn, racial, religious, economic, and other barriers split the total population up into subgroups among which mating is not at random. Insofar as there are differences in the frequencies of the blood-group alleles among these partial *isolates* in the population, we might expect deviations from the random-mating equilibrium in the total population. Such deviations, however, are not statistically evident in the data cited in Table 20-4.

Cousin Marriages. Another interesting gene-frequency consideration in human populations concerns matings between relatives. In the Western world, about one marriage in 200 is between cousins; this is the closest form of "inbreeding" practiced with significant frequency in our population.

If two people (call them John and Mary) are essentially unrelated, their children will have two parents, four different grandparents, and eight different great-grandparents. But if John and Mary are first cousins, their chil-

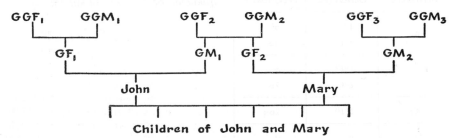

Figure 20-1. *John and Mary are first cousins.*

dren will have only six different great-grandparents; one pair is duplicated in their pedigree (Fig. 20-1).

Now, suppose that one of the common great-grandparents, say great-grandfather 2 (GGF$_2$), was heterozygous for a rare recessive defect. John's mother (GM$_1$) had one chance in two of inheriting this particular allele from him, and the probability that John himself has it is $\frac{1}{4}$ ($\frac{1}{2}$ for the probability that his mother has it × $\frac{1}{2}$ for the probability that if she has it, John inherited it from her = $\frac{1}{4}$, the probability that both events occurred). Similarly, the probability is $\frac{1}{4}$ that Mary is heterozygous for the same recessive defect, tracing back to GGF$_2$. The probability that *both* John and Mary are heterozygous is $\frac{1}{4} \times \frac{1}{4} = \frac{1}{16}$, and if they are both carriers, their children have an average expectation of one chance in four of showing the recessive defect in the homozygous condition.

On the other hand, if John and Mary were unrelated, it would be very unlikely that they would both be carriers of the same rare recessive defect.

We can cite an example of the effect of this situation. Only about one in 20,000 Western Europeans is an albino. The allele for albinism is therefore very rare. About 15 per cent of the albinos in this population come from first-cousin marriages; in other words, the incidence of first-cousin marriages among the parents of albinos is very much higher than it is in the population generally.

Note carefully that we did not say that 15 per cent of cousin marriages produce albinos! On the contrary, albinos are, of course, very rare even among the children of first cousins. Only when we look at the figures the other way around and notice that the frequency of cousin marriages is relatively high among the parents of the rare albinos do we detect the effect of this mild form of inbreeding in human society. In fact, the rarer the allele we are considering, the more likely it is that the allele depends in large part on matings between relatives to reach homozygosity and therefore phenotypic expression in the population. A good method of estimating the frequency of a rare recessive is to determine the incidence of cousin marriages among the parents of children homozygous for the defect.

Cousin marriages represent, by our standards set in Chapter 16, a very slight form of inbreeding. They have little effect, compared with self-fertilization or brother-sister matings, for example, in increasing general homozygosity. They are not, of course, necessarily "harmful," and some of the most prominent men and women in history have had parents who were cousins. But there are many rare recessive defects, carried for the most part hidden in human germ plasm. In view of the increased likelihood that any one of these defects will crop up in the progeny of cousins, an individual does doubtless run a somewhat greater risk of aberrant children if he marries a first cousin than he does if he marries an unrelated person. On the other hand, of course, desirable recessive traits are also more likely to come to expression in the children of related individuals.

There is in most societies a general repugnance to matings between relatives, and this often extends so far as to discourage marriages between people as slightly related as cousins. It has been suggested that part of this repugnance is biological and is based on unsystematic observations of an increased frequency of abnormal children among the progeny of related people. More probably, however, other social and economic considerations are responsible for the taboos against marriages between relatives. In this connection, we might introduce an amusing quotation from Dahlberg:

"It may also be relevant that near relationship brings about an intimate mutual understanding of shortcomings and defects, and that such knowledge is inimical to the production of an illusion which is often a prerequisite for marital union."

Another Application of the Binomial Distribution. An aspect of probability in human families, quite different from the gene-frequency considerations we have been studying, also involves the binomial distribution. To illustrate this, we can ask: "Among families with two children, what proportion will have two boys? A boy and a girl? Two girls?"

There will be four kinds of families of two children, and if we can assume for the present a sex ratio of 1:1, these four types of families will be equal in frequency. Considering the children in order of birth, and letting B stand for boy and G for girl, the families will be:

$$1BB : 1BG : 1GB : 1GG$$

As far as sex ratios are concerned, disregarding birth order, the families will be distributed:

$$1BB : 2BG : 1GG, \text{ or } \tfrac{1}{4}BB : \tfrac{1}{2}BG : \tfrac{1}{4}GG$$

Another way of arriving at this is more direct. If the probability of a boy on any trial is $\tfrac{1}{2}$, then the probability of boys on each of two independent trials is $\tfrac{1}{2} \times \tfrac{1}{2} = \tfrac{1}{4}$. Similarly, the probability of two girls is $\tfrac{1}{2} \times \tfrac{1}{2} = \tfrac{1}{4}$. But there are two ways one could get one boy and one girl—namely, *boy then girl* and *girl then boy*. So this probability is $2 \times \tfrac{1}{2} \times \tfrac{1}{2} = \tfrac{1}{2}$. The probability distribution is therefore:

$$(\tfrac{1}{2})^2 BB : 2(\tfrac{1}{2})(\tfrac{1}{2})BG : (\tfrac{1}{2})^2 GG$$
$$\tfrac{1}{4} \qquad\qquad \tfrac{1}{2} \qquad\qquad\quad \tfrac{1}{4}$$

This checks with our previous result.

How about families of three children? On the same assumption, the experience of different families will be:

	GBB	BGG	
BBB	BGB	GBG	GGG
	BBG	GGB	
1	: 3	: 3	: 1
(3 boys)	(2 boys)	(1 boy)	(3 girls)
	(1 girl)	(2 girls)	
($\tfrac{1}{8}$)	($\tfrac{3}{8}$)	($\tfrac{3}{8}$)	($\tfrac{1}{8}$)

or, on the more direct basis:

$$(\tfrac{1}{2})^3 + 3(\tfrac{1}{2})^2(\tfrac{1}{2}) + 3(\tfrac{1}{2})(\tfrac{1}{2})^2 + (\tfrac{1}{2})^3$$
$$\text{(3 boys)} \quad \text{(2 boys, 1 girl)} \quad \text{(1 boy, 2 girls)} \quad \text{(3 girls)}$$
$$\tfrac{1}{8} \qquad\qquad \tfrac{3}{8} \qquad\qquad\qquad \tfrac{3}{8} \qquad\qquad \tfrac{1}{8}$$

You can work out the distribution in families of four children, and confirm that it would be:

$$(\tfrac{1}{2})^4 \;+\; 4(\tfrac{1}{2})^3(\tfrac{1}{2}) \;+\; 6(\tfrac{1}{2})^2(\tfrac{1}{2})^2 \;+\; 4(\tfrac{1}{2})(\tfrac{1}{2})^3 \;+\; (\tfrac{1}{2})^4$$
(4 boys) (3 boys, 1 girl) (2 boys, 2 girls) (1 boy, 3 girls) (4 girls)
($\tfrac{1}{16}$)   ($\tfrac{4}{16}$)   ($\tfrac{6}{16}$)   ($\tfrac{4}{16}$)   ($\tfrac{1}{16}$)

Such computations become tedious. Fortunately, there is a convenient shortcut. The frequencies of the various combinations correspond to the coefficients of the binomial expansion:

$$(a + b)^2 = a^2 + 2ab + b^2$$
$$(a + b)^3 = a^3 + 3a^2b + 3ab^2 + b^3$$
$$(a + b)^4 = a^4 + 4a^3b + 6a^2b^2 + 4ab^3 + b^4$$

and so on.

The *exponents* of a and b in these expansions correspond to the *number of children of each type* in the family to which the coefficient applies. We can make this clearer by illustrating its use.

The general formula is:

$$(a + b)^s$$

Where a is the probability of a boy($\tfrac{1}{2}$).

b is the probability of a girl($\tfrac{1}{2}$).

s is the number of children per family in the family size under consideration.

Now we can ask: What is the probability that in a family of five children, there will be two boys and three girls? In this example:

$$(a + b)^5 = a^5 + 5a^4b + 10a^3b^2 + 10a^2b^3 + 5ab^4 + b^5$$

We want the value of $10a^2b^3$ (that is, 2 boys, 3 girls). This is:

$$10(\tfrac{1}{2})^2(\tfrac{1}{2})^3 = \tfrac{10}{32} = \tfrac{5}{16}$$

In other words, among sixteen families of five children each, about five such families on the average should have two boys and three girls.

Regularities of the Binomial Expansion. Two symmetries in the binomial expansion make its use easy.

1. Coefficients.   The coefficients of successive powers of the binomial can be arranged in a regular triangle (*Pascal's triangle*).

Powers (s)	Coefficients							
1	1	1						
2	1	2	1					
3	1	3	3	1				
4	1	4	6	4	1			
5	1	5	10	10	5	1		
6	1	6	15	20	15	6	1	
7	1	7	21	35	35	21	7	1
8	1	8	28	56	70	56	28	8	1

You will note that the rows across are symmetrical, and that in the triangle each number is the sum of the numbers immediately above and immediately to the left above. Mathematicians usually prefer symbolical statements of the binomial that make it possible to pick out any coefficient without building up the whole triangle. You may well prefer this, too, if you know the necessary formula and how to use it. But for our present concern it is sufficient to have the "rule of thumb" available in the triangle.

2. Exponents. The exponents in the binomial expansion also follow regular series. For example, in

$$(a + b)^6 = a^6 + 6a^5b + 15a^4b^2 + 20a^3b^3 + 15a^2b^4 + 6ab^5 + b^6,$$

you will note that the exponents of a begin at the power to which the binomial is raised and decrease regularly to 0, while the reverse is true of the exponents of b.

Other Similar Uses of the Binomial. The utility of the binomial is not limited to calculations involving 1:1 ratios. The probabilities a and b can be any fractions whose sum equals unity. Among marriages between heterozygotes, for example,

a = probability of a child showing the dominant characteristic = ¾
b = probability of a child showing the recessive characteristic = ¼
a + b = 1

Among families of eight children whose parents are both heterozygous, how many will have exactly six children showing the dominant and two the recessive characteristic?

$$(a + b)^8 = (¾ + ¼)^8$$

Term needed $= 28a^6b^2 = 28(¾)^6(¼)^2 = 0.31$

This is a rather academic example, but it illustrates one interesting point: Among families of eight, only about one-third will show the ideal ratio of 6:2, and the other families will deviate from this expected value in one direction or the other.

We could also ask questions along this line: How often, in families of eight, would we expect the deviation from the expected 6:2 ratio to be as much as or more than two? In other words, how often would there be eight children showing the dominant, or four or less showing the dominant? We could get the answer by summing the appropriate terms of the binomial. Several statistical tests, including the χ^2 table now familiar to us, are derived more or less directly from the binomial distribution and this kind of consideration.

Probabilities and Independent Events. It is sometimes confusing to note that two apparently similar cases have different probabilities if more information is available on one than on the other. For example, if you are planning to have two children, you have about one chance in four of having both of them be boys. But if you already have one boy, your second also has one chance in two of being a boy. This may seem inconsistent; in the one case the chance for two boys is only one-fourth, while in the second it is one-half.

The difference, of course, is that the probabilities are based on different opportunities in the two cases. In the first, having two boys is one of four equally likely eventualities:

BB   BG   GB   GG

But in the second case, the last two of these eventualities have been eliminated; you already have a "success" on the first trial. Now there are only two equally likely eventualities:

BB and BG

and the probability of BB has increased to ½.

The problems we have been considering all depend on the *independence* of the successive events whose probabilities are computed. Even if a family has nine boys in a row, we assume that the chance of a girl on the tenth trial is still ½.

Keys to the Significance of This Chapter

The extension of Mendelian genetics to the patterns of inheritance in populations is important to many branches of biology, particularly those dealing with human, agricultural, and natural populations. The primary differences between these populations and the usual laboratory populations of the geneticist involve variations in the relative frequencies of alleles and in the patterns of mating.

The relative frequencies of alleles can be computed as gene frequencies and treated as probabilities. Under random mating, a population approximates in a single generation an equilibrium distribution of genotypes and phenotypes for an autosomal allelic pair. This binomial distribution of genotypes provides a basis for analysis of the genetic structure of populations, and suggests useful tools for research and applications in the field of human heredity.

Gene frequency analyses can be extended to such special aspects of genetics as sex linkage, multiple alleles, and cousin marriages.

Besides expressing the relationships of genotype frequencies in populations, binomial distributions describe the characteristics of families of given sizes, segregating for specific attributes in clear-cut ratios.

References

Boyd, W. C., "Blood Groups." *Tabulae Biologicae,* **17**:113–240, 1939. (A general introduction to the blood groups, with frequency data on many populations, and an extensive bibliography.)

Boyd, W. C., *Genetics and the Races of Man*. Boston: Little, Brown & Co., 1950. (See especially Chap. 9, "Use of Blood Groups in Human Classification.")

Dahlberg, G., *Mathematical Methods for Population Genetics*. New York: Interscience, 1948.

————, *Race, Reason, and Rubbish. A Primer of Race Biology for the Plain Man*. London: G. Allen & Unwin, 1942. (Translated from the Swedish by Lancelot Hogben, this is a thoughtful book in popular style.)

Hardy, G. H., "Mendelian Proportions in a Mixed Population." *Science*, 28:49–50, 1908. (With Weinberg's [*op. cit.*], the classic statement of the binomial distribution of genotypes.)

Hogben, L., *An Introduction to Mathematical Genetics*. New York: W. W. Norton & Co., 1946. (Especially, at this point, Chap. 1, "Gene Frequencies, Genotypic Frequencies, and Systems of Mating.")

Li, Ching Chun, *An Introduction to Population Genetics*. Peiping: National Peking University Press, 1948. (This is an excellent textbook on a moderately advanced level. Distributed by the O.S.C. Cooperative Association, Corvallis, Oregon.)

Shapiro, H. L., *The Heritage of the Bounty*. New York: Simon & Schuster, 1936. (An anthropologist's account of the facts of Pitcairn through six generations. See Problems 20-14 to 20-19.)

Simpson, G. G., *Tempo and Mode in Evolution*. New York: Columbia University Press, 1944. (The quotation in the introduction to this chapter was taken from the introduction to this excellent book.)

Snyder, L. H., *The Principles of Heredity*. Boston: D. C. Heath & Co., 1951. (See especially Chap. 30, "The Analysis of Human Family Histories.")

Stern, C., *Principles of Human Genetics*. San Francisco: W. H. Freeman and Co., 1949. (Especially Chap. 10, "The Hardy-Weinberg Law," for material similar to that covered in this chapter.)

Weinberg, W., "Über den Nachweis der Vererbung beim Menschen." *Jahreshefte Verein f. vaterl. Naturk. in Württemberg*, 64:368–382, 1908. (See also Hardy, *op. cit.* An important part of this paper is translated in: C. Stern, "The Hardy-Weinberg Law." *Science*, 97:137–138, 1943.)

Questions and Problems

20- 1. What do the following terms signify?

binomial
gene frequency
random mating

Thalassemia major is a severe anemia, usually fatal in childhood and rather frequent in Mediterranean populations. Thalassemia minor is a very mild anemia, often difficult to detect at all.

20- 2. Among people of southern Italian or Sicilian ancestry now living in Rochester, New York, thalassemia major occurs in about one birth in 2400, and thalassemia minor in about one birth in 25 (Neel and Valentine, 1945). Extrapolating these frequencies to a population of 10,000, the distribution is approximately as follows:

Thalassemia major	Thalassemia minor	Normal
Th Th	*Th +*	*+ +*
4	400	9596

Verify that the frequencies of the *Th* allele and its normal alternative in this population are about 0.02 and 0.98 respectively.

20- 3. Does the population approximate the binomial distribution of genotypes expected from this gene frequency?

Consider the group of alleles controlling positive reactions to the original Rh reagent as a single alternative to the group of alleles controlling negative reactions to this reagent. Thus,

$$R- = \text{Rh-positive}$$
$$rr = \text{Rh-negative},$$

for the Rh grouping of greatest clinical significance. Assume a population in which 16 per cent of the individuals are Rh-negative. This is a convenient figure in the arithmetic to follow, and is not far from the frequency in our own population.

20- 4. Assuming the population to be at equilibrium under random mating for this alternative, what is the calculated frequency of the *r* allele? Of *R*?

20- 5. What is the calculated distribution of genotypes in this population?

20- 6. A man in the above population is Rh-positive and is married to an Rh-negative woman. What is the probability that the man is heterozygous (*Rr*)? If he is heterozygous, what is the probability that their first-born child will be Rh-negative? What is the probability that the first-born child of an Rh-positive man and an Rh-negative woman will be Rh-negative?

20- 7. Assume a large number of five-children families in the above population in which the parents are ♀ *Rr* × ♂ *rr*. What proportion of the families would have all five children Rh-negative? Three Rh-negative and two Rh-positive? Four Rh-positive and one Rh-negative?

20- 8. What reservation would your answer involve if Question 20-7 had been phrased for the reciprocal cross, ♀ *rr* × ♂ *Rr*? (*cf.*, Question 13-5.)

20- 9. What answers would you give to Question 20-7 if the parents had been ♀ *Rr* × ♂ *Rr*?

20-10. Color blindness occurs in about 8 per cent of men in the North American white population, but in only about 4 per cent of Negro men. Assuming sex-linked recessive inheritance, what frequencies of color blindness would you predict for women in each of these populations?

20-11. Actually, about 1 per cent of North American white women, and about 0.8 per cent of Negro women, are color-blind. How might you account for the excess of affected females found in both populations, compared with your prediction in Question 20-10?

20-12. Assume that the Pelger anomaly in man, as in rabbits, is autosomal and lethal when homozygous (Problems 2-15 to 2-19), and that one person in a thousand (in Berlin) is heterozygous. What are the calculated gene frequencies for this allelic pair among living residents of Berlin? Among marriages at random in this regard, what is the probability that both the man and the woman will be heterozygous?

20-13. With regard to the Pelger anomaly in Berlin, what is the probability that two heterozygous parents will have a homozygous child? What is the probability of homozygous children in this population, calculating (a) from the frequency of matings of heterozygotes, and (b) directly from the random combinations of alleles, in terms of their frequencies in this population? Explain the discrepancy between (a) and (b).

In 1790, several British mutineers from H. M. S. *Bounty,* together with a few men and women native to Tahiti, established a settlement on Pitcairn Island. This new island population remained largely isolated for several generations.

The preceding statements represent historical fact; the following are in part deviations from the true history of Pitcairn, as far as it is known, for the purposes of these problems. Assume that:

1. Families were founded by six men from the *Bounty,* of whom three were blue-eyed, two brown-eyed but heterozygous for blue, and one homozygous brown-eyed; and that there were two Tahitian men and eight women, all homozygous for brown.

2. The blue eyes-brown eyes alternative depends on a single autosomal allelic pair with brown (B) dominant, and no modifiers of eye color capable of obscuring this alternative were segregating in this population.

3. Intermarriage among the residents of Pitcairn Island was at random with respect to eye color, with approximately equal numbers of descendants surviving from each type of marriage occurring on a chance basis.

20-14. What were the gene frequencies for the eye-color alleles among the six white men, two Tahitian men, and eight Tahitian women who, we have assumed, established families on Pitcairn Island? Was this population at equilibrium in this regard at the time of its establishment?

20-15. What genotypic and phenotypic proportions would you expect to prevail in this population after it had reached equilibrium?

20-16. Fill in the blank spaces in the following table, illustrating the predicted results of the first generation of marriages on Pitcairn Island.

Type of Marriage ♀ ♂	Number of Marriages	Number of Progeny† BB	Bb	bb
$BB \times BB$	3	6	0	0
$BB \times Bb$	2	2	2	0
$BB \times bb$				
Total	8	8	—	—

† Assuming two children per marriage.

Is the population at equilibrium after one generation? Is this inconsistent with the statement that equilibrium is achieved in one generation of random mating? Why?

20-17. Fill in the blank spaces in the following table, representing marriages among the immediate progeny of the original settlers of Pitcairn Island. (We assume that the eight BB individuals in the preceding table were equally distributed between the sexes, and make similar assumptions for the other classes; and that the ideal chance distribution of mating types was actually realized even in this small population. Note, however, that we need not postulate brother-sister marriages here.)

Type of Marriage ♀ ♂	Number of Marriages	Number of Progeny† BB	Bb	bb
BB × BB	2	4	0	0
BB × Bb	2	2	2	0
Bb × BB	—	—	—	—
Bb × Bb	—	—	—	—
Other types	0	0	0	0
Total	8	9	—	—

† Assuming two children per marriage.

Is the population now at equilibrium?

20-18. Fill in the following table for still another generation of random marriage on Pitcairn Island, utilizing fractions and probabilities rather than absolute numbers of children. Is equilibrium maintained under the assumptions we have made? What advantages has the fraction-and-probability method?

Type of Marriage†	Frequency	Types of Progeny BB	Bb	bb
BB × BB	$(\%_{16})^2$	$81\%_{256}$	0	0
BB × Bb	$2(\%_{16})(\%_{16})$	$54\%_{256}$	$54\%_{256}$	0
BB × bb	$2(\%_{16})(\%_{16})$	0	$18\%_{256}$	0
Bb × Bb	———	$9\%_{256}$	—	—
Bb × bb	———	—	—	—
bb × bb	———	—	—	—
Total	———	—	$96\%_{256}$	—

† Note that the sexes are not distinguished in listing the mating types.

20-19. Dr. H. L. Shapiro, in 1935, six generations after the original settlement, found that about 5.6 per cent of the residents of Pitcairn Island had "light" eyes. Assume that the eye colors of the original settlers, and the inheritance of eye color in this population, were approximately as we have described them. Assume also that the "light" eyes as classified by Shapiro can be taken for our present purposes to represent the "blue" eyes of our series of problems. List several likely deviations from our further assumptions and predictions that might help to explain the eye color of the present-day population.

At the California Institute of Technology 171 students of General Biology found their blood groups to be distributed as follows:

Blood Group	O	A	B	AB	Total
Number	77	60	24	10	171
Percentage	45%	35%	14%	6%	100%

20-20. What blood-group frequencies would be expected among 171 students, if the distribution characteristic of Brooklyn (Table 20-4) represented ideal expectation? Do Cal Tech sophomores differ significantly from the expectation so defined? (Compute p in a χ^2 test using the nearest whole numbers in the *expected* class).

20-21. What are the frequencies of the L^A, L^B, and l alleles among Cal Tech sophomores? Does this population appear to conform to a random, equilibrium distribution, as far as you can judge from the distribution of phenotypes?

20-22. Assuming that Cal Tech men marry at random women from a population like their own, what types of children, and in what proportions, may be expected by Cal Tech men of blood group A, married to group O women? To group A women?

20-23. In our discussion of first-cousin marriages in this chapter, we computed the probability that both John and Mary (Fig. 20-1) would be heterozygous for the same rare recessive carried by GGF_2. Compute similarly the probability that both John and Mary will be heterozygous for a rare recessive carried by their common grandmother, GGM_2. Now, what is the probability that a child of John and Mary will be homozygous for both the GGF_2 recessive and the GGM_2 recessive? For neither?

20-24. Suppose that GGF_2 was heterozygous for two independent, rare recessives not present in any other member of his generation in the pedigree. What is the probability that a child of John and Mary would be homozygous for one or the other or both of these?

CHAPTER 21

Genetics and Evolution

VERY SHORTLY before Mendel started his search for a "generally applicable law governing the formation and development of hybrids," Charles Darwin and Alfred Russell Wallace had independently concluded that the survival in nature of those hereditary variants that were best adapted to their environment was the primary compelling force of evolution. This theory of *natural selection* was a convincing one, and many informed people were won to its support who before had hesitated to believe the evidence for evolution only because they could conceive of no adequate mechanism for it. But the origins of the hereditary variations on which selection was supposed to operate, and the laws governing inheritance, were not understood. In Mendel's day, and indeed long afterward, this constituted one of the primary challenges in science. Even now, the increased understanding of how and why living things have evolved to their present conditions is an aim of much fundamental biological research and a matter of profound curiosity to most thinking people.

Our present concepts of the mechanisms of evolution are based in very large part on our increasing knowledge of the principles of heredity in populations. We recognize that change in gene frequency is the elementary process of evolution. From this point of view, the subject matter of the present chapter is continuous with that of the preceding one. In fact, we can use the terms introduced in Chapter 20 to designate the factors affecting changes in the hereditary qualities of populations as the major points in our outline of genetics and evolution. These are *mutation, selection, random fluctuation,* and *migration.*

Mutation—The Origin of Hereditary Variations

The most common immediate basis for inherent differences among individuals is, of course, the segregation and recombination of Mendelian alternatives in sexual reproduction. And it is these alternatives that through their differences in frequency from one population to another determine the nature and extent of inherent population differences. When we speak of changes in a population, from a genetic viewpoint, we are usually speaking primarily of changes in gene frequencies.

If changes in the relative frequencies of alleles are to contribute to the evolution of populations, there must obviously be alleles there to start with. If segregation and recombination are to result in individual differences, there must be alternatives present to segregate and recombine. From these and other points of view, the phenomenon most fundamental to evolutionary change is the occurrence of the sudden, random, and generally unpredictable changes in germ plasm called *mutations*.

We have already discussed in sufficient detail the characteristics of the process of gene mutation (Chap. 12), and we need now only to capitalize on our familiarity with this process by applying it to evolution.

The Origin of New Alleles. Gene mutations are important in population changes for two rather different reasons. First, they provide the working materials for other factors affecting evolution. If selection is to operate, for example, there must be alternatives to select. Second (and this is our immediate concern here), the process of mutation itself is a force affecting gene frequencies. Whenever gene A mutates to an allele a, the frequency of A is a little bit reduced in the population, and the frequency of a is correspondingly increased. Over a long period of time, if A keeps changing to a, and if no other forces modify the effect of this process, A will have disappeared from the population, and a will have replaced it.

It is as though we had a sack full of red marbles in the classroom, and every year we took out a red marble and replaced it with a white one. It might take a long time, but eventually another class and another professor would find that there were only white marbles in the sack. Under the slow but inexorable pressure of recurrent mutation, a population may change drastically with regard to the characteristics controlled by the mutating gene.

In the usual case, this pressure is balanced by a similar but opposing one. We know that mutation is not only *recurrent;* it is often also *reversible.* Allele a is in turn changing back to A, with measurable frequency. Our model should therefore be modified; instead of drawing out a red marble and replacing it with a white one every time, we draw out any marble and replace it with one of the other color. At first, if we start with all red marbles, we are far more likely to draw red marbles out and to replace them with white. But as white marbles become more and more common in the sack, we are more and more likely to draw a white one out nearly as often as a red. Eventually we arrive at a point at which there are equal numbers of red and white marbles in the sack. From this point on we make no further progress in changing our population of marbles; for each time that we withdraw a red marble and replace it with a white one, there will be a compensating time when we do the opposite.

Returning from marbles to genes, we note that a population in this state is at *equilibrium* with respect to the relative frequencies of the two alleles under the pressures of reversible, recurrent mutation. Genes, however, are different from the marble models in that the mutation rates of alleles in the opposing directions are not often equal. In other words, mutation is usually much less likely to replace *a* with *A* than it is to make the opposite substitution. We can show this relationship symbolically:

$$A \xrightleftharpoons[v]{u} a$$

A mutates to *a* at rate u; *a* back-mutates to *A* at rate v, and u and v are not necessarily equal.

Under these conditions, if q is the frequency of *a* in any generation, and (1−q) is the frequency of *A*, the *change* under mutation, to the next generation, in the frequency of *A* will be:

the *addition* of more *A* alleles to the extent vq
the *subtraction* of *A* alleles to the extent u(1−q).

Now the gene frequencies will be at equilibrium under mutation pressures when these additions just balance the subtractions. In other words:

$$vq = u(1-q)$$
$$vq + uq = u$$
$$q(v + u) = u$$
$$q = \frac{u}{u + v}$$

An example will help to make this more concrete. If *A* mutates to *a* twice as frequently as *a* back-mutates to *A*,

$$u = 2v,$$

then the value of q (the frequency of *a*) at equilibrium under mutation pressures will be: $q = \dfrac{u}{u+v}$; $q = \dfrac{2v}{3v}$; $q = ⅔$.

In other words, the population will become stable with respect to the frequencies of the mutating alleles when the frequency of *A* is 0.33 and that of *a* is 0.67.

We can summarize this algebraic consideration of the effects of mutation pressures on the changing qualities of populations:

1. Recurrent mutation alone tends to spread an allele through a population and to change the relative frequencies of alleles from generation to generation.

2. This pressure toward genetic change is modified by the reversible nature of mutation. Under reversible, recurrent mutation, a population ap-

proaches an equilibrium with respect to the relative frequencies of alleles—a stable point beyond which mutation alone does not change the population. The point at which this stability is reached depends on the relative magnitudes of the component mutation rates.

3. This equilibrium must not be confused with the equilibrium on the level discussed in connection with random mating in Chapter 20. That was a relative stability in the frequencies of *genotypes* and *phenotypes* on the basis of assigned gene frequencies. We are dealing with a more basic kind of stability here—an equilibrium of the gene frequencies themselves, under opposing mutation pressures.

The fact that numerous mutational possibilities are open to a gene complicates the picture somewhat. In our discussion, we have adopted the simplification introduced in Chapter 20: We let A represent one allele at a locus—usually the type allele—and a all other possible alleles. The rates u and v are therefore each made up of a mosaic of component rates.

The Origin of New Genes. It is hardly conceivable that all living things have the same genes, and that the many differences among organisms result simply from the mutation to different allelic forms of genes common to the great variety of plants and animals. Somehow, during evolution *new genes* must have arisen.

We discussed briefly in Chapter 19, page 416, the possible connection that pseudoalleles and complex multiple allelic series might have with the processes through which new genes originate. You will recall that small "repeats" of genic material occur at some points on some chromosomes, and that this process of duplicating small sections of germinal material may be a first step in the origin of new loci. At first, the duplicated material is likely to have the same function as it did when single; it may represent only one gene, duplicated. But through mutation at the duplicated regions, the repeats may diverge so that in time a duplicated portion fulfills a new function, quite different from that of its "twin" on the chromosome. We would then clearly be dealing with two genes where one had been before.

The formation of adjacent "repeats" is not the only way in which new functions can be taken over by genes. J. A. Weir has pointed out that a part of the evolutionary progress of a species may be dependent on the synthetic accomplishments of other species. Compare yourself with Neurospora, for example. No insult is intended when we say that it is questionable which of you, the reader or the mold, comes off better in a comparison. Neurospora is a great deal more self-reliant, biochemically, than you are. The wild type grows nicely on inorganic salts, a carbon source, and biotin, while you require a myriad of vitamins, amino acids, and other compounds that Neurospora makes for itself. But you can think and/or play football, for example—activities at which Neurospora is notoriously incompetent.

The nutritional jobs that the wild-type alleles do for Neurospora, the genes of the plants and animals you eat do for you. Somewhere back in your evolutionary past, these genes have been spared to do other jobs. No doubt a part of your proud superiority over the mold results from the genteel nutritional parasitism on other living things in which your ancestors indulged, and which you now must practice in order to live.

An apparent taking-over of the functions of one gene by another has been studied in Neurospora. A particular strain is genetically unable to synthesize *pyrimidine*, a component of nucleic acid. A mutation occurred that restored the ability of this strain to grow in a pyrimidine-deficient medium. This proved to be not a back-mutation of the original mutant gene, but an independent mutation at an entirely different locus. In other words, a new locus had apparently acquired a function that had belonged to quite a different locus in the original wild type. If, in acquiring its new function, this locus lost its old function, that function was not missed. It had been a spare gene.

Mutant genes that suppress the expression of mutations at other loci are called *suppressors*. We discussed this phenomenon briefly in connection with duplications in Chapter 10.

Chromosomal Mutations. In addition to changes in single genes, the general term *mutation* includes a wide variety of changes in chromosomal structure and number. These also have profound significance to evolution, and many interesting and pertinent studies have been based on them. We considered some of the evolutionary aspects of variations in chromosomal number in Chapter 11.

Selection—The Impact of Environment on Gene Frequencies

The precision with which living forms have grown through evolution to fit their various environments is described as *adaptation*. The adaptations of organisms are many and marvelous. When you consider, for instance, the variety of special characteristics of desert plants that make it possible for them to survive and multiply in their very dry environment, you can scarcely help wondering how these nice adjustments have come about.

Some naturalists and philosophers have speculated that inherent variations in plants and animals may occur in anticipation of particular ends, and may in fact be directed by these ends. Others have speculated that the environment may mold or modify germ plasm in an adaptive and causative way. They have spoken of the acquisition of adaptive characters under the direct impress of the environment, and of the subsequent inheritance of these adaptive, acquired characteristics.

Now we are reasonably sure that both the teleologists and the advocates of the inheritance of adaptive, acquired phenotypes are wrong. This conviction is based on two complementary considerations, a negative one and a positive. On the negative side, no one has been able to detect a mechanism whereby a peculiarity in the ordinary environment can direct a responsive, adaptive change in the germ plasm of the plants and animals we know best. Environment does indeed affect phenotypes; it affects the way genes express themselves, but it does not place an adaptive impress on the genes themselves.

The positive aspect of our conviction that environmental modifications of phenotypes are irrelevant to evolutionary changes in germ plasm is based on the fact that adaptation seems to be adequately explainable in terms of what we do now know to be true about heredity. It is explainable on the basis of the natural selection of spontaneous, inherent variations—the random mutations we have just been discussing. We need now to consider selection in relation to adaptive evolution. Artificial selection, through which man directs the evolution of plants and animals under domestication, will be discussed in later chapters.

An Example of the Effect of Selection on Gene Frequencies.   To illustrate how selection affects the genetic character of a population, we can set up an extreme example. Suppose that we begin with a population at equilibrium under random mating, in which just half the individuals in the population show a recessive trait. The distribution of phenotypes, genotypes, and gene frequencies will be as shown in Table 21-1.

TABLE 21-1. A Population in Which Half of the Individuals Show the Recessive Phenotype.

PHENOTYPES	A−		aa
Phenotypic Frequencies	0.5		0.5
Genotypes	AA	Aa	aa
Approximate Genotypic Frequencies	0.09	0.42	0.5

Approximate Gene Frequencies: p (frequency of A) = 0.3
q (frequency of a) = 0.7

Now suppose that individuals of genotype *aa* are unable, in a particular environment, to mate or to leave any progeny. (This is what we mean by an *extreme* example; it can be described as complete selection against a recessive phenotype.)

The effective breeding population is then reduced to two genotypes, *AA* and *Aa*. They occur in the ratio 0.09*AA* : 0.42*Aa;* or, in terms of the breeding population they represent, $\dfrac{0.09}{0.09 + 0.42} = 0.18AA; \dfrac{0.42}{0.09 + 0.42} = 0.82Aa.$

If these genotypes (constituting a single phenotype) mate at random in becoming the parents of the next generation, and if all of the types of matings can be assumed on the average to be equally prolific, the pattern of the next generation will be determined as shown in Table 21-2.

TABLE 21-2. Results of Random Matings After Elimination of Recessive Phenotype.

TYPE OF MATING	FREQUENCY	PROGENY (FREQUENCIES)		
		AA	Aa	aa
AA $\times$ AA	$(0.18)^2 = 0.03$	0.03		
AA $\times$ Aa	$2(0.18)(0.82) = 0.30$	0.15	0.15	
Aa $\times$ Aa	$(0.82)^2 = 0.67$	0.17	0.34	0.17
Total	(1)	0.35	0.49	0.17

You can verify that this new generation again approximates a binomial distribution of genotypes, as though it were again in equilibrium under random mating. But a fundamental change has occurred in this population. The frequency of allele *a* has *decreased* from its value of 0.7 in the previous generation to a little more than 0.4 in this generation; and there has been a corresponding *increase* in the frequency of A. In terms of phenotypes, the change is even more impressive; the recessive phenotype has declined from a frequency of 0.5 to about 0.17 in a single generation of complete selection against this trait.

Other Kinds and Degrees of Selection. Selection against a dominant allele can be even more effective. In the extreme case, the prevention of all carriers of a dominant allele from mating or leaving progeny can completely eliminate this allele in a single generation.

On the other hand, except in the common case of lethals, natural selection must not often be as intense as the examples we have been considering. Instead of one genotype (or phenotype) being prevented entirely from leaving progeny in the next generation, much more commonly one phenotype will be only a little less effective in reproduction than others. And the situation may be complicated by the fact that heterozygotes may not be quite the same as homozygous dominants in this regard.

As the intensity of selection varies, the effectiveness of selection in changing the population varies too. Intense selection can result in very rapid progress. Even mild selection, in time, may spread a desirable gene through a population, or virtually eliminate an undesirable one. But under very mild selection, the time required for these ends may be more than the time available, even on a geological scale. In other words, as an allele approaches neutrality in terms of its selective value to the organism, selection becomes less and less important compared with other pressures affecting the frequency of the allele in the population.

Dependency of Selection on Gene Frequencies. In populations at equilibrium under random mating, the proportion of individuals carrying the recessive allele hidden in the heterozygous condition, compared with those

TABLE 21-3. Distribution of a Recessive Allele Between Homozygotes and Heterozygotes.

| VALUE OF q | GENOTYPE DISTRIBUTION | | | RATIO $\dfrac{Aa}{aa}$ | VALUE OF $\dfrac{Aa}{aa}$ |
	AA	Aa	aa		
0.9	0.01	0.18	0.81	$\dfrac{0.18}{0.81}$	0.22
0.5	0.25	0.50	0.25	$\dfrac{0.50}{0.25}$	2.0
0.1	0.81	0.18	0.01	$\dfrac{0.18}{0.01}$	18.0
0.01	0.9801	0.0198	0.0001	$\dfrac{0.0198}{0.0001}$	198.0

homozygous for the recessive allele, *increases* as the frequency of the allele *decreases* (Table 21-3).

When *a* is frequent relative to *A*, for example q = 0.9, there are about five times as many homozygous recessives as there are heterozygotes in the population. But when *A* and *a* are equally frequent, there are only half as many homozygous recessives as there are heterozygotes. And when *a* is so rare as to have a frequency of 0.01, about 198 individuals in the population will carry it hidden in the heterozygous condition for every individual that shows the recessive trait.

You can see how this would influence the effectiveness of selection against a recessive trait. When the trait is common, the responsible allele is so distributed among phenotypes that it is very vulnerable to selection. As we have seen, a single generation of complete selection against a recessive trait having a phenotypic frequency of 0.5 can reduce its frequency to 0.17. But in the next generation, a larger proportion of the representatives of the undesired allele in the population will be carried by heterozygotes, where it is

TABLE 21-4. Effectiveness of Selection Against a Recessive Phenotype. (From Snyder, Milbank Mem. Fund Quart., 26:328, 1948.)

GENERATIONS OF COMPLETE ADVERSE SELECTION	FREQUENCY OF A RECESSIVE TRAIT IN THE POPULATION			
0	0.005	0.050	0.500	0.990
1	0.004	0.033	0.172	0.249
2	0.004	0.024	0.086	0.111
3	0.003	0.018	0.051	0.062
4	0.003	0.014	0.034	0.040
5	0.003	0.011	0.024	0.028

screened from selection by its dominant alternative. Instead of eliminating the undesired allele entirely, as one might expect from the remarkable progress in the first generation, another generation of complete selection will only decrease the incidence of the recessive trait from 0.17 to about 0.09. In the next generation the incidence will be about 0.05, then 0.03, then 0.02. And from this point on, progress in eliminating the trait, even with complete selection against the recessive phenotype, is very slow. Table 21-4 summarizes the effects of five generations of complete selection against a recessive trait at several different levels of initial frequency.

This suggests that, with very rare alleles, extremely intense selection over long periods of time is required to change a population significantly. And here, again, other pressures become important in modifying the genetic character of a population. If selection at this level of gene frequency is working in the same direction as recurrent mutation, the two forces together complement each other nicely, and the equilibrium under random mating can move rapidly toward increased frequency of the advantageous trait. But if these two pressures are opposed, mutation can prevent the total elimination of an allele even under intense adverse selection. Lethal genes, for example, are present in surprisingly large numbers in natural populations. They are carried by heterozygotes, and mutation pressure is sufficient to hold them in the populations even though no individual homozygous for any of them survives to reproduce.

Deviations from random mating also profoundly affect the efficiency of selection. We have already seen how inbreeding, for example, exposes hidden recessives to view by increasing the relative frequency of the homozygous classes at the expense of the heterozygotes. The combination of inbreeding and selection, therefore, can go much further in changing the genetic structure of a population, and can proceed much more rapidly, than can either alone. An appreciation of this principle has aided, and will continue to aid, the improvement of plants and animals.

Similarly, in human populations the effectiveness of selection against rare traits under random mating would be slight. But insofar as like individuals tend to marry, selection might be rendered more competent. Of course, if a trait is completely recessive, and if it is so rare as to be carried in large part by heterozygotes, marriage among the unsuspecting heterozygotes is likely to be nearly at random with respect to this trait.

Equilibrium Under Selection Pressures Alone. Under certain circumstances, selection works not toward the complete elimination of an allele, but toward some stable equilibrium value short of loss of the allele from the population. A Brazilian geneticist, A. Brito da Cunha, for example, described experiments with a color-controlling locus in *Drosophila polymorpha*. There is incomplete dominance at this locus, so that genotype EE is dark, Ee is intermediate, and ee is light. When da Cunha studied experimental populations starting with equal numbers of dark and light individuals, or in another experiment with 20 per cent dark and 80 per cent light individuals, he found that in each case the gene frequency of E increased in successive generations to a level of about 0.65, and that the population stabilized at this point. The reason for this appeared to be that under the experimental conditions the heterozygote had a considerable selective advantage over either homozygote. Given the "adaptive value" of the heterozygote as 1.00, the experimental results suggest that the "adaptive value" of the homozygote EE is 0.56, and of ee is 0.23. Thus, the e allele (or at least a section of the chromosome for which e served as a "marker" in the stocks involved in the experiment) when homozygous was selected against. But it appeared to confer sufficient advantage on the heterozygote to maintain a considerable frequency in the population.

Da Cunha found that the situation in natural populations, with regard to this pair of alleles, was much different from that prevailing in his experimental populations. Various other studies have indicated that in many circumstances, selection in both domestic and natural populations favors heterozygous types. In these instances, the population will be expected to reach an equilibrium value at some intermediate level of gene frequency.

Other Aspects of Selection.　Much more complex considerations enter when we turn to interactions among different genes in different environments. We have emphasized that both the physiological environment, controlled in large part by other genes, and the external environment of the individual may modify the expressions of particular alleles. Selection in nature operates upon the organism as a whole, and we cannot accept as a complete picture the conclusions drawn from considerations of one gene at a time, in a specified environment. But we have gone far enough in this elementary discussion to gain at least some idea of how the relative fitness to their environments of inherently different types in a population can affect the character of future generations.

The key to the evolution of adaptive characteristics under natural selection is essentially the analysis provided us by Darwin and Wallace, rephrased in terms of our now much clearer knowledge of the processes of heredity. A proportion of the individuals produced in each generation are eliminated in the struggle for survival. While much of this elimination must be random, in the long run those individuals that are inherently best adapted to their environment are most likely to survive and to leave progeny. The alleles conferring advantages become more frequent in the population, because of these differential reproductive rates; and the less favored alleles decrease in frequency. An increasing nicety of adjustment to the environment results. If the environment were a single, static entity, selection would fix well-adapted types, and further changes would be slow and slight. But the world offers an infinite variety of environments, and these are changing over geologic time. Responsive to a changing environment, a population evolves.

Random Fluctuations and the Effects of Population Size

It must now be clear that to explain *adaptive evolution* we need not postulate either a teleological mechanism or an inheritance of adaptive characteristics impressed in directive fashion on germ plasm by the environment. The natural selection of spontaneous, random mutations meets the general requirements of a mechanism for this kind of evolutionary change. But we may well wonder whether natural selection explains too much. Perhaps only a minority of the characteristics by which a taxonomist distinguishes species can be shown to have selective value. If these important taxonomic characters are really selectively neutral, how could they have become fixed as consistent, distinctive differences at the stage of population divergence that we recognize as the species level?

The phenomenon of random "drift" in gene frequencies, most important in populations of limited size, provides a large part of the answer to this question.

Sampling Errors in Mendelian Inheritance. Throughout our discussion of gene frequencies in evolution we have assumed that we were dealing with populations of infinite size, in which the sampling of the genes of a parent population always achieved the ideal, expected values of Mendelian inheritance. But we are now familiar enough with the laws of chance to know that this is an unrealistic assumption for populations of finite size.

Suppose that in a breeding population of 1000 individuals, 500 males and 500 females, mating in pairs and having two offspring each, a new mutation m has appeared in one female. The ideal expectation is shown in Table 21-5.

We would expect, therefore, that the next generation under these arbitrary conditions would again have 999 homozygotes to 1 carrier of m. But in fact we know that the two offspring of the original heterozygous female would not always show the 1:1 ratio. On the contrary, *both* of these offspring might happen to get m from their mother, or, equally probably, *neither* of them might. The chance is ¼ that the allele will double in frequency the next generation, ½ that it will remain the same, and ¼ that it will be lost, simply as a result of the sampling nature of Mendelian inheritance.

MATING TYPES ♀ × ♂	NUMBER OF MATINGS	PROGENY MM	PROGENY Mm
MM × MM	499	998	0
Mm × MM	1	1	1
Total	500	999	1

TABLE 21-5. Mendelian Expectation for the Transmission of a New Mutation.

If this allele remains in the population, it is subjected to the same kind of sampling errors in the next generation; it might in successive generations "drift" toward higher and higher frequencies. But if it is lost in the sampling process in any generation, it cannot be replaced simply by a compensating variation in sampling in another generation; it can only be replaced by the rare recurrence of the same mutation, again to be subject to the risk of going back over the edge of zero frequency through the vagaries of chance.

This risk of loss from the population is so great for alleles at very low frequency that in a finite population only a little more than one in ten mutations conferring no selective advantage will still be present after 15 generations. Of course, if an allele is beneficial, it has a somewhat better chance of surviving, but R. A. Fisher has calculated that with a 1 per cent selective advantage only about 271 mutations out of 10,000 will be retained after 127 generations. Many mutations are therefore lost within a few generations, regardless of their selective value. Those that do persist may spread by chance fluctuations in frequency through a population, even though they may be selectively neutral, or sometimes even in the face of adverse selection.

These fluctuations are not limited to very rare alleles, although the fluctuations are most critical in connection with very infrequent alleles because the process is not in itself reversible when an allele is lost (or fixed through the loss of its alternative). Even when $p = q = 0.5$, chance may achieve $p = 0.55$, $q = 0.45$ in a generation, and similar fluctuation may occur in the same or the opposite direction in another generation. The probable magnitudes of such chance deviations are related to the size of the breeding population, as we shall see in the following section.

An Effect of Population Size. The significance of chance fluctuation is related to the number of representatives of an allele being sampled, as well as to the frequency of the allele. If an allele has a frequency of 0.01 in a population of 5000 individuals, there are actually 100 representatives of this allele in the population. Almost all of them are in heterozygotes. Some of these representatives will be lost in polar bodies as heterozygous females form eggs; some will be lost in sperm that never fertilize eggs; some will be lost in individuals that die before they can reproduce. But the alternative of the allele in question is subject to the same chance losses in heterozygotes; and with almost 100 individuals carrying the infrequent allele there is a good chance that positive and negative chance variations will come near cancelling each other out.

An allele with a frequency of 0.01 in a population of 50 individuals is in a much more precarious position. There is only one representative of this allele in this population, and it exists in a single individual. If this individual fails to reproduce or leaves only a few offspring, or if the offspring do not survive, for reasons quite independent of their possession of this allele, the allele may well be lost. There is little opportunity for positive and negative chance variations to compensate for each other, and the drift in gene frequency may be extreme.

Similarly, at other levels of gene frequency in a population the absolute number of alleles being sampled affects the probability of wide deviation. If $p = q = 0.5$, a population with the absolute numbers $50A : 50a$ alleles might very well give a chance sample of $41A : 59a$ in the next generation. This would represent an insignificant deviation from the expected 1:1 ratio; that is, it is reasonably probable as a result of chance alone. The gene frequency would change, then, to $p = 0.41$, $q = 0.59$; and there would be no reason to expect that it must drift back the next generation.

In a population with the absolute numbers $500A : 500a$, a similar deviation to $p = 0.41$, $q = 0.59$ would mean a sample of alleles $410A : 590a$. But this is very unlikely, as you can confirm with a chi-square test. In fact, a deviation to $p = 0.47$, $q = 0.53$ in the large population is less probable than a deviation to $p = 0.41$, $q = 0.59$ in the population of 100 alleles.

The Inbreeding Effect in Small Populations.   The fixation or loss of alleles in an inbred population is really a consequence of this same kind of drift. Inbreeding in itself, of course, does not change gene frequencies for the population as a whole; it only results in a relative increase in homozygous genotypes as compared with heterozygotes. But the practical limit on the size of an inbred population automatically results in the frequent selection of homozygous individuals to become the parents of the next generation; and the result of this is the rapid elimination of alleles under intense inbreeding.

The most extreme example is the maintenance of a line by the self-fertilization of an individual in each generation. The size of the breeding population is 1. A given heterozygous gene pair under this condition has a 50-50 chance of being fixed as either homozygote in each generation; and this is going on for all the heterozygous loci in the population at once. About half of the heterozygosity is therefore automatically lost in each generation; the process of fixation and loss of alleles goes on so rapidly that selection cannot hope to keep up with it. About all that a corn breeder can do under this system, for example, is to produce a large number of inbred lines, and to choose, from among the survivors of seven or eight generations of self-fertilization, those that happen through chance to have arrived at homozygosity for alleles that will be useful in further breeding operations.

The process of fixation and loss is slower under less intense inbreeding; even continued brother-sister mating offers considerable opportunity for conscious selection of the particular genotypes that should be used to continue the inbreeding program. As the size of the breeding population increases, the likelihood of chance mating between close relatives decreases, and the inbreeding effect in large populations becomes almost negligible. Sewall Wright has calculated that in a population of N breeding individuals about 1 in 4N alleles are lost and about 1 in 4N are fixed in each generation. Under certain breeding conditions the rate of fixation and loss may be smaller.

The sizes of breeding units in nature are often small; an individual is likely to mate with another born nearby, and the total population is often broken up into a large number of relatively small subpopulations, inter-breeding to some extent but still largely self-sufficient and separate. Further-more, the winter populations of many species are very small, and chance may play a great part in determining which of the large number of individuals of a summer population will successfully "overwinter" to become the parents of the next summer's population. Many ecological observations demonstrate great summer-to-summer changes as a result of drift during the "population bottleneck" represented by the small winter populations.

Some species show cyclic types of fluctuation in population size over a period of years. Species of limited mobility (snails, for example) are likely to be broken up into small, practically isolated breeding units. The homing phenomenon, the restricted breeding range, the phenomenon of "territory" in animal sociology, and many other factors decrease the size of effective breeding populations and therefore increase the significance of nonadaptive drift in the genetic history of these populations.

The "Isolate Effect"—Another Effect of Population Size. In human populations, rare alleles often occur in "pockets" of relatively high frequency; they are not uniformly distributed over a state or a country. A small rural population, centered in a village, may show a remarkably high incidence of polydactyly, or webfeet, or fragile bones with blue sclera, for example—characteristics that are rare in the general population. This is probably in large part an inbreeding effect; although marriages between individuals as closely related as first cousins may occur rarely even in small communities, over a period of generations a network of interrelationships among established families has often developed.

Dahlberg has called attention to an important consequence of the breakdown of such partial *isolates* in human populations. If there are N individuals in Community A, a given locus is represented 2N times. Assume that there are c representatives of an undesirable recessive allele in this population. The frequency of this allele will be $\frac{c}{2N}$, and the incidence of the recessive phenotype at equilibrium will be $\left(\frac{c}{2N}\right)^2 = \frac{c^2}{4N^2}$.

Now suppose that through the establishment of a Ford agency in Community A, and a dance hall and movie theater in nearby Community B of equal size, the boys and girls of Communities A and B come to represent a more freely intermarrying population. If the undesirable recessive allele is absent from Community B (as is likely if this allele is rare in the general population), and if the effective population size becomes 2N individuals, the frequency of this allele becomes $\dfrac{c}{4N}$, and the incidence of the recessive phenotype, in a single generation of random marriage, becomes $\dfrac{c^2}{16N^2}$. The important point is that *doubling* the effective population size has not merely *halved* the incidence of the recessive trait; it has decreased it to one-quarter of its previous level. If the allele is rare, many generations of complete selection against it would have been required to effect the same result.

Mr. Ford's Model T, then, may well have had a most salutary influence on the incidence of undesired recessive traits in human populations.

Migration and Isolation

Our consideration of the mechanisms of evolution up to this point adds up to something like this: Species containing numerous individuals may be subdivided into breeding units of various sizes. Within each of these units, the processes of adaptive evolution through natural selection in the particular environment of the unit, and of nonadaptive change through mutation pressures and chance drift in gene frequencies, progress to some degree independently of the changes going on in other units. Varieties inherently different from each other therefore develop within the species, and these may represent the usual first stage in the origin of new species.

But if the subunits of a population continue to "pool" their genes through migrants that act as a genetic canal among units, the varieties must remain to some degree similar. Unless a unit is reproductively isolated from an adjacent one, the two populations evolve *together,* at least to some extent; they cannot well diverge to the point of consistent and uniform differences represented by distinct species. The role of migration (or perhaps better, from some points of view, the role of *isolation*) in the origin of species is therefore an important one. It is also important through its modification of the effective sizes of breeding populations, discussed in the preceding section, and through its effects on potential recombinations of genes, to be discussed below.

Migration and Recombinations of Genes. Some time before the nature of Mendelian heredity was understood, the importance of isolation in evolution had been emphasized. It was generally believed that the interbreeding of inherently distinct groups of individuals resulted in a dissolution of their differences, and that there was a sort of blending effect in inheritance, so that an intermediate, invariable hybrid type replaced the diverse parent types. The origin of species—of clear-cut and discontinuous groups of plants and animals—was therefore believed to require the reproductive isolation of groups of individuals from each other, so that these groups might diverge and remain distinct. This concept was regarded by some biologists as the key to organic evolution.

You will recognize that the concept contained both fact and fallacy. We now know that inheritance is not a blending process, but is a matter of segregation and recombination of discrete particles. Hybridization does not result in the formation of invariable blends; on the contrary, it can provide for the emergence in later generations of novel forms through the recombinations of alleles that differed in the parent types. On this level, migration among inherently different subunits of a population leads to an increase, not a decline, in variation in the total population. It gives selection a wider variety of phenotypes upon which to operate and therefore facilitates adaptive evolution. And it provides an excellent balancing mechanism against the tendency of small subpopulations to become homozygous through the chance fixation or loss of alleles.

In all these respects, the pre-Mendelian emphasis on isolation as a factor in organic evolution was at variance with what we now know about the machinery of heredity. But in another regard isolation was and still is properly emphasized: The divergence, in time, of subunits of a parent population, until two or more of these subunits reach a point of essential discontinuity and are recognizable as distinct species, depends on the reproductive isolation of these subunits. Insofar as evolution is indeed a matter of the "origin of species," some form of isolation is basic to this process.

Isolating Mechanisms. There are in nature a great many mechanisms effective in preventing the pooling of the genes of diverging groups and therefore in permitting the development of genetic discontinuity among these populations. These isolating mechanisms act at two levels: to prevent the mating of individuals from two populations, or the fertilization of eggs of one population by sperm from another; and to prevent the reproduction of hybrids even when such hybrids are produced. Included in the first category are various geographical, ecological, psychological, and physiological barriers to cross-fertilization. The second category includes the formation of inviable, aberrant, or sterile hybrids. We discussed certain of the bases for hybrid sterility, with particular reference to chromosomal behavior in meiosis, in Chapters 10 and 11.

Keys to the Significance of This Chapter

The recognition of the evolutionary relationships among living plants and animals, and increased understanding of how evolution has come about, continue to be major concerns of biologists working in all parts of the field. The concept of evolution still provides the great integrating basis common to all biology, and makes biology in all its diverse branches still clearly one science.

Population changes in gene frequency under migration, random fluctuation, selection, and mutation pressures are fundamental to evolutionary change. Large populations are typically broken up into smaller subunits, varying in size and in degree of isolation. Since migration provides some degree of genetic continuity throughout the large population, new mutations and new combinations of genes, when they confer advantage on their possessors, can be capitalized upon by the population generally, and there is adequate occasion for adaptive evolution under selection. But at the same time the random fixation and loss of genes continues in the subunits at rates inversely proportional to their sizes. Nonadaptive changes, especially in characteristics near neutrality in selective value, can therefore accumulate in the subunits, and the subunits can also diverge as they become adapted to particular, different niches in the general environment.

When complete isolation occurs, cutting some of the subunits off from the parent population, the "leveling" process of migration stops. Divergence continues in the isolated subunits, and new species come into being.

References

(Many of the references for Chapter 20 are also pertinent here. Also, note an important compendium, "Origin and Evolution of Man," *Cold Spring Harbor Symposia Quant. Biol.*, **15**, 1950, containing numerous papers not individually cited here.)

Da Cunha, A. B., "Genetic Analysis of Polymorphism of Color Pattern in *Drosophila polymorpha.*" *Evolution*, 3:239–251, 1949. (Selection favoring a heterozygote.)

Dahlberg, G., "Genetics of Human Populations." *Advances in Genetics*, **2**:69–98, 1948. (Consideration of factors affecting the genetic structure of human populations, with particular emphasis on isolates.)

Darlington, C. D., *The Evolution of Genetic Systems.* Cambridge: Cambridge University Press, 1939. (Cytological aspects of evolution.)

Darwin, C., *On the Origin of Species by Means of Natural Selection, or the Preservation of Favoured Races in the Struggle for Life.* New York: Appleton, 1860. (The classic, still well worth studying.)

Dobzhansky, Th., *Genetics and the Origin of Species,* 3rd ed. New York: Columbia University Press, 1951. (Thorough, well-written, and interestingly presented survey.)

————, ed. *Biological Symposia,* vol. VI, 1942. (This volume contains three symposia, two of which are pertinent to this chapter. The first, on "Temperature and Evolution," contains interesting papers by eight contributors; the second, on "Isolating Mechanisms" includes four papers on an important aspect of evolution scarcely touched in our discussion).

Fisher, R. A., *The Genetical Theory of Natural Selection.* Oxford: Clarendon Press, 1930. (A pioneer work in the quantitative treatment of the effects of selection.)

Haldane, J. B. S., *The Causes of Evolution.* New York: Harper & Bros., 1931. (See especially the appendix, "Outline of the Mathematical Theory on Natural Selection.")

Horowitz, N. H., "On the Evolution of Biochemical Syntheses." *Proc. Nat. Acad. Sci.,* 31:153–157, 1945. (Consideration of how complex biosynthetic sequences under gene control may have been established.)

Huxley, J., *Evolution, The Modern Synthesis.* New York: Harper & Bros., 1941. (A book rich in biological significance. Note the consideration of industrial melanism, pp. 94–96.)

Mayr, E., *Systematics and the Origin of Species.* New York: Columbia University Press, 1942. (See especially Chap. 5, "The Systematic Categories and the New Species Concept.")

"Natural Selection and Adaptation." *Proc. Am. Phil. Soc.,* 93:459–519, 1949. (Papers read at the annual meeting of the society by H. J. Muller, Sewall Wright, G. L. Jepson, G. L. Stebbins Jr., and E. Mayr. These papers provide a good survey of current thought on this subject.)

Patterson, J. T., and Stone, W. S., *Evolution in the Genus Drosophila.* New York: Macmillan Co., 1952. (A superlatively thorough and interesting account of much we have been unable even to mention, this book will richly repay careful study.)

Shull, A. F., *Evolution.* New York: McGraw-Hill Book Co., 1951. (An elementary textbook—simple, readable, and competent.)

Simpson, G. G., *The Meaning of Evolution.* New Haven: Yale University Press, 1949. (A thoughtful, rather general treatment; note also another book by the same author, cited with the references to Chapter 20.)

Snyder, L. H., "The Principles of Gene Distribution in Human Populations." *Yale J. Biol. and Med.,* 19:817–833, 1947. (Includes data on human gene frequencies.)

Spencer, W. P., "On *Rh* Gene Frequencies." *Am. Naturalist,* 81:237–240, 1947. (Selection in the Rh system.)

Stebbins, G. L., *Variation and Evolution in Plants.* New York: Columbia University Press, 1950. (See especially Chaps. 12 and 13, on "Evolutionary Trends.")

———, "Cataclysmic Evolution." *Sci. American,* 184:54–59, April 1951. (A popular but authoritative account of the importance of polyploidy in plant evolution.)

Sturtevant, A. H., "The Evolution and Function of Genes." *Am. Scientist,* 36:225–236, 1948. (A broad and clear review, including much of the author's own important work.)

Wallace, A. R., *Contributions to the Theory of Natural Selection.* New York: Macmillan Co., 1871. (A series of essays, including classics reprinted after their original appearance in 1855 and 1858.)

Weir, J. A., "Sparing Genes for Further Evolution." *Iowa Acad. Sci.,* 53:313–319, 1946.

Wright, S., "On the Roles of Directed and Random Changes in Gene Frequency in the Genetics of Populations." *Evolution,* 2:279–294, 1948. (Essentially a reply to criticism, with references.)

———, "Evolution in Mendelian Populations." *Genetics,* 16:97–159, 1931. (A classic of the population-genetics approach to evolutionary mechanisms.)

Questions and Problems

21- 1. What do the following terms and phrases signify?

adaptation

evolution

inbreeding effect

isolate effect

isolating mechanism

natural selection

random drift in gene frequencies

suppressor mutation

About one normal allele in 30,000 mutates to the sex-linked recessive allele for hemophilia in each human generation. It is difficult to observe reverse mutation of a human recessive essentially lethal like the allele for hemophilia. Assume for purposes of the following problems that one h allele in 300,000 mutates to the normal alternative in each generation. In terms of the formulation on page 450, this can be described as follows:

$$+ \underset{v}{\overset{u}{\rightleftarrows}} h, \text{ where } u = 10v.$$

21- 2. What gene frequencies would prevail at equilibrium under mutation pressures alone in these circumstances?

21- 3. Check your answer to Problem 21-2 by verifying the following:

a. At the calculated equilibrium frequency, assuming a population with a total of ten million alleles at this locus, about 900,000 of these would be the $+$ allele, and about 9,100,000 would be the h allele.

b. In the above circumstance, about thirty of the $+$ alleles would mutate to h in each generation, and this would be balanced by the mutation of about thirty h alleles to $+$.

21- 4. The conclusions in the above two questions are obviously at variance with the fact that h remains rare relative to its normal allele. Why does h not become increasingly frequent?

21- 5. Suppose that a quick, easy, and effective method of stopping or preventing bleeding in hemophilia should be developed. (Some methods are in fact at hand, but at present they are not effective over long periods of time.) Under the conditions postulated in Problems 21-2 to 21-4, what might you expect to happen to the frequency of hemophilia in successive generations?

21- 6. Carry the complete selection against a recessive trait, illustrated in Table 21-2, another generation, confirming that the frequency of the recessive phenotype will be reduced from 0.17 to about 0.09.

21- 7. Would you expect a sex-linked recessive to be more or less vulnerable to selection than an autosomal recessive? Why?

21- 8. Although breeders of purebred black-and-white cattle have selected completely against the autosomal recessive red phenotype for many generations, there is no tangible evidence of current progress toward the elimination of this rare allele from the black-and-white breeds. Why?

21- 9. Suppose that a method is developed to identify cattle carrying the recessive red allele in the heterozygous condition. What change in the effectiveness of the selection described in Question 21-8 would follow the application of this method to the selection of breeding stock in black-and-white breeds?

21-10. Drosophila trapped in nature and brought in to be bred in the laboratory are often found to be heterozygous for recessive lethals. Why have these lethals not been eliminated by natural selection?

21-11. What characteristic of the usual laboratory mating pattern renders the lethals of Question 21-10 more vulnerable to selection in the laboratory than in nature? Why?

21-12. Animals and plants under domestication typically display a great deal more genetic variation than do comparable populations in the wild. How may the evolutionary forces and mechanisms we have discussed be involved in this contrast between domestic and natural populations?

21-13. What common kind of selection leads to an equilibrium at some intermediate level of gene frequency, rather than to the loss from the population of an allele being selected against?

21-14. There is a suggestion that beef cattle heterozygous for a particular recessive dwarfism have been selected, in preference to homozygous normals, to be used for breeding stock (Gregory, et al., unpubl.). Such heterozygotes may on the average be more efficient producers of the better cuts of meat than are homozygous normal cattle. Homozygous dwarfs are of course very undesirable. In qualitative terms, what would you expect to be the equilibrium situation for this pair of alleles?

Among many species of animals, unusually dark variants have become increasingly frequent in industrial areas during the past century. This is called *industrial melanism;* it regularly depends on dominant genes. In a relatively unfavorable environment, the dark forms seem to enjoy some advantages in hardiness and viability.

21-15. Assuming that mutation to melanism is a random, recurrent process, indicate how selection might have operated to keep the frequency of melanism low in a predominantly light, favorable, nonindustrial environment. (Note that conspicuous coloration is likely to render an organism vulnerable to predators.)

21-16. How might the relatively recent increase in frequency of melanic forms in industrial areas be interpreted in terms of your answer to Question 21-15?

Assume a generally rare kind of recessive mental defect in man, the recessive allele being present with a frequency of 0.2 in Community A but absent from Community B of equal size.

21-17. If Community A is at equilibrium, what proportion of the people in it will show the recessive trait?

21-18. If communities A and B come to represent a freely intermarrying population, what proportion of the people in this new, single population will show the recessive trait at equilibrium?

21-19. Estimate, by comparison with Table 21-4, about how many generations of complete selection against the recessive trait would have been necessary to reduce its frequency to the extent achieved by the breakdown of the isolate under the assumptions made in Problems 21-17 and 21-18.

Erythroblastosis resulting from Rh incompatibility has in the past represented a form of selection, since failure of a proportion of children of a particular genotype to survive affects the frequency of the alleles responsible for their inviability. In the following questions, assume a simple allelic alternative, R = Rh-positive, r = Rh-negative.

21-20. In our population, about one birth in 250 is erythroblastotic. Affected infants are heterozygous, since they are Rh-positive infants born to Rh-negative mothers. Assume for the purposes of this problem that these infants are born alive but do not survive. In a population with the following genotypic frequencies:

$$RR = 0.36 \quad Rr = 0.48 \quad rr = 0.16$$

    a. How many R alleles would be found in a population of 1000 newborn babies the next generation?
    b. How many r alleles?
    c. How many heterozygotes would be eliminated?
    d. How many R alleles would be eliminated?
    e. How many r alleles would be eliminated?
    f. Confirm that the effect of selection in this circumstance would be to reduce slightly the frequency of r in each generation and to increase correspondingly the frequency of R.
    g. What would you expect to be the effect of long-continued selection of this sort?
    h. Why do you suppose that the Chinese, a population of long, relatively unmixed history, are practically homozygous RR?

21-21. Repeat the calculations of Problem 21-20, but beginning with a population in which the initial frequencies are reversed (i.e., p, frequency of R, = 0.4; q = 0.6). In which direction will the allelic frequencies move under selection in this population?

21-22. Present opinion is that the gene frequencies for Rh alleles in the North American White population are the result of relatively recent intermixtures of populations in which one or the other allele had been much more predominant (*cf.*, Spencer, 1947). Why?

21-23. In contrast to their importance in plant evolution, changes in numbers of whole chromosomes or sets of chromosomes are generally believed to have been relatively unimportant to the evolution of higher animals. Discuss the probable relevance of the following statements to this opinion:

    a. Animals frequently depend on a genic balance mechanism for sex determination.
    b. Animals do not often self-fertilize, so that a spontaneous tetraploid, for example, would usually have to mate with a diploid.
    c. The higher animals do not often reproduce asexually.

21-24. We have observed that mutation may be induced by a variety of external agents. Do you regard such induced mutations as examples of the inheritance of acquired characteristics? Why?

21-25. In Chapter 20, we recognized marked differences in the frequencies of red blood cell antigens M and N in different human populations. Discuss briefly why these differences exist.

CHAPTER 22

Breeding Better Plants

To US, the major importance of plants is our absolute dependence upon them for food. The things we eat are, for the most part, either plant stuffs as such or they are secondarily derived from plants, as is true of milk, eggs, and meat. Plants are also the source of material for clothing and for construction. They furnish us with drugs, with tanning and dyeing products, and with latex materials. As ornamentals, they provide us with much that is beautiful as well as useful.

It seems obvious that if we had plants better suited for their various purposes our way of life would be better and richer. There is substantial motivation, then, for men to work at plant improvement, as indeed they have been doing for many years. The American Indians were notable plant breeders; they developed such major crop plants as corn, peanuts, peppers, squashes, tomatoes, and sweet and white potatoes. Similarly, in all parts of the world, many of the plants used by man have for a long time been improved far beyond the state of their wild progenitors. Much of this early improvement, although vast in its effect, was achieved through trial and error, and was accomplished despite ignorance of many of the principles involved. With the advent and development of genetics as a science, plant breeders have been provided with powerful new tools that have enabled plant improvement to proceed at a scale and pace impossible with the earlier methods.

Objectives of Plant Breeding. The greatest emphasis in plant breeding has been placed on the improvement of our food supply. It is significant to economic, social, and political history that in many crop-producing countries the yield per unit of land has been generally increasing over the past fifty years or more. Table 22-1 shows yields of wheat in New York State for ten-year periods starting in 1866. Over the first forty years represented, the average yield per acre was 15.6 bushels; over the next forty years, 20.8 bushels.

A considerable portion of the increase in yield can be ascribed to better cropping practices. In other words, agricultural plants have been provided with more favorable environments. But the growers of crops have also been

PERIOD	AVERAGE YIELD, BUSHELS PER ACRE
1866–1875	14.1
1876–1885	15.5
1886–1895	15.4
1896–1905	17.5
1906–1915	20.2
1916–1925	19.9
1926–1935	19.3
1936–1945	23.8

TABLE 22-1. Yields of Wheat Obtained in New York State Since 1866. (From Love, Cornell Univ. Agr. Exp. Sta. Bull. 828, 22, 1946.)

able to work with inherently better plants. The fact that the years 1936 to 1945, as compared to the previous decade, show an increase of 4.5 bushels per acre in yield of wheat in New York State can partly be credited to the introduction and multiplication of the improved variety Yorkwin. A conservative estimate is that this new high-yielding strain accounted for abou' half of the increase per acre.

Environment must be taken into account not only in evaluating the *results* of plant breeding programs but also in the *planning* of these programs. The plant breeder must constantly face the situation that between the best potential performance of a plant, as designated by its genotype, and its actual performance a wide gap may exist. Much of the breeder's work is concerned with closing up such gaps. Thus, typical objectives in plant improvement programs are disease resistance, insect resistance, and winter hardiness. None of these necessarily brings about increase in yield as such. Insect and disease resistance, however, tend to buffer average yields against decreases resulting from adverse environmental conditions. Winter hardiness and drought resistance may have the same general effect. The achievement of such breeding objectives may permit plants to be grown in regions from which they have previously been excluded.

In many instances, the objectives of plant breeders are determined by special human needs and tastes. Besides the yield of a wheat, the quality of bread stuffs made from its flour is of great concern to cereal breeders. Vegetable breeders must take into account qualities like flavor and tenderness in their products. Plant breeders are also beginning to pay attention to such matters as the vitamin and amino acid content of plants or of particular plant parts.

Under the complex system that brings us our food supply, the desires of growers and processors, as well as of consumers, are significant. Canners are vitally interested in whether or not dry beans turn mushy after the canning process, and bean breeders developing new varieties for the commercial crop must be on the lookout for types that do not mush readily. Strawberry varieties like Sparkle have been developed along lines that make them suitable for quick-freezing. Sorghum breeders have utilized two different genes for dwarf height to create varieties such as Double Dwarf milo, which are short enough to be harvested readily either by machine or by hand. One of the real advantages of hybrid corn is that its greater uniformity of size and strength of stalk make it better adapted to machine harvest.

Since social and economic systems are by no means static, and since man's tastes are often transient, the breeder's job would seem to be never ending.

Methods of Plant Breeding

Selection as the Basis for Plant Improvement. Fundamentally, plant improvement is accomplished through selection. All plants have been subjected to natural selection. Presumably, this has operated in favor of genotypes that, among other things, are balanced to give harmonious and efficient physiological systems. In the case of crop plants, superimposed upon natural selection has been selection by man. More or less systematically over the years he has propagated plants having desirable heritable characters, thus perpetuating these types at the expense of less favored ones. Sometimes, no doubt, artificial selection has worked counter to the trends of natural selection. Cultivated plants live in artificial environments that permit the successful growth of certain types (field corn, for example) that would be poor competitors in nature.

The Efficacy of Selection. All we really need do to assure ourselves that

TABLE 22-2. *Results of Selection of Corn for High and Low Content of Oil and of Protein.* (*From Woodworth, Leng, and Jugenheimer,* Agronomy Journal, **44:61, 1952.**)

Year	Generation	High Oil % Oil	Low Oil % Oil	High Protein % Protein	Low Protein % Protein
1896	0	4.70		10.92	
1901	5	6.24	3.45	13.78	9.63
1906	10	7.38	2.67	14.26	8.65
1911	15	7.52	2.06	13.79	7.90
1916	20	8.51	2.07	15.66	8.68
1921	25	9.94	1.71	16.66	9.14
1926	30	10.21	1.44	18.16	6.50
1931	35	11.80	1.23	20.14	7.12
1936	40	10.16	1.24	22.92	7.99
1941	45	13.73	1.02	17.76	5.79
1949	50	15.36	1.01	19.45	4.91

selection can be effective is to note the differences between our cultivated plants and their ancestors in the wild. But before we proceed to examine certain of the techniques of selection in breeding work, it will be well to have in mind some specific example of the efficacy of selection. Such an example is provided in Table 22-2, which summarizes selection experiments on corn carried out at the Illinois Agricultural Experiment Station for a period of more than fifty years. During this time, open-pollinated corn has been selected for both low and high oil content and for both low and high protein content of the grain. It is clear from the data that selection has been effective in all four directions tried.

The Material with Which the Breeder Works. The basic material with which the plant breeder works is the available supply of germ plasm. He must find sources of variability that include the different kinds of characteristics that constitute his objectives. You will remember, however, that the total variability among organisms has both hereditary and environmental components. One of the primary tasks of the plant breeder is to separate out these components of variability as they refer to characteristics in which he is interested. *Only heritable characters are subject to selection.*

Some of the characters important to the breeder's work are simply inherited. A few examples are to be found in Table 22-3. But most of the

TABLE 22-3. *A Few Heritable Plant Characteristics That Segregate as if They Were Determined by Single Allelic Pairs.*†

KIND OF PLANT	CHARACTERS	
	DOMINANT	RECESSIVE
Beans	Vine-type growth habit	Bush-type
Cabbage	Disease resistance to fusarium yellows	Susceptibility
Celery	Hollow petioles	Solid
Corn	Nonwaxy endosperm	Waxy
	Starchy endosperm	Sugary
	Resistance to loose smut	Susceptibility
Oats	Black grain	Nonblack
	Resistance to loose smut	Susceptibility
Radishes	Corky root	Smooth root
Sorghum	Dry stalk	Juicy stalk
	Susceptibility to red spot	Resistance
Tomatoes	Nonuniform ripening	Uniform

† The fact that a particular characteristic shows simple segregation in some crosses does not preclude a similar characteristic behaving as a quantitative character under other genetic circumstances. For example, low stature in corn may be determined by homozygosity at a single locus for dwarf (*dd*) or by the aggregate effect of multiple genes.

objectives of plant improvement involve quantitative characters, like yield, size, flavor, earliness, and some kinds of hardiness and disease resistance. Many of these are susceptible to environmental influence. And since the breeder carries out experiments on so large a scale that he seldom finds it practical to control environment closely, he faces special problems in the analysis of his results. On the other hand, since the varieties of plants he creates will eventually be grown under varied conditions on farms, he needs to sample the performance of his creations under a variety of environmental circumstances if he is to avoid making wrong recommendations to crop growers. In making the numerous, and often complex, comparisons and evaluations so necessary in plant improvement work, the breeder makes use of a battery of statistical tools, of which the examples given in Chapter 15 are simple representatives.

The First Rule for the Plant Breeder.   The first rule for the plant breeder is: "Know your plant!" It is apparent that the breeder should be thoroughly familiar with the life cycle of any plant with which he works. He needs to know the details of its flower structure and of its reproductive processes, so that he can utilize appropriate techniques in making controlled matings. He needs to know whether self- or cross-pollination is the rule for the plant group, and whether individuals show self-compatibility or self-incompatibility. It is important for him to learn whether the plant is a diploid or a polyploid, and, if it is a diploid, whether it has polyploid relatives. Another important question is: "Do members of the group reproduce asexually?"

There are additional ways in which the breeder should know his plant. He should know the conditions under which the plant grows, and its reaction to different environments. He should know the geographic distribution of the plant, and above all the extent and sources of variability within the group. (Can you think of specific reasons for the value of such information to the breeder?)

Sources of Variability.   Occasionally, a favorable mutation occurs within an already improved plant variety. Then a superior variety may be produced in a few relatively easy steps, largely involving isolation and multiplication of the new kind of plant. Thus the Double Dwarf milo, mentioned earlier in this chapter, originated in a plant of the variety Dwarf Yellow milo, presumably as a mutation. Breeders are always happy when "accidents" of this kind happen. They do not rely upon them, however, and they are prepared to go farther afield to obtain the kinds of genetic differences they want.

Breeders look at a plant species as a vast storehouse of diversity, wherein genetic differences have been accumulating over long time periods. The ultimate origin of this heterogeneity is in mutational processes, including both gene and chromosome changes. In general, however, the immediate source of variability with which breeders work is the genetic diversity provided by the generations of segregation and recombination that have followed mutation.

The Role of Hybridization. Hybridization that occurs in nature gives rise to numerous and diverse segregants, some of which may be favorable for a breeder's purposes. Much plant improvement is centered about the selection of such naturally occurring favorable segregants. The student of general genetics, however, is more likely to be interested in those instances where the breeder finds it necessary to make controlled crosses among different types of plants in an effort to obtain strains combining certain of the desirable qualities of the original parents. There are many examples of this approach to plant improvement.

Yorkwin wheat, for instance, derives from a cross between a variety called Goldcoin and a selection from the variety Dietz. Goldcoin is white-kerneled,

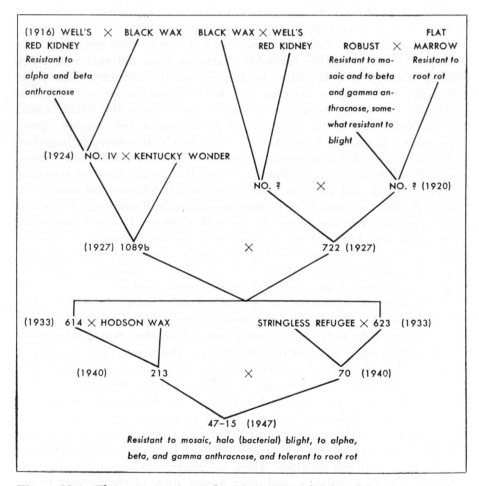

Figure 22-1. *The ancestry of snap bean No. 47-15, developed by R. A. Emerson. Observe that the earliest crosses noted in the figure go back before the 1920's, so that snap bean No. 47-15 has a long history of breeding effort. (Courtesy H. M. Munger.)*

beardless, bronze-chaffed, and has fairly stiff straw and some resistance to loose smut; Dietz is bearded and red-kerneled. Yorkwin has a certain amount of smut resistance, is beardless, white-chaffed, and white-kerneled, and yields well, apparently taking valuable qualities from both parental varieties.

The ancestry of an improved plant variety is often complex, with the favorable genetic material coming from a large number of sources. This is illustrated in Figure 22-1, which traces back part of the pedigree of snap bean selection No. 47-15, developed by R. A. Emerson and characterized by multiple disease resistance as well as desirable attributes of color, time of maturity, and vegetative habit. You will see from the figure how, as a result of recombinations following a number of crosses, resistances to halo blight, mosaic, and to alpha, beta, and gamma anthracnose, in addition to tolerance to root rot, have been brought together in a single line.

Breeders sometimes find it advantageous to resort to wide crosses in their attempts to bring together favorable characters from different sources. A striking illustration is furnished by the cultivated strawberry. This plant originated from crosses between two wild American species: *Fragaria chiloensis,* the beach strawberry, which is found along the Pacific Coast both in North and South America; and *F. virginiana,* the meadow strawberry native to eastern North America. The beach strawberry is large but lacking in flavor, and is adapted for growth only under a relatively narrow range of conditions. The meadow strawberry has a wide range of tolerance for different soils and locations, and has bright-red, delicious but small fruit.

Both *F. chiloensis* and *F. virginiana* were taken to Europe and cultivated there separately for some time. In the 19th Century, however, selections were made after both natural and systematic crosses between the species; these gave rise to our first forms of the garden strawberry. The comment has been made that the strawberry was born in North America, travelled to Europe, and returned home much the better for its journey.

Limitations on Hybridization in Plant Improvement Programs. The potentialities of hybridization and recombination for plant improvement appear at first sight to be so fascinating and so boundless that it is probably wise to reflect upon some of their limitations. The apocryphal experiment in which a strawberry and a milkweed were crossed to give a progeny that provided "strawberries and cream" is, of course, impossible. Even far less exotic combinations are precluded by the fact that interspecific crosses are often difficult, intergeneric crosses are still more rare, and wider crosses than these have seldom been recorded. Not only chromosomal compatibility but also conditions of genic and physiological balance limit the kinds of combinations that can be made. There is evidence, however, that through artificial culture of embryos, and other means, some of the barriers to hybridization can be broken down. From the breeder's point of view this is encouraging, since certain kinds of disease resistance, for example, are found only in wild relatives of cultivated plants.

Another, quite different aspect of hybridization in breeding work should also be considered here. For many of his objectives, the breeder actually finds it desirable to make crosses between plants differing by as few genes as possible. Let us think of the fairly typical situation in which a breeder is dealing with a standard variety, say of tomatoes, that on the whole is highly satisfactory, being well adapted to growers' and consumers' demands, but is susceptible to a common disease. If disease resistance is present in a plant that differs from the standard variety in only a few characters, crosses between the resistant type and the standard variety should give a relatively high frequency of favorable types among the segregants. But if the breeder is compelled to cross his standard variety with a much different sort of tomato to obtain disease resistance, the frequency of favorable segregants will be a great deal lower, and problems of detecting and testing these segregants and establishing them as homogeneous strains will be much more complicated. Hybridization is not something to be undertaken indiscriminately by the plant breeder, or without regard for possible unfavorable consequences. Nor is it likely to lead to plant improvement unless applied toward particular and well-conceived objectives.

Techniques of Selection. In modern breeding practice, principles of selection are utilized in various and sometimes complex ways. We cannot hope to review them in detail here. However, you should be aware that techniques of selection can be adjusted to the demands of different objectives and to the problems peculiar to particular kinds of plants. In the following paragraphs, two general techniques of selection, *mass selection* and *pedigree selection* will be introduced.

Mass Selection. One of the most common techniques of mass selection is simply to rogue out undesirable types and save seed from the rest. This practice is effective as a means of purging genetic deviants that, either through mutation or some other process, have come to appear as contaminants in a variety. In contrast to searching out undesirable plants and preventing their reproduction, breeders may take the more positive approach and look for especially desirable plants, seeds, ears, or the like, and then confine reproduction to this choice material.

Under the right circumstances, mass selection can produce appreciable results with fair rapidity. For example, in the important forage plant big bluestem, it was possible, by five generations of selecting desirable plants as maternal parents in open-pollinated lines, to increase the leaf area of plants in their first season of growth by more than twelve times. In general, however, mass selection has the disadvantage of producing changes relatively slowly, because the breeder utilizing this method has too few experimental controls on his material. In merely selecting among naturally cross-pollinated plants, there is no control over the pollen source, which may be on the average genetically inferior to the selected maternal parents. Lack of strict genetic control accentuates the difficulty—always a great one for the breeder—of untangling differences due to environment from those due to heredity.

Pedigree Selection. Many of the disadvantages of mass selection are minimized in *pedigree selection.* Under this method, individual plants and their progenies are kept separate for study and for breeding purposes. Selec-tion is based upon the comparative performances of these pedigreed lines. Such an approach enables the breeder to control and to define the genetic properties of his material. As a consequence, estimating environmental in-fluences becomes less difficult.

Pedigree selection has been practiced with great success among habitually self-pollinated plants. Here the effect is isolation of different pure lines. When this is accomplished, the breeder's task is to find out by repeated test-ing whether any of the isolates are better for his purpose than varieties already in existence. This is by no means as easy as it sounds, because the differences with which the breeder works may be relatively small, and the problem of demonstrating them satisfactorily under a wide range of field conditions may be a long-term project.

For example in oat breeding, new progenies are usually started from the seed of a single panicle. This original isolation of lines is followed by pre-liminary tests of one to three or more years. During this time, yield is meas-ured, and observations are made on stiffness of straw, disease resistance, and other characteristics. Promising lines are then subjected to larger-scale tests in experimental plots for several more years. Finally, lines which emerge successfully from these earlier trials are studied in different field plots over a period of time. If, after all this examination and cross-checking, a line proves to be superior to varieties already in use, the breeder may decide to release it as a new variety. Before this can be done, however, seed must be multiplied for planting by the farmer. The total process may take from eight to fifteen years or more. This same general procedure has been followed in the breeding of most other small grains, including wheat and barley. Pedi-gree selection as a breeding method is more expensive than mass selection. It has paid huge dividends many times, however, and doubtless will remain a standard breeding technique under appropriate circumstances.

When pedigree selection is applied to crops that are normally cross-pollinated, artificially controlled self-pollination is carried on within the pedigreed lines whenever at all feasible. The effect of continued inbreeding is to produce homozygosity and, therefore, uniformity within selected lines. Moreover, as homozygosis occurs, undesirable characters like albinistic, dwarf, or twisted seedlings appear, and may be selected against.

With some normally cross-pollinated crops, pedigree selection may result in the development of superior, true-breeding varieties. Recall, however, that continued inbreeding of many habitually cross-fertilized plants is at-tended by a general loss in vigor that cannot be attributed to the effects of any small number of genes. Where this is true, mass selection may present advantages over pedigree selection. Through mass selection it is often possible to achieve varietal uniformity for certain key characteristics and still retain sufficient heterozygosity for the maintenance of vigor.

Pedigree selection within self-pollinated lines is being practiced more and more even with normally cross-fertilized crops that show a marked decline in vigor when inbred. Here the purpose of inbreeding is not to produce varieties directly usable by crop growers but to establish uniform lines of predictable behavior, from among which particular lines may be selected to serve as the parents of superior hybrids.

The Practical Utilization of Heterosis. In Chapter 16, heterosis was discussed as a biological phenomenon. We considered its possible bases in the genetically determined physiology of the organism, and its manifestation in various organisms, particularly corn. Now a little more can be said about heterosis as it relates to plant breeding. First, it should be re-emphasized that not all organisms show heterosis, at least in any obvious way. In corn, where heterosis may be strongly manifested, not every hybrid is favorable from the agricultural standpoint. Hybrids which do well under some conditions or in some localities may be poor in others. Again, as in other areas of plant breeding, the breeder who wishes to utilize heterosis must work with specific aims and specific problems in mind.

The performance of a hybrid depends upon its genetic constitution, and therefore stems from the hereditary makeup of its parental inbreds. The fundamental task of the corn breeder is to develop suitable inbred lines. For this work, the effectiveness of selection for particular characteristics, the accurate measurement of these characters, and the degree of certainty with which their heritability can be predicted are all highly important. Corn breeders are continuing to evolve special methods for getting at these vari-

YEAR	NORTH CENTRAL STATES Per Cent	UNITED STATES Per Cent
1933	0.2	0.1
1936	5.1	3.1
1938	25.4	14.9
1940	51.8	30.5
1942	73.0	46.4
1945	88.1	64.4
1949	94.2	77.6
1950‡	94.3	77.1

TABLE 22-4.† Corn Hybrids: Percentage of Total Corn Acreage Planted with Hybrid Seed, North Central States and United States, 1933–50.

† Taken from *Agricultural Statistics 1950*, published by the U. S. Department of Agriculture.
‡ Preliminary figure.

ous problems. In the final analysis, however, the real test of the worth of an inbred is its *combining ability*, i.e., its performance in combination with other inbreds in producing hybrid corn. No shortcuts have yet been found that eliminate the necessity for careful selection and stringent testing of inbred lines.

The Impact of Hybrid Corn. The impact of hybrid corn on our economy has been sudden and strong. Its meteoric rise can be followed in the percentages of total corn acreage planted with hybrid seed over the years following 1933. Representative values for the United States and for the North Central States section of this country are shown in Table 22-4. Today, in the Corn Belt states, almost all the field corn planted is hybrid seed.

Part of the significance of hybrid corn appears in the following quotation from Merle T. Jenkins, Principal Agronomist in charge of corn investigation in the Bureau of Plant Industry of the U. S. Department of Agriculture.

> During the three war years of 1917, 1918, and 1919, we produced 8 billion bushels of corn on a total of 311 million acres. During the three war years of 1942, 1943, and 1944, we produced 9⅓ billion bushels on 281 million acres—1,366,201,000 more bushels than in the earlier period, on 30,-522,000 fewer acres. This is equivalent to 5 billion pounds more meat a year —38 pounds more per person a year. When you look back to the fact that there were times during the last war when meat rationing got down to as low as 115 pounds a person a year, you can appreciate the importance of this extra production.

What this increased efficiency of production of corn meant in terms of release of material, energies, and manpower to other activities essential to the national welfare is difficult to assess. Obviously, the contribution of hybrid corn was significant. When added to other contributions of plant breeding, it constituted one of our most powerful implements of defense.

Likewise, the effects of hybrid corn on our standard of living in peacetime, on farming practice, and on the sociology of large segments of the population cannot yet be properly estimated, but they are certainly vast. We know that the superior standability of hybrid corn, which permits the effective use of mechanical pickers, has resulted in increased all-around mechanization for the farm. The need for hired men to help with corn picking has been significantly reduced, and a variety of more or less subtle socio-economic consequences have followed. Some of these have to do with matters of labor supply, others with the composition of the rural community. Perhaps not the least significant effects have been on the farm housewife who does the cooking. Hybrid corn may prove to be a boon to soil conservation as well as to human conservation. The superior productiveness of hybrid corn is making it feasible for farmers to institute better cropping practices, to rotate their crops, and to restore fertility to the soil by adding fertilizers.

The Production of Hybrid Corn Seed. Important practical considerations for corn breeders have arisen in connection with hybrid corn seed production, now a large and flourishing industry. If seed is used after the first

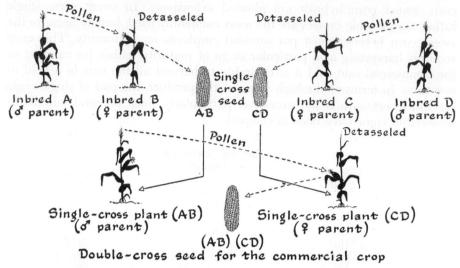

Figure 22-2. *Hybrid seed for field corn is usually produced through double crosses.*

generation following a cross, segregation takes place, and most of the advantages of hybrid corn are lost. The farmer needs, therefore, to obtain a new supply of hybrid corn seed each year.

When hybrid seed is produced simply by crossing two inbred lines, the maternal parent plant, if typical of inbreds, is small and produces small, low-yielding ears. The price of such seed necessarily comes high. To meet this difficulty, hybrid seed for the farmer is generally produced through double crosses, as illustrated in Figure 22-2. This device permits seed for distribution to the farmer to be produced on the large and uniform ears of single-cross plants.

If individual hand pollinations were necessary to produce hybrid corn seed for commercial purposes, again the expense would be prohibitive. Figure 22-2 also indicates how this difficulty is resolved. The parent inbreds to be crossed are planted in fields isolated from the pollen of other corn. One inbred is chosen to act as the female parent (it will bear the hybrid seed), and all its plants have their tassels removed before they begin to shed pollen. Usually these fields for hybridization are planted so that two "female" rows alternate with but one row of the male parent, permitting a greater yield of seed per acre than if male and female parents were in equal numbers. Analogous procedures are followed in the generation that produces the double-cross seed. Note how the nature of its life cycle and of its mechanisms for reproduction makes corn well suited for controlled mass production of hybrid seed.

Other Instances of the Practical Utilization of F_1 Hybrids. First-generation hybrids are beginning to be used in commercial crops other than field corn. Sweet corn hybrids are planted extensively. In sweet corn, single rather than double crosses are the most commonly used, largely because the sweet corn breeder must put unusual emphasis on uniformity. This crop requires harvesting at a particular stage of maturity, either for canning or for commercial sale, and it is desirable to harvest all the ears in a field at one time. In terms of the high value of the product, the cost of single-cross seed in sweet corn is not excessive, particularly since parental inbreds of reasonable vigor have been developed.

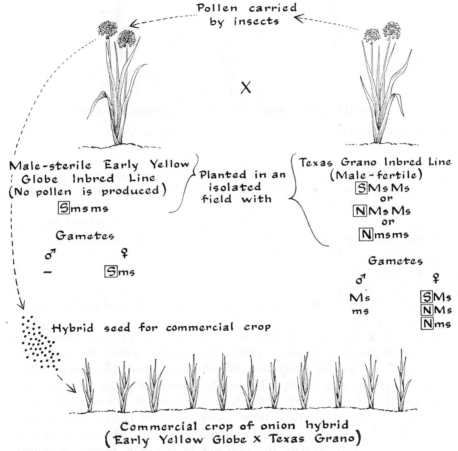

Figure 22-3. *Controlled hybridization in onions may be achieved by utilizing a genetically determined male sterility in the inbred line to be used as the female parent in the cross. This male sterility in onions results from interaction between a cytoplasmic factor* S *and a recessive nuclear gene ms. All plants with* N *(normal) cytoplasm produce viable pollen, and all plants with gene Ms, either homozygous or heterozygous, are also male fertile. Male-sterile plants are* S *ms ms. (After Munger, based on work of Jones and Clarke, Proc. Am. Soc. Hort. Sci., 43:193, 1943.)*

Breeding methods following the general outlines of modern corn improvement programs are successful with onions. However, onions are not well suited for the mass production of hybrid seed. The reason arises from the fact that both male and female organs occur within the same flowers. The emasculation process necessary to control hybridization requires such painstaking work that the expense prohibits commercial production.

In recent years, breeders have made ingenious use of inherited male sterility in onions to produce inbred lines that do not require emasculation. The male sterile character has been introduced into various standard varieties like Crystal Wax, Yellow Bermuda, Yellow Globe Danvers, and Sweet Spanish. Inbred lines have been established, and certain hybrids show exceptional promise. California Hybrid Red No. 1 is already used rather widely. It is larger than either of its parents and combines the relatively early maturity of one with the delayed bolting habit of the other. Figure 22-3 illustrates a method utilizing male sterility in the production of hybrid onion seed on a commercial scale.

Other plants in which first-generation hybrids show promise from the breeder's standpoint include cucumbers, squash, and pine trees. Yankee Hybrid summer squash has an advantage over competing nonhybrid varieties because of its relatively early productiveness. Particular interspecific combinations of pines seem to manifest heterosis in various ways, including greater vigor of growth and superior seed germination. Pine hybrids are being tested extensively in the national forests of California and elsewhere.

The Backcross as a Breeding Tool. A little earlier we mentioned that the male-sterile character was introduced into a number of varieties of onions, but did not describe how this was done. The type of problem involved, which is to transfer particular characters into a standard variety without otherwise changing it, arises frequently in breeding programs. Simply to make appropriate crosses and then to look for desirable segregants may not provide a satisfactory solution for such a problem. If the parent contributing the character to be transferred carries more than a few genes different from those that determine valuable qualities in the standard variety, the probability of recovering the proper segregants is usually so low that impractically large populations would be necessary. A way around this kind of difficulty is offered by the *backcross method* of breeding. This involves first making a cross between members of the types wherein gene transfer is to be accomplished, and then, over a series of generations, backcrossing the progenies to one of the parental lines (called the *recurrent parent*).

The effect of such repeated backcrossing is, in each succeeding generation, roughly to increase by 50 per cent the number of genes characteristic of the recurrent parent. The principle is illustrated in Figure 22-4, which shows how backcrossing can be utilized to develop male-sterile lines of onion varieties such as Crystal Wax. You can see that after only three backcrosses a high proportion of Crystal Wax genes may already be obtained in combination with male sterility. For the sort of purpose illustrated, the backcross method simplifies the breeder's problems. He can concentrate most of his initial efforts on selecting the character or characters desired from the nonrecurrent parent. Meantime, characteristics of the recurrent parent automatically accumulate.

H. H. Smith has reported studies with tobacco that have interesting implications for the theory of the backcross method. Gene *m*, which has occurred several times as a spontaneous mutant in *Nicotiana tabacum*, when homozygous gives rise to plants of exceptional size (mammoths) that flower

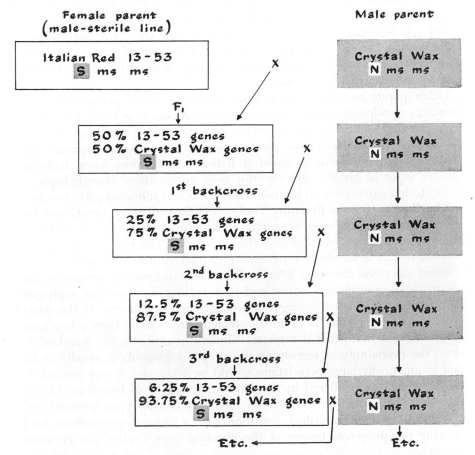

Figure 22-4. *Utilization of the backcross method to develop male-sterile lines of Crystal Wax onions. The percentages in the series to the left indicate the rate at which Crystal Wax genes are incorporated into the male-sterile line (Italian Red), under the assumption of random sampling. In practice, selection for Crystal Wax types in the backcross progenies increases the rate at which a male-sterile Crystal Wax line is approached. (After Jones and Davis, U. S. Dept. Agr. Tech. Bull. No. 874, p. 26, 1944.)*

TABLE 22-5. *Relationship Between Genotype and Photoperiodicity in Tobacco. (From Smith, J. Heredity, 41:202, 1950.)*

RESIDUAL GENOTYPE	GENE	
	MM and Mm	mm
Tabacum strain	Long day—flowers	Long day—no flowers
	Short day—flowers	Short day—flowers
Rustica strain	Long day—flowers	Long day—no flowers
	Short day—flowers	Short day—no flowers

only under short-day light periods. By repeatedly backcrossing plants carrying the *m* gene to members of the species *N. rustica,* Smith was able to transfer this gene from *N. tabacum* to what was essentially a rustica genotype. With this different genetic background for *mm,* the mammoth character is expressed, but plants fail to flower even in short days. The situation is summarized in Table 22-5. The results illustrate again that genes do not express themselves irrespective of environment or of the rest of the genotype of the

Figure 22-5. *The smaller Easter lily was produced on a diploid plant, the larger on a tetraploid. The tetraploid was obtained by means of chromosome doubling induced by colchicine treatment. (Courtesy S. L. Emsweller, Bureau of Plant Industry, U. S. Dept. of Agriculture. Science in Farming, Yearbook of Agriculture, 1943–1947, ff. p. 80.)*

organism. In some instances, then, breeders may not be able to transfer particular characters into varieties without changing either these characters or perhaps some valuable attributes of the varieties.

The Induction of Polyploidy as a Tool in Plant Breeding. You know from the general discussion of polyploidy in Chapter 11 that the addition of genomes sometimes, though not always, results in more luxuriant growth in plants. Also, polyploids may show a wider range of adaptation than their diploid analogues, or they may have other characteristics of practical value. Since techniques are available for doubling chromosome numbers experimentally, it would seem that polyploidy should play an important part in plant improvement programs. Indeed, some enthusiasts who have seen the strikingly large flowers resulting from colchicine-induced polyploidy in ornamentals such as the Easter lily (see Fig. 22-5) have hailed colchicine as a panacea for plant breeding and other practical genetic problems. One correspondent of A. F. Blakeslee asked: "If it will grow better plants, is it good for hair on the head?" Since colchicine is a highly poisonous compound, the experiment would be dangerous, as well as unlikely to succeed. The fact is that plant breeders cannot solve all their problems merely by doubling chromosome numbers. One reason is that a good share of the crop plants presently being grown are already polyploids. In many instances, further reduplication of genomes fails to result in increases in size and vigor.

In some crop plants, especially among diploids, doubling the chromosome number does have favorable results on particular aspects of growth. Tetraploid corn, for example, appears to be appreciably more vigorous than comparable diploid corn, and there is something like 40 per cent more vitamin A in tetraploid yellow corn meal than in meal from the diploid. However, fertility is considerably reduced in the tetraploid lines. (You might expect this. Why?) The picture is brightened by the fact that there are significant differences in fertility among inbred tetraploid lines. Whether it will be possible to select for sufficient fertility to permit the utilization of tetraploid corn for crop purposes remains to be seen.

Very nearly the same difficulties occur in tetraploid red clover, which is vegetatively superior to the diploid but has a poor seed set. On the other hand, Swedish plant breeders have found that tetraploid alsike clover has as good fertility as the diploid and appears to give more persistent growth. Tetraploid varieties of marigolds, snapdragons, and some other garden flowers are listed in seed catalogues. They are at least fertile enough for their seed to be sold at prices comparable to those asked for the seed of excellent new diploid varieties.

In summation, mere doubling of chromosome numbers is not a certain or a short road to plant improvement. Where doubling does gives a favorable type of plant, a more or less laborious program of selection for fertility often needs to follow before the new polyploid can be produced in bulk. Such programs are being carried out with certain polyploids, but in other instances they have been abandoned in favor of lines of approach that promise to be more immediately profitable. Of course, where reproduction is possible by vegetative means, as with certain fruits, problems of fertility are less important, and induced polyploids, if desirable, may be used as quickly as adequate stocks can be established.

The possibilities for producing quite new types of desirable plants through interspecific crosses followed by induced doubling to produce amphidiploids appear to be great. Exploitation of this area of practical genetics is only beginning.

Better Seed Programs

At the time when a plant breeder is convinced that he has a superior new variety, the amount of seed he has on hand, while perhaps adequate for experimental purposes, is insignificant when compared to the amount needed for use by growers. If his results are to be applied, seed of his new variety must be multiplied and distributed. Increase and maintenance of seed stocks must be carefully planned and supervised.

Precautions are necessary, in the first place, to insure that weeds and plant diseases are not spread through seed stocks. More important from the breeder's point of view is the necessity of preserving the genetic identity of the new variety, which has been described and recommended on the basis of particular heritable characteristics. Steps must be taken to prevent mix-

TABLE 22-6. *Classes and Sources of Certified Seed.* (*From* Intern. Crop Improvement Assoc. Pub. No. 17, 1950.)

(a) BREEDER SEED: Breeder seed is seed or vegetative propagating material directly controlled by the originating, or in certain cases the sponsoring, plant breeder or institution, and which provides the source for the initial and recurring increase of foundation seed.

(b) FOUNDATION SEED: Foundation seed, including elite in Canada, shall be seed stocks that are so handled as to most nearly maintain specific genetic identity and purity and that may be designated or distributed by an agricultural experiment station. Production must be carefully supervised or approved by representatives of an agricultural experiment station. Foundation seed shall be the source of all other certified seed classes, either directly or through registered seed.

(c) REGISTERED SEED: Registered seed shall be the progeny of foundation or registered seed that is so handled as to maintain satisfactory genetic identity and purity and that has been approved and certified by the certifying agency. This class of seed should be of a quality suitable for the production of certified seed.

(d) CERTIFIED SEED: Certified seed shall be the progeny of foundation, registered, or certified seed that is so handled as to maintain satisfactory genetic identity and purity and that has been approved and certified by the certifying agency.

ture of seed with that of other varieties. Measures against unintentional hybridization are at least equally important. At appropriate times and places in the seed increase program, rigid selection must be made against off-types that may have appeared either as the result of mutation, chance contamination or unanticipated segregation. Your knowledge of population genetics will tell you why this is essential.

In recognition of the pitfalls we have indicated, more and more of the better seed being grown is produced within a framework of orderly rules and procedures that have emerged from cooperative planning between plant breeders and seed growers. Seed produced according to these standards is *certified* as such. Purchasers can have confidence in it commensurate with the validity of the rules and procedures for certification. These rules and procedures vary for different crops, but the principles are similar for all. An outline procedure for the production of certified seed can be inferred from the description of classes of certified seed found in Table 22-6.

Plant Breeding and Population Genetics

If before we leave the subject of plant breeding you consider its general biological implications, you will find that many of them relate to aspects of population genetics. In fact, the very basis of plant breeding methodology is the manipulation of gene frequencies to establish particular desired genotypes. Apart from this, you should have in mind at least two other phases in which plant breeding has important bearing on concepts of the genetics of populations.

First, plant breeding has contributed much to our understanding of evolution. We know from numerous experiments in plant breeding that selection is effective in achieving large changes within groups of organisms over finite periods of time. These results provide some of our best direct evidence that evolution can actually work on the basis modern biologists have proposed.

Second, and this is a special aspect of the first point, fundamental facets of the dynamics of natural populations appear in relationships of crop plants with the microorganisms that are pathogenic upon them. When Marquis wheat came on the scene many years ago, stinking smut, which had been a major disease problem, almost immediately fell to minor importance. However, scab, to which previously grown varieties had been more or less resistant, spread widely, because Marquis was highly susceptible to this disease although resistant to smut. The death blow to Marquis was an epidemic of stem rust, against which its defenses were totally inadequate. When rust-resistant varieties of bread wheats—notably Ceres—were developed, smut began to build up again. But, ironically, it was an attack of stem rust that eventually almost eliminated Ceres as a variety. Ceres had not kept up with the times. It was the same old variety as always, but the stem rust had changed. Acquisition of a new genotype enabled the rust to break down old barriers to its multiplication and again become a successful and widespread group.

The picture just presented is an essential aspect of the living world seen in microcosm. The brief life cycles of pathogenic microorganisms and the sensitivity of their relationships with their hosts permit us to see with exaggerated clarity the population flux that exists everywhere as selection operates. Variation, as provided by mutation, recombination, or migration, is measured against the demands of environment, and successful groups are those with attributes having superior survival value. Between host and parasite, these issues are clear. The plant breeder must work in anticipation of the results they foster. The effort to keep disease-resistant varieties in the field is a never-ending race between evolution controlled by man and natural evolution, which, although unseeing, grinds away effectively.

Keys to the Significance of This Chapter

The growing of plants has an integral role in our economy. Many valid and feasible objectives of plant improvement are obvious in terms of man's socio-economic needs.

Plant species are sufficiently plastic that man has been able to mold numerous different varieties of plants to fit specific purposes.

To be effective, methods of plant breeding must be based on sound genetic principles. The fundamental operation common to all breeding methods is the *selection* of favored genotypes.

The particular method utilized in any given instance of plant improvement work should be chosen to fit the objective and should take into account the kind of plant. The life cycle of the plant and its previous genetic history are particularly significant.

Once superior varieties have been bred, there remains the problem of increasing them and getting them into the hands of growers. Seed *certification* plays an important part in plant improvement programs.

Analogies between plant breeding and evolution have given us better insight into both processes.

References

Atwood, S. S., "Cytogenetics and Breeding of Forage Crops." *Advances in Genetics*, 1:2–67, 1947. (A condensed but informative review.)

Briggs, F. N., "The Use of the Backcross in Crop Improvement." *Am. Naturalist*, 72:285–292, 1938. (A discussion of the applicability and genetic basis of this method.)

Crabb, A. R., *The Hybrid-corn Makers: Prophets of Plenty*. New Brunswick: Rutgers University Press, 1947. (A human-interest approach to the story of hybrid corn.)

Hayes, H. K., and Immer, F. R., *Methods of Plant Breeding*. New York: McGraw-Hill Book Co., 1942. (A text, dealing with techniques of plant breeding and applied statistics.)

Knight, R. L., "The Role of Major Genes in the Evolution of Economic Characters." *J. Genetics*, **48**:370–387, 1948. (Includes a compilation of economic characters, in a wide variety of plants, known to be at least partly controlled by genes with major effects.)

Krug, C. A., and Carvalho, A., "The Genetics of Coffea." *Advances in Genetics*, **4**:127–158, 1951. (Deals with the genetic basis of characteristics important in coffee breeding. Includes many interesting examples not readily available to students from other sources.)

Mangelsdorf, P. C., "Hybrid Corn: Its Genetic Basis and Its Significance in Human Affairs," in *Genetics in the 20th Century*, pp. 555–571. New York: Macmillan Co., 1951. (A general treatment, well described by the title.)

Müntzing, A., "Cyto-Genetic Properties and Practical Value of Tetraploid Rye." *Hereditas*, **37**:17–84, 1951. (A report of extensive investigations. Includes a picture of "tetraploid rye bread.")

——, "Genetics and Plant Breeding," in *Genetics in the 20th Century*, pp. 473–492. New York: Macmillan Co., 1951. (General, with particularly interesting sections on the utilization of induced mutations and induced polyploidy in breeding work.)

Randolph, L. F., "An Evaluation of Induced Polyploidy as a Method of Breeding Crop Plants." *Biol. Symposia*, **4**:151–167, 1941. (Written soon after the discovery of the colchicine effect on chromosomes but still essentially sound.)

Richey, F. D., "Corn Breeding." *Advances in Genetics*, **3**:159–192, 1950. (A brief summary of corn breeding methods, particularly those relating to the development of superior hybrids. Also contains some discussion of the genetic characters of greatest economic importance.)

Singleton, W. R., "Hybrid Vigor and Its Utilization in Sweet Corn Breeding." *Am. Naturalist*, **75**:48–60, 1941. (Readable and informative to the general student.)

Sprague, G. F., "The Experimental Basis for Hybrid Maize." *Biol. Rev.*, **21**:101–120, 1946. (An authoritative review.)

Stakman, E. C., "Plant Diseases Are Shifty Enemies." *Am. Scientist*, **35**:321–350, 1947. (Deals with the instability of plant diseases and with problems of breeding plants for resistance.)

Walker, J. C., "Genetics and Plant Pathology," in *Genetics in the 20th Century*, pp. 527–554. New York: Macmillan Co., 1951. (An over-all view of the significance of genetic variation in pathogenicity and in disease resistance.)

Yearbook of Agriculture, 1936. Washington: U. S. Govt. Printing Office, 1936. (More than 1000 pages devoted to the development of "Better Plants and Animals" through breeding. On the plant side are extensive summaries of various aspects of the breeding of cereal crops, corn, flax, tobacco, and sugar crops.)

Yearbook of Agriculture, 1937. Washington: U. S. Govt. Printing Office, 1937. (Continues the theme of the 1936 Yearbook. Articles on the improvement of forage crops, vegetable crops, fruits, and flowers.)

Yearbook of Agriculture, 1943–1947. Washington: U. S. Govt. Printing Office, 1947. (Has many short articles relating to plant improvement. See particularly: E. R. Sears, "Genetics and Farming," pp. 245–255; J. H. Martin, "Tailor-Made Sorghums," pp. 413–416; H. A. Jones and A. E. Clarke, "The Story of Hybrid Onions," pp. 320–326; S. L. Emsweller, "Flowers as You Like Them," pp. 284–288; P. Stockwell and F. I. Righter, "Hybrid Forest Trees," pp. 465–472.)

Questions and Problems

22- 1.   What do the following terms signify?

combining ability	open-pollinated variety
double cross	pedigree selection
genetic variability	recurrent parent
male sterility	roguing
mass selection	single cross

22- 2.   What are some of the specific advantages for the plant breeder of working with a plant that reproduces asexually as well as sexually?

22- 3.   In what respects does natural selection operate in favor of the objectives of plant improvement programs? Make your answer as specific as possible.

22- 4.   Does natural selection always work in the same direction a plant breeder might wish? Amplify your answer with examples.

22- 5.   Name two specific circumstances under which the breeder may have to deal with very large populations of plants in order to achieve an objective.

22- 6.   Discuss how particular instances of plant improvement may have rather far-reaching consequences for society, apart from merely giving a greater abundance or finer quality of products.

22- 7.   Until very recently, the artificial induction of mutations has played almost no role in plant improvement programs. Why do you suppose plant breeders have not resorted to this well-known technique of experimental genetics? In other words, do you see any difficulties about utilizing mutagens in plant breeding practice?

22- 8.   In what sorts of instances, and for what kinds of objectives, do you think the artificial induction of mutations might be of practical use in plant improvement programs?

22- 9.   What are some of the difficulties the breeder may have in working with polyploids as compared to diploids?

22-10.   Polyploids are often larger and more vigorous than their diploid analogues. Why not, as part of every breeding program, simply double the chromosome number of all available varieties?

22-11.   Under what circumstances may the breeder find techniques of test tube embryo culture useful?

22-12. What is the breeder's purpose in inbreeding normally cross-pollinated crop plants that show reduction in vigor when they are inbred?

22-13. Under what circumstances might a breeder wish to make *wide* crosses as a step toward plant improvement?

22-14. In oat breeding, for example, which would be more effective for dealing with characters that are sensitive to environmental influence: (a) mass selection, or (b) pedigree selection? Why?

22-15. What problems, if any, do you see in maintaining a pure-line variety of wheat in its original state? What steps might be taken to maintain such a variety?

22-16. Many forage plants have multiple allelic series for self-incompatibility (S alleles). Discuss whether this is advantageous or disadvantageous from the breeder's point of view.

22-17. Suppose that you, as a plant breeder, have on hand a variety of tomato that is satisfactory in every regard except that it is highly susceptible to a certain disease. You also have available a variety with several objectionable features, from the growers' standpoint, but that is disease resistant. You wish to transfer the disease resistance to the first variety through the backcross technique. Will it make any difference in your plans, or in the ease of carrying them out, whether the disease resistance character is inherited as a simple dominant or as a simple recessive? Explain.

22-18. Which of these characters do you think would be simpler to transfer through the backcross method: (a) winter hardiness, or (b) plant color? Why?

22-19. Which is the more realistic criterion for establishing the practical value of a corn hybrid: (a) to compare its performance with the performances of its parental inbreds; or (b) to compare its performance with that of open-pollinated varieties grown in the same area?

22-20. Why, in general, are single-cross progenies more uniform than double-cross progenies?

22-21. Suggest how monoploids might be utilized in a corn breeding program.

22-22. What are some of the various factors that limit yield in crop plants?

22-23. In connection with plant improvement programs, expeditions are sometimes organized for the purpose of collecting wild relatives of our cultivated plants. What practical purposes may such expeditions serve?

22-24. Are there any "improvements" you would like to see made in plants you are familiar with? What improvements? Would it be feasible to achieve them through breeding methods?

22-25. It has been suggested that experiments in plant improvement might well utilize complicated greenhouses that make possible the close control of many environmental factors such as light, temperature, and humidity. What advantages and disadvantages can you see in this suggestion as contrasted with improvement programs practiced in open field culture?

CHAPTER 23

Genetic Aspects of Animal Productivity

NUMEROUS CLEAR-CUT Mendelian alternatives have been observed in domestic animals, and some of these are of immediate economic concern. Most of the characteristics of practical significance in domestic animals are quantitative in nature, however; they depend on the interactions of numerous genes and are subject to phenotypic modification by the environment. We have illustrated some of the principles of heredity by means of examples chosen from the qualitatively inherited characteristics of animals, and some of the problems at the end of this chapter are intended to sample further from this part of the field of animal breeding. For the remainder of our discussion we shall recognize that such attributes as animal productivity and reproductive potential generally constitute continuously variable characteristics in populations of individuals. Particular alleles are often difficult or impossible to identify, and classical Mendelian ratios are usually obscured by the many interacting genes affecting the characteristics under consideration, by the various gene frequencies prevailing in the populations, and by the overlapping effects of environment and genotype on the phenotypic end products of development.

Because it deals primarily with this kind of quantitative inheritance, the developing science of animal breeding has become one of the most specialized segments of genetics. It begins with a broad knowledge of general genetics, and carries on through a whole new battery of essentially statistical techniques that are necessary to the efficient application of the principles of genetics to the problems of animal improvement.

We cannot attempt in this elementary text to present in detail, or to justify in compelling fashion, the various techniques of description, analysis, and evaluation that are now essential parts of animal breeding. We shall only sample from the general methods and the presently available conclusions of this quantitative science.

Bases for Selection

Probably the most important single question that confronts the breeder of any class of livestock is this: "How should I decide which animals to save for breeding stock and which to cull from my breeding population? And if I buy sires or breeding females from outside my own herd, flock, or kennel, how can I best assure that the animals I buy will raise the level of performance of my population in the future?"

Two rather different sources of information about an individual are useful in evaluating his potential breeding worth. One is his own performance or productivity. The other depends on his genetic relatives—ancestral, collateral, and descendent.

Individual Performance. Estimating the breeding value of an animal from his own productivity has long been recognized as a keystone of animal improvement, epitomized in the familiar rule of thumb "Like begets like." Modern animal breeding does not fail to emphasize the value of this guide to selection, but it qualifies the old rule a bit, and places it on a more quantitative basis.

In the discussion to follow, we shall use the term *phenotype* to denote not simply the way an animal looks, but any characteristic that is discernible from the consideration of the individual by himself. Thus we will include a production record achieved by an individual as part of his phenotype, and will assume that this phenotypic characteristic, like others, is based upon a system of genetic potentialities interacting with the environment.

If the characteristics in which we are interested depended on uncomplicated, additive gene effects, then the phenotype of an animal would be a statistically reliable index of his transmitting ability. (Recall our discussion of this kind of quantitative inheritance in Chapter 15.) But the hard fact is that few of the economic characters of animals are really so uncomplicated, and selection on the basis of phenotype alone is likely to make mistakes from a genetic point of view. These mistakes arise from at least three sources:

Environmental Effects. The conditions under which animals are grown, fed, and evaluated affect profoundly the records of productivity they achieve. Environment varies from stall to stall, from season to season, from farm to farm, and from region to region. Even the prenatal environment of the developing animal varies from one dam to another, and from one pregnancy to another in the same dam. Among the most critical problems of the animal breeder are those that deal with the evaluation of these environmental variables and their effects, and with the distinction between inherent merit and the fortunes of environment.

Probably the clearest result of our increasing awareness of these environmental sources of error is the number of "corrections" that are nowadays applied in the standardization of records of performance. In dairy cattle, for instance, statistics are available that make it possible to estimate the mature equivalent of the performance of a young cow; to correct various lactation periods to a constant (usually 305-day) basis; to convert different numbers of daily milkings to a twice-a-day schedule; to correct for the lesser reliability of single or short-term records compared with several records on the same individual; and so on. These corrections are all of unquestionable value in the attempt to eliminate clearly nongenetic sources of error in the selection of individual cows.

But many of the more subtle effects of environment are not subject to such straightforward statistical control. Even when all the "corrections" are made, it is probable that two individuals of similar inherent merit will achieve different records of performance, or that two individuals of different inherent levels of ability may end up with similar records. When the breeder's basis for selection depends upon individual performance alone, therefore, he is likely sometimes to mistake environmental advantage for genetic superiority; and to the extent that this happens, his selection will be unavailing in the genetic improvement of his stock.

Dominance. A quite different source of error in estimating the transmitting ability of an animal from phenotypic data alone involves dominance deviations from simple additive inheritance. You will recall that under the additive scheme the substitution of a given "active allele" A, for a, was assumed to make a constant addition to the phenotype, whether this substitution were to change genotype aa to Aa, or Aa to AA. In other words, the additive scheme is based on a complete lack of dominance at each locus under consideration, so that the heterozygote is exactly intermediate between the two respective homozygotes.

Now if A is dominant to a, the additive scheme in its ideal form cannot apply. Replacing A for a in the genotype aa may have a certain measurable effect, but the same replacement in genotype Aa will have less effect—no effect at all if dominance is complete. The heterozygote may not be intermediate, but may approach the level of the homozygous dominant. Or the heterozygote may even exceed the level of either homozygote (see "overdominance," p. 337).

Some of the effects of dominance on the precision of phenotypic selection will be discussed in connection with the other sources of error in the following section.

Epistasis. Just as dominance at any particular locus results in a deviation from the simple additive scheme, so also interactions among genes at different loci result in epistatic deviations. To cite an easily recognized effect of this sort, we can recall epistasis in color inheritance. If an animal has the dominant allele of albinism, which permits the development of color, then gene substitutions at other loci may affect noticeably the quality or distribution or quantity of pigment. But if the animal is an albino, substitutions at other loci affecting color produce no phenotypic effect; no pigment is present through which other aspects of color diversity may come to expression. There is good reason to believe that in many important characteristics other than color, similar gene interactions occur. In the example of albinism, the effects of epistasis are evident; we would not think of selecting for color characteristics in an albino line. But epistasis in economic characteristics may be much more subtle.

The Selection Differential and Regression. If, from a reasonably large original population, a number of individuals that excel in a particular attribute are chosen to be parents of the next generation, these selected individuals have a higher average value for the characteristic concerned than has the population from which they come (Fig. 23-1). The difference between the mean of those selected and the population mean is called the *selection differential*. It is a measure of the intensity of selection.

You can easily see how environmental effects, dominance, and epistasis reduce the precision of selection based only on phenotype. If the characteristic under selection were determined entirely by additive gene effects, the mean of the selected parents would be a good measure of their average genotype. Different individuals would vary, of course, in the number of "active alleles" they possessed, and in the ways in which the "active alleles" at different loci were combined. Segregation and recombination of these alleles would result in genetic variation among the progeny. But *the mean of the next generation would be the same as the mean of the selected parents,* and in successive generations rapid progress could be made in the improvement of the population (Fig. 23-2). The ultimate level reached would depend on the amount of genetic diversity present in the original population or introduced into it by bringing in "new blood" from outside.

When environmental effects and dominance and epistatic deviations are present, this kind of selection becomes less effective. Among the individuals selected to be parents, a fraction will be animals with only ordinary or even

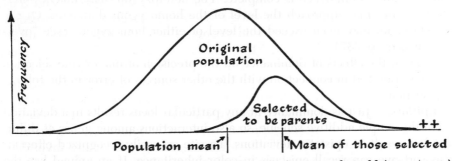

Figure 23-1. *On a scale running from* (— —) *(most undesirable) to* (+ +) *(most desirable) for a trait under selection, the mean of selected parents is higher than the average of the population from which the parents came. (After Lush,* Animal Breeding Plans, *Iowa State College Press, 1945, p. 146.)*

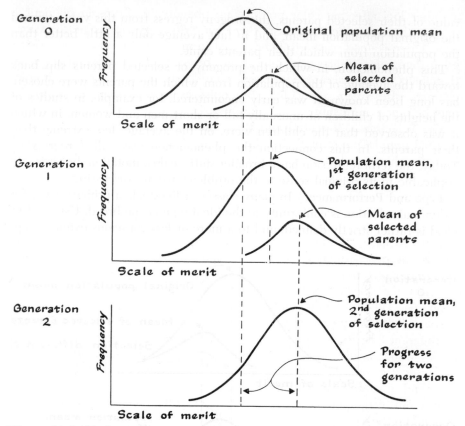

Figure 23-2. *If the trait under selection were determined entirely by additive gene effects, the mean of a generation would be the same as the average of its selected parents, and rapid progress would be made in improving the population.*

inferior genotypes that have been fortunate in their environment and thus have achieved levels of performance high enough to mislead the breeder. Similarly, some animals superior in genotype will, through misfortune in their environment, be left out of the breeding program, and their desirable alleles will be lost. Even among the genotypically superior and selected individuals, undesirable recessives will be present to segregate out in later generations. This will result in progeny that average less than the value predicted by simple additive inheritance (without dominance or recessiveness). And if gene interaction (epistasis) is involved in phenotypic superiority, Mendelian recombination will effect the breaking-up of many favorable, selected gene combinations, again with the result that the progeny may average less than the mean of their selected parents.

For these reasons, the history of a herd or flock under phenotypic selection generally looks something like Figure 23-3. Instead of showing the average value of their selected parents, the progeny regress from this value toward the original population mean, and in fact average only a little better than the population from which their parents came.

This phenomenon, in which the progeny of selected parents slip back toward the average of the population from which the parents were chosen, has long been known. It was early encountered, for example, in studies of the heights of children of unusually tall or short men and women, in which it was observed that the children were, on the average, less extreme than their parents. In this connection the phenomenon was called *regression*. Today, the term regression has a broader statistical connotation, but it is still applicable in its original sense to the problems we are discussing.

Type and Performance. In many classes of livestock, a primary basis for individual selection is conformity to the ideal type of the breed. Usually this ideal is rather strictly defined, and to a more or less conscious extent it rep-

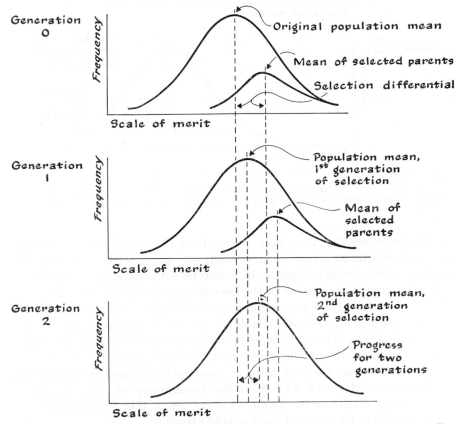

Figure 23-3. *The progeny of selected parents do not usually average as well as the parents did, but regress toward the mean of the population from which the parents came.*

resents an esthetic standard—the standard of beauty for the breed. Breeders who compete for prizes in the show circuits enter their animals in what are essentially "beauty" contests, in which the animals that in the opinion of the judges conform most closely to the breed type win ribbons and prizes. Several of the breed organizations undertake "type classification" of registered animals, and the degree of conformity to type becomes a matter of permanent record for each animal.

There are at least three reasons why conformity to type may be regarded as a justifiable consideration in selecting breeding animals. First, to a great many breeders the esthetic value of owning and working with beautiful animals is one of the primary satisfactions of husbandry. Ruggedly materialistic dairymen, for example, may regard the size of the milk check as the only important aspect of dairying, but to many breeders of dairy cattle the occupation has other values beyond economic evaluation. Second, in the animal breeding world as it is at present constituted, conformity to type has a very real economic aspect. Few breeders who depend for a significant part of their margin of profit on the sale of breeding stock can afford to ignore the looks of their animals, lest they achieve productive animals that few buyers want because they are ugly. The type classification of an animal or his record in the show ring is often reflected in his cash value, and in the value placed on his relatives and progeny. Third, it is often asserted that there is a relationship between type and productivity, so that selection on the basis of type is in fact selecting for higher or more persistent production.

The first two reasons above are matters of things-as-they-are, and each breeder must evaluate them for himself in terms of his own objectives. The third is a point that we may discuss briefly. Probably in all classes of livestock, some of the grounds for type classification are related to the productive merit of the animal. This is probably particularly true of animals grown for meat or for wool or fur, since the potential productivity of the animal is displayed for all to see and to judge. In dairy cattle or in poultry, on the other hand, it is not equally clear that the butterfat or egg production of an individual can be discerned in its appearance. Some of the characteristics observed in judging individuals, while they may not show up in immediate production records, are nevertheless important to the animal's practical, continued performance. No matter how productive, a cow whose udder has broken away from her body to drag on the ground, suspended by loose sheets of skin, is probably not a good cow under most farming conditions. Other similar examples might be cited.

The main difficulty in using type as a means of selecting for productivity, however, is that many of the aspects of type have no clear relationship to productivity, and a few standards of type appear even to be negatively correlated with production. *The effectiveness of selection in any herd or flock of limited size varies in inverse fashion with the number of criteria for culling or saving individuals.* If a dairyman wishes to set up as his single goal the increased butterfat percentage content of his milk, by rigid selection and ignoring all else he should be able to progress toward this goal rather rapidly. If he aims toward increased total butterfat yield, he has two criteria for selection: total yield of milk and butterfat percentage content. These two are negatively correlated; he will be tempted to save some high producers of low-test milk and some low producers of high-test milk. If he computes a single index for selection, the total number of pounds of butterfat per lactation, he will progress somewhat more rapidly than if he selects on the basis of the two components independently.

Now if in addition to this index the breeder must consider the balance and the attachment of the udder, he may be forced to discard some highly productive animals that do not meet this additional standard, and to save some well-uddered heifers that would not otherwise be used in the breeding program. He thereby reduces the effectiveness of his selection for butterfat yield alone. If the animals must also have straight backs and legs, broad muzzles, and the right amount of white spotting in the right places, this breeder must find himself compromising more and more with his primary objective. It is not really relevant to justify selection on the basis of muzzle, back, legs, and udder, because these criteria may be correlated with productivity. Such correlations, if they exist, are generally low, and certainly much less direct and reliable as measures of butterfat productivity than the figure for butterfat yield itself.

This must not be understood to mean that it is unwise to include type as a criterion for selection. As we pointed out earlier, under many circumstances such characteristics as straight backs or the right amount and distribution of white spotting are entirely legitimate ends in themselves, even though they may be independent of productivity. Each breeder must decide for himself what his goals shall be, and then select toward them in as objective a manner as possible, with the firm recognition that as he complicates his criteria for selection he slows down his progress toward any single standard of success. He must be sure that the criteria he uses are really important to him, and he must try to weigh these criteria according to their relative importance and the degree to which they are inherited in some kind of overall index for selection.

Pedigree, Relatives, and Progeny. We have observed that the phenotype of an animal, including all of the aspects of his individual performance, is only an uncertain guide to his breeding value, and that selection on the basis of performance alone is likely to be accompanied by mistakes from a genetic point of view. Some of these mistakes can be avoided if other estimates of the genetic merit of the animal, in addition to those suggested by careful evaluation of his phenotype, can be introduced into the selection index. The obvious way to get such additional information is by studying the ancestors, collateral relatives, and descendants of the individual.

Selection on the basis of pedigree and relatives has for a very long time been a valuable adjunct to animal breeding. Its essential rationale is that we can often get at least some idea of the quality of germ plasm from which an individual came by considering the achievements of his ancestors and relatives. Without discussing the technique in detail, we can make three simple observations:

1. It is indeed true that valuable information regarding the potential breeding worth of an animal can be gained from proper consideration of an informative pedigree. A good animal breeder will not neglect this source of information.

2. The standards for reliable information about the ancestors and relatives of an animal must be as objective and as pertinent as those for evaluating the performance of the individual himself. An informative pedigree should include numerous unselected records on closely related individuals; it should provide as complete and reliable as possible an indication of the genetic background of the individual.

3. As a student of genetics, you are now well aware of the sampling nature of inheritance, and of the regular shuffling and reshuffling of genes between sexual generations. You know that "like" does not automatically "beget like," and that the progeny of highly select parents may be expected to regress toward the mean of the population from which the parents came. In predicting the probable accomplishments of the progeny of an individual from those of his parents, two opportunities for segregation and recombination must be taken into account: that which gave rise to the individual and that which will produce his progeny. In any heterozygous population the opportunities for genetic variation in this situation are very great. For this reason, selection on the basis of pedigree alone is risky, while selection that combines critical pedigree information and a consideration of relatives, with a competent evaluation of the individual himself, is much less likely to go awry. It should go without saying that the significance of pedigree information decreases very rapidly as the ancestors or relatives concerned become more remote in their relationship to the individual under consideration. Uniform excellence in the immediate ancestors and relatives of an individual is immeasurably more trustworthy than is the appearance of outstanding individuals several generations back in his pedigree.

Progeny tests also provide important information about the breeding merit of an animal. They amount to estimating the productive level of transmission of an individual by evaluating a sample of his actual progeny. You can see how such tests would help to correct errors in selection based on phenotype alone; for example, if subtle environmental effects had given a genetically mediocre individual a misleading appearance of excellence, even a small sample of his progeny would be likely to betray his true, inherent mediocrity.

Observations on relatives and progeny are especially useful in evaluating characteristics that are limited in their expression to one sex. One cannot detect directly, for instance, the genetic potentialities for milk production in a bull or for egg production in a cock. One is therefore limited in selecting males for such attributes to estimates based on pedigree, relatives, and progeny plus whatever correlation there may be between the male's physical conformation and the genetic potentialities for productivity he may transmit. In this situation, four or five milking daughters of a bull, from dams of known productivity, can tell as much about the breeding merit of the individual as could the individual's own record. The record of the bull's dam is worth about as much, in terms of information on the bull, as records on four or five half-sisters.

Today, when artificial insemination is making it possible for particular bulls to produce very large numbers of offspring, the wisdom of using sires proved good by progeny tests and by careful observations on relatives has become evident to almost all breeders. A mistake in selecting a sire for an insemination ring can be very costly; the use of information on relatives and progeny can render such mistakes less likely.

The simplest measure of the transmitting merit of a sire from progeny tests is the "mid-parent index." If the progeny can be assumed to have inherited a sample-half of their dams' inherent productive capacities, and similarly a sample-half of their sire's, then

$$\frac{\text{Dams}}{2} + \frac{\text{Sire}}{2} = \text{Daughters.}$$

The words refer to averages for the categories indicated. Solving for *Sire*, which is the unknown we want to estimate,

Sire = (twice the average of the daughters) minus (the average of the dams).

Obviously, this calculation is based on the assumption that the inherent productive capacity of daughters and dams is competently measured by their performance. We have already discussed the limitations of such an hypothesis in individual cases; here, however, since we are dealing with averages of a number of values, some of the chance errors may be expected to be compensated by others in the opposite direction. Such statistical correction factors as are available can of course be used to standardize the dam and daughter records and to make them comparable. Nevertheless, a mid-parent index is at best an approximation, more or less precise depending on the number of dam-daughter pairs it comprises and the nature of the tests it is based on. Like the individual's own record, some "regression" must typically be allowed for in evaluating selected individuals.

In particular instances the loss of time in obtaining progeny test information on superior males may more than offset the additional information to be obtained from such tests. Poultry provide a good example. The evaluation of cockerels on the basis of their sisters' production up to January 1 of their pullet year is probably sufficiently accurate to justify cockerel selection for extensive use in their first breeding season, and it is probably unwise to wait for progeny to come into production before cockerels are selected. Of course, mature cocks with progeny in production can be further evaluated on the basis of these progeny.

Heritability and the Selection Index. We have suggested that the most effective guide to selection would be the computation of an "index" that combines in a single figure as many as possible of the complex bases for deciding whether to cull an animal or to use it in the breeding program. This objective estimate of the breeding worth of an individual would include the information from all the sources of evidence about him, each source weighted according to its estimated value. Pedigree, relatives, performance, and progeny, when they are available, should all be considered. Such an index should weigh all the characteristics to be selected, each according to its relative importance to the breeder's conscious objectives. These objectives should be as clearly defined and as simple as possible, because increasing the number of criteria for selection markedly decreases the rate of progress toward any single goal.

Another consideration should also be taken into account in weighing the characteristics to be selected. This is the degree to which each of them is *heritable;* that is, the extent to which variation in successive generations is predictable in terms of genetic control and is therefore subject to selection in straightforward fashion. For most practical purposes in selection, this straightforward genetic control refers to variation that can be treated as the result of additive gene effects. Estimation of the heritability of characteristics important in domestic animals is a major subject for research in this field. It involves precise experimental design and rather powerful statistical methods, and we cannot elaborate the techniques of estimating heritability here. But we should say a few words about the existence of measures of heritability and about their importance.

It is generally found that only a fraction of the total variation in any generation, with respect to any economic characteristic, is identifiable as genetic in its origin. Table 23-1 lists representative heritability values for a variety of characteristics. We can describe the practical significance of these values in two rather different ways.

First, the figure for heritability is a measure of the importance of heredity, relative to environment and unpredictable interactions, in determining the characteristic designated. For example, about 90 per cent of the variation in weight at fifteen months in beef cattle can be regarded as additive, genetic in its control (in a particular population, under the conditions of a particular experiment). But only 10 per cent of the variation in individual weaning weight in swine (again, in a particular experiment) can be so regarded.

Second, the figure for heritability is an estimate of the amount of regression to be expected among the progeny of selected parents. As a concrete

TABLE 23-1. Representative Heritability Values for Various Characteristics of Farm Animals.†

ANIMAL	CHARACTERISTIC	HERITABILITY
Swine	Litter number at birth	0.2
	Litter number at weaning	0.2
	Weaning weight of litter	0.4
	Individual weaning weight	0.1
	Individual 180-day weight	0.3
	Conformation score	0.2
Sheep	Birth weight	0.3
	Weaning weight	0.3
	Yearling weight	0.4
	Yearling clean fleece yield	0.4
	Face covering	0.6
	Neck folds (Columbia, Corriedale, and Targhee)	0.1
Beef cattle	Birth weight	0.5
	Weaning weight	0.3
	Weight at 15 months	0.9
	Rate of gain in feed lot	0.8
	Slaughter grade	0.5
	Carcass grade	0.3
Fowl	Egg number	0.3
	Viability	0.1
	Production index	0.1
	Sexual maturity	0.3
Dairy cattle	Single annual butterfat record	0.2
	Single annual milk record	0.2
	Single official type classification	0.3
	Single annual butterfat percentage	0.5

† Derived from summaries by Warwick, Henderson, and Lerner. Determinations of heritability in various studies differ considerably; these are selected values, corrected to one decimal place.

example, consider Table 23-2. You will see that the use of the heritability value for 180-day weight in swine provides a measure of expected genetic gain in terms of a given intensity of selection. Highly heritable traits are easily subject to effective selection; slightly heritable ones require intense selection to provide significant genetic progress.

Knowledge of the heritability of selected traits is therefore of obvious value in deciding what emphasis should be put on these traits in selection. Estimates of heritability are, however, subject to some variation in themselves, because they are affected by the amount of environmental fluctuation

TABLE 23-2. Use of the Heritability Value for Average Individual 180-Day Weight in Swine to Estimate Performance of Progeny of Selected Parents. (After Warwick, in Breeding and Improvement of Farm Animals, by Rice and Andrews, McGraw-Hill Book Co., 1951, p. 663.)

AVERAGE OF HERD	SELECTED INDIVIDUALS	SELECTION DIFFERENTIAL	HERITABILITY	EXPECTED PERFORMANCE OF PROGENY
180 lb	195 lb	15 lb	0.3	184.5 lb

in the herd or flock in which they are determined, and by the system of mating and the degree of genetic heterozygosity within that herd or flock. We will consider mating systems briefly later in this chapter.

An Example of a Planned Selection Program. The computation of a selection index is a major undertaking. In fact, there are at present only a few instances in which our knowledge is sufficient to approximate a complete index. One of these is the selection of market swine. Here, the extensive work of the U. S. Department of Agriculture and cooperating state experiment stations since 1937, together with the pioneering thought of Lush and, later, of Hazel, at Iowa State College, have resulted in selection indexes based on characteristics of economic importance and their heritability. Chapman, of Wisconsin, has adapted this scheme to farm conditions, and through his generosity in making an outline of the Wisconsin program available to us, we can describe briefly a modern swine selective cooperative.

One of the primary necessities in conducting intelligent selection is to keep a set of records on each individual. These should include:

1. *Dates* of breeding, of farrowing, and of weaning the pigs.
2. *Numbers* of pigs at farrowing and at weaning.
3. *Weights* of pigs at specified ages—preferably at weaning and at five or six months of age.

All too often such records are not kept by breeders who select in haphazard fashion; emphasis on the need for these measures and help in obtaining and recording them is in itself a valuable service of the cooperative.

To be useful, these records must of course be used. In this program the objectives are listed as improved *fertility, vigor, nursing ability, economy of gain,* and *type.* All of these except type can be estimated from the simple records specified above. Sows that have a relatively large number of pigs at farrowing, rear a large number of them, and raise them to a desirable weaning weight meet the standards for fertility, vigor, and nursing ability. The weight of a pig at five or six months of age has been shown to be an acceptable measure of his economy of gain. Type, in terms of general body conformation and such details as are clearly related to the production of market hogs, can be evaluated with fair reliability.

These criteria can be incorporated into a single index by a "point system," in which the number of points attainable in any category is dependent on the relative economic importance and on the heritability of the characteristic. Table 23-3 shows the number of points assigned in this program for values in each category. These point values are of course somewhat arbitrary; they may require changes to suit the needs and the objectives of individual breeders. If you are interested in swine breeding, however, you can get a good idea of the general relative importance of the characteristics

TABLE 23-3. Point Values for Number of Pigs Farrowed and Weaned, Litter Weight at Weaning, and 5-Month Weight of Individual. (Courtesy of A. B. Chapman.)

POINTS FOR NUMBER OF PIGS FARROWED

Number of Pigs Farrowed	1	2	3	4	5	6	7	8	9	10	11	12	13	14	15
Points	1	2	3	4	5	6	7	8	9	10	11	12	12	12	12

POINTS FOR NUMBER OF PIGS WEANED

Number of Pigs Weaned	0	1	2	3	4	5	6	7	8	9	10	11	12	13	14	15
Points	0	2	4	6	8	10	12	14	16	18	20	22	24	26	28	30

POINTS FOR LITTER WEIGHT AT WEANING				POINTS FOR 5-MONTH WEIGHT OF INDIVIDUAL			
Weaning Weight of Litter (lb)	Points	Weaning Weight of Litter (lb)	Points	Weight of Individual at 5 Months (lb)	Points	Weight of Individual at 5 Months (lb)	Points
Less than 30	0	255–269	17	Less than 75	0	145–149	54
30–44	2	270–284	18	75–79	5	150–154	58
45–59	3	285–299	19	80–84	9	155–159	61
60–74	4	300–314	20	85–89	12	160–164	65
75–89	5	315–329	21	90–94	16	165–169	68
90–104	6	330–344	22	95–99	19	170–174	72
105–119	7	345–359	23	100–104	23	175–179	75
120–134	8	360–374	24	105–109	26	180–184	79
135–149	9	375–389	25	110–114	30	185–189	82
150–164	10	390–404	26	115–119	33	190–194	86
165–179	11	405–419	27	120–124	37	195–199	89
180–194	12	420–434	28	125–129	40	200–204	93
195–209	13	435–449	29	130–134	44	205–209	96
210–224	14	450–464	30	135–139	47	210–214	100
225–239	15	465–479	31	140–144	51		
240–254	16	480–494	32				

considered here by comparing the point values assigned to them. The general bases for the point weighting arc, for the most part, rather obvious. For example, a sow deserves more points for a large number of pigs weaned than she does for a large number farrowed, in part because it is the pigs surviving to be weaned that have economic value. The precise choice of *doubling* the number of pigs weaned, however, is based upon careful study of genetic and economic data.

In practice, it has been found possible to substitute the weight and numbers of the litter at five months for the same data at weaning, because these two measures are closely correlated. This saves the time-consuming operation of weighing the pigs at weaning. When the substitution is made, the 154-day litter weight is divided by 100 to give about the same number of points as result in the 56-day scheme.

When the 154-day weights of a litter are available, the pigs are indexed according to the point scale shown. A sow's index can be computed from the information now available, as shown for three sows in Table 23-4.

Item A, the "Sow's Own 'Pig Index,'" is a carry-over from her record as a 154-day pig, and is a combined measure of her own economy of gain as a pig and of her dam's productivity (see the computation of "Pig Index" for this generation, line F). You will note that the sows shown in the table each had the same pig index—90. Item E indicates the sow's productivity, in terms of points for numbers of pigs farrowed and weaned and litter weaning weight. Item H is the average pig index of the pigs in the litter. The "Sow's Index," line I, is computed as line A + twice line E + line H. It combines into a single figure all of the characteristics, except type, listed as goals in the selection program. These characteristics have been weighted through the point system and the method of averaging according to their estimated importance and their heritability. Type and conformation are considered separately by arbitrarily listing defective animals as "not acceptable" in the record and by further selection from among animals with top indexes at the time of culling.

The pig indexes provide the bases for selection of the young boars and gilts, while the sow indexes help to determine which of the old sows to keep for breeding and which to discard. Thus, pig 5 from sow 5, with the top index of 106, seems to be the most promising pig of the three litters studied, assuming that his type is not unacceptable. Pig 2 from sow 10, with a pig index of 93, is second. Sow 10, with an index of only 184, is the poorest of the three sows. She is not much different from sow 5 in number of pigs farrowed and is superior to both of the others in average weight of pigs at 5 months, but only three of her eight pigs survived to weaning, and her litter weaning weight was low. The fact that her index combines all of these considerations in a single figure is testimony to its utility.

While the Wisconsin Swine Selection Cooperative is too young to have accumulated much evidence of its economic value to the three hundred or so

TABLE 23-4. Computation of Selection Index for Each of Three Sows. (Courtesy of A. B. Chapman.)

SOW'S IDENTIFICATION	5			10			12		
A. Sow's Own "Pig Index"	90			90			90		
Spring 1944	NUMBER OR WEIGHT	POINTS		NUMBER OR WEIGHT	POINTS		NUMBER OR WEIGHT	POINTS	
B. Number of pigs farrowed	9	9		8	8		12	12	
C. Number of pigs weaned	8	16		3	6		9	18	
D. Litter weaning weight (adjusted to 56 days of age)	200	13		105	7		195	13	
E. Sow's productivity (total points lines B, C, D)		38			21			43	
F. Weight of individual pigs at 5 months (adjusted to 154 days of age):	WEIGHT	POINTS	PIG INDEX (POINTS E + F)	WEIGHT	POINTS	PIG INDEX (POINTS E + F)	WEIGHT	POINTS	PIG INDEX (POINTS E + F)
1.	120	37	75	170	72	93	95	19	62
2.	113	30	68	138	47	68	90	16	59
3.	130	44	82	123	37	58	110	30	73
4.	142	51	89				98	19	62
5.	167	68	106				89	12	55
6.	102	23	61				80	9	52
7.							100	23	66
8.							104	23	66
9.									
10.									
G. Total points lines F-1 to F-10		253			156			151	
H. Average points lines F-1 to F-10		42			52			19	
I. Sow's Index (points line A + twice line E + line H)		208			184			195	

507

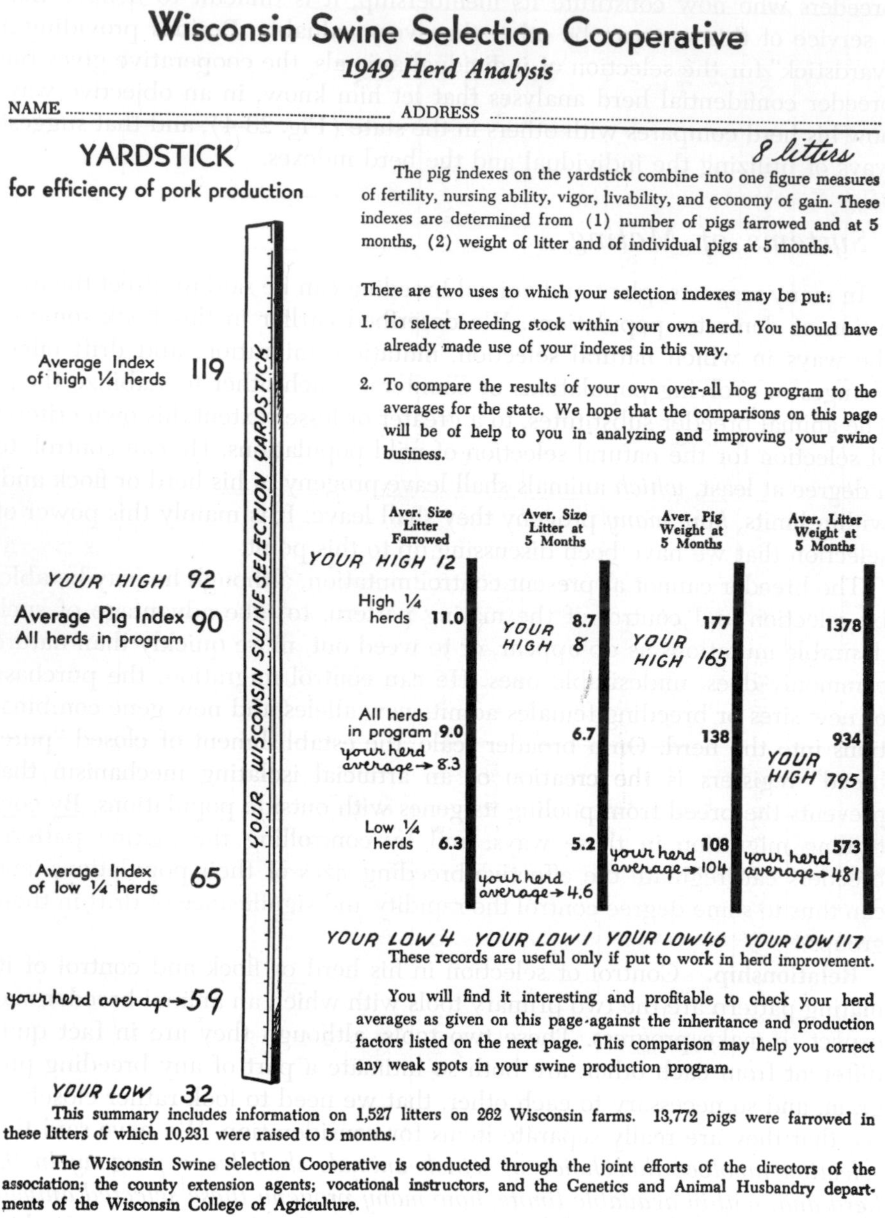

Wisconsin Swine Selection Cooperative
1949 Herd Analysis

NAME .... ADDRESS ....

YARDSTICK
for efficiency of pork production

8 litters

The pig indexes on the yardstick combine into one figure measures of fertility, nursing ability, vigor, livability, and economy of gain. These indexes are determined from (1) number of pigs farrowed and at 5 months, (2) weight of litter and of individual pigs at 5 months.

There are two uses to which your selection indexes may be put:

1. To select breeding stock within your own herd. You should have already made use of your indexes in this way.

2. To compare the results of your own over-all hog program to the averages for the state. We hope that the comparisons on this page will be of help to you in analyzing and improving your swine business.

Average Index of high ¼ herds 119

YOUR WISCONSIN SWINE SELECTION YARDSTICK

YOUR HIGH 92

Average Pig Index 90
All herds in program

Average Index of low ¼ herds 65

your herd average→59

YOUR LOW 32

	Aver. Size Litter Farrowed	Aver. Size Litter at 5 Months	Aver. Pig Weight at 5 Months	Aver. Litter Weight at 5 Months
	YOUR HIGH 12			
High ¼ herds	11.0	YOUR HIGH 8.7	177	1378
		YOUR HIGH 8	YOUR HIGH 165	
All herds in program	9.0	6.7	138	934
	your herd average→ 8.3			YOUR HIGH 795
Low ¼ herds	6.3	5.2	108	573
		your herd average→ 4.6	your herd average→104	your herd average→481

YOUR LOW 4   YOUR LOW 1   YOUR LOW 46   YOUR LOW 117

These records are useful only if put to work in herd improvement.

You will find it interesting and profitable to check your herd averages as given on this page-against the inheritance and production factors listed on the next page. This comparison may help you correct any weak spots in your swine production program.

This summary includes information on 1,527 litters on 262 Wisconsin farms. 13,772 pigs were farrowed in these litters of which 10,231 were raised to 5 months.

The Wisconsin Swine Selection Cooperative is conducted through the joint efforts of the directors of the association; the county extension agents; vocational instructors, and the Genetics and Animal Husbandry departments of the Wisconsin College of Agriculture.

Figure 23-4. *The herd analysis sheet provided members of the Wisconsin Swine Selection Cooperative gives the breeders objective measures of their positions and progress. (Courtesy of A. B. Chapman.)*

breeders who now constitute its membership, it is difficult to believe that a service of this sort can be other than very valuable. Besides providing a "yardstick" for the selection of individual animals, the cooperative gives the breeder confidential herd analyses that let him know, in an objective way, how his herd compares with others in the state (Fig. 23-4), and that suggest ways of utilizing the individual and the herd indexes.

Systems of Mating

In many respects, plant and animal breeding can be said to direct the evolution of domestic populations. We described earlier in this book some of the ways in which natural selection, mutation, migration, and drift effect changes in evolving populations or counteract each other to stabilize them. The animal breeder substitutes, to a greater or lesser extent, his own criteria of selection for the natural selection of wild populations. He can control, to a degree at least, *which* animals shall leave progeny in his herd or flock and, within limits, *how many* progeny they shall leave. It is mainly this power of selection that we have been discussing up to this point.

The breeder cannot at present control mutation, although he may be able, by selection and control of the mating pattern, to take advantage of such desirable mutations as do appear, or to weed out, more quickly than nature commonly does, undesirable ones. He can control migration; the purchase of new sires or breeding females admits new alleles and new gene combinations into the herd. On a broader scale, the establishment of closed "purebreed" registers is the creation of an artificial isolating mechanism that prevents the breed from pooling its genes with outside populations. By controlling migration in these ways, and by controlling the mating pattern, breeders can regulate the effective breeding sizes of their populations, and can thus to some degree control the rapidity and significance of drift in these groups.

Relationship. Control of selection in his herd or flock and control of its mating pattern are the two primary tools with which an animal breeder may expect to make progress. These two tools, although they are in fact quite different from each other, are both so intimate a part of any breeding program, and so necessary to each other, that we need to look rather closely to see that they are really separate items for consideration. We have said that *selection involves the choice of which animals shall leave progeny in the herd and, within available limits, how many progeny these selected animals shall leave. The choice of a mating pattern is the determination of which of these selected animals shall mate with which. This can practically be summed up, from a genetic point of view, by observing that it involves control of the extent to which the parents of a forthcoming generation shall be genetically related to each other.*

Genetic relationship is obviously a variable quantity for which we need

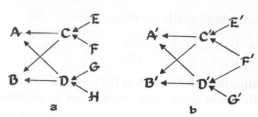

Figure 23-5. *A and B are full sibs, having the same parents, C and D. Similarly, A' and B' are full sibs. But A' and B' are more closely related than are A and B.*

some kind of quantitative measure. All animals are related to some degree, because they have evolved from common ancestors. All the members of a breed are related; commonly almost all of the individuals trace back, more or less directly, to a few foundation animals. Exceptionally popular or outstanding individuals have had substantial genetic influence on each breed, and living animals are related through their common descent from such individuals. Most of the members of a herd are often even more closely related, tracing back, for example, to the limited number of herd sires and female families existing in the herd during the past few generations. Second cousins are related to a degree; first cousins even more closely related but less closely than parents and offspring or full sibs (sisters and brothers).

Figure 23-5 shows two degrees of full-sib relationship. In Figure 23-5a, individuals A and B are full sibs, having common parents C and D. Similarly, in Figure 23-5b, individuals A' and B' have common parents C' and D'. But A and B are really less closely related than are A' and B', because the parents of the latter are in turn related (half-sibs), while no relationship is shown for C and D. A and B have gene samples from four different grandparents, while A' and B' depend on only three.

Relationship on this scale can be measured by the *coefficient of relationship,* which depends on the knowledge that each individual receives a sample half of the genes of each of his parents. The simplest way of calculating the coefficient of relationship for two individuals is from arrow diagrams like those in Figure 23-5. One need only count the number of "samplehalving" processes that separate the related individuals from a common ancestor in the diagram, and use this sum as the exponent of one-half to arrive at the contribution of that ancestor to the relationship of the individuals in question. The total relationship is the sum of the separate contributions of all the common ancestors.

Thus, in Figure 23-5a, a path from A to B involving two "sample-halving" processes can be traced through C: $\qquad$ A $\longleftarrow$ C

B $\longleftarrow$

and another through D: $\qquad$ A $\longleftarrow$

B $\longleftarrow$ D

The contributions of these paths are then:

$$A \longleftarrow C \longrightarrow B = (\frac{1}{2})^2 = 0.25$$
$$A \longleftarrow D \longrightarrow B = (\frac{1}{2})^2 = 0.25$$

and the total relationship of A and B is $0.25 + 0.25 = 0.5$.

In Figure 23-5b, these same paths occur, but in addition there are two through F':

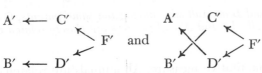

Each of these involves four "sample-halvings," so that the total relationship of A' and B' is $0.5 + (\frac{1}{2})^4 + (\frac{1}{2})^4 = 0.625$.

The coefficient of relationship really measures the extent to which animals may have genes in common because of their descent from the same ancestral individuals. This figure is relative to the amount of diversity in the population concerned, and to the average relationship in this population. We have already pointed out that all the members of a breed are to some extent related and have many genes in common. The coefficient of relationship measures the extent of genetic similarity arising from specific relationships in excess of this common store of similarity.

Inbreeding. A mating system that involves the breeding together of individuals *more closely related than the average for the population concerned* comprises some form and degree of inbreeding. The degree of inbreeding in any particular mating is therefore a function of the relationship between the animals mated. For our present purposes, we can define the inbreeding coefficient for any individual as approximately one-half of the relationship between its parents. Thus, if A and B in Figure 23-5 were to be mated, their progeny would be inbred to the extent measured by an inbreeding coefficient of 0.25. If A' and B' were mated, their offspring would have an inbreeding coefficient of about 0.31.

We have observed earlier in this book that the primary genetic effect of inbreeding is to reduce heterozygosity in the population. The inbreeding coefficient measures the extent to which heterozygosity may be expected to be reduced in any individual as a consequence of relationship between his parents. As is true of the relationship coefficient, the absolute genetic value of this measure depends on the extent of diversity in the population concerned. If a random-bred individual in a given breed is on the average heterozygous at 400 loci, then an individual with an inbreeding coefficient of 0.25 is estimated to be heterozygous at about 300 loci. But if a random-bred individual in another breed is on the average heterozygous for 4000 loci, then an individual with this same inbreeding coefficient is probably heterozygous for about 3000 allelic pairs. On the whole, we recognize this situation when we observe that one breed is "more uniform" than the other. But we do not have at hand accurate measures of the number of heterozygous loci in any domestic population. Such measures as have been applied have sometimes suggested that the statistical estimation of heterozygosity after inbreeding may be in error, perhaps because unknown mechanisms may act to maintain heterozygosity in excess of that predicted from the inbreeding coefficients. Much remains to be learned in establishing that such mechanisms really exist and, if they do, in ascertaining their nature.

Types of Mating Patterns. Our consideration of plant breeding in the previous chapter, and of inbreeding and heterosis in Chapter 16, has emphasized the utility of inbreeding in bringing to light, and rendering vulnerable to selection, genetic qualities that might otherwise remain largely hidden in heterozygotes. We have also emphasized the uniformity within inbred lines and the uniformity and vigor of certain plant hybrids between inbred lines. The possibility of equivalent progress in animal improvement through the use of similar techniques has prompted a great deal of research into the effects and potential utility of close inbreeding and crossing in animals.

The investment in an individual animal is of course much greater than that in a plant, and one cannot speak lightly of the establishment of numerous inbred lines of animals, most of them defective or weak, in order to select a few lines that might survive the random fixation of genes that comes with close inbreeding. On the other hand, inbreeding approximating the intensity of self-fertilization is in any case impossible in domestic animals; and the rapidity with which random fixation or loss of genes occurs becomes much less as the intensity of inbreeding decreases. Even under a system that calls for successive generations of full-sib or parent-offspring matings, the most intense inbreeding possible in farm animals, the rate of "drift" may be slow enough so that intense selection can keep up with it. (Recall our discussion of this subject in Chapter 21, pp. 460–461.)

This means that in animal breeding one need not depend, as one does in corn, on selecting from among a large number of inbred lines the few in which chance has fixed a desirable combination of genes. Selection may be effectively applied as the inbreeding continues, and the resultant lines may be less a product of chance than of design. Under these conditions, large-scale inbreeding programs in swine and poultry are now under way, and there is indication that the uniformity and vigor of hybrid progeny will prove to be of practical value.

Individual breeders, however, can seldom afford to take the chances involved in the rapid establishment of truly inbred lines. They must experiment with milder inbreeding if they are to take advantage of the desirable genetic effects of this mating system without risking its undesirable consequences. A form of inbreeding of longstanding value in animal improvement in this regard is known as *linebreeding*. This is an effort to intensify the contribution of particular admired individuals to the herd or flock while keeping the relationship among contemporary individuals at a minimum. There is much opportunity for the exercise of ingenuity and originality in achieving this end.

The use of "family systems" of mating is usually another method of attaining the same kind of objective. But "families" are in general so poorly defined that it would be difficult to discuss this technique briefly. Similar objections apply to the discussion of "blood lines" and their use in mating systems.

Some mating systems attempt the opposite of inbreeding, and breed together individuals less closely related than the average for the population concerned. As one might expect, insofar as such systems increase heterozygosity they result in improved individuals with uncertain breeding value. An extreme of such "outbreeding" is involved in *crossbreeding,* in which the parents are of different breeds. Gains from such systems are usually debatable, and such gains as may occur must be weighed against the costs of replacing the breeding stock from pure breeds in each generation.

Other mating patterns may ignore genetic relationships and be based only upon phenotypic similarity or dissimilarity (*assortative* or *disassortative mating*). Except in simple and infrequent circumstances, such systems appear to have little effect on homozygosity or heterozygosity. Assortative mating approaches its full possible effect quite rapidly, so that after a few generations this system loses much of its potentiality for further progress. Its effects disappear very rapidly if the system is abandoned. Disassortative mating is sometimes useful when the desired type is a heterozygote (for example, maintaining blue Andalusians by mating blacks with whites).

Keys to the Significance of This Chapter

Although many instances may be cited of simply inherited, qualitative characteristics important to animal breeding, the improvement of domestic animals is largely concerned with quantitative inheritance. The description and analysis of the continuous variation involved in characteristics like productivity and reproductive potential, and the construction of practical programs for improvement with regard to these economic characteristics, require a variety of statistical techniques.

The two most important tools available to the breeder are selection and control of the mating pattern.

By constructing an index for selection, which weighs the minimum number of characteristics that can represent the goals of his breeding program in terms of the relative economic importance and the heritability of these characteristics, a breeder may render his selection of breeding stock more objective and effective. Pedigree and relatives, individual performance, and progeny tests can provide important guides for the selection of individuals.

By careful choice of the system of mating that will best implement his selection and suit his facilities and objectives, a breeder can direct the evolution of his herd or flock toward increased productivity and value.

References

Bonnier, G., and Hansson, A., "Identical Twin Genetics in Cattle." *Heredity,* 2:1–27, 1948. (A summary of the uses of twins in animal breeding research, a powerful technique we have not discussed. See, however, the somewhat similar studies of human twins in Chap. 24.)

Castle, W. E., "New Evidence on the Genetics of the Palomino Horse." *J. Heredity,* 42:60–64, 1951. (Includes identification of several color-controlling genes; the dominant dilution of the Palomino is of particular interest.)

Chapman, A. B., "Genetic and Nongenetic Sources of Variation in the Weight Response of the Immature Rat Ovary to a Gonadotrophic Hormone." *Genetics,* 31:494–507, 1946. (Illustrates in a laboratory population the significance of current animal breeding methods.)

Dempster, E. R., and Lerner, I. M., "The Optimum Structure of Breeding Flocks." *Genetics,* 32:555–579, 1947. (A sequence of two papers on rates of genetic improvement under different breeding plans.)

Dickerson, G. E., and Grimes, J. C., "Effectiveness of Selection for Efficiency of Gain in Duroc Swine." *J. Animal Sci.,* 6:265–287, 1947. (Results of a selection program for high and low feed requirement per pound gain, including estimates of heritability and correlated characters.)

Donald, H. P., and El-Itriby, A. A., "The Duration of Pedigree Herds in Three Breeds of Cattle in Relation to Selective Breeding." *J. Agr. Sci.,* 36:100–110, 1946.

Gowen, J. W., "Genetics and Disease Resistance," in *Genetics in the 20th Century,* pp. 401–429. New York: Macmillan Co., 1951. (Competent consideration of a problem significant in animal breeding.)

Hazel, L. N., "The Genetic Basis for Constructing Selection Indexes." *Genetics,* 28:476–490, 1943. (A key paper for the professional animal breeder).

Johnson, L. E., " 'Streamlined' Pigs, A New Legless Mutation." *J. Heredity,* 31:239–242, 1940. (Source of Problem 23-3.)

Landauer, W., and Chang, T. K., "The Ancon or Otter Sheep." *J. Heredity,* 40:105–112, 1949. (An interesting historical account, the source of Problem 23-9.)

Lerner, I. M., *Population Genetics and Animal Improvement.* Cambridge: Cambridge University Press, 1950. (An excellent, up-to-date book, with emphasis on the author's experience with poultry. See especially Chap. 8, "The Principles of Selection"; Chap. 10, "Mating Systems"; and Chap. 15, "The Outlook.")

————, and Dempster, E. R., "Some Aspects of Evolutionary Theory in the Light of Recent Work on Animal Breeding." *Evolution,* 2:19–28, 1948. (A concise and competent summary, emphasizing the importance of quantitative inheritance and techniques for analysis and control.)

Lush, J. L., *Animal Breeding Plans.* Ames: Collegiate Press, 1945. (Standard textbook by a pioneer and consistent contributor in the field.)

Lush, J. L., "Genetics and Animal Breeding," in *Genetics in the 20th Century*, pp. 493–525. New York: Macmillan Co., 1951. (Primarily an evaluation of the important interactions between formal genetics and applied animal breeding, with interesting factual data.)

Mohr, O. L., "Yellow Fat in Sheep." *J. Heredity*, 25:246–247, 1934. (A letter to W. E. Castle, with comments by Dr. Castle. Source of Problem 23-4.)

Pearl, R., and Surface, F. M., "Selection Index Numbers and Their Use in Breeding." *Am. Naturalist*, 43:385–400, 1909. (A classic paper presenting early recognition of the importance of constructing an index for selection, and suggesting indexes for poultry and sweet corn.)

Phillips, J. M., and Knight, E. D., "Merle or Calico Foxhounds." *J. Heredity*, 29:365–367, 1938. (Source of Problem 23-6.)

Serra, J. A., *Génétique du Mouton*. Lisbon: Ministerio da Economia, Publ. Junta Nacion. dos Prod. Pecuarios. Ser. A No. 1, 1948. (A broad and critical review, in French, of the genetics of sheep, with many references.)

Sierk, C. F., and Winters, L. M., "A Study of Heterosis in Swine." *J. Animal Sci.*, 10:104–111, 1951. (Reports the results of experiments evaluating hybrid vigor and uniformity in swine.)

Stormont, C., Owen, R. D., and Irwin, M. R., "The B and C Systems of Bovine Blood Groups." *Genetics*, 36:134–161, 1951. (Listed here as a key to the literature on the red blood cell antigens of cattle, *cf.*, Problem 23-5.)

Winge, Ö., *Inheritance in Dogs*. New York: Comstock, 1950. (An interesting general discussion, followed by specific considerations of the sporting breeds.)

Wright, S., "Systems of Mating." *Genetics*, 6:111–178, 1921. (A series of five papers, written while Wright was with the U.S.D.A. These papers provide the foundation of our current appreciation of the processes of both evolution and animal improvement.)

————, "The Analysis of Variance and the Correlations Between Relatives with Respect to Deviations from an Optimum." *J. Genetics*, 30:243–256, 1935. (A technical paper, highly significant, with particular reference to the probably common situation in which the favored class is an intermediate type.)

————, "Genetic Principles Governing the Rate of Progress in Livestock Breeding." *Am. Soc. Animal Prod.*, *32nd Ann. Meet.*, pp. 18–26, 1939.

Yearbooks of Agriculture. Washington: U. S. Govt. Printing Office. (These volumes include extensive general and specific considerations, by numerous authorities, of the problems of obtaining better plants and animals. See the references to Chapter 22 for specific citations.)

Questions and Problems

23- 1.   What do the following terms and phrases signify?

additive gene effects	progeny test
coefficient of inbreeding	regression
coefficient of relationship	selection differential
heritability	selection index
pedigree selection	system of mating

Each of the following statements relates to a simply inherited characteristic of a domestic animal. Indicate how the genetic knowledge you have acquired might be used to serve breeders of these animals.

23- 2.   Palomino horses, highly favored because of their attractive color, are essentially like chestnut and sorrel horses in their "color genotype," except that palominos are heterozygous for a semidominant autosomal allele (D), which in the homozygous condition produces white or near-white (Castle, 1951). Chestnuts and sorrels are dd. Breeders would like to establish true-breeding palominos, or, if this is impossible, at least to be able to predict that palomino foals would regularly result from particular matings.

23- 3.   A swine breeder finds that about one-eighth of the progeny of matings between a particular boar and his paternal half-sisters are born completely without legs. The abnormal pigs are born alive, but die in a few days, probably from starvation (cf., Johnson, 1940). The breeder wants to rid his herd of this defect.

23- 4.   In Iceland, matings between sheep having white fat occasionally produce offspring having yellow fat (Mohr, 1934). In some flocks, more than a quarter of the lambs born in a particular year have yellow fat. Carcasses with yellow fat are very objectionable on the market; in fact, the meat cannot be sold. Yellow fat in sheep appears to be comparable in its inheritance to the similar characteristic in rabbits (p. 25). The characteristic is difficult to detect until the animal is slaughtered. Breeders would like to eliminate the characteristic from their flocks, and anyone importing breeding stock from Iceland would want to be sure that this undesirable allele is not being introduced, to be disseminated as a hidden recessive.

23- 5.   Numerous red blood cell antigens, similar in their patterns of inheritance to those we have discussed in man, are known in dairy cattle (cf., Stormont et al., 1951). Uncertainty as to the paternity of purebred dairy calves bars rather numerous potentially valuable animals from registration each year. In the typical case, the dam is known, but the sire may be either of two particular bulls. If one of the possible sires can be excluded as the true parent, the breed associations will accept registration of the calf in question as by the other sire.

23- 6.   Foxhounds homozygous for the allele for "calico" coat color are deaf and have "china eyes." Heterozygotes are calico in color, sometimes china eyed, rarely deaf (Phillips and Knight, 1938). Breeders would sometimes like to be able to make matings that would be assured of a maximal frequency of calico progeny without deafness or china eyes. They wonder which would be better—to mate calico × calico and discard china-eyed pups, or to mate calico × noncalico consistently.

23- 7.   Several of the heavy breeds of fowl show delayed feathering in young birds; such "barebacks" at broiler age are at a disadvantage in the present market. It would be desirable (in fact, it has been done, primarily by D. C. Warren) to incorporate the sex-linked recessive allele for rapid feathering, which is homozygous in Leghorns, into the heavy breeds, with a minimum of loss of the other desirable aspects of these breeds as meat producers.

23- 8.   Almost a quarter of the beef calves born on a particular ranch are dwarfs. The breeder would like to take advantage of the desirable characteristics of individuals heterozygous for this autosomal recessive (cf., Problem 21-14), but to avoid the risk of matings that might produce dwarfs. There are indications that almost all heterozygotes for this particular type of dwarfing may be identified by a careful consideration of their phenotype (Gregory, et al., unpubl.).

23- 9.   In 1791, Seth Wright, on his small farm sixteen miles from Boston, found an unusual male lamb born to one of his fifteen ewes. The lamb was very short legged, and in those days of low rock and rail fences a breed of his sort offered the considerable potential advantage of being unable to jump fences. How might you, knowing what you now do about heredity, have advised Wright to go about attempting to establish such a breed? (*Note:* Wright, on the basis of his neighbors' advice, did pretty well. See Landauer and Chang, 1949.)

23-10. A new color characteristic of potential commercial value appears in a group of poor-quality, scrub red foxes in a zoo. The characteristic appears to depend on a simple autosomal recessive. It is desirable to fix this allele as rapidly as possible in a strain of high-quality, ranch-bred standard silver-black foxes, meanwhile contaminating the superior strain as little as possible with the inferior "residual genotype" of the scrub reds. In attacking this problem, you have the amazing good fortune to find that the new recessive is linked, with 10 per cent recombination, with the locus controlling the difference between red and standard silver-black, in which the allele for red is semidominant (*cf.*, Problems 4-13 to 4-15).

Assume a characteristic controlled by five pairs of alleles, acting in equal and additive fashion and uncomplicated by environmental effects. Assign a value of 50 units to the complete recessive, and assume that each substitution of an "active" allele (represented by a large letter) gives a phenotypic increment of 5 units.

For example,

$$
\begin{array}{llllll}
aa & bb & cc & dd & ee & = & 50 \\
Aa & bb & cc & dd & ee & = & 55 \\
Aa & Bb & cc & DD & ee & = & 70 \\
AA & BB & CC & DD & EE & = & 100
\end{array}
$$

23-11. Suppose that in a population with a phenotypic range from 50 to 70 units and an average value of 60, you selected to be parents of the next generation only individuals with the top rating of 70.

   a. List at random five different genotypes that might be represented among the individuals selected.
   b. Confirm by inspection that the average gamete produced by the selected individuals listed in (a) would contain two active alleles, and that the gametes might range from 0 to 4 active alleles.
   c. Confirm from (b) above that the average zygote in the next generation would have a phenotypic value of 70, and the range would be from 50 to 90.

23-12. Repeat the arbitrary analysis in Question 23-11 for another generation of selection, choosing the individuals with a phenotypic value of 90 to be parents of this next generation. What would be the average and the range of phenotypic values in the progeny?

23-13. Under the simple, additive inheritance postulated in Problems 23-11 and 23-12,

   a. How does the mean of the progeny compare with the mean of the selected parents?
   b. Make a general statement about the effectiveness of selection under these circumstances, using the term *selection differential*.
   c. What sets the limits to be achieved by selection under these conditions, and what determines the rapidity with which these limits are approached?

23-14. Now, postulate an arbitrary environmental effect on the expression of the characteristics discussed in Problems 23-11 to 23-13. Assume that the conditions described prevail for an "average" environment, but that a "poor" environment subtracts ten units from the phenotypic value of any particular genotype, and a "good" environment adds ten units. Describe, in a general way, the effects of this circumstance on the achievements of selection, if allowance for environmental effects cannot be made in the selection of individuals for breeding.

23-15. How would complete dominance of the "active" alleles affect the selection discussed above? Why?

23-16. Suppose that the situation is that described in the introduction to this series of problems (equal and additive gene effects, no environmental modification or dominance), except that the substitution of B for b has no effect unless A is also present in either the homozygous or heterozygous condition. For example,

$$Aa\ bb\ Cc\ Dd\ ee = 65, \text{ and}$$
$$Aa\ Bb\ Cc\ Dd\ ee = 70, \text{ but}$$
$$\left.\begin{array}{l} aa\ bb\ Cc\ Dd\ ee \\ aa\ Bb\ Cc\ Dd\ ee \\ aa\ BB\ Cc\ Dd\ ee \end{array}\right\} \text{ all} = 60.$$

Describe in a general way how this epistatic interaction may affect the progress of selection.

23-17. Frequently, in a comparison of two genotypes, one is found to be more effective in a given environment while the other is better in a different environment. How might this kind of interaction between genotype and environment affect a selection program?

23-18. How do the effects of environment, dominance, and epistasis, illustrated in Questions 23-14 to 23-17, explain the phenomenon of regression?

23-19. Why would you expect progeny tests to be particularly useful in the improvement of poultry and dairy cattle? In each of these classes of livestock, what advantages can you discern in estimating the breeding value of a male by indexes based on his dam and sisters, rather than on his progeny?

23-20. In terms of practical poultry production, how might you utilize a selection index based on pullet egg production to January 1 of the first laying year to select cockerels for the breeding flock (*cf.*, Lerner, 1950)?

23-21. Following are dam-daughter comparisons in butterfat yields (corrected to maturity, 305 days, twice-daily milkings) for five Guernsey bulls in use in a single large herd. Considering butterfat production alone, and on the basis of the information given, which bull would you be likely to select for use in your Guernsey herd?

Bull	Corrected Average, Five Daughters	Corrected Average, Corresponding Dams
1	380	390
2	385	360
3	405	385
4	405	415
5	425	440

23-22. Compute coefficients of relationship for individuals A and B on the basis of the diagram below. If these two individuals are mated, what will be the inbreeding coefficient of their progeny?

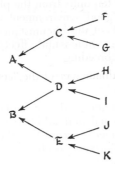

23-23. Studying the men and women of Pitcairn Island (Problems 20-14 to 20-19), Shapiro attempted to estimate the degree of inbreeding that had occurred by dividing the actual number of ancestors in a given generation of the pedigree of an individual by the total number he would have had in that generation if there had been no inbreeding. For example, a marriage between first cousins otherwise unrelated would have children with a coefficient of $\%$ = 0.75, if the computation is based on great-grandparental generation (Fig. 20-1, p. 437).

Compute the inbreeding coefficients for individuals P and P′ in the diagrams given below, assuming that the individuals in the most remote generation shown (great-grandparents) were unrelated.

   a. Use the method described in this chapter.
   b. Use the measure Shapiro utilized, counting ancestors in the great-grandparental generation. (Note that P is the result of a mating between half-sibs, while P′ is the result of a mating between first cousins.)
   c. Which of the two measures describe the genetic situation better? Why?

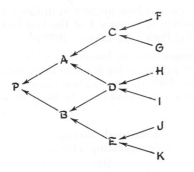
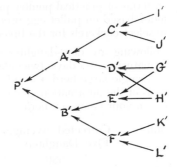

23-24. Characterize in general terms the usual genetic effects of the following systems of mating: (a) inbreeding, (b) outbreeding, (c) assortative mating, (d) disassortative mating, (e) linebreeding.

23-25. Work out a plan for the improvement of some animal population in which you are interested—e.g., a breed of dogs used as hunters; a herd of Jerseys, or a population of earthworms to be used as fish bait. How might you select your foundation stock and your breeding stock from generation to generation? What mating patterns might you adopt? What information would you need for most efficient progress?

CHAPTER 24

Genetics and the Welfare of the Human Individual

IF WE ARE to achieve true self-understanding, especially to the point of being able to improve our lot as human beings, an appreciation of the implications of our biological as well as our cultural heritage is of great significance. The fundamental genetic mechanisms that operate in man seem to be essentially the same as those of molds, mice, flies, or higher plants. You will remember that in previous chapters, examples from human heredity have been used together with other material in the exposition of general genetic principles. But though man may be reasonably ordinary as a genetic subject, his genetics has had to be studied in extraordinary ways.

Limitations on the Study of Human Genetics. Man is not a particularly favorable object for genetic investigation. He has a long life cycle and comparatively small individual progenies. Contrast him in these important (from the geneticist's standpoint) respects with Drosophila or Neurospora, or even corn, rats, or mice. Another limiting factor is that human cytology is at best still in the stage of promising beginnings. Recent studies indicate that effective cytological work with man's chromosomes will be possible, but a great impediment to rapid progress is the practical difficulty of obtaining sufficient suitable material. (For studying human chromosomes, cytologists have depended upon incidental sources of supply, for example surgical operations involving removal of the testes, as performed for the alleviation of prostatic cancer.)

The most important general restriction on the study of human genetics is that our society is so constituted that we are neither able to subject ourselves to rigorous experimental conditions nor are we desirous of doing so. In the usual genetic approach, closely controlled matings and standardized environment are prerequisite. Where man is concerned, these experimental ideals are not feasible.

Human Heredity and Environment

Our understanding of the genetics of any organism depends first of all upon a knowledge of what characteristics are *inherited*. Until such information is at hand, studies of the mode of action of genes or studies of population genetics within the group must be deferred, as must be attempts to apply genetic principles to more or less practical ends.

A great deal of what we know about the inheritance of different traits in man has come from the analysis of pedigrees, like the one discussed in Chapter 5. But the characteristics of humans, as well as those of other organisms, are determined by the compounded influences of heredity and environment. When a character being studied can be easily and reliably diagnosed, and is little affected within the usual scope of environmental change, pedigree analysis may serve well for arriving at the mode of its inheritance. The blood antigens, ability to taste phenylthiourea, and color perception fall into this category. But attributes such as intelligence, certain size characteristics, and personality traits are complex in their manifestations. They are sensitive to environmental influences and are probably under the influence of many genes. For these, the pedigree method is inadequate and far less effective than the general genetic method of studying controlled matings under defined experimental conditions.

The Use of Twins in Studying Human Genetics

Nature has provided an admirable kind of compensation for some of the difficulties in studying human genetics. This compensation is in the form of human twins, which turn up about once in 88 births in the United States. Twins have sometimes been called "experiments in nature," because they provide certain controls ordinarily lacking in human genetic studies.

One-Egg and Two-Egg Twins. Figure 24-1 shows the essential difference between two kinds of twins. *One-egg*, or *identical*, twins originate from the division and separation of a single fertilized egg cell, or very young embryo. Members of such a pair are genotypically identical, at least as to genes in chromosomes, since the nuclei of their cells have arisen by mitosis from a single common source. *Two-egg* twins, or *fraternal* twins, result from the nearly simultaneous fertilization of two different egg cells by different sperm. Members of such twin pairs are no closer genetic relatives than are sibs of different birth. *Sibs*, or *siblings*, are offspring of the same parents. You can see that, whereas members of a one-egg twin pair must always be of the same sex, members of a two-egg pair may be either of the same sex or of different sexes. Among human twin births in this country, on the average about one in three is a one-egg twin birth.

Methods for Utilizing Twins in Genetic Studies. A standard procedure in experimentation is to study the effects of some one variable while other

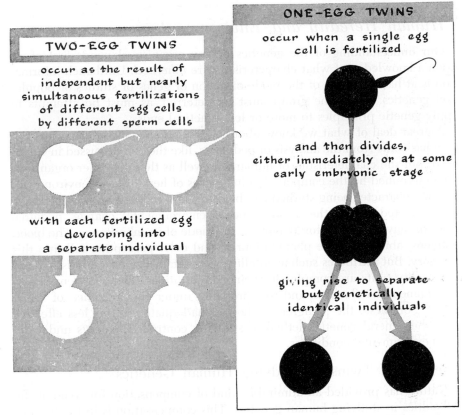

TWO-EGG TWINS

occur as the result of independent but nearly simultaneous fertilizations of different egg cells by different sperm cells

with each fertilized egg developing into a separate individual

ONE-EGG TWINS

occur when a single egg cell is fertilized

and then divides, either immediately or at some early embryonic stage

giving rise to separate but genetically identical individuals

Figure 24-1. *The origin of one-egg and two-egg twins, showing the basic genetic difference between these two types.*

possible variables are nullified or controlled. Twins give control over the two important groups of variables that can be designated the *hereditary* and the *environmental*. One-egg twins provide genetic control, since each pair includes two individuals that are genotypically identical. Both kinds of twins may provide environmental control. Members of a twin pair are *in utero* at the same time, and while this does not insure uniformity of prenatal environment, it at least may reduce some of the variables associated with siblings born at different times. After birth, except where pair members are raised in separate homes, the environment for twins is as nearly the same as one might hope for without imposing experimental conditions. Certainly the environment of twins is usually much more alike than is the environment of two single-born individuals, even within the same family.

Triplets, quadruplets, and quintuplets may be one-egg, two-egg, or multiple-egg, and can be utilized for genetic studies in the same way twins are. But any widespread use of multiple birth individuals in genetic studies has been precluded by their relative rarity.

Figure 24-2. *Four sets of twins from the island of Lanai. From the outside going in, the Tesoros, the Nakaos, and the Sakamotos are all one-egg twin pairs. However, the Soridas (center), although also very similar in appearance, can only be two-egg twins, since Molly is blood type AB and Polly is blood type A. (Courtesy Hawaiian Pineapple Co., Ltd., from* Pine Parade, *p. 4, April, 1951.)*

Comparison of Physical Characteristics of Twin Pair Members. Identical twins are almost always strikingly similar in facial features, in hair and skin color and texture, in eye color, in various characteristics of the teeth, and in certain proportions of the body and limbs. Fraternal twins may also look very much alike (Fig. 24-2). This is not surprising, since they are, after all, close relatives, and may be expected to have many of the same genes. But it is nearly impossible for fraternal twins to be genotypically identical for all their physical characteristics. Usually, enough segregation has taken place that pair members, even of the same sex, are somewhat dissimilar in looks.

Figure 24-3 shows a pair of identical twins that are remarkably alike. In fact, H. H. Newman, an outstanding authority on twins, states that despite many interviews and conversations he never learned to distinguish them. Their similarity is all the more impressive because they were separated eight days after they were born. They were reared apart, one in an urban community and one in a rural area, and, except for brief visits, spent no time together until they entered the same university as freshmen. Differences in environment clearly had no appreciable effects on the obvious physical features of these individuals. Louise and Lois, the girls in the picture, are perhaps more alike than most one-egg twins, but they are valid representatives of the proposition that heredity exerts a strong influence on many of our physical features.

When one turns to characters that can be described rather precisely in quantitative terms, it becomes obvious that even the most similar of one-egg twins are not truly "identical." Actually, Lois and Louise, when examined by Dr. Newman, were both 5 feet 4¾ inches tall and had a head length of exactly 17 centimeters. But Lois had a head width 0.25 cm greater than the corresponding measurement for Louise, and Louise was a few pounds heavier. Weight comparisons do not always have permanent significance, however. At a later date than that of the first comparison, Lois and Louise weighed about the same. An analysis of the fingerprint patterns of the two girls gave ridge counts as follows:

	Left	Right	Total
Louise	72	67	139
Lois	75	69	144

Louise's left hand, in this regard, is more like Lois's than like her own right hand! Differences between these twins can be found, but the total picture is one of great similarity.

More meaningful to our general understanding of the influences of heredity and environment on physical characteristics are studies which compare one-egg twin groups with two-egg twin groups and with groups of paired siblings not twins. Table 24-1 summarizes such comparisons. The values are average pair differences for certain physical traits. Values for one-egg twins reared apart are also included. The two-egg twins and the paired sibs all represent instances where the pair members are of the same sex.

Figure 24-3. *Lois and Louise are strikingly similar one-egg twins. They were separated eight days after birth, and except for brief visits had no contact until they entered college at the age of eighteen. (From Gardner and Newman, J. Heredity, 31:120, 1940.)*

TABLE 24-1. Average Pair Differences in Certain Physical Traits for Identical and Fraternal Twins and for Siblings Reared Together, and for Identical Twins Reared Apart. (Data from Newman, Freeman, and Holzinger, Twins: A Study of Heredity and Environment, University of Chicago Press, 1937.)

	AVERAGE PAIR DIFFERENCES			
SELECTED TRAITS	IDENTICAL TWINS (50 pairs)	FRATERNAL TWINS (52 pairs)	PAIRED SIBLINGS OF LIKE SEX† (52 pairs)	IDENTICAL TWINS REARED APART (20 pairs)
Standing Height	1.7 cm	4.4 cm	4.5 cm	1.8 cm
Weight	4.1 lb	10.0 lb	10.4 lb	9.90 lb
Head length	2.9 mm	6.2 mm	‡	2.20 mm
Head width	2.8 mm	4.2 mm	‡	2.85 mm
Cephalic index	0.016	0.028	‡	‡

† Values represent brothers or sisters whose height and weight had been measured at the same age.
‡ The investigators report no values in these categories.

The first point to be observed in the data is that differences between pair members occur within each biological group. From this it appears that environment has some effect on each of the traits studied. Secondly, the average pair differences are not the same for the various biological groups. Take height, for example. Pair differences for fraternal twins and for sibs are about the same, and in each case the value is appreciably greater than the average difference between identical twins. The greater divergence between fraternal twins and between paired siblings, as compared to identical twins, can be attributed to heredity. Moreover, whatever may be the comparative differences of environment between fraternals as against sibs, these differences are not reflected in the mean pair height differences for the two groups. There is another potent reason for thinking that ordinary environmental circumstances do not greatly affect the expression of height. Sets of identical twins reared apart show almost the same mean pair differences for height as do identical twins reared together.

Similarly, width and length of head are not sensitive to the kind of environment over which the twin method of study gives control. The situation is otherwise in regard to body weight. Identical twins reared apart are much more different than identical twins reared together. In fact, the former group shows an average pair difference much like that for fraternal twins or sibs. We can conclude that body weight responds to environmental change more readily than height or the dimensions of the head.

Heredity and I. Q. Doubtless it would be wrong to refer to human intelligence as if it represented some single, well-defined characteristic. Nevertheless, we agree that intelligence is important. We think of it as being the foundation for rational behavior and as enabling us to make competent judgments on all sorts of matters that affect our well-being. Differences in intelligence no doubt account for many of the misunderstandings among individuals and for many of the maladjustments of individuals to society. A knowledge of the bases of this important but elusive trait would do much to promote the understanding of man by man.

In a few cases of grossly subnormal intelligence, as in *amaurotic idiocy* or *phenylpyruvic amentia,* we know that simple genic alternatives account quite directly for the differences between defectives and so-called normals. But among the vast bulk of people whom we consider "normal" there appears to be a wide range of continuous differences in intelligence. What is the basis of this variation? Pedigree studies have been of little aid in answering this question, because intelligence appears to involve highly complex relationships between heredity and environment. This is the kind of situation in which the twin method offers special advantages over other methods available to human geneticists.

Before reviewing what twin studies imply about differences in intelligence, we need to consider briefly the essential matter of measuring these differences. The best and most usable measures of intelligence so far available are the I. Q. (*intelligence quotient*) ratings devised by psychologists. These ratings depend upon scores made by individuals on certain standardized tests. The tests are so contrived that the test behavior, insofar as possible, reflects certain aspects of rational behavior. While I. Q.'s are not considered wholly reliable or all-inclusive measures of "innate" intelligence, they may represent a fairly reproducible estimate of capacity for some kinds of rational behavior.

Table 24-2 provides the same kind of comparison of average pair differences in intelligence as was given in Table 24-1 for certain physical traits. You will notice at once that identical twins reared apart show an appreciably greater average difference than identical twins reared together, indicating an effective environmental influence on I. Q. The former group shows a smaller average pair difference than that found in fraternal twins or sibs, suggesting that heredity is also important. This difference between group averages is relatively small, however, and must be interpreted with caution,

TABLE 24-2. Average Pair Differences for Binet I.Q. Scores. (Data from Newman, Freeman, and Holzinger, Twins: A Study of Heredity and Environment, University of Chicago Press, 1937.)

IDENTICAL TWINS (50 PAIRS)	FRATERNAL TWINS (52 PAIRS)	PAIRED SIBLINGS OF LIKE SEX (47 PAIRS)	IDENTICAL TWINS REARED APART (19 PAIRS)
5.9	9.9	9.8	8.2

especially since I. Q. tests are sampling methods, so that scoring is subject to errors of chance. The fact that mean pair differences between fraternal twins and sibs are essentially the same implies that the kind of environmental influences that affect I. Q. are not the sort that vary significantly between individuals born at the same time as against those born at different times within a family.

Further insight into the effects of environment on I. Q. may be obtained from the case studies of identical twins reared apart. One thing the unsupplemented average pair difference value does not tell is that, for the majority of the 19 separated pairs that were studied, the individual differences were about the same as those found for unseparated pairs. But most of these separated pair members were not reared under drastically different environments. The few instances of large discrepancies in formal schooling, or in opportunities for education, could be correlated with differences in I. Q. test performance. The case histories of Gladys and Helen provide an illustration.†

> Gladys and Helen were separated at the age of 18 months. They did not meet again until they were 28 years old. *Helen* was adopted out of an orphanage into a farm family living in Michigan. After going through high school she did four years of college work and took a bachelor's degree. She was then employed as a school teacher. *Gladys* was adopted into a Canadian family. Her foster father, a railway conductor, became ill, and in the interests of health moved to the Canadian Rockies for a two-year period. This was just at the time when *Gladys* was ready for third grade. No school was available at her new home, and when the family returned to Ontario she did not resume her formal education. From 17 years on she worked at several occupations. At the time she and her sister were examined, she was employed in a printing house. On the Stanford-Binet test for I. Q. *Helen* scored 116 and *Gladys* 92.

This difference in I. Q. scores is the largest in the group of identical twin pairs tested by Newman and his associates. In fact, about 69 per cent of the scores of the general population lie between the scores of Gladys and Helen. It seems significant that this striking difference in I. Q. was found for the pair members having the greatest difference in educational experience of any of the twins studied.

On the basis of similar findings in other case histories, a number of authorities have drawn the conclusion that fairly large environmental differences may produce proportional differences in the I. Q. of genetically identical individuals, but that the effects of smaller environmental differences may not be detectable. The concept of a threshold, to which you were introduced in Chapter 5, has been invoked to explain this phenomenon.

Any present judgment as to the genetic basis of I. Q. must be tentative, for these reasons: (1) Twin studies have been carried out with only small

† Condensed from Newman, Freeman, and Holzinger, *Twins: A Study of Heredity and Environment*. Chicago: University of Chicago Press, 1937.

numbers of individuals. (2) We can question whether fraternal twins reared together may not experience greater environmental differences than do identical twins. (3) The inability of the twin method to clarify which factors in heredity and which in environment are effective in modifying I. Q. leaves an unfortunate gap in our information. (4) Problems of the relative potency of postnatal and prenatal environment in producing certain kinds of differences have not been resolved.

When all difficulties, these and others, are taken into account, we are, at best, left with a very general picture of the relationships of genetics to intelligence. Heredity seems to provide the individual with upper and lower limits, between which some level of intelligence is realized. The realization of a particular I. Q. depends upon a number, probably large, of environmental factors. The possibility of shifting the I. Q. of an individual, within limits, by modifying his environment seems to be very real.

If this concept is at all correct, it has significant implications for us, even though it is in the stage of broad generality. One of the foremost of these implications is that a person with relatively favorable heredity for intelligence may fall short, in the achievement of intelligent behavior, of a person with relatively unfavorable heredity. The idea is illustrated in Figure 24-4. We may presume, then, that even if the genetic component of intelligence

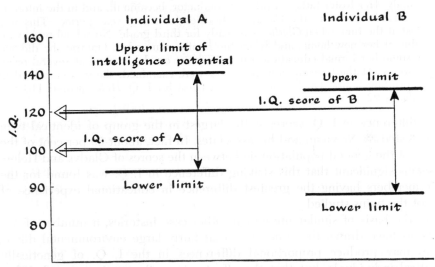

Figure 24-4. *One interpretation of the relationship of genetics to intelligence is that each individual has a fairly wide range of potentialities for intelligence, with the upper and lower limits of this range being determined by heredity. The actual realization of intelligence, as measured for example by an I. Q. score, is determined in complex fashion by a variety of factors of the internal and external environment. Thus the performance of individual A, with a higher potentiality for intelligent behavior, may fall short of that of individual B, whose I. Q. test score may lie much nearer to the upper limits of his capacity.*

is large, there is a real point in working to achieve favorable environments for the expression of intelligence. In fact, the genetic component of intelligence in different individuals will continue to be difficult to define until environment is so manipulated that for all individuals the most favorable expression of intelligence is possible. It is highly probable that the conditions most favorable for the utmost realization of one set of genetic potentialities will not be those most favorable for the realization of potentialities of some other genotype.

Other Twin Studies. We have sampled only a few of the areas in which twin studies have increased our insight into complex relationships between human heredity and environment. Other studies have evaluated the role of heredity in such diverse human characteristics as cancer, criminality, and sleep habits. Knowing about the extent of genetic control of such human differences is, of course, quite different from being able to do something about them. It should go without saying, however, that increasing knowledge of this kind, besides being important in itself, is basic to human welfare, both social and individual.

Genetics and Medicine

Since the constitution of a man is so much a product of his heredity, as well as of his environment, genetics has important relationships with medicine. The most obvious point of contact between genetics and medicine lies in the fact that many impairments of normal human function that fall into the category of "disease" are heritable characters. These may be relatively inconsequential departures from the normal, like color blindness, albinism, or polydactyly, or they may be much more serious, as hemophilia, Huntington's chorea, juvenile amaurotic idiocy, or glioma retina.

Utilization of Genetic Knowledge in Medical Practice. The recognition that many problems in disease have a genetic component has considerably enlarged the scope of medical research, and our understanding of these problems has been correspondingly amplified. At the level of medical practice, the use of genetics, unfortunately, has lagged somewhat behind. L. H. Snyder, of the University of Oklahoma, has analyzed the uses of genetic considerations in medical practice into three categories: diagnosis, prevention, and prognosis.

Diagnosis. One of the important concepts you will have gained from your study of genetics is that the same, or nearly the same, phenotypic characters of an organism may be based on quite different combinations of hereditary and environmental factors. This principle applies to many of the symptoms that the physician is called upon to diagnose. The fundamental problem in diagnosis is to arrive at the correct causation of symptoms; otherwise treatment is likely to be ineffective or possibly damaging.

M. T. Macklin has recorded a striking example of how genetic knowledge can be utilized to determine the causation of pathological symptoms that are otherwise difficult to diagnose. The patient was a child whose symptoms were scanty hair, undeveloped teeth, dry skin, and a tendency to fever. An early diagnosis suggested deficiency in the functioning of the thyroid gland, but this was reconsidered when thyroid treatment accentuated rather than reduced the symptoms. Further inquiry revealed that one parent and other relatives of the child showed similar pathological symptoms. Converging trails of genetic and physiological approach led to the correct conclusion that the patient's difficulty was a dominant hereditary condition, *ectodermal dysplasia*, which, although rare, is well known. It is characterized by absence of the sweat glands as well as by deficiencies in the development of hair and teeth. With accurate diagnosis, the reason for trouble with temperature control became clear. At the same time, the undesirable effects of the original thyroid medication became explainable. Since the thyroid treatment stimulated metabolic activity, the patient's body temperature became even higher, and more difficult to control.

Prevention. Genetic knowledge that facilitates accurate diagnosis may be useful also in disease prevention. For an example, let us consider *xanthoma tuberosum*, a noninfectious hereditary disease. The overt symptoms of this condition, which appears to be transmitted on the basis of a dominant gene, are numerous nodules and tumors, largely present on the elbows, knees, fingers, heels, buttocks, and over certain tendons. Lesions of the heart sometimes occur, and implication of the cardiovascular system often culminates in death. The fundamental error in metabolism, however, is *hypercholesterolemia*, an excess of cholesterol in the blood. Indeed, increased cholesterol in the blood presages the appearance of the lesions described above. If this warning signal is detected in time, an affected person can be placed on a suitable diet, and years may be added to his life.

In cases like this, an awareness of genetic principles may lead to the detection of individuals with hypercholesterolemia who have not reached the stage where lesions appear. For whereas it is scarcely feasible to test periodically the level of cholesterol in the blood of each of us, it is quite practical and justifiable to apply such tests to the relatives of persons with xanthoma tuberosum. When this type of procedure can be applied in many instead of only a few kinds of disease, medical men will be able to forego certain "shotgun" methods of prevention in favor of "sharpshooting" methods. The consequent advantages to precision and effectiveness of treatment are obvious.

In the future, even infectious diseases are likely to be considered in the light of heredity. Man's resistance or susceptibility to certain pathogens appears to have a genetic basis just as does disease resistance in crop plants and domestic animals. Identical twins, for example, show a much greater concordance for tuberculosis than do fraternals. This is revealed in similarity of time of onset, and in the organs involved, as well as in the mere fact of infection. The ability to recognize persons with genetic susceptibility might be of great value in the prevention of infectious diseases where immunizations or other preventive methods are difficult to apply on a mass scale. It is conceivable that susceptible individuals could take unusual precautions against infection—precautions that might be impracticable for the population at large. Or, susceptibles might be able to undertake special measures to build up resistance to infection.

Prognosis. One of the duties of the physician is to employ his special knowledge to make forecasts, or *prognoses,* that can be utilized for the well-being of his patients. You have already seen how genetic knowledge serves as the basis for prognosis in another sphere as well—the sphere of marriage counselling. The physician should be prepared, for example, to advise a father affected with dominant *ectodermal dysplasia* that half his offspring can be expected to suffer from the same difficulties he experiences. He should be able to explain to two normal parents who have had an albino child that the expectancy of another of their offspring being albino is one in four. He should recognize the importance of being able to make encouraging as well as discouraging forecasts. For instance, it would be desirable that normal brothers and sisters of a man with ectodermal dysplasia be assured that they will not transmit the disease. In short, for the welfare of his patients, the medical advisor should be able to deal with their problems from a well-rounded genetic point of view. And it is to be hoped that agencies such as clinics of human heredity will be established in increasing number, for handling such problems on a more specialized basis.

The Detection of Carriers of Hereditary Disease. Individuals who do not exhibit the symptoms of an hereditary disease but nevertheless are able to transmit it are called genetic *carriers.* Persons heterozygous for a recessive character, as for example the mothers of sons with hemophilia, are carriers. The term is also applied when genes manifest themselves late in development, or are incompletely penetrant, or are otherwise irregular in their expression.

In Chapter 2, we mentioned thalassemia major (Cooley's anemia) as a heritable condition based upon the action of an incompletely recessive gene. Thalassemia major is a severe anemia, usually fatal quite early in life. Occurring frequently in the same families with thalassemia major is an anemia having some of the same characteristics but much milder and nonfatal. The milder disease results from a heterozygous condition at the genetic locus for the major anemia. This less severe anemia, appropriately, is called *thalassemia minor.*

The frequency of the gene involved in these anemias is rather high in certain populations. A study of the Italian population of Rochester, New York, for example, disclosed a carrier frequency of about 0.04 (the value calculated for 2pq in the formula for a population in equilibrium). Investigations conducted in certain cities in north-central Italy have found values

TABLE 24-3. Summary of Criteria Used in Designation of Carriers of Thalassemia (i.e., Criteria for Diagnosing Thalassemia Minor). To designate carriers accurately, not one but several criteria must be applicable. (After Neel, Am. J. Human Genetics, 1:22, 1949.)

1. Appearance of certain abnormal erythrocyte types in a stained blood smear.
2. Decreased cell size.
3. Decreased fragility of the erythrocytes in hypotonic salt solutions.
4. Lack of evidence of iron deficiency, chronic blood loss, or other disease which might produce a hematological picture comparable to that of thalassemia minor.
5. Failure to respond to any known therapy.
6. Familial incidence of a similar blood picture.

higher than this. Since the gene for thalassemia does have a relatively high frequency in some parts of the world, ability to detect carriers is of considerable importance. Now of course every person with a mild anemia is not a potential parent of a victim of thalassemia major. But actual carriers for this disease can be accurately designated if several criteria are carefully applied as summarized in Table 24-3. The genetic aspect plays an important part.

Besides thalassemia, there are other heritable conditions where the carrier state can be defined with reasonable precision. Analysis of the uric acid content of the blood helps to reveal carriers for *gout*. It appears, too, that carriers for Huntington's chorea, a severe nervous disorder, may be singled out on the basis of "brain wave" patterns revealed by an electroencephalogram. Additional instances might be mentioned, but the total number is yet too small to have had any great effect on medical practice in general.

In his several functions of diagnosis, prevention, and prognosis, the physician would be in a position to work more effectively if carriers of the hereditary diseases could be detected. Moreover, the ability to detect carriers would offer new opportunities for the medical research worker to study interrelationships of genetics and environment that have important implications for therapy and for the prevention of disease. In the search for specific criteria for different carriers, biochemical and physiological approaches appear likely to be the most fruitful. The reliability of such criteria, for the most part, will depend rather directly on how closely they relate to the primary activities of the appropriate genes or to their primary sites of action. Many morphological characters and attributes of behavior have turned out to be unreliable indicators of carriers because such traits are often far removed from the primary action of the genes with which they are associated. Hence the opportunities for variation in such characters and attributes, based on intervening factors of environment and heredity, are great.

If any considerable number of carrier states are to be detectable, we will need to know a great deal about the genetically determined biochemical individuality of man. Investigations carried out by R. J. Williams and co-workers at the University of Texas emphasize that such individuality does in fact exist, and that it can be revealed and defined through appropriate experiments. For example, urinary excretion patterns for the substances creatinine, glucose, alanine, glycine, serine, glutamic acid, and lysine have been studied. Among the persons whose excretion patterns were investigated, a rather surprising diversity was found. However, the excretion patterns of members of an identical twin pair were very similar, indeed much more similar than those of any other persons investigated.

Genetics and the Pathogens of Man. The repeated experience of scientists working in practical fields of biology has been that their problems are usually most successfully dealt with when approached on a broad biological basis. An important element in the success of plant breeders in dealing with problems in disease has been the appreciation by breeders and pathologists that the attributes of plant pathogens as well as of their hosts are based on genetic systems. It is also being taken into greater account that the bacteria and viruses preying on man are "genetic" organisms.

The Development of Resistance to Antibiotics by Bacteria. Some of man's most effective weapons in his struggle against infectious disease have been antibiotics such as penicillin, aureomycin, streptomycin, and the sulfas. There was early promise that antibiotics might neutralize completely the attacks by certain groups of bacteria on man. However, in a number of cases where patients were being treated, for example with penicillin, treatment was ineffective, even though the pathogenic organisms were of a kind ordinarily sensitive to the antibiotic. Now we recognize that strains of bacteria originally sensitive to an antibiotic can become resistant to it.

Investigations in laboratories have shown that bacterial resistance to antibiotics may originate through mutations. The detection of mutants of this kind is exceptionally easy, even when the mutation rate is low. Suppose, for example, that an investigator wishes to look for streptomycin-resistant mutants. Essentially all he needs do is to distribute bacteria of a sensitive type into Petri dishes containing a medium which includes streptomycin at a concentration that normally will not permit survival of the bacteria. If resistant mutants occur, they grow and form colonies. Under this system the mutants literally detect themselves. Since as many as several billion bacteria can be accommodated comfortably in a single Petri dish, the investigator can test almost unlimited numbers of individuals with relatively small effort.

M. Demerec, of the Biological Laboratories at Cold Spring Harbor, Long Island, has pointed out the interesting circumstance that bacteria may show different patterns in acquiring resistance to different antibiotics. He has found that a high degree of resistance to streptomycin can be acquired in a single mutational step. On the other hand, a high degree of resistance to penicillin is attained only as the cumulative result of a series of mutations. Under this pattern of resistance, first-step mutants show a tolerance to

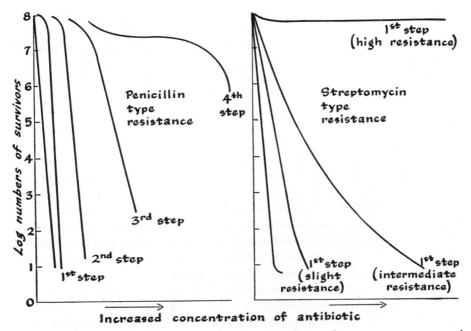

Figure 24-5. *Survival curves, showing the penicillin and streptomycin types of resistance pattern. Note that fewer cells survive at the higher concentrations of antibiotic. But within populations, differences in antibiotic resistance occur. If survivors from a population initially grown in the presence of an antibiotic are selected for reproduction, one may obtain a culture with an average resistance higher than that of the original population. By selecting mutants, through a series of steps of this kind, strains of bacteria quite tolerant to penicillin may be obtained. The curves show, however, that it is possible for bacteria to attain a high degree of resistance to streptomycin in what appears to be a single mutational step. (After Bryson and Demerec, Annals N. Y. Acad. Sci., 53:285, 1950.)*

penicillin that is only a modest advance over the lack of resistance characteristic of the original sensitive bacteria. However, further mutation in the new, mildly resistant strain can give somewhat greater tolerance. Subsequent accumulation of mutations may eventually give rise to strains that are highly resistant to penicillin. The penicillin and streptomycin patterns of resistance are compared in Figure 24-5.

The findings of Demerec have an important bearing on the clinical use of antibiotics. It appears that with penicillin the development of resistant strains can be avoided if initial concentrations of the antibiotic are high enough to eliminate first-step mutants, and if these effective concentrations are maintained as long as any of the pathogenic bacteria persist. Otherwise, mutation may produce first-step resistant bacteria which might multiply and eventually give rise to even more resistant types. On the other hand, since treatment with even fairly massive initial doses of streptomycin does not preclude the occurrence of resistant bacteria, the clinician must be prepared for the occasional appearance of pathogens resistant to this antibiotic. In view of this, the use of streptomycin should perhaps be reserved for cases that cannot be effectively treated in other ways.

Mutation sometimes leads to the curious reversal of situation where a microorganism, far from remaining sensitive to an antibiotic, actually develops a requirement for it. An example is the sulfonamide-requiring strain of Neurospora mentioned in Chapter 16. But perhaps the ultimate in irony has been reached in an investigation conducted with a streptomycin-requiring strain of Meningococcus. Mice inoculated with this strain initially showed no symptoms of infection. When treated with streptomycin, however, they developed meningococcal sepsis and died.

Increase in Production of Penicillin as the Result of Gene Mutation. That mutation can sometimes work in our favor is dramatically illustrated in a story involving penicillin production. Penicillin, as you know, is a chemical produced by the mold Penicillium. When the antibiotic's tremendous clinical importance, especially during wartime, was realized in the early 1940's, great efforts were made to increase its production. One plan of attack was to irradiate the mold, in hopes of inducing a mutation favorable to a larger output of penicillin. You can see a basis for this hope if you will recall instances where genetic blocks in metabolism have led to the accumulation of particular substances.

At least one lucky hit seems to have been made. From spores that were X-rayed, a culture of *Penicillium chrysogenum* was isolated that yielded approximately twice the amount of penicillin obtained from the original parent strain. Further irradiation experiments, in which conidia of the new mutant type were treated with ultraviolet light, produced a strain that yielded about 900 units of penicillin per milliliter in comparison with the 500 average obtained from the earlier X-ray mutant.

Implications of Bacterial and Viral Recombinations. The discoveries that certain bacteria and viruses have some sort of mechanism for producing genetic recombinations have opened the way to new kinds of research relating to problems of disease. There is growing evidence that the antibiotics as a whole are less effective against today's populations of human pathogens than they were against those of only a few years ago. As in plant breeding, a continuous struggle between the potentials for variation in pathogens and the ingenuity of biologists seems in prospect. Genetic recombination, long known to be an important source of variation in the fungi that parasitize plants, is now seen to be available to the bacteria and viruses that plague man as well.

Until there is an actual demonstration of sexuality in viruses and bacteria pathogenic to man, the issue raised in this section is speculative. But some preliminary evidence suggests that recombination may occur among the influenza viruses. It will not be too surprising to find similar phenomena among other human pathogens.

Genetics and the Races of Mankind

Problems of race differences concern us all. Not the least reason is that race prejudice and the misunderstanding of race differences account for a substantial portion of human misery. False notions of race superiority have led to extremes of irrational behavior so recently in man's history that there is no need to document this point here. What does need to be said is that such irrational behavior has no justification, even though dogmatists of race superiority have sometimes pretended scientific support for their views.

Unfortunately, the views on race problems of far too many persons, even among the well-intentioned, are based on habit rather than reason, and on hearsay rather than knowledge. Even the ready facility with which the word *race* is used in everyday speech is painfully inconsistent with the difficulties most people would have in satisfactorily defining it. However, many people who use the word *race* have an idea with some validity in mind, although they may perceive it as a distorted image. Genetics has much to contribute toward bringing such distorted images into truer focus.

Individual Diversity and Racial Diversity. The primary implication of *race* would seem surely to be that people have similarities and differences that permit them to be put into some sort of meaningful classification. We know, of course, that people have similarities and differences. Are these of a kind and distribution that permit classification? And, if so, is there any possible meaningful classification that fits at all with widely held preconceived notions of race?

First, let us examine two attributes common to the usual concepts of race. One of these is that by racial differences we mean heritable biological differences, not cultural differences as might be found in language, dress, or economic systems. The other is that race has something to do with geography, and with common origin. We might, for example, separate, quite accurately, all the people of the world into color blind and not color blind. But such a classification would in itself have little to do with our concepts of race. There are color-blind individuals among the Japanese, among American whites, Indians, and Negroes, and among different groups of Europeans, Asiatics, and Africans. If you think about the matter, you will find that your ideas of race involve natural populations rather than artificial groupings of scattered individuals.

With the foregoing in mind, it may be asked: Are there heritable traits that distinctively characterize groups of people who have had geographic origin within a more or less limited area? Despite commonly held beliefs, we will be hard pressed to point to more than a few traits representing anything

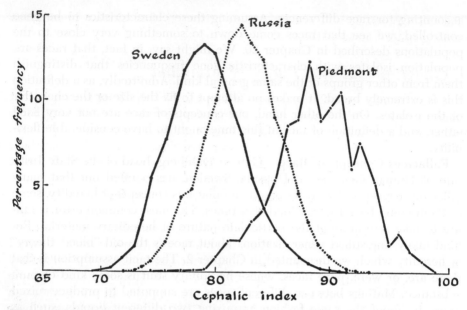

Figure 24-6. *Frequency distributions of cephalic index (breadth as percentage of length). Represented are a Swedish population (after Lamborg and Linders); a Russian population from the region of Smolensk (after Tchepowkovsky); and a population of Piedmontese (after Livi). (From Haldane, Heredity and Politics, 1938. By permission of George Allen & Unwin Ltd. and of W. W. Norton.)*

like absolute differences among groups of people that fit the usual concepts of race. The combination of dark skin, thick lips, and kinky hair serves to set apart most Negroes into a distinct racial group. But within the group so set apart, there is a tremendous range of variation for other heritable characteristics. And when we turn to different groups that by some definition or other have qualified as races, for example Caucasoids, we can scarcely find a single criterion to which all members of the group conform and which excludes all members of different groups.

The key to the problem of defining race differences is that popular stereotypes of race are wrong in expecting absolute differences among racial groups. The most frequent real situation is that represented in Figure 24-6, which shows frequency distributions of cephalic index in three rather diverse European groups—Swedes, Russians, and Piedmontese. We see that there are significant differences among the groups, but that they are differences of average. With reference to individuals, the groups show a large overlap. In other words, the skull measurements of an individual are not diagnostic as to his "racial" origin. (Lacking other information, in what group would you place, for example, an individual whose cephalic index was 80?)

A Genetic Definition of Race. What is true of distributions of cephalic index is true for most other characteristics of the kind that we think of as accounting for race differences. Assuming these characteristics to be gene controlled, we see that races come down to something very close to the populations described in Chapter 20. We might say, in fact, that races are population isolates with characteristic gene frequencies that distinguish them from other groups of the same general kind. Admittedly, as a definition this is extremely broad. It makes no attempt to fix the size or the character of the isolates. On the other hand, our concepts of race are not very fixed either, and a definition of race at this time ought to have considerable flexibility.

Fallacious Concepts of Race. Gunnar Dahlberg, head of the State Institute of Human Genetics, at Uppsala, Sweden, has pointed out that many fallacious concepts of race are based on fallacious concepts of heredity, some of them going back to pre-Mendelian times. The most common error is failure to take into account the particulate nature of hereditary material. Behind many unjustified generalizations about race is the old "blood theory" of heredity which we discounted in Chapter 2. The tacit assumption is that there are, or were, pure races, whose hereditary stuff is some kind of pure substance. Matings between different races are supposed to produce mixed races, in about the same fashion as mixing two different liquids, such as grape juice and ginger ale, gives rise to a mixed drink with definite but "hybrid" characteristics of its own. A further implication is that a series of matings between members of two different races will always give the same results. On such a basis, the character of the race assumes great importance in determining the character of its individual members. Persons belonging to races with "superior blood" are presumed to be predictably better than people who are members of races with less desirable hereditary stuff.

You realize at once, from your knowledge of genetics, that concepts of the sort we have just outlined are nonsensical. If in addition you realize that group differences are differences in frequencies of genes, not absolute differences, many widely accepted race concepts are laid bare as fallacies. If all of us can come to recognize these fallacies, and behave toward our fellow men in ways which recognition of these fallacies suggests, then human welfare and understanding will be truly promoted. To comment more particularly:

1. Pure races are fictional. A *pure* race would have to be one in which all individuals were homozygous and had the same allelic substitutions at each genetic locus. Except for one-egg twins, genetic identity is not approached even within families, and still less within the much larger groups called races. Complete homozygosity probably never occurs.

There is no reason to suppose that pure races existed even in the remote past. The available fossil evidence tends to refute rather than support the idea of a biological past in which the earth was peopled with pure races.

2. Judging an individual on the basis of some type or ideal which has been set up for his racial group is unfair and will frequently lead to false conclusions. Races, for the most part, are distinguishable only on the basis of gene

frequencies. An individual member of a group may have heritable traits considerably different from those characteristic of the most frequent type or of the average type for the group.

3. Evidence is lacking for associations between particular mental or psychological characteristics and the common heritable physical traits by which certain racial groups are identified. Black skins are sometimes supposed to go with shiftlessness and lack of ambition, or with uncanny musical talent. At the same time it may be forgotten that white skins may go with these traits as well, or that black skins are often not associated with these characteristics. Incorrect thinking along these lines is in some measure due to failure to understand the particulate nature of hereditary materials.

4. It is by no means established that there are racial differences in frequencies of genes determining mental and psychological traits. In fact, such genes have not yet been accurately identified in individuals, let alone studied in racial groups. Moreover, the considerable difficulty of obtaining precise measurements of such traits as I. Q. is magnified when comparisons between racial groups are made. For example, can mental tests based on the culture of western Europeans and white Americans give anything like a true picture of the mental capacities of individual American Indians? From several points of view, judgments as to racial differences in mental and psychological traits are premature.

On the other hand, to assert dogmatically that all racial groups have an identical mental and psychological heritage is also at present unjustified. If genes have some influence in determining the various facets of intelligence, it would be remarkable if the frequencies of such genes were identical in different racial groups. *But to speak of differences is not to imply, at the same time, a scale of superiority and inferiority.*

5. On the basis of what has been said before, it follows quite obviously that ideas of race superiority are ill founded. First of all, no race has a monopoly on "good" genes or is entirely free from "bad" genes. And what are "good" and "bad" genes anyway? Quite a few genes that are unfavorable under one geographical and cultural environment may be relatively favorable under another. Secondly, many of the so-called "superior" and "inferior" characteristics sometimes presumed to be associated with particular racial groups may be largely or entirely the effect of environment. Shiftlessness and lack of ambition have been said to characterize certain racial groups. These are the same groups that have lived under circumstances providing small opportunity for the exercise of initiative or ambition.

Eugenics

Many people would like to see genetic principles applied toward the biological improvement of man. Programs for achieving this *eugenic* goal have been formulated, and to a certain extent are being carried out. The approach to eugenics has been two-sided. *Negative* eugenic measures, such as the sterilization or segregation of persons with genetic defects, are designed to prevent the propagation of unfavorable genes. *Positive* eugenic measures are those intended to increase the frequency of favored genetic traits.

The general eugenic ideal is no doubt a noble concept, and acceptable to most persons. But specific eugenic objectives are controversial, both from a biological and a sociological point of view. And the suggested means for attaining eugenic objectives involve a number of questionable assumptions. We cannot deal with so complex a subject in this broad treatment of genetics. Probably, in any case, really effective consideration of eugenics must await a much greater accumulation of genetic knowledge than is now available. This does not mean that we should cease consideration of eugenics or fail to employ measures that seem immediately desirable and well justified.

Probably it is fitting that our book should end at a place where the need for further genetic knowledge is apparent. Genetics has not been, and should not be, a static science.

As indicated in our introductory chapter, the problems of genetics are numerous and are intimately related to progress in diverse fields. When some of these problems are solved, others, often unforeseen, take their place. But this is not a cause for pessimism, since what is really involved is an unfolding and an integration of fundamental aspects of biology.

Insofar as problems of genetics relate particularly to man, they offer the hope of increased self-understanding and well-being. We must now recognize that there is a great diversity of genetic potentiality among men, and that these various potentialities are not to be evaluated in terms of superior and inferior qualities. A primary aim of democratic society, to provide each individual with opportunities for the realization of the best of his unique pattern of potentialities, thus makes sense on genetic as well as on social grounds.

References

Boyd, W. C., *Genetics and the Races of Man.* Boston: Little, Brown & Co., 1950. (Authoritative, this book at the same time makes excellent reading for pleasure. Chap. 7, "The Concept of Race," and Chap. 9, "Use of Blood Groups in Human Classification," should be read in supplement to material presented in this text.)

Dunn, L. C., and Dobzhansky, Th., *Heredity, Race, and Society.* New York: Penguin Books, 1946. (Elementary but sound. Worth reading in its entirety.)

Haldane, J. B. S., *Heredity and Politics.* New York: W. W. Norton & Co., 1938. (Interesting both for the casual and the professional genetic reader. Chaps. 3 and

4 are valuable for pointing to some of the possible pitfalls in eugenics programs as presently conceived. Chaps. 5 and 6 deal with problems of race differences.)

Lange, J., *Verbrechen als Schicksal*. Leipzig: Thieme, 1929. Translation *Crime and Destiny*. New York: Charles Boni, 1930. (Twin studies indicating a possible hereditary basis for criminality.)

Montagu, M. F. A., *Statement on Race*. New York: Henry Schuman, 1951. (A discussion and amplification of the "Statement by Experts on Race Problems" issued by the United Nations Educational, Scientific, and Cultural Organization [UNESCO]. Brief enough to be read in its entirety, and of great contemporary interest.)

Muller, H. J., "Progress and Prospects in Human Genetics." *Am. J. Human Genetics*, 1:1–18, 1949. (The preface to a new journal of human genetics. A general statement of problems and trends in the field.)

———, "Our Load of Mutations." *Am. J. Human Genetics*, 2:111–176, 1950. (Possible deleterious consequences of increased mutation rate in man due to exposure to irradiations and other mutagens.)

———, Little, C. C., and Snyder, L. H., *Genetics, Medicine, and Man*. Ithaca: Cornell University Press, 1947. (A series of six excellent lectures given for a nonprofessional audience.)

Newman, H. H., *Multiple Human Births*. New York: Doubleday, Doran & Co., 1940. (This very readable book contains a wealth of information covering various aspects of multiple births.)

———, Freeman, F. N., and Holzinger, K. J., *Twins: A Study of Heredity and Environment*. Chicago: University of Chicago Press, 1937. (The major publication on twin studies in this country. Chap. 5 is most likely to be useful to the general student. Chap. 10 summarizes the fascinating case studies of identical twins reared apart.)

Neel, J. V., "The Detection of the Genetic Carriers of Hereditary Disease." *Am. J. Human Genetics*, 1:19–36, 1949. (Gives the details of several important and interesting examples of this subject.)

Osborn, F., *Preface to Eugenics*. New York: Harper & Bros., 1951. (Broad and temperate treatment of the case for eugenics.)

Scheinfeld, A., *The New You and Heredity*. Philadelphia: Lippincott Co., 1950. (For the general reader. Touches on many interesting facets of human genetics not often dealt with in technical books on the subject.)

Schwesinger, G., *Heredity and Environment*. New York: Macmillan Co., 1933. (A voluminous summary of earlier studies bearing on the genesis of psychological characters in man.)

Stern, C., *Principles of Human Genetics*. San Francisco: W. H. Freeman and Co., 1949. (An admirable text, with many examples thoroughly discussed. Note the lists of references for human genetics, pp. 5 and 6.)

Williams, R. J., "Introduction, General Discussion and Tentative Conclusions," Article I in "Individual Metabolic Patterns and Human Disease: An Exploratory Study Utilizing Predominantly Paper Chromatographic Methods." *Biochemical Institute Studies IV, University of Texas Pub. No. 5109*, 7–21, 1951. (Discussion of the biochemical basis of human individuality. Article XVI, same publication, by H. K. Berry, L. Cain, and L. L. Rogers, reports the urinary excretion patterns of different human individuals, including a pair of one-egg twins.)

"Origin and Evolution of Man," *Cold Spring Harbor Symposia Quant. Biol.*, 15: 425 pp., 1950. (Entirely devoted to aspects of human genetics, with separate articles by different authors. Consult the index for subjects that interest you particularly.)

Questions and Problems

24- 1. What do the following signify?

antibiotic	one-egg quintuplets
average pair differences	one-egg twins
carrier	prevention
diagnosis	race
eugenics	streptomycin resistance
hypercholesterolemia	siblings
identical twins	two-egg quadruplets
I.Q.	two-egg twins

24- 2. What are some factors of the prenatal environment that might produce differences in one-egg twins?

24- 3. How might difficulties in procuring adequate material for cytological analysis impede progress in our understanding of the genetics of man?

24- 4. In the extensive studies involving comparisons of one-egg and two-egg twins carried out by Newman, Freeman, and Holzinger, all of the two-egg pairs investigated were like-sexed. Why do you suppose that no boy-girl pairs were included in the comparisons?

24- 5. An investigation involving a fairly large number of twin pairs revealed that, among one-egg twins, in 95 per cent of all cases where one pair member had been infected with measles, the partner twin had a case history for measles too. Discuss whether this finding implies that susceptibility to measles is strongly hereditary.

24- 6. Among two-egg twins where one pair member had a case history for measles, in 87 per cent of all the instances the partner member also had a case history for measles. Adding this information to that given in the preceding question, what can you say about a possible hereditary basis for susceptibility to measles?

24- 7. J. B. Nichols studied the sex ratios of twins recorded in the 1900 census report for the U. S. and found that 717,907 pairs of twins were born between 1890 and 1900. Of these, 234,497 were boy-boy pairs, 219,312 were girl-girl pairs, and 264,098 were boy-girl pairs. Assuming for practical purposes a 1:1 sex ratio in man, estimate the number of one-egg twin pairs included in these data. Now, calculate the probability of male and female births from the data above, and estimate the number of one-egg twin pairs on this basis.

24- 8. Give reasons why it would be a good idea for every medical practitioner to have training in genetics.

24- 9. Why is it that in the establishment of criteria for the detection of carriers of hereditary disease biochemical and physiological criteria are likely, for the most part, to be more useful than morphological criteria?

24-10. What are some of the practical advantages of being able to detect the carriers of hereditary diseases?

24-11. There is a tendency among many people to view heritable diseases as somehow more hopeless and horrible than infectious diseases or accidental mutilations. What arguments and examples could you muster to refute this idea?

24-12. It has been suggested that in the treatment of certain infectious diseases two effective antibiotics should be utilized simultaneously. Can you see any "genetic" arguments in favor of such a practice?

24-13. Are there any kinds of genetic studies for which man, as compared with a standard experimental organism such as Drosophila, is a more favorable object?

24-14. For the increased welfare of the human individual, what are some of the directions research in human genetics should take?

24-15. Within certain social groups it appears that members of families that are somewhat larger than average for the group tend in turn to have relatively large families themselves. Is this convincing evidence for a hereditary basis for human fertility? What alternative explanations might the situation have?

24-16. Xeroderma pigmentosum is a severe recessive disease. Affected persons are photosensitive, and portions of their skin that have been exposed to the light show intensive pigmentation, freckling, and warty growths that often become malignant. Those afflicted with this heritable disease seldom live beyond the age of 15. Pedigree studies have led to the discovery that individuals heterozygous for the gene for xeroderma pigmentosum are characterized by very heavy freckling. This is quite independent of the freckling associated with red hair. Haldane has suggested that it may be undesirable for two heavily freckled persons to get married unless at least one is a red head. Explain the basis of his proposal.

24-17. Point out fundamental similarities in these two phenomena: (a) Plant varieties with established disease resistance against a pathogen sometimes suddenly fall prey to it. (b) Occasionally, antibiotics unexpectedly fail to work against human pathogens that previously were sensitive to them.

24-18. The following has been given as the definition of a race: "A race is a human group all of whose members are alike in physical and mental characters." Is this a tenable definition? If so, support it with appropriate examples. If not, tell where it is unsatisfactory.

24-19. Defend the statement that "Race is a statistical concept."

24-20. Why is it dangerous to classify an individual according to a racial stereotype?

24-21. Do the people of the United States constitute a race?

24-22. W. C. Boyd and others have proposed tentative classifications of mankind on the basis of frequencies of the blood group alleles. As compared with skin color or morphological characteristics, what genetic advantages do the blood groups have for purposes of race classification?

24-23. Does your knowledge of genetics supply any reason for believing that interracial marriages are biologically undesirable? Discuss.

(C5)